Understanding Fiction

CLEANTH BROOKS

ROBERT PENN WARREN

Understanding FICTION

SECOND EDITION

PRENTICE-HALL, INC., *Englewood Cliffs, New Jersey*

PRENTICE-HALL INTERNATIONAL, INC., *London*
PRENTICE-HALL OF AUSTRALIA, PTY. LTD., *Sydney*
PRENTICE-HALL OF CANADA, LTD., *Toronto*
PRENTICE-HALL OF INDIA PRIVATE LIMITED, *New Delhi*
PRENTICE-HALL OF JAPAN, INC., *Tokyo*

ACKNOWLEDGMENTS

Albert & Charles Boni: for "An Occurrence at Owl Creek Bridge" by Ambrose Bierce, from *In the Midst of Life*.

Brandt & Brandt: for "Cruel and Barbarous Treatment" by Mary McCarthy, from *The Company She Keeps*, published by Simon and Schuster, Inc., copyright, 1939, by Mary McCarthy.

Dino Buzzati: for his story "The Killing of the Dragon."

Criterion Books, Inc.: for "Crossing into Poland" by Isaac Babel.

J. M. Dent & Sons, Ltd.: for "Amy Foster" by Joseph Conrad, from *Typhoon*; and for "The Fight" by Dylan Thomas from *Portrait of the Artist as a Young Dog*, Canadian rights.

Doubleday & Company, Inc.: for "I See You Never" by Ray Bradbury, from *The Golden Apples of the Sun*, copyright, 1947, by The New Yorker Magazine, Inc., reprinted by permission of Doubleday & Co., Inc.; for "The Furnished Room" by O. Henry, from *The Four Million*, copyright, 1904, by Doubleday & Co., Inc., reprinted by permission of the publisher; and for "The Man Who Would be King" by Rudyard Kipling, from *Under the Deodars*, reprinted by permission of Mrs. George Bambridge and Doubleday & Co., Inc.

E. P. Dutton & Co., Inc.: for "War" by Luigi Pirandello, from *The Medals and Other Stories*, copyright, 1939, by E. P. Dutton, the publishers.

Farrar, Straus and Cudahy, Inc.: for "The Bitch" by Colette, from *Creatures Great and Small*, used by permission of the publishers, Farrar, Straus and Cudahy, Inc.; and for "The Lottery" by Shirley Jackson, from *The Lottery*, copyright, 1949, by Shirley Jackson, copyright, 1948, by The New Yorker Magazine, Inc.

Funk & Wagnalls Company: for "Goodbye, My Brother" by John Cheever. Reprinted from *The Enormous Radio and Other Stories* by John Cheever. By permission of the publishers, Funk & Wagnalls, N.Y.

Harcourt, Brace and Company, Inc.: for "A Good Man Is Hard to Find" by Flannery O'Connor, from *A Good Man Is Hard to Find and Other Stories* by Flannery O'Connor, © copyright, 1953, 1954, 1955, by Flannery O'Connor, reprinted by permission of Harcourt, Brace and Company, Inc.; for "Noon Wine" by Katherine Anne Porter, from *Pale Horse, Pale Rider*, copyright, 1936, 1937, 1939, by Katherine Anne Porter, reprinted by permission of Harcourt, Brace and Company, Inc.; for "Blackberry Winter" by Robert Penn Warren, from *The Circus in the Attic and Other Stories*, copyright, 1947, by Robert Penn Warren, reprinted by permission of Harcourt, Brace and Company, Inc.; for "A Piece of News" by Eudora Welty, from *A Curtain of Green and Other Stories*, copyright, 1936, 1937, 1938, 1939, 1941, by Eudora Welty, reprinted by permission of Harcourt, Brace and Company, Inc.; and for "No Place for You, My Love" by Eudora Welty, reprinted by permission of Harcourt, Brace and Company, Inc., from *The Bride of the Innisfallen* © 1955, by Eudora Welty.

Harper & Brothers: for "Dermuche" by Marcel Aymé, from *Across Paris*, translated by Norman Denny, copyright 1947, by Librairie Gallimard.

The Hogarth Press, Ltd.: for "Through the Quinquina Glass" by William Sansom, from *Fireman Flower*, Canadian rights.

Houghton Mifflin Company: for "Tennessee's Partner" by Bret Harte; and for "A Domestic Dilemma" by Carson McCullers, from *The Ballad of the Sad Cafe*.

Alfred A. Knopf, Inc.: for "The Adulterous Woman" by Albert Camus, from *Exile and the Kingdom*, translated by Justin O'Brien, copyright, 1958, by Alfred A. Knopf, Inc.; for "The Bride Comes to Yellow Sky" by Stephen Crane, from *Stephen Crane: An Omnibus*, copyright, 1952, by Alfred A. Knopf, Inc.; for "Disorder and Early Sorrow" by Thomas Mann, from *Stories of Three Decades* by Thomas Mann, translated by H. T. Lowe-Porter, copyright, 1936, by Alfred A. Knopf, Inc.; for "The Fly" by Katherine Mansfield, from *The Short Stories of Katherine Mansfield*, copyright, 1922, 1937, by Alfred A. Knopf, Inc.; and for "The Drunkard" by Frank O'Connor, originally appeared in the *New Yorker*, from *The Stories of Frank O'Connor*, copyright, 1948, 1952, by Frank O'Connor.

John Lane: The Bodley Head, Ltd.: for "Dermuche" by Marcel Aymé, from *Across Paris*, Canadian rights.

Harold Matson Company: for "De Mortuis" by John Collier, originally appeared in the *New Yorker*, from *Fancies and Goodnights*, copyright, 1942, by John Collier; and for "The Drunkard" by Frank O'Connor, originally appeared in the *New Yorker*, from *The Stories of Frank O'Connor*, copyright, 1948, 1952, by Frank O'Connor.

William Morrow and Company, Inc.: for "Realpolitik" by Angus Wilson, from *The Wrong Set and Other Stories* by Angus Wilson, copyright, 1949, by Angus Wilson.

ACKNOWLEDGMENTS

New Directions: for "Eventide" by James Purdy from *Color of Darkness,* copyright, 1956, 1957, by James Purdy, reprinted by permission of New Directions; and for "The Fight" by Dylan Thomas, from *Portrait of the Artist as a Young Dog,* copyright, 1940, by New Directions, reprinted by permission of New Directions.

The New Yorker Magazine, Inc.: for "The Secret Life of Walter Mitty" by James Thurber. Permission the author; copr. © 1939 The New Yorker Magazine, Inc.

The New York Times: "Blackberry Winter: A Recollection," by Robert Penn Warren, originally appeared in a somewhat different version in *The New York Times Book Review.*

Harold Ober Associates, Inc.: for "I Want to Know Why" by Sherwood Anderson, from *The Triumph of the Egg,* published by B. W. Huebsch, Inc., copyright © 1921, by Eleanor Anderson, reprinted by permission of Harold Ober Associates, Incorporated.

Putnam & Company, Ltd.: for "The Sailor Boy's Tale" by Isak Dinesen, from *Winter's Tales,* Canadian rights.

Random House, Inc.: for "A Christmas Memory" by Truman Capote, from *Breakfast at Tiffany's,* by Truman Capote, © copyright, 1956, by Truman Capote, reprinted by permission of *Mademoiselle* and Random House, Inc.; for "The Sailor Boy's Tale" by Isak Dinesen, from *Winter's Tales,* by Isak Dinesen, copyright, 1942, by Random House, Inc., reprinted by permission of the publishers; for "A Rose for Emily" by William Faulkner, from *Collected Stories of William Faulkner,* copyright, 1930, and renewed, 1957, by William Faulkner, reprinted by permission of Random House, Inc.; and for "The Girls in Their Summer Dresses" by Irwin Shaw, from *Mixed Company* by Irwin Shaw, copyright, 1939, by Irwin Shaw, reprinted by permission of Random House, Inc.

Russell & Volkening, Inc.: for "Through the Quinquina Glass" by William Sansom, from *Fireman Flower* by William Sansom, copyright, 1945, by William Sansom.

Schocken Books, Inc.: for "In the Penal Colony" by Franz Kafka, by permission of *The Partisan Review,* publishers in the United States; copyright, 1941.

Charles Scribner's Sons: for "The Sensible Thing" by F. Scott Fitzgerald, copyright, 1924, Colorato Corp., renewal copyright, 1952, Francis Scott Fitzgerald Lanahan, reprinted from *All the Sad Young Men* by F. Scott Fitzgerald with permission of Charles Scribner's Sons; for "Old Red" by Caroline Gordon, copyright, 1933, Charles Scribner's Sons, reprinted from *Forest of the South* by Caroline Gordon with permission of Charles Scribner's Sons; for "The Killers" by Ernest Hemingway, copyright, 1927, Charles Scribner's Sons, renewal copyright, 1955, reprinted from *Men Without Women* by Ernest Hemingway with permission of Charles Scribner's Sons; for "Haircut" by Ring Lardner, copyright, 1925, Ellis A. Lardner, renewal copyright, 1953, reprinted from *The Love Nest and Other Stories* by Ring Lardner with permission of Charles Scribner's Sons; and for "The Far and the Near" by Thomas Wolfe, copyright, 1935, International Magazines, Inc., reprinted from *From Death to Morning* by Thomas Wolfe with permission of Charles Scribner's Sons.

Martin Secker & Warburg, Ltd.: for "Realpolitick" by Angus Wilson, from *The Wrong Set and Other Stories;* and for "The Bitch" by Colette, from *Creatures Great and Small,* Canadian rights.

Jesse Stuart: for his story "Love"

The Viking Press, Inc.: for "A Father-to-Be" by Saul Bellow, from *Seize the Day* by Saul Bellow, copyright, 1955, by Saul Bellow, originally appeared in the *New Yorker,* reprinted by permission of The Viking Press, Inc.; for "Araby" by James Joyce, from *Dubliners* by James Joyce, included in *The Portable James Joyce,* copyright, 1946, 1947, by The Viking Press, Inc., reprinted by permission of The Viking Press, Inc.; for "Tickets, Please" by D. H. Lawrence, from *England, My England* by D. H. Lawrence, included in *The Portable D. H. Lawrence,* copyright, 1922, by Thomas Seltzer, Inc., 1950, by Frieda Lawrence, reprinted by permission of The Viking Press, Inc.; and for "Lady Blessington" by Peter Quennell, from *Byron in Italy* by Peter Quennell, copyright, 1941, by Peter Quennell, reprinted by permission of The Viking Press, Inc.

The Virginia Quarterly Review: for "How I Write" by Eudora Welty, which originally appeared in the Spring, 1955, issue.

A. P. Watt & Son: for "The Man Who Would Be King" by Rudyard Kipling, Canadian rights.

Willis Kingsley Wing: for "R.M.S. *Titanic*" by Hanson Baldwin, originally appeared in *Harper's Magazine,* reprinted by permission of Willis Kingsley Wing, copyright, 1934, by Hanson Baldwin.

The Yale Review: for "Noon Wine: The Sources" by Katherine Anne Porter, which originally appeared in the Autumn, 1956, issue.

TO DONALD DAVIDSON

Preface

THE general principles on which this revision has been undertaken are the same as those of the original edition, of 1943. We might state those principles a little differently now, and under present circumstances make some shifts of emphasis, but in the original "Letter to the Teacher," here reprinted, we are leaving our old formulations for whoever has the curiosity to glance at them. Though our principles have remained fundamentally the same, our application of them in this new edition has resulted in a book very different from, and we hope better than, the old one.

First, there is the question of scale. The old edition had thirty-four stories, this has fifty. But the comparison of mere number is misleading. Only seventeen, that is, just half, of the stories in the original edition remain. We wish, in other words, to give not only more stories, but a greater variety of kind among the older writers and a representation of the substantial number of distinguished writers who have emerged in the last fifteen years.

We have, we trust, given a richer and more balanced picture of the short story, but our purpose has never been merely to make a representative anthology. It has been to devise a textbook that would help toward an understanding of the art and significance of fiction. So our motive in enlarging the book is primarily pedagogical. We are perfectly aware that some teachers will not be able to use all the stories here, but we hope that the number and variety now available will allow a teacher to tailor the course to the needs and tastes of his particular class.

Second, as another device to allow the teacher such flexibility, we now give a section of thirteen stories, by authors as various as Truman Capote, Mary McCarthy, and Joseph Conrad, with no interpretations, comments, or exercises. These stories have been carefully chosen to furnish links with previous stories—contrasts and comparisons, reapplications of principles and methods. They are not intended to be used only when the class has finished the previous sections. The teacher may use them at his discretion, feeding them in here and there to put the student on his mettle, to test him, to set him the task not only of discussing, but also of locating, the problems and cruxes in a piece of fiction.

Third, the central sections of the book have been drastically over-hauled. After years of using the book, our confidence in the inductive method has been fortified rather than shaken, but we have come to feel that the discussion of individual stories in the three sections on plot, character, and theme should be given more of a context. So we now have section introductions to set up some of the theoretical questions for guidance. Further, we have been more systematic in the scheme for each section, trying to make the progression from one story to another embody more definitely the development of critical principles, and giving more elaborate cross references and comparisons.

Fourth, in Section VI, as an entirely new feature, we present four essays, especially prepared for this book, in each of which an author undertakes to give the genesis of a story and its relation to his personal life. This section is not addressed primarily to students who want to write—though it may be useful to them. We hope that the section will serve all readers by making a dramatic presentation of the fact that fiction—serious fiction, at least—is grounded in experience and has a significant relation to the world of actuality, and that formal considerations spring from deep personal urgencies and are not finally to be thought of in isolation.

As we have said, this book is devised as a textbook, and the first virtue of a textbook is to be teachable. This book is, we are certain, richer and fuller than the old book. We hope that it is more practical, for on that question, it must stand or fall.

We wish to express our deep gratitude to Eudora Welty, Katherine Anne Porter, and John Cheever for preparing especially for this book the accounts of the backgrounds and origins of their several stories which appear in Section VI.

C. B.
R. P. W.

Letter to the Teacher*

MOST students read some kind of fiction of their own free will and for pleasure. This fact may lull the teacher of fiction into a false sense of security. He does not, he feels, have to "make" the student read fiction as he has to "make"the student read poetry or essays. He simply sets himself the easier problem of persuading the student that some fiction that is "good literature" or that has historical importance, is also interesting in itself. Frequently the student does discover that the "good" story or novel is interesting to him. Then the teacher says, in substance: "Look, you did like that story, and that story is literature. Therefore, you like literature, after all. You see, literature is not so bad." And having reached this conclusion, the teacher may feel that the objective of the course in fiction has been achieved.

But let us suppose that the student should read any number of stories which are called literature. No doubt, if he is somewhat more intelligent and sensitive than most, he will begin to ask questions of himself and to make comparisons, and his general taste will, as a result, be improved. But, unless he does attempt to read with deeper comprehension, it is doubtful whether any beneficial result can be had, no matter how many stories he reads or how many details of plot he can remember or how many characters he can name. The editors of this book believe that before extensive reading can be profitable, the student must have some practice in intensive reading. Otherwise, the interests which he originally brings to his reading will remain unchanged.

It is probably true, however, that a teacher must always build upon the interests which the student already possesses. But it is one thing to build upon those interests and quite another to take them as the standard of values by which the course is to be conducted. If the critical standards which the student possesses when he begins the course are adequate, then the course is superfluous and merely flatters him in his convictions. If the course merely encourages the student to systematize his views somewhat—to try to say why he likes or dislikes a story—some gain has certainly been made, for this process is essential to the development of taste. But if the views re-

* For convenience, the titles of a few stories used for illustration have been changed to conform to the contents of this edition.

main substantially unchanged, if the interests which he brings to fiction in the first place are not broadened and refined, the course has scarcely fulfilled its purpose: the student has merely grown more glib and complacent in his limitations.

Let us take a particular case. A student likes Kipling's "The Man Who Would Be King" because it is a story of romantic adventure, because he wants to know how it "comes out," but does not like Chekhov's "The Lament" because "nothing happens in it." One immediately realizes that the student is not giving a clear account of either story or even of his own reactions; that, in fact, he has not really "read" either story. In the first place, it is improbable that he likes "The Man Who Would Be King" simply because of the suspense concerning the external action. Matters of character, psychological development, and moral decision are inextricably involved with the action. It is true that the student may have a perfectly usual bias toward fiction of romantic setting and violent action, but it is only through a failure of introspection that he bases his case for the story merely on those elements. A little reflection should bring him to the conclusion that, even in the crudest story of violent action, he demands a certain modicum of characterization, a certain concern with the psychological basis of action, a certain interest in moral content and general meaning. And a little further reflection should lead him to the conclusion that his liking for the story may depend upon the organic relation existing among these elements—that his interest did not depend upon the element of violent plot, or the element of romantic setting, taken in isolation. If he has once faced this question, he may realize that his liking for a story does not depend finally upon his threshold interests, but rather depends, in one sense at least, upon the total structure, upon the logic of the whole, the relationships existing among elements of character and psychology, action, social situation, ideas and attitudes, style, and so on.

There are innumerable types of threshold interest which bring readers to fiction. Some of these types are clearly defined and well recognized in the field of magazine fiction. There are "sport" stories, "young love" stories, "marriage problem" stories, "moral" stories, "child" stories, "sea" stories, "Wild West" stories, "farm" stories, "business" stories, "crime" stories, and the like. Such threshold interests as are appealed to by these types may derive from a variety of factors. A man who knows the world of baseball may come to fiction that deals with that subject expecting the pleasure of recognition, of dwelling on what he knows and likes in real life. Such a reader demands a high degree of fidelity to the external facts of the world in which he is interested. But another reader may come, let us say, to baseball stories or to Wild West stories, expecting the pleasure of escape from a life which does not afford him sport or adventure. He is scarcely concerned with incidental realism, with recognizing a world which he already knows, but with extending his experience into a world which he does not know.

Both of these impulses, the impulse to dwell on the known world in fiction and to judge the fictional rendering by the facts of observation, and the impulse to enlarge experience through fiction, are perfectly normal and admirable; they are, in rudimentary form, the impulse toward contemplation and the impulse toward fulfillment, the demand for logic and the demand for imagination. They are pernicious only when they operate in isolation from each other and when they stop at the level of the threshold interest. For instance, if the baseball player or fan who reads only baseball stories should apply his criteria of realism, his tests of recognition and logic, to matters of characterization and psychology and theme as well as to the technical questions concerning the world of baseball, he would probably find unsatisfactory many of the stories which ordinarily satisfy his threshold interest. Or, if the reader who goes to adventure stories for escape from a humdrum existence could realize that his experience could be extended more fully by reading fiction which does not merely emphasize the elements of violent action and romantic setting but which also leads to some understanding of the inner lives of other people, or to some understanding of his own life, he might be less content with the escape based on merely external differences from the circumstances of his own experience.

Our hypothetical student may object that he has lost, and not gained, by such a process, for his area of potential enjoyment has been limited by the process. But actually the process which leads him past the mere threshold interest to the fuller interests implicit in fiction causes an enlargement of the area of his potential enjoyment. As a human being, he has interests wider than baseball or Western adventure, and he may come to realize that, even in the shoddiest story dealing with baseball or the Wild West, his other more fundamental interests have been covertly engaged. And he may realize, further, that without the appeal to those other interests there would be no story at all. The Wild West and baseball, finally, interest him in terms of certain persons, with certain motivations and with certain characteristics, who have certain experiences; and these experiences themselves are of little interest to him except in so far as they involve certain meanings—success and failure, courage and cowardice, generosity and cruelty, and the like—which are dramatized in character and action. This returns us to the notion that the liking for a piece of fiction does not depend upon the satisfaction of the threshold interest, whatever it may be, football or moral message-hunting or sociological documentation, but upon the total structure, upon a set of organic relationships, upon the logic of the whole.

This book is based on the belief that the student can best be brought to an appreciation of the more broadly human values implicit in fiction by a course of study which aims at the close analytical and interpretative reading of concrete examples. It seems to us that the student may best come to understand a given piece of fiction by understanding the functions of the various elements which go to make up fiction and by understanding their relationships to each other in the whole construct. The editors believe that such an end may best be achieved by the use of an inductive method, by the use of concrete cases which can be investigated and interpreted and compared with each other. The organization of the book is based on that principle.

The problem of the nature and structure of fiction is first approached (pp. 2–21) through the investigation of five negative examples: one, which is almost pure action, an anecdote from Parkman's *The Oregon Trail;* three, which are almost pure descriptions of character; one, which is narrative developed almost as pure symbol, the account of the sinking of the *Titanic.* Each of these examples, although interesting in itself, lacks some element which is vital to fiction. In other words, the attempt is here made to illustrate by particular examples the difference between the interest which specifically attaches to fiction and the interests which may merely be involved in the materials of fiction. Further, the fact that all of the examples used are drawn from history raises a second question, that of the kind of truth aimed at by fiction. It is not pretended that these complicated questions are answered in these first pages, but the editors believe that an awareness of their importance is an absolutely necessary preliminary to the proper reading of fiction. . . .

The method is now reversed, and the rest of Section I is devoted to the presentation of three fully developed stories: one which emphasizes action, one which emphasizes character, and one which emphasizes theme in terms of allegory and symbol. The purpose here is to illustrate, by the analysis and interpretation of the various stories, the fact that the particular emphases in the individual stories—on plot, on character, on theme—are merely superficial, that the element which is emphasized in each case is inextricably involved with other elements in the fictional construct.

Sections II, III, and IV are closely related to each other and really represent an extension and development of the principles touched on in Section I. Section II deals primarily with problems of plot. This is not to say that the stories involved are stories in which the plot interest obtrudes itself— that they are examples of what is called "the plot story." As a matter of fact, some of the stories in this section, such as "War," by Pirandello, and "A Piece of News," by Eudora Welty, scarcely involve overt action at all. Rather, the stories chosen for this section, along with their interpretations and exercises, are intended to illustrate a variety of types and functions of plot with a constant emphasis on the relationship of the plot to other factors. In Section III the same method is used in regard to certain problems of character in fiction; and in Section IV, in regard to certain problems of realizing theme in fiction. But in all of these sections other questions have been raised in the course of the discussions and in the exercises, questions of style and tone, for example, as related to the basic intentions of the stories.

Section V* raises a number of special problems, and re-emphasizes certain problems already discussed: irony, tragic and comic and humorous effects, indirection, fantasy, allegory and symbolism, style and tone, scale, pace, and focus. The stories used in Section V are not intended, and could not well be expected, to exhaust the special problems which appear in fiction. And certainly it cannot be expected that an exhaustive treatment of these questions could be given in the accompanying discussions. The editors simply hope to raise these questions in concrete terms for the student and to increase his awareness of the various subtle means by which an author of fiction may achieve his total communication.

The Appendix will have, it is hoped, a double function, a function for the student reader of fiction and for the student writer of fiction. It has no doubt been observed that the discussions of stories in this book have not frequently touched on the questions which are usually called "technical" in the narrow sense of the word: questions of exposition, complication, climax, proportion, focus of interest, focus of narration, and the like. The editors feel, rather, that it is usually fruitless to raise such superficially technical questions until the student has some grasp of the more fundamental considerations, some notion of the relationships among the elements which go to make up the fictional structure.

Therefore, it is suggested that, for classes in which the reading of fiction is the sole objective, the study of the Appendix may well be undertaken after the completion of Section V. At that time certain of the stories already studied may be investigated anew in the light of the technical questions discussed in the Appendix. To facilitate this process, the Appendix draws all of its examples from the stories in this collection.

For classes in which the students are expected to write stories, it is suggested that a similar program may be followed, though such classes may find it profitable to undertake the study of the Appendix after the completion of Section IV. The editors would justify this delay in the study of the Appendix on the following grounds. First, the early concern with questions of exposition, complication, climax, and so on, tends to encourage the student in the all too ordinary view that the composition of fiction is primarily a mechanical activity, that to write fiction he has only to get the hang of a bag of tricks. It tends to distract him from the more fundamental considerations which, it is hoped, are the subject matter of the discussions and exercises up through Section V. Further, this book does not pretend to be a collection of "models" for short-story writers. The editors believe, in fact, that the tendency to emphasize certain stories as models

---

* The section referred to here is, of course, Section V of the first edition, not of the present book.

encourages imitation at the wrong level. It encourages imitation of particular effects found in the model and not imitation in terms of principles by which effects are rendered. The imitation of particular effects distracts the student from the candid exploration of his own feelings and attitudes; the imitation in terms of principles should give him the instruments by which he can explore his own feelings and attitudes and realize them in form. This is only one way of saying that the only way to teach something about writing may be through a discipline in critical reading.

The selection of stories has been undertaken with the hope of providing as wide a range of examples in terms of fictional method as could be reasonably expected in a book of this size. There has been no attempt at great novelty in selection. Rather, the editors have, in large part, chosen stories which are popular and widely anthologized. Nor has there been any attempt at making this book a representative collection or a collection of masterpieces. Many authors of great importance, and many stories for which the editors feel the keenest admiration, are omitted. Furthermore, certain stories which are definitely inferior are included in order to give the student exercise in destructive analysis and criticism. Again, there has been no attempt to present key examples in the history of the short story. In fact, the history of the short story, except at the narrowest technical level, can scarcely be discussed at all in isolation from the history of fiction in general and of poetry. But the editors have undertaken to give materials for some historical investigation of the influences and methods found in the modern short story. For instance, exercises might be framed on the comparisons or contrasts between Katherine Mansfield and Chekhov; between Buzzati and Kafka or Shirley Jackson; between Bret Harte or Kipling and Hemingway; between Poe and Faulkner; and between other pairs. The selection is necessarily smaller than the editors would have wished, for the number of stories which can be admitted to a single volume is limited.

It will no doubt be observed, and by some readers objected to, that for the most part the interpretations in this book are descriptive and analytical rather than evaluative. But the editors feel that, in general, the matter of the relative grading of stories, except for broad distinctions, should arise late rather than early in the critical process. The first problem is to understand the nature of fictional structure, to become acquainted with the idiom in terms of which the art operates, and to broaden the imaginative sympathies so that the student can transcend stock responses and threshold interests. But this process necessarily will lead to evaluation in a broad sense. A student does not have to go very far in the investigation of fictional structure before he understands that O. Henry's "The Furnished Room" depends for its effect not on a functional relationship among its elements but on arbitrary manipulation by the author, or before he understands that the irony here is accidental as compared with the irony in Pirandello's "War," or in Chekhov's "The Lament." Such a discrimination as this should come early and naturally, but an attempt to discriminate between the value of "The Lament" and that of "Tickets, Please," by Lawrence ought probably to come rather late. It is very important, to be sure, to be able to discriminate between the methods and effects of "The Lament" and those of "Tickets, Please," for such discrimination should lead to a fuller appreciation of both pieces; but an early effort to grade two such successful stories on their relative merits may encourage critical vindictiveness and literary priggishness. It has been aptly said that a literary dictator has no place in the republic of letters.

Another and more specific objection which may be raised concerns the apparent emphasis on formal considerations in the evaluation of fiction— what may be thought the editors' failure to give adequate heed to the importance, on ethical, religious, philosophical, or sociological grounds, of the "idea" in a piece of fiction. In attempting to reply to such an objection the editors would first say that idea or theme is one of the elements in the fictional structure, but that the structure is not to be set over against the idea in any mechanical fashion. Rather, it is their first article of faith that the structure of a piece of fiction, in so far as that piece of fiction is successful, must involve a vital and functional relationship between the idea and the other elements in that structure—plot, style, character, and the like. In the second place, they would agree that to be good, a piece of fiction must involve an idea of some real significance for mature and thoughtful human beings. This does not mean that to appreciate a piece of fiction such a mature and thoughtful reader must *agree* with the idea realized in it; but it does mean that the question raised by the piece of fiction must seem to him worthy of serious exploration. For instance, the mature and thoughtful reader whom we have posited might not accept the view of the world which underlies Hemingway's fiction, but he might very well realize the difficulty of transcending such a view of the world. That is, he might admit that the question implicit in Hemingway's fiction is a real question, even though he might feel that he himself had transcended Hemingway's solution. If, on the other hand, he is of such an unrelentingly dogmatic disposition that he restricts his approbation to works which involve ideas with which he is in precise accord, he will probably find himself subsisting on very poverty-stricken literary diet. Worse still, he will not even be able to receive nourishment from the diet which he accepts, for he will be reading merely in terms of his threshold interest and will not be submitting his beliefs to the test of imaginative experience. In literature, ideas leave their cloisters and descend into the dust and heat to prove their virtue anew.

But the editors would wish to make a further remark on this general point, a remark concerning the level at which an idea in fiction becomes important. The mere presence in a piece of fiction of an idea which is held to be important in itself on ethical, religious, philosophical, sociological, or other grounds, does not necessarily indicate anything about the importance of the piece of fiction. One might almost as well commend a piece of fiction for exemplifying good grammatical usage. The mere presence of the "good" idea or the "good" grammar tells us nothing about the final success of the item in question. The idea is important in a story in so far as it is incorporated into the total structure—in so far as the story lives out the idea and, in the process of living, modifies the idea. The idea as an abstraction is absolute; but the idea in a story forfeits that privilege of absoluteness and must accept the dangers of qualification and modification. Everyone is familiar with stories in which "good" ideas emerge as cruel parodies of themselves, brutally debased by insensitive style and crude characterization and arbitrary psychology, for instance, or else sentimentalized by defects in logic and mechanical plot management. In fact, most popular fiction aims at flattering the ethical sense of the public. That such fiction is often, in the last analysis, corrupt derives from the fact that the author does not recognize the necessity of attempting to realize the idea fully in the experience of his characters and in the structure of his story. The villain bites the dust; the good heart triumphs over all. The author does not recognize the difficulty, let us say, in making a moral decision, and simply follows the idea as blueprint, as dogma. Situations which qualify an idea of virtue and emphasize the difficulty of moral decision—such as the situation which confronts Cordelia in the first scene of *King Lear* or that which confronts Isabella in her condemned brother's cell in *Measure for Measure* —do not flourish in the fiction of our best family magazines. . . .

A piece of fiction is a unity, in so far as the piece of fiction is successful. Its elements are so related that we feel an expressive interpenetration among them, a set of vital relationships. But the unity which the fictional structure possesses is of a very special kind. It is not the result of a purely genial conspiracy among the constituent elements. There is conflict and tension present, and the structure involves almost as much of vindictive opposition as of genial conspiracy. One says "almost" because some sort of resolution, however provisional and marginal, must be implicit in the tensions of the fictional structure, if the unity is to be achieved—if the revelation is to be had. The fact of conflict as an essential aspect of fiction is clearly stated in every handbook. In its most obvious form it concerns a collision of interests in the external world. In a somewhat more subtle and sophisticated form conflict concerns a division of interests or obligations in the self. In an even more subtle and sophisticated form, it concerns the alignment of judgments and sympathies on the part of the author—the problem of his own self-division.

The dogmatist who is author paints a world of black and white, a world in which right and wrong, truth and falsehood, are clear with statutory distinctness, a world of villain and hero. The artist who is author paints a world in which there is, in the beginning, neither black nor white, neither right nor wrong which can be defined with absolute certainty. The certainty can only come in terms of the process, and must be *earned*, as it were, through the process. In other words, the artist is sporting enough to put the best case possible for the opposition. But this is not mere sportsmanship. The artist realizes that, if the opponent—"villain" or "idea"—is a straw man, the conflict will lack interest. In a simple example such as *Richard III*, we observe that Shakespeare makes the traditional and historical Tudor villain the vessel of certain virtues which the Tudor age seems to have admired inordinately. Without this ironical ambivalence, the play would be a tedious recital of butcheries to prove that you can't kill all of the people all of the time. It would have had no psychological center for tension, either in terms of the main character or in terms of the audience. Or, to glance at other simple cases, we may recall that in *Uncle Tom's Cabin* Simon Legree is a Yankee, and that in Hemingway's *For Whom the Bell Tolls* the scene of greatest brutality is that of the massacre of Fascists by Loyalists, or that the book closes with the distant figure of the young Fascist lieutenant (whom Hemingway has previously presented as a sympathetic character) caught in the gunsights of the hero. In all of these cases, the irony is intended, on the one hand, to intensify the implications of the conflict, and on the other, to raise the issue above the level of merely dogmatic and partisan vilification. But these two functions are closely interrelated and only by an act of abstraction can one, in many cases, separate them out.

Another function, also closely related, is to indicate an awareness of the multiplicity of options in conduct, idea, or attitude—an awareness of the full context. This suggests one of the objections which may be brought against the emphasis on irony; the objection that such an emphasis ends in the celebration of a smug and futile skepticism which is at variance with the actual effect which most successful literary compositions leave upon the reader. The editors would hope that, by this time, the grounds upon which they would answer this particular objection are clear. They would not endorse an irony which precluded resolution but they would endorse an irony which forced the resolution to take stock of as full a context as possible. The reader wants the resolution, but he does not want it too easy or too soon. He wants to see the knockout, but he does not want to see it until the fifteenth round. And, if he feels that the fight has been fixed, he will want to stop at the box office on the way out and demand his money back. . . .

The editors perhaps should crave the indulgence of the teacher for intruding this discussion of their general views into what should be a mere description of the aims and methods of this textbook. But they hope that the utility of this book for the individual teacher will not stand or fall by the teacher's assent to those views, just as they hope that it will not stand or fall by the teachers' assent to the editors' interpretation of particular stories. Certainly they do not wish to be dogmatic, for they realize too acutely the pitfalls in the way of even the most elementary critical analysis. They merely hope that this book raises certain profitable questions in a relatively systematic form for the student, and that by so doing it may render the task of the teacher a little easier. For the editors feel that no book, however much better than this, can do more than be of some slight assistance to the teacher in the classroom, upon whom the final responsibility must rest.

C. B.
R. P. W.
1943

Contents

SECTION III
What Character Reveals

SECTION IV
What Theme Reveals

SECTION V
Stories for Study

SECTION VI

Fiction and Human Experience:
How Four Stories Came to Be Written

SECTION I

The Intentions of Fiction

THIS is a book about the reading of fiction, and it might seem desirable to begin with a definition of the subject. But in one sense a definition is unnecessary, because everyone feels that he knows what fiction is. It is a story, a made-up story, about characters. (Even when the "characters" are animals, it is the human trait read into the animal which makes it a character at all.) But the trouble with this definition is that it is too easy, too simple, and throws little light on the stories which one encounters. It would be possible to construct a much more elaborate definition, but such a definition would necessarily be complicated and abstract. At this point, therefore, it may be more fruitful to work toward an understanding of our subject through an investigation of individual stories. Furthermore it may be helpful to consider first some pieces of writing which do not pretend to be fiction, but which, because they exhibit some of the qualities of fiction, may throw light on fiction itself.

Consider first, for example, the following paragraphs taken from Francis Parkman's *The Oregon Trail*, a work in which Parkman, who actually went West in the early days, tells what life on the Great Plains was like.

1

FRANCIS PARKMAN

The Attack on the Fort

SIX years ago, a fellow named Jim Beckworth, a mongrel of French, American, and Negro blood, was trading for the Fur Company, in a large village of the Crows. Jim Beckworth was last summer at St. Louis. He is a ruffian of the worst stamp, bloody and treacherous, without honor or honesty; such at least is the character he bears upon the prairie. Yet in his case the standard rules of character fail, for though he will stab a man in his sleep, he will also perform most desperate acts of daring; such, for instance, as the following: While he was in the Crow village, a Blackfoot war-party, between thirty and forty in number, came stealing through the country, killing stragglers and carrying off horses. The Crow warriors got upon their trail and pressed them so closely that they could not escape, at which the Blackfeet, throwing up a semi-circular breastwork of logs at the foot of a precipice, coolly awaited their approach. The logs and sticks, piled four or five feet high, protected them in front. The Crows might have swept over the breastwork and exterminated their enemies; but though outnumbering them tenfold, they did not dream of storming the little fortification. Such a proceeding would be altogether repugnant to their notions of warfare. Whooping and yelling, and jumping from side to side like devils incarnate, they showered bullets and arrows upon the logs; not a Blackfoot was hurt, but several Crows, in spite of their leaping and dodging, were shot down. In this childish manner, the fight went on for an hour or two. Now and then a Crow warrior, in an ecstasy of valor and vainglory, would scream forth his war song, boast himself the bravest and greatest of mankind, grasp his hatchet, rush up, strike it upon the breastwork, and then, as he retreated to his companions, fall dead under a shower of arrows; yet no combined attack was made. The Blackfeet remained secure in their intrenchment. At last Jim Beckworth lost patience.

"You are all fools and old women," he said to the Crows; "come with me, if any of you are brave enough, and I will show you how to fight."

He threw off his trapper's frock of buckskin and stripped himself naked, like the Indians themselves. He left his rifle on the ground, took in his hand a small light hatchet, and ran over the prairie to the right, concealed by a hollow from the eyes of the Blackfeet. Then climbing up the rocks, he gained the top of the precipice behind them. Forty or fifty young

Crow warriors followed him. By the cries and whoops that rose from below he knew that the Blackfeet were just beneath him; and running forward, he leaped down the rock into the midst of them. As he fell he caught one by the long loose hair, and dragging him down, tomahawked him; then grasping another by the belt at his waist, he struck him also a stunning blow, and, gaining his feet, shouted the Crow war cry. He swung his hatchet so fiercely around him that the astonished Blackfeet bore back and gave him room. He might, had he chosen, have leaped over the breastwork and escaped; but this was not necessary, for with devilish yells the Crow warriors came dropping in quick succession over the rock among their enemies. The main body of the Crows, too, answered the cry from the front, and rushed up simultaneously. The convulsive struggle within the breastwork was frightful; for an instant the Blackfeet fought and yelled like pent-up tigers; but the butchery was soon complete, and the mangled bodies lay piled together under the precipice. Not a Blackfoot made his escape.

There are two preliminary observations which one may make on this anecdote. First, it really happened, it is not made up. Second, Parkman wrote it, not primarily because it was spirited and interesting in itself, but because it illustrated one aspect of the life which he wanted to describe to the people back at home. These observations raise two questions. First, would this anecdote be fiction if Parkman had simply made it up out of his head? Second, would it be fiction if Parkman had written it, not to instruct his readers, but because it was interesting in itself? The answer to both of these questions is "no."

We must answer "no" to the first question because, though fiction is not tied to fact, it may use fact. Many pieces of fiction make as much use of historical fact as does this. We must answer "no" to the second question because, though many pieces of fiction are written with a desire to instruct the reader, they are not written with the purpose to instruct the reader merely about matters of fact.

If we are not debarred from calling this anecdote fiction because it is true and not because the author's purpose was to instruct the reader, why, then, is it not to be considered fiction? To answer this question, we must look at the nature of the anecdote itself.

The anecdote proper is simply a spirited piece of action which, as a piece of action, is unified. That is, we have the situation precipitating the fight, the cunning defense by the Blackfeet Indians which creates a problem for the attackers, the failure of the attackers to solve their problem, then the daring solution by Beckworth. The anecdote, as action, is unified because it presents problem and solution, because it has a beginning, middle, and end. Our curiosity about the outcome is satisfied. But does this outcome satisfy fully the interest which we bring to fiction?

Certainly, our curiosity about the outcome of an action, as action, is one of the elements of our interest in fiction. A great deal of fiction is written with the appeal to this curiosity in the foreground, as for instance, detective stories and adventure stories. But even in these types of fiction, there are other important interests involved. In a detective story, one wants to know not only who did "it," but why "it" was done. The author of even the crudest detective or adventure story always feels obligated to satisfy this interest: he attributes *motive* to his characters.

Does Parkman's anecdote satisfy this interest? Why did Jim Beckworth undertake the daring feat? It is a question which is raised in the mind of anyone who reads the episode, but it is a question for which the author gives no answer. We can guess at a number of answers, but the author takes no responsibility for any of our guesses; he simply gives us the *external* action, what was said and done, and does not give us any real inkling as to the *internal* action, as to what went on inside Jim Beckworth's head. We must confess, however, that Parkman does raise a general question about Beckworth's character: "in his case the standard rules of character fail, for though he will stab a man in his sleep, he will also perform most desperate acts of daring." But this remark is merely preliminary to the anecdote, which illustrates the author's statement, and does not do anything to answer the question as to why Beckworth behaves in this fashion, and does not help us to understand more clearly the process by which Beckworth arrives at his decision.

Why, then, do we not call this anecdote fiction? Certainly one reason is that its action is purely *external;* it does not sufficiently involve character and motive; it does not answer fully enough our basic interest about human action.

Let us look at another example, a modern description of the author's great-great-grandfather, who was born in the eighteenth century.

CHRISTOPHER SYKES

Sir Tatton Sykes

HE was famous in his day. In such centers of sporting culture as Yorkshire, Melton Mowbray, and Newmarket, he is not quite forgotten even now. He was called Sir Tatton Sykes. Frequent references to this baronet occur in the novels of Surtees, in which he figures generally as "old Tat," also as "Sir Tat," and "Tatters";

and I have noticed that it is often difficult to determine whether he is treated as a figure of fun or veneration in those splendid romances. Possibly as both. He lived to extreme old age, being born before the Duke of Wellington and not dying till the eighteen sixties. From youth to death he never weakened in an almost insane passion for fox-hunting, racing, and the very companionship of horses. It formed the whole basis of his life and character. He never sold a horse if he could avoid doing so, and yet, oddly enough, he parted at a cheap price with the best and most famous of his breed. Taking Surtees as my authority once more, I find myself in doubt as to whether he was looked on as an astute or a poor judge of the animal he so madly worshipped.

As might be expected, he was an eccentric. Until his death in the age of peg-top trousers he wore the long high-collared coat of the regency, chokers, frills, and mahogany topped boots. Although he had received the education of a gentleman, at Westminster and Brasenose College, Oxford, he spoke in the dialect of Yorkshire throughout his life, using extreme modes of that extreme variation of English speech. This affectation was very typical of the English eighteenth century. He was very vain, he exploited the then meager arts of publicity with shrewdness. His engraved picture and later his daguerreotype, taken in the act of patting or, as portrayed by Sir Francis Grant, riding one of his numerous favorite horses, or reposing in his boots after hunting, with a smile on his countenance fairly bursting with benevolence and cunning, these likenesses were widely circulated among sportsmen of the time. Ludicrous and yet respected, a charlatan in some ways, and yet a homely, comforting, familiar figure, a symbol and a caricature of England, I dare say he was revered and mocked in equal degrees. He was much loved too. To the credit of our humanity, the last departing tenant of an age received an affectionate farewell as a rule. "Tat" was almost the last human being of the eighteenth century to leave the world, and his fellowmen honoured him greatly for it. But they would have honored him a little less, I feel, if they had known how he preserved to the last the more revolting vices of the brutal age which produced him.

His pleasant Adamesque house was a barbaric hell. He ruled over his family with the vicious rage of a stone-age tyrant. That fierce and obscure revival of parental oppression which, according to its historian, Samuel Butler, first became noticeable in the mid-eighteenth century and did not decline till some eighty or ninety years later, this extraordinary relapse found absolute personification in the home life of the old sportsman. He begot a large family: two sons and six daughters. On them he imposed simple and intolerable rules of life: that the virtues resided in rising at dawn in Winter and Summer, on no hot water, on no creature comforts (the girls slept in one small room), and on submission to frequent applications of the paternal whip. An enigmatical portrait survives of his wife, painted by Sir Francis Grant. Resignation and hardness are oddly combined in her features; one wonders whether she made this bestial manner of life less unbearable for her children.

Obviously, this is not a piece of fiction. Even if Sir Tatton Sykes were a creation of the writer's imagination, and not a real person who died a century ago, the fact would not render this a piece of fiction. This is a character sketch. The author describes Sir Tatton's personal appearance and gives a brief account of the kind of life that he led. There is even a little character analysis.

Fiction, to be sure, exhibits all these properties: description, the portrayal of character, and most of all the rendition of the vivid, concrete details that present a mode of life—"the long high-collared coat of the regency," "mahogany topped boots," a "pleasant Adamesque house," and the like. But this sketch is static in its presentation, whereas fiction characteristically makes its presentation through action: *fiction gives us character primarily through action.*

How overt the action in a piece of fiction should be is not a matter easily determined. Frequently the action may be very slight in the physical sense, but may involve very important psychological changes, as for example in the story "Old Red," p. 232 or "The Lament," p. 203. But no matter how slight the action in a piece of fiction may appear to be, it always provides us with a "line," a progression of events which may be either external or internal in emphasis, and comes to some definite conclusion. The conclusion may result in very positive external changes or merely in a new awareness on the part of a character, but things are not as they were before. *A story involves change.*

The basic reason for regarding this piece of writing as a character sketch and not as fiction is that it has no "line" and shows no change. It is static. But though this sketch is not a story, yet it uses, as we have pointed out above, a number of the methods which fiction uses; and indeed it is full of incipient stories.

These are, for instance, suggestions of stories about fox hunting. Indeed, as our author has pointed out, the novelist Robert Surtees has made references to Sir Tatton in his sporting stories. But it is easy to imagine other stories in which such a character might figure; for example, a story of conflict between Sir Tatton and his sons, or a story about Sir Tatton's being forced to sell one of his horses, or a story of how Sir Tatton found, or failed to find, something to sustain him when age took him away from the active sports which had been his whole life. Indeed, from the standpoint of fiction we have *too many* stories implied by this sketch. We can see that all of them attach logically to such a personality, but unfortunately no one of them is developed. Had the author cared to develop this sketch as a piece of fiction, he would have been compelled to choose what story he wanted to tell and to omit the other possible stories or scale them into positions subordinate to it.

Let us consider another character sketch, one that presents another personality and indeed another world. Here is Mark Twain's brief account of an old Mississippi River steamboat pilot.

MARK TWAIN

Captain Isaiah Sellers

WE had some talk about Captain Isaiah Sellers, now many years dead. He was a fine man, a high-minded man, and greatly respected both ashore and on the river. He was very tall, well built, and handsome; and in his old age—as I remember him—his hair was as black as an Indian's, and his eye and hand were as strong and steady and his nerve and judgment as firm and clear as anybody's, young or old, among the fraternity of pilots. He was the patriarch of the craft; he had been a keelboat pilot before the day of steamboats; and a steamboat pilot before any other steamboat pilot, still surviving at the time I speak of, had ever turned a wheel. Consequently, his brethren held him in the sort of awe in which illustrious survivors of a bygone age are always held by their associates. He knew how he was regarded, and perhaps this fact added some trifle of stiffening to his natural dignity, which had been sufficiently stiff in its original state.

He left a diary behind him; but apparently it did not date back to his first steamboat trip, which was said to be 1811, the year the first steamboat disturbed the waters of the Mississippi. . . .

Whenever Captain Sellers approached a body of gossiping pilots, a chill fell there, and talking ceased. For this reason: whenever six pilots were gathered together, there would always be one or two newly fledged ones in the lot, and the elder ones would be always "showing off" before these poor fellows; making them sorrowfully feel how callow they were, how recent their nobility, and how humble their degree, by talking largely and vaporously of old-time experiences on the river; always making it a point to date everything back as far as they could, so as to make the new men feel their newness to the sharpest degree possible, and envy the old stagers in the like degree. And how these complacent baldheads *would* swell, and brag, and lie, and date back—ten, fifteen, twenty years, and how they did enjoy the effect produced upon the marveling and envying youngsters!

And perhaps just at this happy stage of the proceedings, the stately figure of Captain Isaiah Sellers, that real and only genuine Son of Antiquity, would drift solemnly into the midst. Imagine the size of the silence that would result on the instant! And imagine the feelings of those baldheads, and the exultation of their recent audience, when the ancient captain would begin to drop casual and indifferent remarks of a reminiscent nature—about islands that had disappeared, and cut-offs that had been made, a generation before the oldest baldhead in the company had ever set his foot in a pilot-house!

Many and many a time did this ancient mariner appear on the scene in the above fashion, and spread disaster and humiliation around him. If one might believe the pilots, he always dated his islands back to the misty dawn of river history; and he never used the same island twice; and never did he employ an island that still existed, or give one a name which anybody present was old enough to have heard of before. If you might believe the pilots, he was always conscientiously particular about little details; never spoke "the state of Mississippi," for instance—no, he would say, "When the state of Mississippi was where Arkansas now is"; and would never speak of Louisiana or Missouri in a general way, and leave an incorrect impression on your mind—no, he would say, "When Louisiana was up the river farther," or "When Missouri was on the Illinois side."

In this sketch Captain Isaiah is treated humorously, though affectionately, as a repository of stories about the river. His stories are obviously marvelous and grandiose and put those told by the other pilots very much in the shade. As Mark Twain develops his sketch, he has placed little stress on the Captain's stories as aborbing tales of adventure in their own right. They are rather legends out of the "misty dawn of river history," and Mark Twain more than hints that they are fabulous rather than real.

It is easy, however, to imagine that some of these stories of life on the river, told with a different inflection, might become the material of serious fiction involving moral conflict, heroism, or ethical decisions agonizingly made. After all, as Mark Twain tells us, Captain Isaiah was a high-minded man with an iron hand "as strong and steady and [a] nerve and judgment as firm and clear as anybody's." And in a further paragraph Mark Twain refers to Captain Isaiah as "a man who . . . would have stayed [at the pilot wheel] till he burned to a cinder, if duty required it." So much for the possibility of the Captain's figuring in a heroic tale of the river. But it is also easy to see how Captain Isaiah might figure in a humorous story whose spirit would be close to that of this character sketch. One can imagine his exposing some boaster of deeds of derring-do on the Mississippi or perhaps his outdoing them with a superior boasting of his own. But clearly we could not substitute Captain Isaiah in a story into which Sir Tatton would fit admirably, nor could we make Sir Tatton exchange places with our steamboat pilot. A heroic action or a humorous action appropriate to one would not be appropriate to the other.

Let us consider one more brief sketch, that of Lady Blessington as Peter Quennell describes her in his *Byron in Italy*.

PETER QUENNELL

Lady Blessington

MARGUERITE Blessington was an adventurous and amusing personage. The daughter of a petty landowner in County Waterford, at the age of fifteen she had been forced into a miserable marriage with a certain Captain St. Leger Farmer of the 47th Foot. After three months, Mrs. Farmer had left her husband; Lawrence had painted her portrait in 1807; and she next re-emerges as the mistress of a Captain Jenkins with whom for several years she had lived in placid domestic retirement. From Captain Jenkins's arms Marguerite Farmer had moved to those of the plutocratic, extravagant, fashionable Lord Mountjoy, and from Stidmanton in Hampshire to a house in Manchester Square. By falling while he was drunk out of the window of a debtor's jail, Captain Farmer had removed the last obstacle to his wife's good fortune, and from that moment she had swept onward with superb assurance. Lord Blessington, an indistinct but kindly figure, was as lavish as he was rich, and as complaisant or unsuspicious as he was devoted. With the Blessingtons travelled that dazzling ephebus Count Alfred d'Orsay, paragon of elegance and model of manly grace, whom the world regarded, no doubt correctly, as Lady Blessington's lover.

At thirty-five, with her shining dark· hair, neatly parted down the middle of the scalp and drawn back from the smooth white forehead, her delicate skin, noble brow, and lustrous expressive eyes, Marguerite Blessington retained all her power of pleasing. To good looks she added a brisk intelligence, and to vivacity and curiosity some touches of literary aptitude. Naturally, she was eager to visit Byron; and, though Tom Moore when she met him in Paris had alarmed her by the announcement that the poet was growing corpulent—"a fat poet is an anomaly in my opinion"— it was full of tremulous interest, not unmixed with awe, that she arrived at Genoa. To her diary she expressed her hopes and fears by means of a rhetorical question: ". . . Am I indeed in the same town with Byron? Tomorrow I may, perhaps, behold him. I never before felt the same impatient longing to see any one known to me only by his work." Next day, with Lord Blessington's help, the longing was gratified; and following her first impressions came a tiny earthquake tremor of disappointment.

With this last example of the character sketch, we have moved quite a distance from the static description with which we tend to associate such sketches. Quennell has given us Lady Blessington's character largely through a summary of her past actions. At the beginning of the second paragraph to be sure, Quennell paints a striking picture of her. But then the sketch moves on into action once more as we enter into her anticipation of her meeting with the poet. Quennell gives us a bit of the conversation that passed between her and one of her friends, and quotes from her diary on the eve of her meeting with Byron. Though our excerpt is taken from a biography, the method is very close to that of fiction. Lady Blessington's character is presented to us dramatically, which means through action.

One can easily imagine Lady Blessington's becoming a character in a historical novel. The writer of fiction might well try to imagine what actually went on in her mind and heart when "at the age of fifteen she had been forced into a miserable marriage with a certain Captain St. Leger Farmer of the 47th Foot." Since we know very little of this period of her life beyond the facts so cursorily summarized, an author would have to use his imagination to present in concrete detail the inner stress of her life at this period, though undoubtedly he would make use of what had been preserved of her writings and conversations in later life as useful hints of what she had been earlier and what she must have suffered and what she must have done.

But the excerpt that we have quoted from *Byron in Italy* is not fiction. Nothing "happens"; even if we extended the excerpt to include the meeting between Byron and Lady Blessington and their later relationship, we still would not have a piece of fiction. For the account is not focused upon a significant happening. The "tiny earthquake tremor of disappointment" does not become a shattering event, changing Lady Blessington's life, or even giving her a new insight into human beings, or telling her something about herself, or bringing her into a new understanding of reality. The meaning of her meeting with Byron is—quite properly for Quennell's purposes—never brought into sharp focus.

What is involved in fiction's characteristic focus on meaning is best observed, however, by considering a piece of nonfiction in which there is a great deal of action. Let us look at the following account of the sinking of the *Titanic.*

HANSON BALDWIN

R.M.S. *Titanic*

THE White Star liner *Titanic*, largest ship the world had ever known, sailed from Southampton on her maiden voyage to New York on April 10, 1912. The paint on her strakes was fair and bright; she was fresh from Harland and Wolff's Belfast yards, strong in the strength of her forty-six thousand tons of steel, bent, hammered, shaped and riveted through the three years of her slow birth.

There was little fuss and fanfare at her sailing; her sister ship, the *Olympic*—slightly smaller than the *Titanic*—had been in service for some months and to her had gone the thunder of the cheers.

But the *Titanic* needed no whistling steamers or shouting crowds to call attention to her superlative qualities. Her bulk dwarfed the ships near her as longshoremen singled up her mooring lines and cast off the turns of heavy rope from the dock bollards. She was not only the largest ship afloat, but was believed to be the safest. Carlisle, her builder, had given her double bottoms and had divided her hull into sixteen watertight compartments, which made her, men thought, unsinkable. She had been built to be and had been described as a gigantic lifeboat. Her designers' dreams of a triple-screw giant, a luxurious, floating hotel, which could speed to New York at twenty-three knots, had been carefully translated from blue prints and mold-loft lines at the Belfast yards into a living reality.

The *Titanic's* sailing from Southampton, though quiet, was not wholly uneventful. As the liner moved slowly toward the end of her dock that April day, the surge of her passing sucked away from the quay the steamer *New York*, moored just to seaward of the *Titanic's* berth. There were sharp cracks as the manila mooring lines of the *New York* parted under the strain. The frayed ropes writhed and whistled through the air and snapped down among the waving crowd on the pier; the *New York* swung toward the *Titanic's* bow, was checked and dragged back to the dock barely in time to avert a collision. Seamen muttered, thought it an ominous start.

Past Spithead and the Isle of Wight the *Titanic* steamed. She called at Cherbourg at dusk and then laid her course for Queenstown. At 1:30 P.M. on Thursday, April 11, she stood out of Queenstown harbor, screaming gulls soaring in her wake, with 2,201 persons—men, women, and children—aboard.

Occupying the Empire bedrooms and Georgian suites of the first-class accommodations were many well-known men and women—Colonel John Jacob Astor and his young bride; Major Archibald Butt, military aide to President Taft, and his friend, Frank D. Millet, the painter; John B. Thayer, vice-president of the Pennsylvania Railroad, and Charles M. Hays, president of the Grand Trunk Railway of Canada; W. T. Stead, the English journalist; Jacques Futrelle, French novelist; H. B. Harris, theatrical manager, and Mrs. Harris; Mr. and Mrs. Isidor Straus; and J. Bruce Ismay, chairman and managing director of the White Star line.

Down in the plain wooden cabins of the steerage class were 706 immigrants to the land of promise, and trimly stowed in the great holds was a cargo valued at $420,000: oak beams, sponges, wine, calabashes, and an odd miscellany of the common and the rare.

The *Titanic* took her departure on Fastnet Light and, heading into the night, laid her course for New York. She was due at Quarantine the following Wednesday morning.

Sunday dawned fair and clear. The *Titanic* steamed smoothly toward the west, faint streamers of brownish smoke trailing from the funnels. The purser held services in the saloon in the morning; on the steerage deck aft the immigrants were playing games and a Scotsman was puffing "The Campbells Are Coming" on his bagpipes in the midst of the uproar.

At 9 A.M. a message from the steamer *Caronia* sputtered into the wireless shack:

> CAPTAIN, TITANIC—WESTBOUND STEAMERS REPORT
> BERGS GROWLERS AND FIELD ICE IN 42 DEGREES N. FROM 49
> DEGREES TO 51 DEGREES W. 12TH APRIL.
>
> COMPLIMENTS—
>
> BARR.

It was cold in the afternoon; the sun was brilliant, but the *Titanic*, her screws turning over at 75 revolutions per minute, was approaching the Banks.

In the Marconi cabin Second Operator Harold Bride, earphones clamped on his head, was figuring accounts; he did not stop to answer when he heard MWL, Continental Morse for the nearby Leyland liner, *Californian*, calling the *Titanic*. The *Californian* had some message about three icebergs; he didn't bother then to take it down. About 1:42 P.M. the rasping spark of those days spoke again across the water. It was the *Baltic*, calling the *Titanic*, warning her of ice on the steamer track. Bride took the message down and sent it up to the bridge. The officer-of-the-deck glanced at it; sent it to the bearded master of the *Titanic*, Captain E. C. Smith, a veteran of the White Star service. It was lunch time then; the Captain, walking along the promenade deck, saw Mr. Ismay, stopped, and handed him the message without comment. Ismay read it, stuffed it in his pocket, told two ladies about the icebergs, and resumed his walk. Later, about 7:15 P.M., the Captain requested the return of the message in order to post it in the chart room for the information of officers.

Dinner that night in the Jacobean dining room was gay. It was bitter on deck, but the night was calm and fine; the sky was moonless but studded with stars twinkling coldly in the clear air.

After dinner some of the second-class passengers gathered in the saloon, where the Reverend Mr. Carter conducted a "hymn sing-song." It was almost ten o'clock and the stewards were waiting with biscuits and coffee as the group sang:

> *O, hear us when we cry to Thee*
> *For those in peril on the sea.*

On the bridge Second Officer Lightoller—short, stocky, efficient—was relieved at ten o'clock by First Officer Murdock. Lightoller had talked with other officers about the proximity of ice; at least five wireless ice warnings had reached the ship; lookouts had been cautioned to be alert; captains and officers expected to reach the field at any time after 9:30 P.M. At twenty-two knots its speed unslackened, the *Titanic* plowed on through the night.

Lightoller left the darkened bridge to his relief and turned in. Captain Smith went to his cabin. The steerage was long since quiet; in the first and second cabins lights were going out; voices were growing still, people were asleep. Murdock paced back and forth on the bridge, peering out over the dark water, glancing now and then at the compass in front of Quartermaster Hichens at the wheel.

In the crow's-nest, Lookout Frederick Fleet and his partner, Leigh, gazed down at the water, still and unruffled in the dim, starlit darkness. Behind and below them the ship, a white shadow with here and there a last winking light; ahead of them a dark and silent and cold ocean.

There was a sudden clang. "Dong-dong. Dong-dong. Dong-dong. Dong!" The metal clapper of the great ship's bell struck out 11:30. Mindful of the warnings, Fleet strained his eyes, searching the darkness for the dreaded ice. But there were only the stars and the sea.

In the wireless room, where Phillips, first operator, had relieved Bride, the buzz of the *Californian's* set again crackled into the earphones:

Californian: "Say, old man, we are stuck here, surrounded by ice."
Titanic: "Shut up, shut up; keep out. I am talking to Cape Race; you are jamming my signals."

Then, a few minutes later—about 11:40 . . .

Out of the dark she came, a vast, dim, white, monstrous shape, directly in the *Titanic's* path. For a moment Fleet doubted his eyes. But she was a deadly reality, this ghastly *thing*. Frantically, Fleet struck three bells—*something dead ahead*. He snatched the telephone and called the bridge: "Iceberg! Right ahead!"

The First Officer heard but did not stop to acknowledge the message. "Hard astarboard!"

Hichens strained at the wheel; the bow swung slowly to port. The monster was almost upon them now.

Murdock leaped to the engine-room telegraph. Bells clanged. Far below in the engine room those bells struck the first warning. Danger! The indicators on the dial faces swung round to "Stop!" Then "Full speed astern!" Frantically the engineers turned great valve wheels; answered the bridge bells. . . .

There was a slight shock, a brief scraping, a small list to port. Shell ice—slabs and chunks of it—fell on the foredeck. Slowly the *Titanic* stopped.

Captain Smith hurried out of his cabin.

"What has the ship struck?"

Murdock answered, "An iceberg, sir. I hard-astarboarded and reversed the engines, and I was going to hard-aport around it, but she was too close. I could not do any more. I have closed the watertight doors."

Fourth Officer Boxhall, other officers, the carpenter, came to the bridge. The Captain sent Boxhall and the carpenter below to ascertain the damage.

A few lights switched on in the first and second cabins; sleepy passengers peered through porthole glass; some casually asked the stewards: "Why have we stopped?"

"I don't know, sir, but I don't suppose it is anything much."

In the smoking room a quorum of gamblers and their prey were still sitting round a poker table; the usual crowd of kibitzers looked on. They had felt the slight jar of the collision and had seen an eighty-foot ice mountain glide by the smoking-room windows, but the night was calm and clear, the *Titanic* was "unsinkable"; they hadn't bothered to go on deck.

But far below, in the warren of passages on the starboard side forward, in the forward holds and boiler rooms, men could see that the *Titanic's* hurt was mortal. In No. 6 boiler room, where the red glow from the furnaces lighted up the naked, sweaty chests of coal-blackened firemen, water was pouring through a great gash about two feet above the floor plates. This was no slow leak; the ship was open to the sea; in ten minutes there were eight feet of water in No. 6. Long before then the stokers had raked the flaming fires out of the furnaces and had scrambled through the watertight doors into No. 5 or had climbed up the long steel ladders to safety. When Boxhall looked at the mail room in No. 3 hold, twenty-four feet above the keel, the mailbags were already floating about in the slushing water. In No. 5 boiler room a stream of water spurted into an empty bunker. All six compartments forward of No. 4 were open to the sea; in ten seconds the iceberg's jagged claw had ripped a three-hundred-foot slash in the bottom of the great *Titanic*.

Reports came to the bridge; Ismay in dressing gown ran out on deck in the cold, still, starlit night, climbed up the bridge ladder.

"What has happened?"

Captain Smith: "We have struck ice."

"Do you think she is seriously damaged?"

Captain: "I'm afraid she is."

Ismay went below and passed Chief Engineer William Bell fresh from an inspection of the damaged compartments. Bell corroborated the Captain's statement; hurried back down the glistening steel ladders to his duty. Man after man followed him—Thomas Andrews, one of the ship's designers, Archie Frost, the builder's chief engineer, and his twenty assistants—men who had no posts of duty in the engine room but whose traditions called them there.

On deck, in corridor and stateroom, life flowed again. Men, women, and children awoke and questioned; orders were given to uncover the lifeboats; water rose into the firemen's quarters; half-dressed stokers streamed up on deck. But the passengers—most of them—did not know that the *Titanic* was sinking. The shock of the collision had been so slight that some were not awakened by it; the *Titanic* was so huge that she must be unsinkable; the night was too calm, too beautiful, to think of death at sea.

Captain Smith ran to the door of the radio shack. Bride, partly dressed, eyes dulled with sleep, was standing behind Phillips, waiting.

"Send the call for assistance."

The blue spark danced: "CQD—CQD—CQD—CQ—"

Miles away Marconi men heard. Cape Race heard it, and the steamships *La Provence* and *Mt. Temple*.

The sea was surging into the *Titanic's* hold. At 12:20 the water burst into the seamen's quarters through a collapsed fore-and-aft wooden bulkhead. Pumps strained in the engine rooms—men and machinery making a futile fight against the sea. Steadily the water rose.

The boats were swung out—slowly; for the deckhands were late in reaching their stations, there had been no boat drill, and many of the crew did not know to what boats they were assigned. Orders were shouted; the safety valves had lifted, and steam was blowing off in a great rushing roar. In the chart house Fourth Officer Boxhall bent above a chart, working rapidly with pencil and dividers.

12:15 A.M.   Boxhall's position is sent out to a fleet of vessels: "Come at once; we have struck a berg."

To the Cunarder *Carpathia* (Arthur Henry Rostron, Master, New

York to Liverpool, fifty-eight miles away): "It's a CQD, old man. Position 41–46 N.; 50–14 W."

The blue spark dancing: "Sinking; cannot hear for noise of steam."

12:30 A.M.   The word is passed: "Women and children in the boats." Stewards finish waking their passengers below; life preservers are tied on; some men smile at the precaution. "The *Titanic* is unsinkable." The *Mt. Temple* starts for the *Titanic;* the *Carpathia*, with a double watch in her stokeholds, radios, "Coming hard." The CQD changes the course of many ships—but not of one; the operator of the *Californian*, near by, has just put down his earphones and turned in.

The CQD flashes over land and sea from Cape Race to New York; newspaper city rooms leap to life and presses whir.

On the *Titanic*, water creeps over the bulkhead between Nos. 5 and 6 firerooms. She is going down by the head; the engineers—fighting a losing battle—are forced back foot by foot by the rising water. Down the promenade deck, Happy Jock Hume, the bandsman, runs with his instrument.

12:45 A.M.   Murdock, in charge on the starboard side, eyes tragic, but calm and cool, orders boat No. 7 lowered. The women hang back; they want no boat ride on an ice-strewn sea; the *Titanic* is unsinkable. The men encourage them, explain that this is just a precautionary measure: "We'll see you again at breakfast." There is little confusion; passengers stream slowly to the boat deck. In the steerage the immigrants chatter excitedly.

A sudden sharp hiss—a streaked flare against the night; Boxhall sends a rocket toward the sky. It explodes, and a parachute of white stars lights up the icy sea. "God! Rockets!" The band plays ragtime.

No. 8 is lowered, and No. 5. Ismay, still in dressing gown, calls for women and children, handles lines, stumbles in the way of an officer, is told to "get the hell out of here." Third Officer Pitman takes charge of No. 5; as he swings into the boat Murdock grasps his hand. "Good-by and good luck, old man."

No. 6 goes over the side. There are only twenty-eight people in a lifeboat with a capacity of sixty-five.

A light stabs from the bridge; Boxhall is calling in Morse flashes, again and again, to a strange ship stopped in the ice jam five to ten miles away. Another rocket drops its shower of sparks above the ice-strewn sea and the dying ship.

1:00 A.M.   Slowly the water creeps higher; the fore ports of the *Titanic* are dipping into the sea. Rope squeaks through blocks; lifeboats drop jerkily seaward. Through the shouting on the decks comes the sound of the band playing ragtime.

The "Millionaires' Special" leaves the ship—boat No. 1, with a capacity of forty people, carries only Sir Cosmo and Lady Duff Gordon and ten others. Aft, the frightened immigrants mill and jostle and rush for a boat.

An officer's fist flies out; three shots are fired into the air, and the panic is quelled. . . . Four Chinese sneak unseen into a boat and hide in its bottom.

1:20 A.M.   Water is coming into No. 4 boiler room. Stokers slice and shovel as water laps about their ankles—steam for the dynamos, steam for the dancing spark! As the water rises, great ash hoes rake the flaming coals from the furnaces. Safety valves pop; the stokers retreat aft, and the water-tight doors clang shut behind them.

The rockets fling their splendor toward the stars. The boats are more heavily loaded now, for the passengers know the *Titanic* is sinking. Women cling and sob. The great screws aft are rising clear of the sea. Half-filled boats are ordered to come alongside the cargo ports and take on more passengers, but the ports are never opened—and the boats are never filled. Others pull for the steamer's light miles away but never reach it; the light disappears, the unknown ship steams off.

The water rises and the band plays ragtime.

1:30 A.M.   Lightoller is getting the port boats off; Murdock the starboard. As one boat is lowered into the sea a boat officer fires his gun along the ship's side to stop a rush from the lower decks. A woman tries to take her great Dane into a boat with her; she is refused and steps out of the boat to die with her dog. Millet's "little smile which played on his lips all through the voyage" plays no more; his lips are grim, but he waves good-by and brings wraps for the women.

Benjamin Guggenheim, in evening clothes, smiles and says, "We've dressed up in our best and are prepared to go down like gentlemen."

1:40 A.M.   Boat 14 is clear, and then 13, 16, 15, and C. The lights still shine, but the *Baltic* hears the blue spark say, "Engine room getting flooded."

The *Olympic* signals, "Am lighting up all possible boilers as fast as can."

Major Butt helps women into the last boats and waves good-by to them. Mrs. Straus puts her foot on the gunwale of a lifeboat, then she draws back and goes to her husband: "We have been together many years; where you go I will go." Colonel John Jacob Astor puts his young wife in a lifeboat, steps back, taps cigarette on fing rnail: "Good-by, dearie; I'll join you later."

1:45 A.M.   The foredeck is under water, the fo'c'sle head almost awash; the great stern is lifted high toward the bright stars; and still the band plays. Mr. and Mrs. Harris approach a lifeboat arm in arm.

Officer: "Ladies first, please."

Harris bows, smiles, steps back: "Of course, certainly; ladies first."

Boxhall fires the last rocket, then leaves in charge of boat No. 2.

2:00 A.M.   She is dying now; her bow goes deeper, her stern higher. But there must be steam. Below in the stokeholds the sweaty firemen keep steam up for the flaring lights and the dancing spark. The glowing coals slide and tumble over the slanted grate bars; the sea pounds behind that yielding bulkhead. But the spark dances on.

The *Asian* hears Phillips try the new signal—SOS.

Boat No. 4 has left now; boat D leaves ten minutes later. Jacques Futrelle clasps his wife: "For God's sake, go! It's your last chance; go!" Madame Futrelle is half forced into the boat. It clears the side.

There are about 660 people in the boats, and 1,500 still on the sinking *Titanic.*

On top of the officers' quarters men work frantically to get the two collapsibles stowed there over the side. Water is over the forward part of A deck now; it surges up the companionways toward the boat deck. In the radio shack, Bride has slipped a coat and lifejacket about Phillips as the first operator sits hunched over his key, sending—still sending—"41–46 N.; 50–14 W. CQD—CQD—SOS—SOS—"

The Captain's tired white face appears at the radio-room door: "Men, you have done your full duty. You can do no more. Now, it's every man for himself." The Captain disappears—back to his sinking bridge, where Painter, his personal steward, stands quietly waiting for orders. The spark dances on. Bride turns his back and goes into the inner cabin. As he does so, a stoker, grimed with coal, mad with fear, steals into the shack and reaches for the lifejacket on Phillips' back. Bride wheels about and brains him with a wrench.

2:10 A.M.   Below decks the steam is still holding, though the pressure is falling—rapidly. In the gymnasium on the boat deck the athletic instructor watches quietly as two gentlemen ride the bicycles and another swings casually at the punching bag. Mail clerks stagger up the boat-deck stairways, dragging soaked mail sacks. The spark still dances. The band still plays—but not ragtime:

> *Nearer my God to Thee,*
> *Nearer to Thee . . .*

A few men take up the refrain; others kneel on the slanting decks to pray. Many run and scramble aft, where hundreds are clinging above the silent screws on the great uptilted stern. The spark still dances and the lights still flare; the engineers are on the job. The hymn comes to its close. Bandmaster Hartley, Yorkshireman violinist, taps his bow against a bulkhead, calls for "Autumn" as the water curls about his feet, and the eight musicians brace themselves against the ship's slant. People are leaping from the decks into the near by water—the icy water. A woman cries, "Oh, save me, save me!" A man answers, "Good lady, save yourself. Only God can save you now." The band plays "Autumn":

> *God of Mercy and Compassion!*
> *Look with pity on my pain . . .*

The water creeps over the bridge where the *Titanic's* master stands; heavily he steps out to meet it.

2:17 A.M. "CQ—" The *Virginian* hears a ragged, blurred CQ, then an abrupt stop. The blue spark dances no more. The lights flicker out; the engineers have lost their battle.

2:18 A.M. Men run about blackened decks; leap into the night; are swept into the sea by the curling wave which licks up the *Titanic's* length. Lightoller does not leave the ship; the ship leaves him; there are hundreds like him, but only a few who live to tell of it. The funnels still swim above the water, but the ship is climbing to the perpendicular; the bridge is under and most of the foremast; the great stern rises like a squat leviathan. Men swim away from the sinking ship; other drop from the stern.

The band plays in the darkness, the water lapping upwards:

> *Hold me up in mighty waters,*
> *Keep my eyes on things above,*
> *Righteousness, divine atonement,*
> *Peace and everlas . . .*

The forward funnel snaps and crashes into the sea; its steel tons hammer out of existence swimmers struggling in the freezing water. Streams of sparks, of smoke and steam, burst from the after funnels. The ship upends to fifty—to sixty degrees.

Down in the black abyss of the stokeholds, of the engine rooms, where the dynamos have whirred at long last to a stop, the stokers and the engineers are reeling against hot metal, the rising water clutching at their knees. The boilers, the engine cylinders, rip from their bed plates; crash through bulkheads; rumble—steel against steel.

The *Titanic* stands on end, poised briefly for the plunge. Slowly she slides to her grave—slowly at first, and then more quickly—quickly—quickly.

2:20 A.M. The greatest ship in the world has sunk. From the calm, dark waters, where the floating lifeboats move, there goes up, in the white wake of her passing, "one long continuous moan."

The boats that the *Titanic* had launched pulled safely away from the slight suction of the sinking ship, pulled away from the screams that came from the lips of the freezing men and women in the water. The boats were poorly manned and badly equipped, and they had been unevenly loaded. Some carried so few seamen that women bent to the oars. Mrs. Astor tugged at an oar handle; the Countess of Rothes took a tiller. Shivering stokers in sweaty, coal-blackened singlets and light trousers steered in some boats; stewards in white coats rowed in others. Ismay was in the last boat that left the ship from the starboard side; with Mr. Carter of Philadelphia and two seamen he tugged at the oars. In one of the lifeboats an

Italian with a broken wrist—disguised in a woman's shawl and hat—huddled on the floor boards, ashamed now that fear had left him. In another rode the only baggage saved from the *Titanic*—the carry-all of Samuel L. Goldenberg, one of the rescued passengers.

There were only a few boats that were heavily loaded; most of those that were half empty made but perfunctory efforts to pick up the moaning swimmers, their officers and crew fearing that they would endanger the living if they pulled back into the midst of the dying. Some boats beat off the freezing victims; fear-crazed men and women struck with oars at the heads of swimmers. One woman drove her fist into the face of a half-dead man as he tried feebly to climb over the gunwale. Two other women helped him in and stanched the flow of blood from the ring cuts on his face.

One of the collapsible boats, which had floated off the top of the officers' quarters when the *Titanic* sank, was an icy haven for thirty or forty men. The boat had capsized as the ship sank; men swam to it, clung to it, climbed upon its slippery bottom, stood knee-deep in water in the freezing air. Chunks of ice swirled about their legs; their soaked clothing clutched their bodies in icy folds. Colonel Archibald Gracie was cast up there, Gracie who had leaped from the stern as the *Titanic* sank; young Thayer who had seen his father die; Lightoller who had twice been sucked down with the ship and twice blown to the surface by a belch of air; Bride, the second operator, and Phillips, the first. There were many stokers, half-naked; it was a shivering company. They stood there in the icy sea, under the far stars, and sang and prayed—the Lord's Prayer. After a while a lifeboat came and picked them off, but Phillips was dead then or died soon afterward in the boat.

Only a few of the boats had lights; only one—No. 2—had a light that was of any use to the *Carpathia*, twisting through the ice field to the rescue. Other ships were "coming hard" too; one, the *Californian*, was still dead to opportunity.

The blue sparks still danced, but not the *Titanic's*. *La Provence* to *Celtic:* "Nobody has heard the *Titanic* for about two hours."

It was 2:40 when the *Carpathia* first sighted the green light from No. 2 boat; it was 4:10 when she picked up the first boat and learned that the *Titanic* had foundered. The last of the moaning cries had just died away then.

Captain Rostron took the survivors aboard, boatload by boatload. He was ready for them, but only a small minority of them required much medical attention. Bride's feet were twisted and frozen; others were suffering from exposure; one died, and seven were dead when taken from the boats, and were buried at sea.

It was then that the fleet of racing ships learned they were too late; the *Parisian* heard the weak signals of MPA, the *Carpathia*, report the death of the *Titanic*. It was then—or soon afterward, when her radio operator put on his earphones—that the *Californian*, the ship that had been within sight as the *Titanic* was sinking, first learned of the disaster.

And it was then, in all its white-green majesty, that the *Titanic's* survivors saw the iceberg, tinted with the sunrise, floating idly, pack ice jammed about its base, other bergs heaving slowly near by on the blue breast of the sea.

This selection, like our previous selections, does not pretend to be fiction, but it has one important aspect of fiction which is lacking in the examples of nonfiction hitherto presented. It has "point," or "idea," or "meaning." We may, perhaps, arrive at an understanding of this "point" or "meaning" by asking ourselves why the sinking of the *Titanic* continues to appeal to the imagination of mankind whereas the loss of other fine ships with thousands of lives has been forgotten. The *Lusitania*, for example, was a great ship and its sinking gave rise to deeds of heroism, but the loss of the *Titanic* is somehow more memorable. How can one account for this?

We notice in the first sentence that the *Titanic* was the "largest ship the world had ever known." Another thing, it was her maiden voyage, and her paint was "fair and bright." Most of all, "she was believed to be the safest." Baldwin goes on to point out how the designers planned to make her "unsinkable," a "luxurious floating hotel." It is true, there was a slight accident at her start, but this was taken to be an ill omen only by common seamen, known by nature to be superstitious. The event was without meaning for the great and famous people who had chosen to be passengers on this maiden voyage and who trusted in the skill of designers and officers.

With this introduction, Baldwin skips over to the day of the disaster, which dawned "fair and clear." Messages began to come in from other ships that ice had been sighted, but one of the messages was not even taken down, and the others did not cause the ship to slacken speed. In the evening, the second-class passengers gathered for a "hymn sing-song." While coffee and sandwiches were being passed, they sang:

> *O, hear us when we cry to Thee*
> *For those in peril on the sea.*

At eleven-thirty that night the ship was still rushing ahead, without diminished speed, when the *Californian* reported that it had hove to, surrounded by ice. But the operator on the *Titanic* asked the *Californian* to "shut up . . . you are jamming my signals." This was less than ten minutes before the great ship crashed into the iceberg.

We can find running through all of these details a basic contrast between what people expected to happen and what actually happened; between the assumption by the passengers that the designers and the ship's officers had conquered the perils of nature, and the actual disaster to the ship; between the scene in which the passengers, almost in a festive mood (as the word "sing-song" indicates), sing a hymn praying for the safety of others at sea, and the scene, a few minutes later, in which they will sing in bitter earnest,

Hold me up in mighty waters,
Keep my eyes on things above.

These contrasts are *ironical* (see Glossary): that is, they involve a disparity. In this case, the irony is simply inherent in a situation: the passengers assume one meaning in the situation while its true meaning is quite different. Men feel that the maiden voyage of the great ship marks the conquest by man of the perils of the sea; in fact, they take it to be another milestone toward man's total conquest of nature.

We can see that on this basis Baldwin has chosen the details which he emphasizes. He never states this general "point," but his selection of events, great and trivial, leads us inevitably to this conclusion. For instance, he quotes from the hymns the lines which bear most positively on the actual situation; he might have referred to other hymns sung on the same occasion. This is not to say that Baldwin puts this general meaning into the situation; he merely sharpens meanings which were actually inherent in the situation. That they were inherent in the situation probably accounts for the fact that the sinking of the *Titanic* has held such a grip on man's imagination for a number of years.

In the description of the actual collision and the reaction of the passengers in the hours which follow, Baldwin develops further the irony of the situation. For instance, in the smoking room the gamblers see the great shape glide by the windows, but they do not even go on deck. When the first boats are lowered the men encourage the women by saying, "We'll see you again at breakfast." But the lifeboats are not filled to capacity and there is great confusion because boat drill had not been thought necessary on such a ship. The *Californian* radio operator, who had been told to "shut up," has "shut up," and consequently that ship, which is almost within sight of the *Titanic*, cannot be reached to come to the rescue. In this connection, we might even examine the author's intention in the last paragraph:

"And it was then, in all its white-green majesty, that the *Titanic's* survivors saw the iceberg, tinted with the sunrise, floating idly, pack ice jammed about its base, other bergs heaving slowly near by on the blue breast of the sea."

The instrument of terror is observed here in its majestic placidity, and appears not horrible, but delicately tinted and beautiful. Nature, in other words, is both terrible and beautiful, and it acts with a bland unawareness of humanity.

Thus far we have been dealing with the general irony underlying the situation. But there are many types of response among the passengers. Some behave with shameful cowardice, some with hysterical irrationality, some with fortitude, some with heroism. Some of the passengers speak their feelings with direct earnestness. Others cover their feelings, or even their courageous actions, with jokes and banter.

In the behavior of the passengers, there emerges another level of irony, different from the general underlying irony of "pride before the fall." If the general situation reflects on the folly of man's overweening pride in his confidence that he has, actually, conquered nature, there remains, after all, a sense in which man can rise superior to nature. Those men who meet the circumstance heroically do, actually, conquer nature: though dying, they keep their dignity as men and do not behave like trapped animals. This irony hinges on two contrasts: First, the men, though dying, are victorious. Second, these men, who had been confident of conquering nature by the machine, finally conquer it by means of something within themselves.

What makes this story meaningful is what the event represents in our minds: it typifies an aspect of the human situation. In one form or another, man is constantly engaged in the attempt to conquer nature, and sooner or later he must confront a situation in which the only victory possible is a victory over himself. In its baldest terms, the matter may be stated thus: every man must die, but there are many ways in which man can confront this fact.

Every *tragedy* (see Glossary) is concerned with this question, and the sinking of the *Titanic* as given here involves some of the elements of the tragic experience. This is no place to undertake a definition of tragedy, but surely this much is true: the tragic hero is always defeated—his sin, by the way, is usually an overweening pride—but he always manages to wrest something from the defeat and from death.

The account of the sinking of the *Titanic*, then, has in it certain elements of the tragic experience, but it is not a tragedy in the formal sense. In fact, it is not even a piece of fiction. The reason why Baldwin's account is not to be so regarded we shall consider in a moment, but first it is only fair to indicate that it exhibits one important aspect of fiction which is lacking in either of the other two examples which we have considered. It is built to convey a definite "point," a definite idea or meaning, which, though it is never expressed explicitly—and fiction itself rarely expresses its idea explicitly—nevertheless is felt by almost any reader.

In this connection, we might profitably glance again at two of our earlier examples of nonfiction. It is true that a fiction writer, in using the story of Jim Beckworth, could give the episode a "point." Parkman himself indicates something of this when he says: in Beckworth's case "the standard rules of character fail, for though he will stab a man in his sleep, he will also perform the most desperate acts of daring." Parkman's intention in using the episode is simply to show that the characters of the plainsmen do not fit the "standard rules of character" which are accepted in more civilized societies. He is merely using the episode as a sociological example. But if a fiction writer should undertake to employ the episode, he might, by developing the character of Beckworth (which is exactly what Parkman does not do) arrive at some such point as this: individuals cannot be judged by rule of thumb; every individual character is unique and has mixtures of good and evil within it. Of course, it is not to be thought that this would be the only possible point in this episode for a fiction writer, but it is the one hinted at but not developed by Parkman.

In the portrait of Sir Tatton Sykes, the author suggests that Sir Tatton's eccentricities are typical of the English eighteenth century. But this again is a sociological and not a fictional point. We have already suggested that the fiction writer would find many potential stories suggested by Sir Tatton's character. In the same way he would find many potential points *appropriate to fiction.*

To return to our question concerning the account of the loss of the *Titanic:* why is it not fiction? The primary objection, although there may be other objections, is fairly obvious. It lacks a character or characters. We have only fleeting glimpses of the individuals. Moreover, it cannot be argued that the ship itself will serve as a character; it stands merely as a *symbol* (see Glossary) for certain human attitudes—pride, confidence, and the like. Even if the account were extended to give fairly full portraits of some of the individuals, of some of the passengers and officers, this added characterization would not, in itself, remove the objection. The characterizations would have to be *functional* (see Glossary), would have to have some bearing on the total situation, would have to be tied into the total account in terms of both action and meaning. For example, a fiction writer might develop the character of the captain to show why, under the special circumstances, he neglected ordinary precautions; or develop the character of the wireless operator to show why he ordered the operator on the *Californian* off the air; or develop the character of some passenger or seaman to show why he behaved courageously or shamefully. Such a process would do much to convert the account into fiction, but it would raise the whole problem of *unity* (see Glossary). That is, the following questions would arise for the fiction writer: Whose story is this? Is there a central character? As a rule, in most pieces of fiction, there is a central character, but there are instances in which this is not true. In such cases, however, the fiction writer is not freed from the obligation to maintain a unity, that is, to build his story so that the characters in action are related to each other and to a dominating idea or theme.*

The reader will observe that in none of the instances we have examined has the matter of the historical truth or falsity been taken as the basis for distinguishing fiction from nonfiction. At first glance this may seem strange, for ordinarily people think of "fiction" as being opposed to "fact." Instead, we have considered the decisive matter to be the *structure* (see Glossary) of the particular example under consideration; that is, the way in which the elements (character, events, meanings) are related to each other.

To make the structure the important matter, not the question of historical truth or untruth, is not mere perversity. Certainly, fiction may make use of facts. Most fiction writers get their suggestions for stories from real life. But real life, either present or past, never fully gives the fiction writer the kind of facts in which he, and the reader, are most interested. For those facts concern psychological processes and human motives. It is easy enough, for instance, to check the tonnage of the *Titanic*, or get the names of the passenger list, but it is very hard to know what passed in the captain's mind in the moment when he stepped forward from the slanting bridge to meet the rising waters.

The historian and the biographer, as a matter of fact, are up against the same sort of problem when they attempt to interpret a historical character. The biographer finds certain recorded facts about his subject and certain recorded opinions expressed by his subject or expressed by other people concerning his subject; but the biographer must, on the basis of this recorded evidence, try, by an act of his own imagination, to tell us what his subject was like as a man. The proof of this may be found in the fact that no two biographers present us with exactly the same interpretation of any historical personage. Of course, the interpretation presented by a biographer should never violate the facts, but the same facts can sometimes bear different interpretations; what the biographer is trying to do is to see the logic behind the facts. Certainly, the logic by which a biographer must interpret his subject involves consistency of character, a logic of motivation, and the cause-and-effect relationship of one action to another.

To turn once more to the fiction writer, it is perfectly true that he may make use of facts. Indeed, many pieces of fiction find their germ in some actual happening which stirred the writer's imagination, and a writer may even stay very close to the facts. If the biographer, as we have said, is interested, not in the mere assemblage of facts, but in the interpreta-

* In such cases, although there is no single dominating character, all characters must be related to the governing idea. It is conceivable that a fiction writer might make such a story out of the *Titanic* disaster, but this type of story is always more difficult to handle successfully than the type in which the action is strongly centralized.

tion of facts, the fiction writer, who is not bound by facts as such, has an even more obvious concern with the matter of interpretation. We can summarize in this way: the biographer or historian is concerned to discover the pattern implied by the facts; the fiction writer may choose or create "facts" in accordance with the pattern of human conduct which he wishes to present.

Thus a biographer of Lady Blessington would be concerned to see into what pattern of meaning the various facts of her life could be fitted. The fiction writer, on the other hand, who chose to write the story of an "adventurous and amusing personage" with a personality something like that of Lady Blessington would be concerned to invent facts appropriate to the pattern of Marguerite Blessington's character and personality. In saying that the fiction writer can "invent" his facts, we do not, of course, mean to imply that he is bound by no laws whatsoever. Obviously he must convince his reader that the story does not violate the probabilities of human action.

This distinction between the problem which the biographer must face and that which the fiction writer must face is sharply illustrated by Baldwin's account of the sinking of the *Titanic*. In the actual circumstances of the event the ironical coincidences are so numerous and so obvious that a fiction writer might well have feared to make such full use of them as Baldwin does. For a fiction writer to make so full a use might seem to strain the reader's sense of probability. If this account were pure fiction, the reader would have to be convinced simply in terms of probability, but Baldwin is merely presenting certain facts which are matters of history. We have in Baldwin's account, then, an example of the old saying that truth is stranger than fiction. A fiction writer would probably feel constrained to "play down" the ironical coincidences and suggest his ironical theme more subtly. To approach this matter in another way: one often thinks of "fiction" as being opposed to "fact." But in one real sense, this is a false opposition. It is simply a matter of what kind of facts fiction can use and of the way in which it can use them.

For this reason, one should not conceive of fiction as being a "make-believe." It is make-believe only in so far as it does not claim that the *particular* persons or events of which it treats are historically real. Instead of being primarily concerned with make-believe, fiction is primarily concerned with "truth." In discussing the stories which appear in this book we shall frequently deal with the kind of "truth" which is involved in fiction. But for the present it can be said that the truth of fiction involves such matters as the following: (1) the consistency and comprehensibility of character; (2) the motivation and credibility of action; and (3) the acceptability of the total meaning. As for the method of fiction, it should also be evident, even at this point, that these three matters, character, action, and theme (see Glossary), are bound up together. For instance, many stories never state their themes at all; in such cases the theme is simply presented in terms of the characters and the action. In the same way, character is usually defined by action, and action is to be understood in terms of its effect on character or as a result of character.

We ought to make one further comment upon the distinction between history and fiction (let us remember that all the five samples of nonfiction that we have thus far examined are drawn from history, including biography). History and biography give us what may called truth of correspondence. What a true history says "corresponds" to the facts. A true biography matches the life of its subject. But fiction is not fact, and its "truth" does not involve a correspondence to something outside itself— at least not in the way in which history and biography involve such correspondence. It may be useful, therefore, to note that in fiction truth of coherence is the primary truth. A few sentences earlier we wrote that the truth of fiction involves such matters as "(1) the *consistency* and *comprehensibility* of character; (2) the motivation and *credibility* of action; and (3) the *acceptability* of the total meaning." The terms in italics imply an inner consistency or coherence rather than truth of correspondence to outside facts. This distinction is presumably the sort of thing that Aristotle had in mind when he indicated that in "poetry" (fiction) a probable falsehood is better than an improbable truth, or when he said that fiction was more "philosophical" than history.

It should be pointed out, however, that in recognizing the special meaning of truth as it applies to fiction, we are not cutting off fiction from its relevance to the world of human values. If we ask, not that a story correspond to historical fact but rather that it merely conform to the laws of probability, one must not forget that our judgment of probability and our notion of credibility in general are based firmly upon the way in which the human mind works and upon the experience that we have had as human beings. The relevance of fiction to our lives is not lessened one bit by the fact that we recognize that fiction is typical of human action rather than factually true.

There are positive advantages in clearly distinguishing between truth of correspondence and truth of coherence, and fixing upon the latter as the peculiar province of fiction. Successful fiction always involves a coherent relating of action, character, and meaning. And as we shall see, most of the failures in fiction could be stated as failures in coherence. Some of these would be: the empty and meaningless depiction of action for its own sake; the use of obscure and confused motivation; or the incoherent appeal to emotion for emotion's sake. Even the mere "slice of life" in which the author attempts to foist off on us a raw transcript of reality instead of a focused perception of reality, represents a failure of coherence —that is, a failure to make action truly meaningful. (This kind of incoherence may spring from the false assumption that fiction is some kind of "scientific" account of reality—a kind of uninterpreted sociology.) Later in this book we shall have occasion to refer to the various kinds of incoherence. At this point in our study, however, what is to be emphasized once more is the special way in which character and action must hang together (must cohere) to produce meaning. Keeping in mind this relationship, the student will do well in reading any story to ask himself such questions as the following:

1. What are the characters like?
2. Are they "real"?
3. What do they want? (motivation)
4. Why do they do what they do? (motivation)
5. Do their actions logically follow from their natures? (consistency of character)
6. What do their actions tell about their characters?
7. How are the individual pieces of action—the special incidents—related to each other? (plot organization)
8. How are the characters related to each other? (subordination and emphasis among characters; conflict among characters)
9. What is the theme?
10. How are the characters and incidents related to the theme?

RUDYARD KIPLING

The Man Who Would Be King

"Brother to a Prince and fellow to a beggar if he be found worthy."

THE law, as quoted, lays down a fair conduct of life, and one not easy to follow. I have been fellow to a beggar again and again under circumstances which prevented either of us finding out whether the other was worthy. I have still to be brother to a Prince, though I once came near to kinship with what might have been a veritable King and was promised the reversion of a Kingdom—army, law courts, revenue and policy all complete. But, today, I greatly fear that my King is dead, and if I want a crown I must go and hunt it for myself.

The beginning of everything was in a railway train upon the road to Mhow from Ajmir. There had been a Deficit in the Budget, which necessitated traveling, not Second-class, which is only half as dear as First-class, but by Intermediate, which is very awful indeed. There are no cushions in the Intermediate class, and the population are either Intermediate, which is Eurasian, or native, which for a long night journey is nasty, or Loafer, which is amusing though intoxicated. Intermediates do not patronize refreshment rooms. They carry their food in bundles and pots, and buy sweets from the native sweetmeat-sellers, and drink the roadside water. That is why in the hot weather Intermediates are taken out of the carriages dead, and in all weathers are most properly looked down upon.

My particular Intermediate happened to be empty till I reached Nasirabad, when a huge gentleman in shirt sleeves entered, and, following the custom of Intermediates, passed the time of day. He was a wanderer and a vagabond like myself, but with an educated taste for whisky. He told tales of things he had seen and done, of out-of-the-way corners of the Empire into which he had penetrated, and of adventures in which he risked his life for a few days' food. "If India was filled with men like you and me, not knowing more than the crows where they'd get their next day's rations, it isn't seventy millions of revenue the land would be paying —it's seven hundred millions," said he; and as I looked at his mouth and chin I was disposed to agree with him. We talked politics—the politics of Loaferdom that sees things from the underside where the lath and plaster is not smoothed off—and we talked postal arrangements because my friend wanted to send a telegram back from the next station to Ajmir, which is the turning-off place from the Bombay to the Mhow line as you travel westward. My friend had no money beyond eight annas which he wanted for dinner, and I had no money at all, owing to the hitch in the Budget before-mentioned. Further, I was going into a wilderness where, though I should resume touch with the Treasury, there were no telegraph offices. I was, therefore, unable to help him in any way.

"We might threaten a Stationmaster, and make him send a wire on tick," said my friend, "but that'd mean inquiries for you and for me, and I've got my hands full these days. Did you say you are traveling back along this line within any days?"

"Within ten," I said.

"Can't you make it eight?" said he. "Mine is rather urgent business."

"I can send your telegram within ten days if that will serve you," I said.

"I couldn't trust the wire to fetch him now I think of it. It's this way. He leaves Delhi on the twenty-third for Bombay. That means he'll be running through Ajmir about the night of the twenty-third."

"But I'm going into the Indian Desert," I explained.

"Well *and* good," said he. "You'll be changing at Marwar Junction to get into Jodhpore territory—you must do that—and he'll be coming through Marwar Junction in the early morning of the twenty-fourth by the Bombay Mail. Can you be at Marwar Junction on that time? 'Twon't be inconveniencing you because I know that there's precious few pickings to be got out of these Central India States—even though you pretend to be correspondent of the *Backwoodsman*."

"Have you ever tried that trick?" I asked.

"Again and again, but the Residents find you out, and then you get escorted to the Border before you've time to get your knife into them. But about my friend here. I *must* give him a word o' mouth to tell him what's come to me or else he won't know where to go. I would take it more than kind of you if you was to come out of Central India in time to catch him at Marwar Junction, and say to him, 'He has gone South for the week.' He'll know what that means. He's a big man with a red beard, and a great swell he is. You'll find him sleeping like a gentleman with all his luggage round him in a Second-class compartment. But don't you be afraid. Slip down the window, and say, 'He has gone South for the week,' and he'll tumble. It's only cutting your time of stay in those parts by two days. I ask you as a stranger—going to the West," he said, with emphasis.

"Where have *you* come from?" said I.

"From the East," said he, "and I am hoping that you will give him the message on the Square—for the sake of my Mother as well as your own."

Englishmen are not usually softened by appeals to the memory of their mothers, but for certain reasons, which will be fully apparent, I saw fit to agree.

"It's more than a little matter," said he, "and that's why I ask you to do it—and now I know that I can depend on you doing it. A Second-class carriage at Marwar Junction, and a red-haired man asleep in it. You'll be sure to remember. I get out at the next station, and I must hold on there till he comes or sends me what I want."

"I'll give the message if I catch him," I said, "and for the sake of your Mother as well as mine I'll give you a word of advice. Don't try to run the Central India States just now as the correspondent of the *Backwoodsman*. There's a real one knocking about here, and it might lead to trouble."

"Thank you," said he, simply, "and when will the swine be gone? I can't starve because he's ruining my work. I wanted to get hold of the Degumber Rajah down here about his father's widow, and give him a jump."

"What did he do to his father's widow, then?"

"Filled her up with red pepper and slippered her to death as she hung from a beam. I found that out myself, and I'm the only man that would dare going into the State to get hush money for it. They'll try to poison me, same as they did in Chortumna when I went on the loot there. But you'll give the man at Marwar Junction my message?"

He got out at a little roadside station, and I reflected. I had heard, more than once, of men personating correspondents of newspapers and bleeding small Native States with threats of exposure, but I had never met any of the caste before. They lead a hard life, and generally die with great suddenness. The Native States have a wholesome horror of English newspapers, which may throw light on their peculiar methods of government, and do their best to choke correspondents with champagne, or drive them out of their mind with four-in-hand barouches. They do not understand that nobody cares a straw for the internal administration of Native States so long as oppression and crime are kept within decent limits, and the ruler is not drugged, drunk, or diseased from one end of the year to the other. Native States were created by Providence in order to supply picturesque scenery, tigers, and tall writing. They are the dark places of the earth, full of unimaginable cruelty, touching the Railway and the Telegraph on one side, and, on the other, the days of Harun-al-Raschid. When I left the train I did business with divers Kings, and in eight days passed through many changes of life. Sometimes I wore dress clothes and consorted with Princes and Politicals, drinking from crystal and eating from silver. Sometimes I lay out upon the ground and devoured what I could get, from a plate made of a flapjack, and drank the running water, and slept under the same rug as my servant. It was all in the day's work.

Then I headed for the Great Indian Desert upon the proper date, as I had promised, and the night Mail set me down at Marwar Junction, where a funny little, happy-go-lucky, native-managed railway runs to Jodhpore. The Bombay Mail from Delhi makes a short halt at Marwar. She arrived as I got in, and I had just time to hurry to her platform and go down the carriages. There was only one Second-class on the train. I slipped the window, and looked down upon a flaming red beard, half covered by a railway rug. That was my man, fast asleep, and I dug him gently in the ribs. He woke with a grunt, and I saw his face in the light of the lamps. It was a great and shining face.

"Tickets again?" said he.

"No," said I. "I am to tell you that he is gone South for the week. He is gone South for the week!"

The train had begun to move out. The red man rubbed his eyes. "He has gone South for the week," he repeated. "Now that's just like his impidence. Did he say that I was to give you anything?—'Cause I won't."

"He didn't," I said, and dropped away, and watched the red lights die out in the dark. It was horribly cold, because the wind was blowing off the sands. I climbed into my own train—not an Intermediate Carriage this time—and went to sleep.

If the man with the beard had given me a rupee I should have kept it as a memento of a rather curious affair. But the consciousness of having done my duty was my only reward.

Later on I reflected that two gentlemen like my friends could not do any good if they foregathered and personated correspondents of newspapers, and might, if they "stuck up" one of the little rat-trap states of

Central India or Southern Rajputana, get themselves into serious difficulties. I therefore took some trouble to describe them as accurately as I could remember to people who would be interested in deporting them; and succeeded, so I was later informed, in having them headed back from Degumber borders.

Then I became respectable, and returned to an Office where there were no Kings and no incidents except the daily manufacture of a newspaper. A newspaper office seems to attract every conceivable sort of person, to the prejudice of discipline. Zenana-mission ladies arrive, and beg that the Editor will instantly abandon all his duties to describe a Christian prize-giving in a back-slum of a perfectly inaccessible village; Colonels who have been overpassed for commands sit down and sketch the outline of a series of ten, twelve, or twenty-four leading articles on Seniority *versus* Selection; missionaries wish to know why they have not been permitted to escape from their regular vehicles of abuse and swear at a brother missionary under special patronage of the editorial We; stranded theatrical companies troop up to explain that they cannot pay for their advertisements, but on their return from New Zealand or Tahiti will do so with interest; inventors of patent punkah-pulling machines, carriage couplings, and unbreakable swords and axletrees call with specifications in their pockets and hours at their disposal; tea companies enter and elaborate their prospectuses with the office pens; secretaries of ball committees clamor to have the glories of their last dance more fully expounded; strange ladies rustle in and say, "I want a hundred lady's cards printed *at once,* please," which is manifestly part of an Editor's duty; and every dissolute ruffian that ever tramped the Grand Trunk Road makes it his business to ask for employment as a proofreader. And, all the time, the telephone bell is ringing madly, and Kings are being killed on the Continent, and Empires are saying—"You're another," and Mister Gladstone is calling down brimstone upon the British Dominions, and the little black copy boys are whining, "*kaa-pi chay-ha-yeh*" (copy wanted) like tired bees, and most of the paper is as blank as Modred's shield.

But that is the amusing part of the year. There are other six months wherein none ever come to call, and the thermometer walks inch by inch up to the top of the glass, and the office is darkened to just above reading light, and the press machines are red-hot of touch, and nobody writes anything but accounts of amusements in the Hill stations or obituary notices. Then the telephone becomes a tinkling terror, because it tells you of the sudden deaths of men and women that you knew intimately, and the prickly heat covers you as with a garment, and you sit down and write: "A slight increase of sickness is reported from the Khuda Janta Khan District. The outbreak is purely sporadic in its nature, and, thanks to the energetic efforts of the District authorities, is now almost at an end. It is, however, with deep regret we record the death, etc."

Then the sickness really breaks out, and the less recording and reporting the better for the peace of the subscribers. But the Empires and the Kings continue to divert themselves as selfishly as before, and the Foreman thinks that a daily paper really ought to come out once in twenty-four hours, and all the people at the Hill stations in the middle of their amusements say, "Good gracious! Why can't the paper be sparkling? I'm sure there's plenty going on up here."

That is the dark half of the moon, and, as the advertisements say, "must be experienced to be appreciated."

It was in that season, and a remarkably evil season, that the paper began running the last issue of the week on Saturday night, which is to say, Sunday morning, after the custom of a London paper. This was a great convenience, for immediately after the paper was put to bed, the dawn would lower the thermometer from 96° to almost 84° for half an hour, and in that chill—you have no idea how cold is 84° on the grass until you begin to pray for it—a very tired man could set off to sleep ere the heat roused him.

One Saturday night it was my pleasant duty to put the paper to bed alone. A King or courtier or a courtesan or a community was going to die or get a new Constitution, or do something that was important on the other side of the world, and the paper was to be held open till the latest possible minute in order to catch the telegram. It was a pitchy black night, as stifling as a June night can be, and the *loo*, the red-hot wind from the westward, was booming among the tinder-dry trees and pretending that the rain was on its heels. Now and again a spot of almost boiling water would fall on the dust with the flop of a frog, but all our weary world knew that was only pretense. It was a shade cooler in the press room than the office, so I sat there, while the type clicked and clicked and the nightjars hooted at the windows, and the all but naked compositors wiped the sweat from their foreheads and called for water. The thing that was keeping us back, whatever it was, would not come off, though the *loo* dropped and the last type was set, and the whole round earth stood still in the choking heat, with its finger on its lip, to wait the event. I drowsed, and wondered whether the telegraph was a blessing, and whether this dying man, or struggling people, was aware of the inconvenience the delay was causing. There was no special reason beyond the heat and worry to make tension, but, as the clock hands crept up to three o'clock and the machines spun their flywheels two or three times to see that all was in order, before I said the word that would set them off, I could have shrieked aloud.

Then the roar and rattle of the wheels shivered the quiet into little bits. I rose to go away, but two men in white clothes stood in front of me. The first one said, "It's him!" The second said, "So it is!" And they both laughed almost as loudly as the machinery roared, and mopped their foreheads. "We see there was a light burning across the road and we were sleeping in that ditch there for coolness, and I said to my friend here, 'The office is open. Let's come along and speak to him as turned us back from the Degumber State.' " said the smaller of the two. He was the man I had met in the Mhow train, and his fellow was the red-bearded man of Marwar Junction. There was no mistaking the eyebrows of the one or the beard of the other.

I was not pleased, because I wished to go to sleep, not to squabble with loafers. "What do you want?" I asked.

"Half an hour's talk with you cool and comfortable, in the office," said the red-bearded man. "We'd *like* some drink—the Contrack doesn't begin yet, Peachey, so you needn't look—but what we really want is advice. We don't want money. We ask you as a favor, because you did us a bad turn about Degumber."

I led from the press room to the stifling office with the maps on the walls, and the red-haired man rubbed his hands. "That's something like," said he. "This was the proper shop to come to. Now, Sir, let me introduce to you Brother Peachey Carnehan, that's him, and Brother Daniel Dravot, that is *me*, and the less said about our professions the better, for we have been most things in our time. Soldier, sailor, compositor, photographer, proofreader, street preacher, and correspondents of the *Backwoodsman* when we thought the paper wanted one. Carnehan is sober, and so am I. Look at us first and see that's sure. It will save you cutting into my talk. We'll take one of your cigars apiece, and you shall see us light."

I watched the test. The men were absolutely sober, so I gave them each a tepid peg.

"Well *and* good," said Carnehan of the eyebrows, wiping the froth from his mustache. "Let me talk now, Dan. We have been all over India, mostly on foot. We have been boiler-fitters, engine-drivers, petty contractors, and all that, and we have decided that India isn't big enough for such as us."

They certainly were too big for the office. Dravot's beard seemed to fill half the room and Carnehan's shoulders the other half, as they sat on the big table. Carnehan continued: "The country isn't half worked out because they that governs it won't let you touch it. They spend all their blessed time in governing it, and you can't lift a spade, nor chip a rock, nor look for oil, nor anything like that without all the Government saying, 'Leave it alone and let us govern.' Therefore, such as it is, we will let it alone, and go away to some other place where a man isn't crowded and can come to his own. We are not little men, and there is nothing that we are afraid of except Drink, and we have signed a Contrack on that. *Therefore*, we are going away to be Kings."

"Kings in our own right," muttered Dravot.

"Yes, of course," I said. "You've been tramping in the sun, and it's a very warm night, and hadn't you better sleep over the notion? Come to-morrow."

"Neither drunk nor sunstruck," said Dravot. "We have slept over the notion half a year, and require to see Books and Atlases, and we have decided that there is only one place now in the world that two strong men can Sar-a-*whack*. They call it Kafiristan. By my reckoning it's the top right-hand corner of Afghanistan, not more than three hundred miles from Peshawur. They have two and thirty heathen idols there, and we'll be the thirty-third. It's a mountainous country, and the women of those parts are very beautiful."

"But that is provided against in the Contrack," said Carnehan. "Neither Women nor Liqu-or, Daniel."

"And that's all we know, except that no one has gone there, and they fight, and in any place where they fight, a man who knows how to drill men can always be a King. We shall go to those parts and say to any King we find, 'D'you want to vanquish your foes?' and we will show him how to drill men; for that we know better than anything else. Then we will sub-vert that King and seize his Throne and establish a Dy-nasty."

"You'll be cut to pieces before you're fifty miles across the Border," I said. "You have to travel through Afghanistan to get to that country. It's one mass of mountains and peaks and glaciers, and no Englishman has been through it. The people are utter brutes, and even if you reached them you couldn't do anything."

"That's more like," said Carnehan. "If you could think us a little more mad we would be more pleased. We have come to you to know about this country, to read a book about it, and be shown maps. We want you to tell us that we are fools and to show us your books." He turned to the bookcases.

"Are you at all in earnest?" I said.

"A little," said Dravot, sweetly. "As big a map as you have got, even if it's all blank where Kafiristan is, and any books you've got. We can read, though we aren't very educated."

I uncased the big thirty-two-miles-to-the-inch map of India, and two smaller Frontier maps, hauled down volume INF-KAN of the *Encyclo-paedia Britannica*, and the men consulted them.

"See here!" said Dravot, his thumb on the map. "Up to Jagdallak, Peachey and me know the road. We was there with Roberts's Army. We'll have to turn off to the right at Jagdallak through Laghmann territory. Then we get among the hills—fourteen thousand feet—fifteen thousand—it will be cold work there, but it don't look very far on the map."

I handed him Wood on the *Sources of the Oxus*. Carnehan was deep in the *Encyclopaedia*.

"They're a mixed lot," said Dravot, reflectively; "and it won't help us to know the names of their tribes. The more tribes the more they'll fight, and the better for us. From Jagdallak to Ashang. H'mm!"

"But all the information about the country is as sketchy and inaccurate as can be," I protested. "No one knows anything about it really. Here's the file of the *United Services' Institute*. Read what Bellew says."

"Blow Bellew!" said Carnehan. "Dan, they're an all-fired lot of heathens, but this book here says they think they're related to us English."

I smoked while the men pored over *Raverty, Wood,* the maps, and the *Encyclopaedia.*

"There is no use your waiting," said Dravot, politely. "It's about four o'clock now. We'll go before six o'clock if you want to sleep, and we won't steal any of the papers. Don't you sit up. We're two harmless lunatics and if you come, tomorrow evening, down to the Serai we'll say good-by to you."

"You *are* two fools," I answered. "You'll be turned back at the Frontier or cut up the minute you set foot in Afghanistan. Do you want any money or a recommendation down-country? I can help you to the chance of work next week."

"Next week we shall be hard at work ourselves, thank you," said Dravot. "It isn't so easy being a King as it looks. When we've got our Kingdom in going order we'll let you know, and you can come up and help us to govern it."

"Would two lunatics make a Contrack like that?" said Carnehan, with subdued pride, showing me a greasy half sheet of note paper on which was written the following. I copied it, then and there, as a curiosity:

This Contract between me and you pursuing witnesseth in the name of God—Amen and so forth.

(ONE)   *That me and you will settle this matter together: i.e., to be Kings of Kafiristan.*

(Two)   *That you and me will not, while this matter is being settled, look at any Liquor, nor any Woman, black, white or brown, so as to get mixed up with one or the other harmful.*

(THREE)   *That we conduct ourselves with dignity and discretion and if one of us gets into trouble the other will stay by him.*

Signed by you and me this day.
        PEACHEY TALIAFERRO CARNEHAN.
        DANIEL DRAVOT.
        Both Gentlemen at Large.

"There was no need for the last article," said Carnehan, blushing modestly; "but it looks regular. Now you know the sort of men that Loafers are—we *are* Loafers, Dan, until we get out of India—and *do* you think that we would sign a Contrack like that unless we was in earnest? We have kept away from the two things that make life worth having."

"You won't enjoy your lives much longer if you are going to try this idiotic adventure. Don't set the office on fire," I said, "and go away before nine o'clock."

I left them still poring over the maps and making notes on the back of the "Contrack." "Be sure to come down to the Serai tomorrow," were their parting words.

The Kumharsen Serai is the great four-square sink of humanity where the strings of camels and horses from the North load and unload. All the nationalities of Central Asia may be found there, and most of the folk of India proper. Balkh and Bokhara there meet Bengal and Bombay, and try to draw eyeteeth. You can buy ponies, turquoises, Persian pussy cats, saddlebags, fat-tailed sheep, and musk in the Kumharsen Serai, and get many strange things for nothing. In the afternoon I went down there to see whether my friends intended to keep their word or were lying about drunk.

A priest attired in fragments of ribbons and rags stalked up to me, gravely twisting a child's paper whirligig. Behind was his servant bending under the load of a crate of mud toys. The two were loading up two camels, and the inhabitants of the Serai watched them with shrieks of laughter.

"The priest is mad," said a horse-dealer to me. "He is going up to Kabul to sell toys to the Amir. He will either be raised to honor or have his head cut off. He came in here this morning and has been behaving madly ever since."

"The witless are under the protection of God," stammered a flat-cheeked Usbeg in broken Hindi. "They foretell future events."

"Would they could have foretold that my caravan would have been cut up by the Shinwaris almost within shadow of the Pass!" grunted the Eusufzai agent of a Rajputana trading house whose goods had been feloniously diverted into the hands of other robbers just across the Border, and whose misfortunes were the laughingstock of the bazaar. "Ohé, priest, whence come you and whither do you go?"

"From Roum have I come," shouted the priest, waving his whirligig; "from Roum, blown by the breath of a hundred devils across the sea! O thieves, robbers, liars, the blessing of Pir Khan on pigs, dogs, and perjurers! Who will take the Protected of God to the North to sell charms that are never still to the Amir? The camels shall not gall, the sons shall not fall sick, and the wives shall remain faithful while they are away, of the men who give me place in their caravan. Who will assist me to slipper the King of the Roos with a golden slipper with a silver heel? The protection of Pir Khan be upon his labors!" He spread out the skirts of his garberdine and pirouetted between the lines of tethered horses.

"There starts a caravan from Peshawur to Kabul in twenty days, *Huzrut*," said the Eusufzai trader. "My camels go therewith. Do thou also go and bring us good luck."

"I will go even now!" shouted the priest. "I will depart upon my winged camels, and be at Peshawur in a day! Ho! Hazar Mir Khan," he yelled to his servant, "drive out the camels, but let me first mount my own."

He leaped on the back of his beast as it knelt, and, turning round to me, cried, "Come thou also, Sahib, a little along the road, and I will sell thee a charm—an amulet that shall make thee King of Kafiristan."

Then the light broke upon me, and I followed the two camels out of the Serai till we reached open road and the priest halted.

"What d'you think o' that?" said he in English. "Carnehan can't talk their patter, so I've made him my servant. He makes a handsome servant. 'Tisn't for nothing that I've been knocking about the country for fourteen years. Didn't I do that talk neat? We'll hitch on to a caravan at Peshawur till we get to Jagdallak, and then we'll see if we can get donkeys for our camels, and strike into Kafiristan. Whirligigs for the Amir, O Lor'! Put your hand under the camel bags and tell me what you feel."

I felt the butt of a Martini, and another and another.

"Twenty of 'em," said Dravot, placidly. "Twenty of 'em, and ammunition to correspond, under the whirligigs and the mud dolls."

"Heaven help you if you are caught with those things!" I said. "A Martini is worth her weight in silver among the Pathans."

"Fifteen hundred rupees of capital—every rupee we could beg, borrow, or steal—are invested on these two camels," said Dravot. "We won't get caught. We're going through the Khyber with a regular caravan. Who'd touch a poor mad priest?"

"Have you got everything you want?" I asked, overcome with astonishment.

"Not yet, but we shall soon. Give us a memento of your kindness, *Brother*. You did me a service yesterday, and that time in Marwar. Half my Kingdom shall you have, as the saying is." I slipped a small charm compass from my watch chain and handed it up to the priest.

"Good-by," said Dravot, giving me hand cautiously. "It's the last time we'll shake hands with an Englishman these many days. Shake hands with him, Carnehan," he cried, as the second camel passed me.

Carnehan leaned down and shook hands. Then the camels passed away along the dusty road, and I was left alone to wonder. My eye could detect no failure in the disguises. The scene in Serai attested that they were complete to the native mind. There was just the chance, therefore, that Carnehan and Dravot would be able to wander through Afghanistan without detection. But, beyond, they would find death, certain and awful death.

Ten days later a native friend of mine, giving me the news of the day from Peshawur, wound up his letter with:—"There has been much laughter here on account of a certain mad priest who is going in his estimation to sell petty gauds and insignificant trinkets which he ascribes as great charms to H. H. the Amir of Bokhara. He passed through Peshawur and associated himself to the Second Summer caravan that goes to Kabul. The merchants are pleased, because through superstition they imagine that such mad fellows bring good fortune."

The two, then, were beyond the Border. I would have prayed for them, but, that night, a real King died in Europe, and demanded an obituary notice.

* * * *

The wheel of the world swings through the same phases again and again. Summer passed and winter thereafter, and came and passed again. The daily paper continued and I with it, and upon the third summer there fell a hot night, a night issue, and a strained waiting for something to be telegraphed from the other side of the world, exactly as had happened before. A few great men had died in the past two years, the machines worked with more clatter, and some of the trees in the Office garden were a few feet taller. But that was all the difference.

I passed over to the press room, and went through just such a scene as I have already described. The nervous tension was stronger than it had been two years before, and I felt the heat more acutely. At three o'clock I cried, "Print off," and turned to go, when there crept to my chair what was left of a man. He was bent into a circle, his head was sunk between his shoulders, and he moved his feet one over the other like a bear. I could hardly see whether he walked or crawled—this rag-wrapped, whining cripple who addressed me by name, crying that he was come back. "Can you give me a drink?" he whimpered. "For the Lord's sake, give me a drink!"

I went back to the office, the man followed with groans of pain, and I turned up the lamp.

"Don't you know me?" he gasped, dropping into a chair, and he turned his drawn face, surmounted by a shock of gray hair, to the light.

I looked at him intently. Once before had I seen eyebrows that met over the nose in an inch-broad black band, but for the life of me I could not tell where.

"I don't know you," I said, handing him the whisky. "What can I do for you?"

He took a gulp of the spirit raw, and shivered in spite of the suffocating heat.

"I've come back," he repeated; "and I was the King of Kafiristan—me and Dravot—crowned Kings we was! In this office we settled it—you setting there and giving us the books. I am Peachey—Peachey Taliaferro Carnehan, and you've been setting here ever since—O Lord!"

I was more than a little astonished, and expressed my feelings accordingly.

"It's true," said Carnehan, with a dry cackle, nursing his feet, which were wrapped in rags. "True as gospel. Kings we were, with crowns upon our heads—me and Dravot—poor. Dan—oh, poor, poor Dan, that would never take advice, not though I begged of him!"

"Take the whisky," I said, "and take your own time. Tell me all you can recollect of everything from beginning to end. You got across the border on your camels, Dravot dressed as a mad priest and you his servant. Do you remember that?"

"I ain't mad—yet, but I shall be that way soon. Of course I remember. Keep looking at me, or maybe my words will go all to pieces. Keep looking at me in my eyes and don't say anything."

I leaned forward and looked into his face as steadily as I could. He dropped one hand upon the table and I grasped it by the wrist. It was twisted like a bird's claw, and upon the back was a ragged, red, diamond-shaped scar.

"No, don't look there. Look at *me*," said Carnehan.

"That comes afterward, but for the Lord's sake don't distrack me. We left with that caravan, me and Dravot playing all sorts of antics to amuse the people we were with. Dravot used to make us laugh in the evenings when all the people was cooking their dinners—cooking their dinners, and . . . what did they do then? They lit little fires with sparks that went into Dravot's beard, and we all laughed—fit to die. Little red fires they was, going into Dravot's big red beard—so funny." His eyes left mine and he smiled foolishly.

"You went as far as Jagdallak with that caravan," I said, at a venture, "after you had lit those fires. To Jagdallak, where you turned off to try to get into Kafiristan."

"No, we didn't neither. What are you talking about? We turned off before Jagdallak, because we heard the roads was good. But they wasn't good enough for our two camels—mine and Dravot's. When we left the caravan, Dravot took off all his clothes and mine too, and said we would be heathen, because the Kafirs didn't allow Mohammedans to talk to them. So we dressed betwixt and between, and such a sight as Daniel Dravot I never saw yet nor expect to see again. He burned half his beard, and slung a sheepskin over his shoulder, and shaved his head into patterns. He shaved mine, too, and made me wear outrageous things to look like a heathen. That was in a most mountaineous country, and our camels couldn't go along any more because of the mountains. They were tall and black, and coming home I saw them fight like wild goats—there are lots of goats in Kafiristan. And these mountains, they never keep still, no more than goats. Always fighting they are, and don't let you sleep at night."

"Take some more whisky," I said, very slowly. "What did you and Daniel Dravot do when the camels could go no further because of the rough roads that led into Kafiristan?"

"What did which do? There was a party called Peachey Taliaferro Carnehan that was with Dravot. Shall I tell you about him? He died out there in the cold. Slap from the bridge fell old Peachey, turning and twisting in the air like a penny whirligig that you can sell to the Amir— No; they was two for three ha'pence, those whirligigs, or I am much mistaken and woeful sore. And then these camels were no use, and Peachey said to Dravot—'For the Lord's sake, let's get out of this before our heads are chopped off,' and with that they killed the camels all among the mountains, not having anything in particular to eat, but first they took off the boxes with the guns and the ammunition, till two men came along driving four mules. Dravot up and dances in front of them, singing,—'Sell me four mules.' Says the first man,—'If you are rich enough to buy, you are rich enough to rob'; but before ever he could put his hand to his knife, Dravot breaks his neck over his knee, and the other party runs away. So Carnehan loaded the mules with the rifles that was taken off the camels, and together we starts forward into those bitter cold mountaineous parts, and never a road broader than the back of your hand."

He paused for a moment, while I asked him if he could remember the nature of the country through which he had journeyed.

"I am telling you as straight as I can, but my head isn't as good as it might be. They drove nails through it to make me hear better how Dravot died. The country was mountaineous and the mules were most contrary, and the inhabitants was dispersed and solitary. They went up and up, and down and down, and that other party, Carnehan, was imploring of Dravot not to sing and whistle so loud, for fear of bringing down the tremenjus avalanches. But Dravot says that if a King couldn't sing it wasn't worth being King, and whacked the mules over the rump, and never took no heed for ten cold days. We came to a big level valley all among the mountains, and the mules were near dead, so we killed them, not having anything in special for them or us to eat. We sat upon the boxes, and played odd and even with the cartridges that was jolted out.

"Then ten men with bows and arrows ran down that valley, chasing twenty men with bows and arrows, and the row was tremenjus. They was fair men—fairer than you or more—with yellow hair and remarkable well built. Says Dravot, unpacking the guns—'This is the beginning of the business. We'll fight for the ten men,' and with that he fires two rifles at the twenty men, and drops one of them at two hundred yards from the rock where we was sitting. The other men began to run, but Carnehan and Dravot sits on the boxes picking them off at all ranges, up and down the valley. Then we goes up to the ten men that had run across the snow too, and they fires a footy little arrow at us. Dravot he shoots above their heads and they all falls down flat. Then he walks over and kicks them, and then he lifts them up and shakes hands all around to make them friendly like. He calls them and gives them the boxes to carry, and waves his hand for all the world as though he was King already. They takes the boxes and him across the valley and up the hill into a pine wood on the top, where there was half a dozen big stone idols. Dravot he goes to the biggest—a fellow they call Imbra—and lays a rifle and a cartridge at his feet, rubbing his nose respectful with his own nose, patting him on the head, and saluting in front of it. He turns round to the men and nods his head, and says, 'That's all right. I'm in the know too, and all these old jim-jams are my friends.' Then he opens his mouth and points down it, and when the first man brings him food, he says 'No'; and when the second man brings him food, he says 'No'; but when one of the old priests and the boss of the village brings him food, he says 'Yes'; very haughty, and eats it slow. That was how we came to our first village, without any trouble, just as though we had tumbled from the skies. But we tumbled from one of those damned rope bridges, you see, and you couldn't expect a man to laugh much after that."

"Take some more whisky and go on," I said. "That was the first village you came into. How did you get to be King?"

"I wasn't King," said Carnehan. "Dravot he was the King, and a handsome man he looked with the gold crown on his head and all. Him and the other party stayed in that village, and every morning Dravot sat by the side of old Imbra, and the people came and worshiped. That was Dravot's order. Then a lot of men came into the valley, and Carnehan and Dravot picks them off with the rifles before they knew where they was, and runs down into the valley and up again the other side, and finds another village, same as the first one, and the people all falls down flat on their faces, and Dravot says, 'Now what is the trouble between you two villages?' and the people points to a woman, as fair as you or me, that was carried off, and Dravot takes her back to the first village and counts up the dead—eight there was. For each dead man Dravot pours a little milk on the ground and waves his arms like a whirligig and 'That's all right,' says he. Then he and Carnehan takes the big boss of each village by the arm and walks them down into the valley, and shows them how to scratch a line with a spear right down the valley, and gives each a sod of turf from both sides o' the line. Then all the people comes down and shouts like the devil and all, and Dravot says, 'Go and dig the land, and be fruitful and multiply,' which they did, though they didn't understand. Then we asks the names of things in their lingo—bread and water and fire and idols and such, and Dravot leads the priest of each village up to the idol, and says he must sit there and judge the people, and if anything goes wrong he is to be shot.

"Next week they was all turning up the land in the valley as quiet as bees and much prettier, and the priests heard all the complaints and told Dravot in dumb show what it was about. 'That's just the beginning,' says Dravot. 'They think we're Gods.' He and Carnehan picks out twenty good men and shows them how to click off a rifle, and form fours, and advance in line, and they was very pleased to do so, and clever to see the hang of it. Then he takes out his pipe and his 'baccy pouch and leaves one at one village and one at the other, and off we two goes to see what was to be done in the next valley. That was all rock, and there was a little village there, and Carnehan says, 'Send 'em to the old valley to plant,' and takes 'em there and gives 'em some land that wasn't took before. They were a poor lot, and we blooded 'em with a kid before letting 'em into the new Kingdom. That was to impress the people, and then they settled down quiet, and Carnehan went back to Dravot, who had got into another valley, all snow and ice and most mountaineous. There was no people there, and the Army got afraid, so Dravot shoots one of them, and goes on till he finds some people in a village, and the Army explains that unless the people wants to be killed they had better not shoot their little matchlocks; for they had matchlocks. We makes friends with the priest and I stays there alone with two of the Army, teaching the men how to drill, and a thundering big Chief comes across the snow with kettledrums and horns twanging, because he heard there was a new God kicking about. Carnehan sights for the brown of the men half a mile across the snow and wings one of them. Then he sends a message to the Chief that, unless he wished to be killed, he must come and shake hands with me and leave his arms behind. The Chief comes alone first, and Carnehan shakes hands with him and whirls his arms about, same as Dravot used, and very much surprised that Chief was, and strokes my eyebrows. Then Carnehan goes alone to the Chief, and asks him in dumb show if he had an enemy he hated. 'I have,' says the Chief. So Carnehan weeds out the pick of his men, and sets the two of the Army to show them drill, and at the end of two weeks the men can maneuver about as well as Volunteers. So he marches with the Chief to a great big plain on the top of a mountain, and the Chief's men rushes into a village and takes it; we three Martinis firing into the brown of the enemy. So we took that village too, and I gives the Chief a rag from my coat and says, 'Occupy till I come'; which was scriptural. By way of a reminder, when me and the Army was eighteen hundred yards away, I drops a bullet near him standing on the snow, and all the people falls flat on their faces. Then I sends a letter to Dravot, wherever he be by land or by sea."

At the risk of throwing the creature out of train I interrupted, "How could you write a letter up yonder?"

"The letter?—Oh!—The letter! Keep looking at me between the eyes, please. It was a string-talk letter, that we'd learned the way of it from a blind beggar in the Punjab."

I remember that there had once come to the office a blind man with a knotted twig and a piece of string which he wound round the twig according to some cipher of his own. He could, after the lapse of days or hours, repeat the sentence which he had reeled up. He had reduced the alphabet to eleven primitive sounds; and tried to teach me his method, but failed.

"I sent that letter to Dravot," said Carnehan; "and told him to come back because this Kingdom was growing too big for me to handle, and then I struck for the first valley, to see how the priests were working. They called the village we took along with the Chief, Bashkai, and the first village we took, Er-Heb. The priests at Er-Heb was doing all right, but they had a lot of pending cases about land to show me, and some men from another village had been firing arrows at night. I went out and looked for that village and fired four rounds at it from a thousand yards. That used all the cartridges I cared to spend, and I waited for Dravot, who had been away two or three months, and I kept my people quiet.

"One morning I heard the devil's own noise of drums and horns, and Dan Dravot marches down the hill with his Army and a tail of hundreds of men, and, which was the most amazing—a great gold crown on his head. 'My Gord, Carnehan,' says Daniel, 'this is a tremenjus business, and we've got the whole country as far as it's worth having. I am the son of Alexander by Queen Semiramis, and you're my younger brother and a God too! It's the biggest thing we've ever seen. I've been marching and fighting for six weeks with the Army, and every footy little village for fifty miles has come in rejoiceful; and more than that, I've got the key of the whole show, as you'll see, and I've got a crown for you! I told 'em to make two of 'em at a place called Shu, where the gold lies in the rock like suet in mutton. Gold I've seen, and turquoise I've kicked out of the cliffs, and there's garnets in the sands of the river, and here's a chunk of amber that a man brought me. Call up all the priests and, here, take your crown.'

"One of the men opens a black hair bag and I slips the crown on. It was too small and too heavy, but I wore it for the glory. Hammered gold it was—five pound weight, like a hoop of a barrel.

"'Peachey,' says Dravot, 'we don't want to fight no more. The Craft's the trick, so help me!' and he brings forward that same Chief that I left at Bashkai—Billy Fish we called him afterward, because he was so like Billy Fish that drove the big tank engine at Mach on the Bolan in the old days. 'Shake hands with him,' says Dravot, and I shook hands and nearly dropped, for Billy Fish gave me the Grip. I said nothing, but tried him with the Fellow Craft Grip. He answers, all right, and I tried the Master's Grip, but that was a slip. 'A Fellow Craft he is!' I says to Dan. 'Does he know the word?' 'He does,' says Dan, 'and all the priests know. It's a miracle! The Chiefs and the priests can work a Fellow Craft Lodge in a way that's very like ours, and they've cut the marks on the rocks, but they don't know the Third Degree, and they've come to find out. It's Gord's Truth. I've known these long years that the Afghans knew up to the Fellow Craft Degree, but this is a miracle. A God and a Grand Master of the Craft am I, and a Lodge in the Third Degree I will open, and we'll raise the head priests and the Chiefs of the villages.'

" 'It's against all the law,' I says, 'holding a Lodge without warrant from anyone; and we never held office in any Lodge.'

" 'It's a master stroke of policy,' says Dravot. 'It means running the country as easy as a four-wheeled bogy on a down grade. We can't stop to inquire now, or they'll turn against us. I've forty Chiefs at my heel, and passed and raised according to their merit they shall be. Billet these men on the villages and see that we run up a Lodge of some kind. The temple of Imbra will do for the Lodge room. The women must make aprons as you show them. I'll hold a levee of Chiefs tonight and Lodge tomorrow.'

"I was fair run off my legs, but I wasn't such a fool as not to see what a pull this Craft business gave us. I showed the priests' families how to make aprons of the degrees, but for Dravot's apron the blue border and marks was made of turquoise lumps on white hide, not cloth. We took a great square stone in the temple for the Master's chair, and little stones for the officers' chairs, and painted the black pavement with white squares, and did what we could to make things regular.

"At the levee which was held that night on the hillside with big bonfires, Dravot gives out that him and me were Gods and sons of Alexander, and Past Grand Masters in the Craft, and was come to make Kafiristan a country where every man should eat in peace and drink in quiet, and specially obey us. Then the Chiefs come round to shake hands, and they was so hairy and white and fair it was just shaking hands with old friends. We gave them names according as they was like men we had known in India—Billy Fish, Holly Wilworth, Pikky Kergan that was Bazaar-master when I was at Mhow, and so on and so on.

"*The* most amazing miracle was at Lodge next night. One of the old priests was watching us continuous, and I felt uneasy, for I knew we'd have to fudge the Ritual, and I didn't know what the men knew. The old priest was a stranger come in from beyond the village of Bashkai. The minute Dravot puts on the Master's apron that the girls had made for him, the priest fetches a whoop and a howl, and tried to overturn the stone that Dravot was sitting on. 'It's all up now,' I says. 'That comes of meddling with the Craft without warrant!' Dravot never winked an eye, not when ten priests took and tilted over the Grand Master's chair—which was to say the stone of Imbra. The priest begins rubbing the bottom end of it to clear away the black dirt, and presently he shows all the other priests the Master's Mark, same as was on Dravot's apron, cut into the stone. Not even the priests of the temple of Imbra knew it was there. The old chap falls flat on his face at Dravot's feet and kisses 'em. 'Luck again,' says Dravot, across the Lodge to me, 'they say it's the missing Mark that no one could understand the why of. We're more than safe now.' Then he bangs the butt of his gun for a gavel and says, 'By virtue of the authority vested in

me by my own right hand and the help of Peachey, I declare myself Grand
Master of all Freemasonry in Kafiristan in this the Mother Lodge o' the
country, and King of Kafiristan equally with Peachey!' At that he puts on
his crown and I puts on mine—I was doing Senior Warden—and we opens
the Lodge in most ample form. It was a amazing miracle! The priests
moved in Lodge through the first two degrees almost without telling, as if
the memory was coming back to them. After that, Peachey and Dravot
raised such as was worthy—high priests and Chiefs of far-off villages. Billy
Fish was the first, and I can tell you we scared the soul out of him. It was
not in any way according to Ritual, but it served our turn. We didn't
raise more than ten of the biggest men, because we didn't want to make
the Degree common. And they was clamoring to be raised.

" 'In another six months,' says Dravot, 'we'll hold another Communication and see how you are working.' Then he asks them about their villages, and learns that they was fighting one against the other and were fair
sick and tired of it. And when they wasn't doing that they was fighting
with the Mohammedans. 'You can fight those when they come into our
country,' says Dravot. 'Tell off every tenth man of your tribes for a
Frontier guard, and send two hundred at a time to this valley to be drilled.
Nobody is going to be shot or speared any more so long as he does well,
and I know that you won't cheat me because you're white people—sons of
Alexander—and not like common, black Mohammedans. You are *my* people
and by God,' says he, running off into English at the end—'I'll make a
damned fine Nation of you, or I'll die in the making!'

"I can't tell all we did for the next six months because Dravot did a lot
I couldn't see the hang of, and he learned their lingo in a way I never could.
My work was to help the people plow, and now and again go out with
some of the Army and see what the other villages were doing, and make
'em throw rope bridges across the ravines which cut up the country horrid.
Dravot was very kind to me, but when he walked up and down in the
pine wood pulling that bloody red beard of his with both fists I knew
he was thinking plans I could not advise him about, and I just waited for
orders.

"But Dravot never showed me disrespect before the people. They
were afraid of me and the Army, but they loved Dan. He was the best of
friends with the priests and the Chiefs; but anyone could come across the
hills with a complaint and Dravot would hear him out fair, and call four
priests together and say what was to be done. He used to call in Billy Fish
from Bashkai, and Pikky Kergan from Shu, and an old Chief we called
Kafuzelum—it was like enough to his real name—and hold councils with
'em when there was any fighting to be done in small villages. That was
his Council of War, and the four priests of Bashkai, Shu, Khawak, and
Madora was his Privy Council. Between the lot of 'em they sent me, with
forty men and twenty rifles, and sixty men carrying turquoises, into the

Ghorband country to buy those hand-made Martini rifles, that come out of the Amir's workshops at Kabul, from one of the Amir's Herati regiments that would have sold the very teeth out of their mouths for turquoises.

"I stayed in Ghorband a month, and gave the Governor there the pick of my baskets for hush money, and bribed the Colonel of the regiment some more, and, between the two and the tribespeople, we got more than a hundred hand-made Martinis, a hundred good Kohat Jezails that'll throw to six hundred yards, and forty manloads of very bad ammunition for the rifles. I came back with what I had, and distributed 'em among the men that the Chiefs sent to me to drill. Dravot was too busy to attend to those things, but the old Army that we first made helped me, and we turned out five hundred men that could drill, and two hundred that knew how to hold arms pretty straight. Even those corkscrewed, hand-made guns was a miracle to them. Dravot talked big about powder shops and factories, walking up and down in the pine wood when the winter was coming on.

" 'I won't make a Nation,' says he. 'I'll make an Empire! These men aren't niggers; they're English! Look at their eyes—look at their mouths. Look at the way they stand up. They sit on chairs in their own houses. They're the Lost Tribes, or something like it, and they've grown to be English. I'll take a census in the spring if the priests don't get frightened. There must be a fair two million of 'em in these hills. The villages are full o' little children. Two million people—two hundred and fifty thousand fighting men—and all English! They only want the rifles and a little drilling. Two hundred and fifty thousand men, ready to cut in on Russia's right flank when she tries for India! Peachey, man,' he says, chewing his beard in great hunks, 'we shall be Emperors—Emperors of the Earth! Rajah Brooke will be a suckling to us. I'll treat with the Vice-roy on equal terms. I'll ask him to send me twelve picked English—twelve that I know of—to help us govern a bit. There's Mackray, Sergeant-pensioner at Segowli—many's the good dinner he's given me, and his wife a pair of trousers. There's Donkin, the Warder of Tounghoo Jail; there's hundreds that I could lay my hand on if I was in India. The Vice-roy shall do it for me. I'll send a man through in the spring for those men, and I'll write for a dispensation from the Grand Lodge for what I've done as Grand Master. That—and all the Sniders that'll be thrown out when the native troops in India take up the Martini. They'll be worn smooth, but they'll do for fighting in these hills. Twelve English, a hundred thousand Sniders run through the Amir's country in driblets—I'd be content with twenty thousand in one year—and we'd be an Empire. When everything was shipshape, I'd hand over the crown—this crown I'm wearing now—to Queen Victoria on my knees, and she'd say: "Rise up, Sir Daniel Dravot." Oh, it's big! It's big, I tell you! But there's so much to be done in every place—Bashkai, Khawak, Shu, and everywhere else.'

" 'What is it?' I says. 'There are no more men coming in to be drilled this autumn. Look at those fat, black clouds. They're bringing the snow.'

" 'It isn't that,' says Daniel, putting his hand very hard on my shoulder; 'and I don't wish to say anything that's against you, for no other living man would have followed me and made me what I am as you have done. You're a first-class Commander-in-Chief, and the people know you; but—it's a big country, and somehow you can't help me, Peachey, in the way I want to be helped.'

" 'Go to your blasted priests, then!' I said, and I was sorry when I made that remark, but it did hurt me sore to find Daniel talking so superior when I'd drilled all the men, and done all he told me.

" 'Don't let's quarrel, Peachey,' says Daniel, without cursing. 'You're a King, too, and the half of this Kingdom is yours; but can't you see, Peachey, we want cleverer men than us now—three or four of 'em, that we can scatter about for our Deputies. It's a hugeous great State, and I can't always tell the right thing to do, and I haven't time for all I want to do, and here's the winter coming on and all.' He put half his beard into his mouth, and it was as red as the gold of his crown.

" 'I'm sorry, Daniel,' says I. 'I've done all I could. I've drilled the men and shown the people how to stack their oats better; and I've brought in those tinware rifles from Ghorband—but I know what you're driving at. I take it Kings always feel oppressed that way.'

" 'There's another thing too,' says Dravot, walking up and down. 'The winter's coming and these people won't be giving much trouble and if they do we can't move about. I want a wife.'

" 'For Gord's sake leave the women alone!' I says. 'We've both got all the work we can, though I *am* a fool. Remember the Contrack, and keep clear o' women.'

" 'The Contrack only lasted till such time as we was Kings; and Kings we have been these months past,' says Dravot, weighing his crown in his hand. 'You go get a wife too, Peachey—a nice, strappin', plump girl that'll keep you warm in the winter. They're prettier than English girls, and we can take the pick of 'em. Boil 'em once or twice in hot water, and they'll come as fair as chicken and ham.'

" 'Don't tempt me!' I says. 'I will not have any dealings with a woman not till we are a dam' side more settled than we are now. I've been doing the work o' two men, and you've been doing the work o' three. Let's lie off a bit, and see if we can get some better tobacco from Afghan country and run in some good liquor; but no women.'

" 'Who's talking o' *women?*' says Dravot. 'I said *wife*—a Queen to breed a King's son for the King. A Queen out of the strongest tribe, that'll make them your blood brothers, and that'll lie by your side and tell you all the people thinks about you and their own affairs. That's what I want.'

" 'Do you remember that Bengali woman I kept at Mogul Serai when

I was a plate layer?' says I. 'A fat lot o' good she was to me. She taught me the lingo and one or two other things; but what happened? She ran away with the Stationmaster's servant and half my month's pay. Then she turned up at Dadur Junction in tow of a half-caste, and had the impidence to say I was her husband—all among the drivers in the running shed!'

" 'We've done with that,' says Dravot. 'These women are whiter than you or me, and a Queen I will have for the winter months.'

" 'For the last time o' asking, Dan, do *not*,' I says. 'It'll only bring us harm. The Bible says that Kings ain't to waste their strength on women, 'specially when they've got a new raw Kingdom to work over.'

" 'For the last time of answering, I will,' said Dravot, and he went away through the pine trees looking like a big red devil. The low sun hit his crown and beard on one side and the two blazed like hot coals.

"But getting a wife was not as easy as Dan thought. He put it before the Council, and there was no answer till Billy Fish said that he'd better ask the girls. Dravot damned them all round. 'What's wrong with me?' he shouts, standing by the idol Imbra. 'Am I a dog or am I not enough of a man for your wenches? Haven't I put the shadow of my hand over this country? Who stopped the last Afghan raid?' It was me really, but Dravot was too angry to remember. 'Who brought your guns? Who repaired the bridges? Who's the Grand Master of the sign cut in the stone?' and he thumped his hand on the block that he used to sit on in Lodge, and at Council, which opened like Lodge always. Billy Fish said nothing, and no more did the others. 'Keep your hair on, Dan,' said I; 'and ask the girls. That's how it's done at Home, and these people are quite English.'

" 'The marriage of the King is a matter of State,' says Dan, in a white-hot rage, for he could feel, I hope, that he was going against his better mind. He walked out of the Council room, and the others sat still, looking at the ground.

" 'Billy Fish,' says I to the Chief of Bashkai, 'what's the difficulty here? A straight answer to a true friend.' 'You know,' says Billy Fish. 'How should a man tell you who know everything? How can daughters of men marry Gods or Devils? It's not proper.'

"I remembered something like that in the Bible; but if, after seeing us as long as they had, they still believed we were Gods, it wasn't for me to undeceive them.

" 'A God can do anything,' says I. 'If the King is fond of a girl he'll not let her die.' 'She'll have to,' said Billy Fish. 'There are all sorts of Gods and Devils in these mountains, and now and again a girl marries one of them and isn't seen any more. Besides, you two know the Mark cut in the stone. Only the Gods know that. We thought you were men till you showed the sign of the Master.'

"I wished then that we had explained about the loss of the genuine secrets of a Master Mason at the first go-off; but I said nothing. All that night there was a blowing of horns in a little dark temple halfway down the hill, and I heard a girl crying fit to die. One of the priests told us that she was being prepared to marry the King.

" 'I'll have no nonsense of that kind,' says Dan. 'I don't want to interfere with your customs, but I'll take my own wife.' 'The girl's a little bit afraid,' says the priest. 'She thinks she's going to die, and they are a-heartening of her up down in the temple.'

" 'Hearten her very tender, then,' says Dravot, 'or I'll hearten you with the butt of a gun so that you'll never want to be heartened again.' He licked his lips, did Dan, and stayed up walking about more than half the night, thinking of the wife that he was going to get in the morning. I wasn't any means comfortable, for I knew that dealings with a woman in foreign parts, though you was a crowned King twenty times over, could not but be risky. I got up very early in the morning while Dravot was asleep, and I saw the priests talking together in whispers, and the Chiefs talking together too, and they looked at me out of the corners of their eyes.

" 'What is up, Fish?' I says to the Bashkai man, who was wrapped up in his furs and looking splendid to behold.

" 'I can't rightly say,' says he; 'but if you can induce the King to drop all this nonsense about marriage, you'll be doing him and me and yourself a great service.'

" 'That I do believe,' says I. 'But sure, you know, Billy, as well as me, having fought against and for us, that the King and me are nothing more than two of the finest men that God Almighty ever made. Nothing more, I do assure you.'

" 'That may be,' says Billy Fish, 'and yet I should be sorry if it was.' He sinks his head upon his great fur cloak for a minute and thinks. 'King,' says he, 'be you man or God or Devil, I'll stick by you today. I have twenty of my men with me, and they will follow me. We'll go to Bashkai until the storm blows over.'

"A little snow had fallen in the night, and everything was white except the greasy fat clouds that blew down and down from the north. Dravot came out with his crown on his head, swinging his arms and stamping his feet, and looking more pleased than Punch.

" 'For the last time, drop it, Dan,' says I, in a whisper. 'Billy Fish here says that there will be a row.'

" 'A row among my people!' says Dravot. 'Not much. Peachey, you're a fool not to get a wife too. Where's the girl?' says he, with a voice as loud as the braying of a jackass. 'Call up all the Chiefs and priests, and let the Emperor see if his wife suits him.'

"There was no need to call anyone. They were all there leaning on their guns and spears round the clearing in the center of the pine wood. A deputation of priests went down to the little temple to bring up the girl, and the horns blew up fit to wake the dead. Billy Fish saunters round and gets as close to Daniel as he could, and behind him stood his twenty men with matchlocks. Not a man of them under six feet. I was next to Dravot, and behind me was twenty men of the regular Army. Up comes the girl, and a strapping wench she was, covered with silver and turquoises, but white as death, and looking back every minute at the priests.

" 'She'll do,' said Dan, looking her over. 'What's to be afraid of, lass? Come and kiss me.' He puts his arm round her. She shuts her eyes, gives a bit of a squeak, and down goes her face in the side of Dan's flaming red beard.

" 'The slut's bitten me!' says he, clapping his hand to his neck, and, sure enough, his hand was red with blood. Billy Fish and two of his matchlock men catches hold of Dan by the shoulders and drags him into the Bashkai lot, while the priests howl in their lingo, 'Neither God nor Devil, but a man!' I was all taken aback, for a priest cut at me in front, and the Army behind began firing into the Bashkai men.

" 'God A-mighty!' says Dan. 'What is the meaning o' this?'

" 'Come back! Come away!' says Billy Fish, 'Ruin and Mutiny is the matter. We'll break for Bashkai if we can.'

"I tried to give some sort of orders to my men—the men o' the regular Army—but it was no use, so I fired into the brown of 'em with an English Martini and drilled three beggars in a line. The valley was full of shouting, howling creatures, and every soul was shrieking, 'Not a God not a Devil, but only a man!' The Bashkai troops stuck to Billy Fish all they were worth, but their matchlocks wasn't half as good as the Kabul breechloaders, and four of them dropped. Dan was bellowing like a bull, for he was very wrathy; and Billy Fish had a hard job to prevent him running out at the crowd.

" 'We can't stand,' says Billy Fish. 'Make a run for it down the valley! The whole place is against us.' The matchlock men ran, and we went down the valley in spite of Dravot's protestations. He was swearing horribly and crying out that he was a King. The priests rolled great stones on us, and the regular Army fired hard, and there wasn't more than six men, not counting Dan, Billy Fish, and Me, that came down to the bottom of the valley alive.

"Then they stopped firing and the horns in the temple blew again. 'Come away—for Gord's sake come away!' says Billy Fish. 'They'll send runners out to all the villages before ever we get to Bashkai. I can protect you there, but I can't do anything now.'

"My own notion is that Dan began to go mad in his head from that hour. He stared up and down like a stuck pig. Then he was all for walking back alone and killing the priests with his bare hands; which he could have done. 'An Emperor am I,' says Daniel, 'and next year I shall be a Knight of the Queen.'

" 'All right, Dan,' says I; 'but come along now while there's time.'

" 'It's your fault,' says he, 'for not looking after your Army better. There was mutiny in the midst and you didn't know—you damned engine-driving, plate-laying, missionary's-pass-hunting hound!' He sat upon a rock and called me every foul name he could lay tongue to. I was too heartsick to care, though it was all his foolishness that brought the smash.

" 'I'm sorry, Dan,' says I, 'but there's no accounting for natives. This business is our Fifty-Seven. Maybe we'll make something out of it yet, when we've got to Bashkai.'

" 'Let's get to Bashkai, then,' says Dan, 'and, by God, when I come back here again I'll sweep the valley so there isn't a bug in a blanket left!'

"We walked all that day, and all that night Dan was stumping up and down on the snow, chewing his beard and muttering to himself.

" 'There's no hope o' getting clear,' said Billy Fish. 'The priests will have sent runners to the villages to say that you are only men. Why didn't you stick on as Gods till things was more settled? I'm a dead man,' says Billy Fish, and he throws himself down on the snow and begins to pray to his Gods.

"Next morning we was in a cruel bad country—all up and down, no level ground at all, and no food either. The six Bashkai men looked at Billy Fish hungrywise as if they wanted to ask something, but they said never a word. At noon we came to the top of a flat mountain all covered with snow, and when we climbed up into it, behold, there was an Army in position waiting in the middle!

" 'The runners have been very quick,' says Billy Fish, with a little bit of a laugh. 'They are waiting for us.'

"Three or four men began to fire from the enemy's side, and a chance shot took Daniel in the calf of the leg. That brought him to his senses. He looks across the snow at the Army, and sees the rifles that we had brought into the country.

" 'We're done for,' says he. 'They are Englishmen, these people—and it's my blasted nonsense that has brought you to this. Get back, Billy Fish, and take your men away; you've done what you could, and now cut for it. Carnehan,' says he, 'shake hands with me and go along with Billy. Maybe they won't kill you. I'll go and meet 'em alone. It's me that did it. Me, the King!'

" 'Go!' says I. 'Go to Hell, Dan. I'm with you here. Billy Fish, you clear out, and we two will meet those folk.'

" 'I'm a Chief,' says Billy Fish, quite quiet. 'I stay with you. My men can go.'

"The Bashkai fellows didn't wait for a second word, but ran off, and Dan and Me and Billy Fish walked across to where the drums were drumming and the horns were horning. It was cold—awful cold. I've got that cold in the back of my head now. There's a lump of it there."

The punkah coolies had gone to sleep. Two kerosene lamps were blazing in the office, and the perspiration poured down my face and splashed on the blotter as I leaned forward. Carnehan was shivering, and I feared that his mind might go. I wiped my face, took a fresh grip of the piteously mangled hands, and said, "What happened after that?"

The momentary shift of my eyes had broken the clear current.

"What was you pleased to say?" whined Carnehan. "They took them without any sound. Not a little whisper all along the snow, not though the King knocked down the first man that set hand on him—not though old Peachey fired his last cartridge into the brown of 'em. Not a single solitary sound did those swines make. They just closed up tight, and I tell you their furs stunk. There was a man called Billy Fish, a good friend of us all, and they cut his throat, Sir, then and there, like a jig; and the King kicks up the bloody snow and says, 'We've had a dashed fine run for our money. What's coming next?' But Peachey, Peachey Taliaferro, I tell you, Sir, in confidence as betwixt two friends, he lost his head, Sir. No, he didn't neither. The King lost his head, so he did, all along o' one of those cunning rope bridges. Kindly let me have the paper cutter, Sir. It tilted this way. They marched him a mile across that snow to a rope bridge over a ravine with a river at the bottom. You may have seen such. They prodded him behind like an ox. 'Damn your eyes!' says the King. 'D'you suppose I can't die like a gentleman?' He turns to Peachey—Peachey that was crying like a child. 'I've brought you to this, Peachey,' says he. 'Brought you out of your happy life to be killed in Kafiristan, where you was late Commander-in-Chief of the Emperor's forces. Say you forgive me, Peachey,' 'I do,' says Peachey. 'Fully and freely do I forgive you, Dan.' 'Shake hands, Peachey,' says he. 'I'm going now.' Out he goes, looking neither right nor left, and when he was plumb in the middle of those dizzy dancing ropes, 'Cut, you beggars,' he shouts; and they cut, and old Dan fell, turning round and round and round twenty thousand miles, for he took half an hour to fall till he struck the water, and I could see his body caught on a rock with the gold crown close beside.

"But do you know what they did to Peachey between two pine trees? They crucified him, Sir, as Peachey's hand will show. They used wooden pegs for his hands and his feet; and he didn't die. He hung there and screamed, and they took him down next day, and said it was a miracle that he wasn't dead. They took him down—poor old Peachey that hadn't done them any harm—that hadn't done them any . . ."

He rocked to and fro and wept bitterly, wiping his eyes with the back of his scarred hands and moaning like a child for some ten minutes.

"They was cruel enough to feed him up in the temple, because they said he was more of a God than old Daniel that was a man. Then they turned him out on the snow, and told him to go home, and Peachey came home in about a year, begging along the roads quite safe; for Daniel

Dravot he walked before and said, 'Come along, Peachey. It's a big thing we're doing.' The mountains they danced at night, and the mountains they tried to fall on Peachey's head, but Dan he held up his hand, and Peachey came along bent double. He never let go of Dan's hand, and he never let go of Dan's head. They gave it to him as a present in the temple, to remind him not to come again, and though the crown was pure gold, and Peachey was starving, never would Peachey sell the same. You knew Dravot, Sir! You knew Right Worshipful Brother Dravot! Look at him now!"

He fumbled in the mass of rags round his bent waist; brought out a black horsehair bag embroidered with silver thread; and shook therefrom on to my table—the dried, withered head of Daniel Dravot! The morning sun that had long been paling the lamps struck the red beard and blind sunken eyes; struck, too, a heavy circlet of gold studded with raw turquoises, that Carnehan placed tenderly on the battered temples.

"You behold now," said Carnehan, "the Emperor in his habit as he lived—the King of Kafiristan with his crown upon his head. Poor old Daniel that was a monarch once!"

I shuddered, for, in spite of defacements manifold, I recognized the head of the man of Marwar Junction. Carnehan rose to go. I attempted to stop him. He was not fit to walk abroad. "Let me take away the whisky, and give me a little money," he gasped. "I was a King once. I'll go to the Deputy Commissioner and ask to set in the Poorhouse till I get my health. No, thank you, I can't wait till you get a carriage for me. I've urgent private affairs—in the South—at Marwar."

He shambled out of the office and departed in the direction of the Deputy Commissioner's house. That day at noon I had occasion to go down the blinding hot Mall, and I saw a crooked man crawling along the white dust of the roadside, his hat in his hand, quavering dolorously after the fashion of street-singers at Home. There was not a soul in sight, and he was out of all possible earshot of the houses. And he sang through his nose, turning his head from right to left:

> *The Son of Man goes forth to war,*
> *A golden crown to gain;*
> *His blood-red banner streams afar—*
> *Who follows in his train?*

I waited to hear no more, but put the poor wretch into my carriage and drove him off to the nearest missionary for eventual transfer to the Asylum. He repeated the hymn twice while he was with me, whom he did not in the least recognize, and I left him singing it to the missionary.

Two days later I inquired after his welfare of the Superintendent of the Asylum.

"He was admitted suffering from sunstroke. He died early yesterday morning," said the Superintendent. "Is it true that he was half an hour bareheaded in the sun at midday?"

"Yes," said I, "but do you happen to know if he had anything upon him by any chance when he died?"

"Not to my knowledge," said the Superintendent.

And there the matter rests.

INTERPRETATION

At first glance, this seems to be merely a good story of adventure in a far-off and exotic place. There are difficult journeys, mysterious strangers, battles, pagan temples, madness, a crucifixion. The reader's curiosity about the turn of events is whetted by many cunning devices for provoking suspense. (For instance, the first stranger's mysterious message leads to the red-bearded man in the second-class carriage. The trader and his servant in the bazaar turn out to be the adventurers ready for their journey. Or, to go further, in the episode (see Glossary) concerning the mark on the stone, everything hangs for a moment in the balance until the mark is disclosed. Kipling, in other words, not only plays on the reader's curiosity about the final outcome, but plays up our suspense as to the outcome of the individual steps in the story's development.)

Furthermore, we can see how, in this story in which *plot* (see Glossary) seems to be so dominant in interest, one incident is caused by another. For instance, the marriage causes the discovery which brings on the ruin of the kings. But though we can link up the various episodes into a chain of cause and effect, we can see that this chain really depends upon the characters themselves.

Again, considered superficially, the matter of *motivation* (see Glossary) seems to present little difficulty. Many men desire riches and power, as do Peachey and Dravot; and it may seem that we need go no further into the matter in our discussion of motivation and character. (Indeed, this is as far as most adventure stories do go in presenting motivation.) But we can see that in this story, despite its apparent emphasis on action, the motivation is more complicated. For example, as the kings acquire their power, the simple desire for riches and power begins to change. There is a growing sense of responsibility for, and pride in, the people that they rule. Dravot begins to talk about bringing in skilled administrators, recognizing with an unexpected kind of humility that the business of kingship is more complicated than he had thought. He even begins to dream of turning over his kingdom to Queen Victoria—of taking his place in history as one of the Empire Builders. Actually, it is this development of character that proves to be one of the factors leading to his downfall, for the desire for marriage is not merely his simple human desire for companionship—though this is present—but it is also a desire to found a royal line, to leave someone to carry on the kingdom after his death. The wedding, therefore, must be public, and it must be carried out with due ceremony and ritual.

The course of the adventure itself has gone hand in hand with a development of character. That is, the men whom we meet at the beginning of the story are loafers—even if rather unusual loafers—yet men who are outcasts and who see "things from the underside where the lath and plaster is not smoothed off." But Dravot does not die like the loafer: "They prodded him behind like an ox. 'Damn your eyes!' says the King. 'D'you suppose I can't die like a gentleman?' "

He dies like a king, "like a gentleman," not like the trapped animal, the ox. And even Peachey, whose position is subordinate to Dravot's throughout the story, participates in this new dignity. Peachey comes back through the wild mountains, through terrors and hardships, but he never relinquishes the bag in which are the head of the King, and the crown, the symbol of kingship. So, as a *paradox* (see Glossary), the two loafers become most truly kings in the moment when their false kingship is taken from them. That is, when external kingship is lost, internal kingship is achieved.

This idea may prompt us to look back again at the meaning of the situation which brings about the ruin of the adventurers. The natives have thought of them as gods—not as human kings. The power of Peachey and Dravot is, thus, that of the king-as-god, not that of the king-as-man. But Dravot, the king-as-god, wants to be a man—he has human instincts which the mere exercise of godlike power cannot satisfy. He wants to have power, to be a god (for, to have power over the natives, he must be a god, as we discover), and he longs to be a man. This is the dilemma in which he is caught, and the dilemma which ruins him. The story at this point shows itself to be in a sense, then, a study of kingship; and there is a continuation of this study of kingship as the story goes on to recount Dravot's death, where, as we have seen, Dravot achieves another kind of kingship, and the nature of kingship is redefined.

Perhaps the general point may be summarized as follows: The loafers are impelled by a dream of kingship, but not a kingship hedged about by constitutional limitations, not a kingship which depends upon a mere social arrangement, not a kingship which is a mere figurehead or symbol for the real power of the state, but a "real" kingship, a kingship of absolute power. Such power depends upon their remaining aloof from humanity as gods; yet they are men, and man, not even for power, will forfeit his humanity. It is ironical that Dravot finally exercises his godlike power only in order to become a man—to satisfy his basic human desires. This step brings ruin, but there is a further irony in the fact that Dravot becomes most truly kingly at the moment of his ruin. Especially is this true for the reader who sees simply a kind of tawdry showmanship and deception in the parade of godlike power over the ignorant tribesmen, but who admires the way in which Dravot meets his death. Thus the story involves a contrast between kinds of kingship, between kinds of power, external and internal, power over others and power over oneself.

At this point, it may have occurred to the student that the theme of this story is closely related to the basic idea that seems involved in and implied by "R.M.S. *Titanic*." In "The Man Who Would Be King," true kingship is found to lie in the exercise of power over the self; in "R.M.S. *Titanic*" the attempt to conquer nature fails except in so far as men conquer their own human nature.

To recur to the list of questions suggested earlier on page 28: it ought to be apparent that the account of "The Man Who Would Be King" just given represents what may be regarded as at least a beginning to an answer to those questions. But the account also makes it very plain that the questions are all interrelated, and that a full answer to one of them tends to involve the answers to the others. It should also be plain that such questions as are suggested at the beginning of this story actually go on to raise many further questions. The account of the story given above does not pretend to provide a full interpretation of the story. For instance, the following are some of the questions which would be involved in a full analysis of the story:

1. Why is it appropriate that Peachey should be heard singing the particular hymn which he sings? Is it in his character to sing this particular hymn? How is the hymn related to the "meaning" of the story? Define the ironies involved in this incident.

2. Is Billy Fish loyal to Dravot as "god" or as "man"? What light does the fact of his loyalty shed on the rest of the story?

3. Is the contract signed by Dravot and Peachey humorous, pathetic, or heroic?

4. How does the fact that this story is told by a first-person narrator help us to define the characters?

5. What is the significance of the crucifixion of Peachey?

These are only a few of the possible questions which might be raised about the story. The student should choose several of these topics as exercises and write a full discussion of them.

JAMES THURBER

The Secret Life of Walter Mitty

"WE'RE going through!" The Commander's voice was like thin ice breaking. He wore his full-dress uniform, with the heavily braided white cap pulled down rakishly over one cold gray eye. "We can't make it, sir. It's spoiling for a hurricane, if you ask me." "I'm not asking you, Lieutenant Berg," said the Commander. "Throw on the power lights! Rev her up to 8,500! We're going through!" The pounding of the cylinders increased; ta-pocketa-pocketa-pocketa-*pocketa-pocketa*. The Commander stared at the ice forming on the pilot window. He walked over and twisted a row of complicated dials. "Switch on No. 8 auxiliary!" he shouted. "Switch on No. 8 auxiliary!" repeated Lieutenant Berg. "Full strength in No. 3 turret!" shouted the Commander. "Full strength in No. 3 turret!" The crew, bending to their various tasks in the huge, hurtling eight-engined Navy hydroplane, looked at each other and grinned. "The Old Man'll get us through," they said to one another. "The Old Man ain't afraid of Hell!" . . .

"Not so fast! You're driving too fast!" said Mrs. Mitty. "What are you driving so fast for?"

"Hmm?" said Walter Mitty. He looked at his wife, in the seat beside him, with shocked astonishment. She seemed grossly unfamiliar, like a strange woman who had yelled at him in a crowd. "You were up to fifty-five," she said. "You know I don't like to go more than forty. You were up to fifty-five." Walter Mitty drove on toward Waterbury in silence, the roaring of the SN202 through the worst storm in twenty years of Navy flying fading in the remote, intimate airways of his mind. "You're tensed up again," said Mrs. Mitty. "It's one of your days. I wish you'd let Dr. Renshaw look you over."

Walter Mitty stopped the car in front of the building where his wife went to have her hair done. "Remember to get those overshoes while I'm having my hair done," she said. "I don't need overshoes," said Mitty. She put her mirror back into her bag. "We've been all through that," she said, getting out of the car. "You're not a young man any longer." He raced the engine a little. "Why don't you wear your gloves? Have you lost your gloves?" Walter Mitty reached in a pocket and brought out the gloves. He put them on, but after she had turned and gone into the building and he had driven on to a red light, he took them off again. "Pick it up, brother!" snapped a cop as the light changed, and Mitty hastily pulled on his gloves and lurched ahead. He drove around the streets aimlessly for a time, and then he drove past the hospital on his way to the parking lot.

. . . "It's the millionaire banker, Wellington McMillan," said the pretty nurse. "Yes?" said Walter Mitty, removing his gloves slowly. "Who has the case?" "Dr. Renshaw and Dr. Benbow, but there are two specialists here, Dr. Remington from New York and Dr. Pritchard-Mitford from London. He flew over." A door opened down a long, cool corridor and Dr. Renshaw came out. He looked distraught and haggard. "Hello, Mitty," he said. "We're having the devil's own time with McMillan, the millionaire banker and close personal friend of Roosevelt. Obstreosis of the ductal tract. Tertiary. Wish you'd take a look at him." "Glad to." said Mitty.

In the operating room there were whispered introductions: "Dr. Remington, Dr. Mitty. Dr. Pritchard-Mitford, Dr. Mitty." "I've read your book on streptothricosis," said Pritchard-Mitford, shaking hands. "A brilliant performance, sir." "Thank you," said Walter Mitty. "Didn't know you were in the States, Mitty," grumbled Remington. "Coals to Newcastle, bringing Mitford and me up here for a tertiary." "You are very kind," said Mitty. A huge, complicated machine, connected to the operating table, with many tubes and wires, began at this moment to go pocketa-pocketa-pocketa. "The new anaesthetizer is giving away!" shouted an interne. "There is no one in the East who knows how to fix it!" "Quiet, man!" said Mitty, in a low, cool voice. He sprang to the machine, which was now going pocketa-pocketa-queep-pocketa-queep. He began fingering delicately a row of glistening dials. "Give me a fountain pen!" he snapped. Someone handed him a fountain pen. He pulled a faulty piston out of the machine and inserted the pen in its place. "That will hold for ten minutes," he said. "Get on with the operation." A nurse hurried over and whispered to Renshaw, and Mitty saw the man turn pale. "Coreopsis has set in," said Renshaw nervously. "If you would take over, Mitty?" Mitty looked at him and at the craven figure of Benbow, who drank, and at the grave, uncertain faces of the two great specialists. "If you wish," he said. They slipped a white gown on him; he adjusted a mask and drew on thin gloves; nurses handed him shining . . .

"Back it up, Mac! Look out for that Buick!" Walter Mitty jammed on the brakes. "Wrong lane, Mac," said the parking-lot attendant, looking at Mitty closely. "Gee. Yeh," muttered Mitty. He began cautiously to back out of the lane marked "Exit Only." "Leave her sit there," said the attendant. "I'll put her away." Mitty got out of the car. "Hey, better leave the key." "Oh," said Mitty, handing the man the ignition key. The attendant vaulted into the car, backed it up with insolent skill, and put it where it belonged.

They're so damn cocky, thought Walter Mitty, walking along Main Street; they think they know everything. Once he had tried to take his chains off, outside New Milford, and he had got them wound around the axles. A man had had to come out in a wrecking car and unwind them, a young, grinning garage man. Since then Mrs. Mitty always made him drive to a garage to have the chains taken off. The next time, he thought, I'll wear my right arm in a sling; they won't grin at me then. I'll have my right arm in a sling and they'll see I couldn't possibly take the chains off myself. He kicked at the slush on the sidewalk. "Overshoes," he said to himself, and he began looking for a shoe store.

When he came out into the street again, with the overshoes in a box under his arm, Walter Mitty began to wonder what the other thing was his wife had told him to get. She had told him, twice before they set out from their house for Waterbury. In a way he hated these weekly trips to town—he was always getting something wrong. Kleenex, he thought, Squibb's, razor blades? No. Toothpaste, toothbrush, bicarbonate, carborundum, initiative and referendum? He gave it up. But she would remember it. "Where's the what's-its-name?" she would ask. "Don't tell me you forgot the what's-its-name." A newsboy went by shouting something about the Waterbury trial.

. . . "Perhaps this will refresh your memory." The District Attorney suddenly thrust a heavy automatic at the quiet figure on the witness stand. "Have you ever seen this before?" Walter Mitty took the gun and examined it expertly. "This is my Webley-Vickers 50.80," he said calmly. An excited buzz ran around the courtroom. The judge rapped for order. "You are a crack shot with any sort of firearms, I believe?" said the District Attorney, insinuatingly. "Objection!" shouted Mitty's attorney. "We have shown the the defendant could not have fired the shot. We have shown that he wore his right arm in a sling on the night of the fourteenth of July." Walter Mitty raised his hand briefly and the bickering attorneys were stilled. "With any known make of gun," he said evenly, "I could have killed Gregory Fitzhurst at three hundred feet *with my left hand*." Pandemonium broke loose in the courtroom. A woman's scream rose above the bedlam and suddenly a lovely, dark-haired girl was in Walter Mitty's arms. The District Attorney struck at her savagely. Without rising from his chair, Mitty let the man have it on the point of the chin. "You miserable cur!" . . .

"Puppy biscuit," said Walter Mitty. He stopped walking and the buildings of Waterbury rose up out of the misty courtroom and surrounded him again. A woman who was passing laughed. "He said 'Puppy biscuit,'" she said to her companion. "That man said 'Puppy biscuit' to himself." Walter Mitty hurried on. He went into an A. & P., not the first one he came to but a smaller one farther up the street. "I want some biscuit for small, young dogs," he said to the clerk. "Any special brand, sir?" The greatest pistol shot in the world thought a moment. "It says 'Puppies Bark for It' on the box," said Walter Mitty.

His wife would be through at the hairdresser's in fifteen minutes, Mitty saw in looking at his watch, unless they had trouble drying it; sometimes they had trouble drying it. She didn't like to get to the hotel first; she would want him to be there waiting for her as usual. He found a big leather chair in the lobby, facing a window, and he put the overshoes and the puppy biscuit on the floor beside it. He picked up an old copy of *Liberty* and sank down into the chair. "Can Germany Conquer the World through the Air?" Walter Mitty looked at the pictures of bombing planes and of ruined streets.

. . . "The cannonading has got the wind up in young Raleigh, sir," said the sergeant. Captain Mitty looked up at him through tousled hair. "Get him to bed," he said wearily, "with the others. I'll fly alone." "But you can't, sir," said the sergeant anxiously. "It takes two men to handle that bomber and the Archies are pounding hell out of the air. Von Richtman's circus is between here and Saulier." "Somebody's got to get that ammunition dump," said Mitty. "I'm going over. Spot of brandy?" He poured a drink for the sergeant and one for himself. War thundered and whined around the dugout and battered at the door. There was a rending of wood and splinters flew through the room. "A bit of a near thing," said Captain Mitty carelessly. "The box barrage is closing in," said the sergeant. "We only live once, sergeant," said Mitty, with his faint, fleeting smile. "Or do we?" He poured another brandy and tossed it off. "I never see a man could hold his brandy like you, sir," said the sergeant. "Begging your pardon, sir." Captain Mitty stood up and strapped on his huge Webley-Vickers automatic. "It's forty kilometers through hell, sir," said the sergeant. Mitty finished one last brandy. "After all," he said softly, "what isn't?" The pounding of the cannon increased; there was the rat-tat-tatting of machine guns, and from somewhere came the menacing pocketa-pocketa-pocketa of the new flame-throwers. Walter Mitty walked to the door of the dugout humming *"Après de Ma Blonde."* He turned and waved to the sergeant. "Cheerio!" he said. . . .

Something struck his shoulder. "I've been looking all over this hotel for you," said Mrs. Mitty. "Why do you have to hide in this old chair? How did you expect me to find you?" "Things close in," said Walter Mitty vaguely. "What?" Mrs. Mitty said. "Did you get the what's-its-name? The puppy biscuit? What's in that box?" "Overshoes," said Mitty. "Couldn't you have put them on in the store?" "I was thinking," said Walter Mitty. "Does it ever occur to you that I am sometimes thinking?" She looked at him. "I'm going to take your temperature when I get you home," she said.

They went out through the revolving doors that made a faintly derisive whistling sound when you pushed them. It was two blocks to the parking lot. At the drugstore on the corner she said, "Wait here for me. I forgot something. I won't be a minute." She was more than a minute.

Walter Mitty lighted a cigarette. It began to rain, rain with sleet in it. He stood up against the wall of the drugstore, smoking. . . . He put his shoulders back and his heels together. "To hell with the handkerchief," said Walter Mitty scornfully. He took one last drag on his cigarette and snapped it away. Then, with that faint, fleeting smile playing about his lips, he faced the firing squad; erect and motionless, proud and disdainful, Walter Mitty the Undefeated, inscrutable to the last.

INTERPRETATION

This story may seem to be merely another character sketch somewhat like that of Sir Tatton Sykes or that of Captain Isaiah Sellers, though a more elaborate one, and not fiction at all. True, certain things do happen here, but are the happenings meaningful? Mr. Mitty, a suburbanite, drives his wife into the center for some shopping. After having been reproved for driving too fast, he lets her out at the hairdresser's, and leaves his car at the parking lot. He buys a pair of overshoes and a box of dog biscuit, and goes to the lobby of the hotel where his wife is to meet him. On their way back to the parking lot, his wife remembers something that she needs to buy in the drugstore and the story ends as Mr. Mitty waits for her outside. If we call this the "action" of the story, then indeed precious little happens. And if we go on to say that Mr. Mitty's daydreaming, which actually makes up most of the story, is not really connected with the action at all, being a direct expression of character, then the case for denying that the story is fiction becomes rather grave. It looks as if the very sketchy "plot" is simply a convenient rack on which to hang the various manifestations of Mr. Mitty's interior life. Looking at the story in this way, we may be tempted to deny that Thurber's story constitutes that revelation of character *through* action which we have said is essential to fiction.

There is a sense, of course, in which the foregoing account of the story is true: the whole narrative *is* constructed to reveal the character of the man, and aside from that revelation, very little does happen. This story, it must be confessed, is very close to a mere character sketch. Yet, it will not be difficult to show that it is a genuine piece of fiction after all.

In the first place, the author never once makes a direct comment upon Walter Mitty's character. We have no statements about Mitty comparable to "[Sir Tatton] was very vain, he exploited the then meagre arts of publicity with shrewdness" or "To good looks [Lady Blessington] added a brisk intelligence. . . ." We have no difficulty, it is true, in deducing what kind of figure Mitty cuts in the eyes of the parking-lot attendant or of the woman who passes him as he mutters "puppy biscuit." But the author never tells us in his own person what we are to think. He is really quite objective in his report of what happens. We learn what people think of Walter Mitty through the actions and comments of those people—not through any summary made by the author.

In the second place, when it comes to a matter of the way in which Mitty sees himself, that too is mediated through "action." We see Mitty at his business of daydreaming. We see how Mrs. Mitty's mention of the family physician, Dr. Renshaw, sends Mitty into a fantasy in which he becomes the medical hero in the operating room of a great hospital, or how his withering retort to the District Attorney, "You miserable cur"—itself a part of one of his daydreams—suddenly reminds him that it is puppy biscuit that he is to remember to purchase.

Most important of all, however, the "action," trivial though it is, gives point and meaning to Mitty's daydreams. It indicates the motivation for these fantasies by revealing Mitty's need to escape from the world in which he lives. His is not only a trivial and boring world; it is a world in which his own role is that of the husband henpecked by an overbearing and unimaginative wife who evidently long ago effectually suppressed Mr. Mitty's yearnings for the heroic and venturesome. The "action" in this little story effectively dramatizes this relationship, and though the events in question are in themselves commonplace—Mitty's driving at 55 miles an hour or Mitty's protest at wearing overshoes—they illuminate the very core of Mitty's life.

What attitude are we to take toward Walter Mitty? The situation portrayed is in essence the Maggie-and-Jiggs comic-strip sort of situation. Yet the effect aimed at here is not so blatant as that of the comic strip. Walter Mitty, though his daydreams embody the stalest of clichés of adventure fiction and the movies, is not made farcically grotesque. He is allowed a certain kind of pathos, even though his creator is obviously amused at his ineffectuality. Are we to take him rather seriously, then, and see in his plight the imprisonment of a high-hearted soul condemned to frustration? Scarcely that, either. The nature of the daydreams and the way in which they are grotesquely piled up one upon another effectually prevent our taking the plight of Walter Mitty really seriously. But the reader will need no special help in deciding how to "take" this story. Here again the "action" of the story serves to suggest the proper blend of sympathy and amusement with which we are to view Mr. Mitty. Far from telling us what to feel, the author gives us a dramatic presentation of a few hours of Mr. Mitty's life and leaves it up to us to make our own inferences. The "point" of the story is thus also rendered by the drama of presentation.

We began the previous paragraph by asking what attitude we should take toward Walter Mitty. We might have put this question by asking: What is the *tone* (see Glossary) of the story. For the tone is the reflection in the makeup of the story of the author's attitudes—toward his material and toward his reader. The tone of a story may be characterized as grave or gay, reserved or ebullient, straightforward or mocking, merry or melancholy, solemn, playful, prim, sentimental—and one might continue through a hundred other adjectives. Actually, however, the tone of most stories will usually be too special and too complicated to be adequately described by any one adjective. The tone of Thurber's story, for example, is one of amused playfulness, but we have seen that it has nothing of scorn in it and that it even allows for a trace of pathos. But to give an exact description of the tone will involve us in the same difficulties as those met with in the attempt to characterize the author's attitude.

Tone as a term used to characterize style derives from the tone of the voice. The tone in which a thing is uttered modifies what is said and may even reverse the meaning. "He's a fine fellow" delivered in a sarcastic tone, means that the speaker does not think that the person in question is a fine fellow at all. In our spoken language, we are constantly giving exact qualifications to what our words literally say by the tone in which we say them. The literary artist usually cannot read us his work aloud; yet if he is an artist, he can control very powerfully and exactly the way in which we are to "take" what he puts on the page. In the stories that follow, the problem of the "tone" is frequently a matter of primary importance. We shall often have to ask what is the tone of a passage or of a whole story. (If we are thinking primarily not of the story but of the author we may prefer to transpose our question from the tone of the story to the attitude of the author.)

1. In its distortion, the portrait of Walter Mitty may be regarded as a kind of caricature. In this instance is the distortion, like that employed by a good cartoonist, justified?

2. May the last sentence of the story be said to be an appropriate conclusion? Literally, of course, this sentence refers to the pose he assumes in the particular fantasy in which he is absorbed, but can it be said to apply at another level? Is there a sense in which Walter Mitty is indeed "the Undefeated, inscrutable to the last"?

3. Consider the function of the following items in making for the humorous effect: Mr. Mitty's fondness for the syllables "pocketa-pocketa" as expressive of certain sounds; the *alliteration* (see Glossary) involved in such phrases as "sir, said the sergeant"; the use, in the parts of the story which recount Mitty's various fantasies, of *clichés* (see Glossary) drawn from thriller stories.

SHIRLEY JACKSON

The Lottery

THE morning of June 27th was clear and sunny, with the fresh warmth of a full-summer day; the flowers were blossoming profusely and the grass was richly green. The people of the village began to gather in the square, between the post office and the bank, around ten o'clock; in some towns there were so many people that the lottery took two days and had to be started on June 26th, but in this village, where there were only about three hundred people, the whole lottery took less than two hours, so it could begin at ten o'clock in the morning and still be through in time to allow the villagers to get home for noon dinner.

The children assembled first, of course. School was recently over for the summer, and the feeling of liberty sat uneasily on most of them; they tended to gather together quietly for a while before they broke into boisterous play, and their talk was still of the classroom and the teacher, of books and reprimands. Bobby Martin had already stuffed his pockets full of stones, and the other boys soon followed his example, selecting the smoothest and roundest stones; Bobby and Harry Jones and Dickie Delacroix—the villagers pronounced this name "Dellacroy"—eventually made a great pile of stones in one corner of the square and guarded it against the raids of the other boys. The girls stood aside, talking among themselves, looking over their shoulders at the boys, and the very small children rolled in the dust or clung to the hands of their older brothers or sisters.

Soon the men began to gather, surveying their own children, speaking of planting and rain, tractors and taxes. They stood together, away from the pile of stones in the corner, and their jokes were quiet and they smiled rather than laughed. The women, wearing faded house dresses and sweaters, came shortly after their menfolk. They greeted one another and exchanged bits of gossip as they went to join their husbands. Soon the women, standing by their husbands, began to call to their children, and the children came reluctantly, having to be called four or five times. Bobby Martin ducked under his mother's grasping hand and ran, laughing, back to the pile of stones. His father spoke up sharply, and Bobby came quickly and took his place between his father and his oldest brother.

The lottery was conducted—as were the square dances, the teen-age club, the Halloween program—by Mr. Summers, who had time and energy to devote to civic activities. He was a round-faced, jovial man and he ran the coal business, and people were sorry for him, because he had no children and his wife was a scold. When he arrived in the square, carrying the black wooden box, there was a murmur of conversation among the villagers, and he waved and called, "Little late today, folks." The postmaster, Mr. Graves, followed him, carrying a three-legged stool, and the stool was put in the center of the square and Mr. Summers set the black box down on it. The villagers kept their distance, leaving a space between themselves and the stool, and when Mr. Summers said, "Some of you fellows want to give me a hand?" there was a hesitation before two men, Mr. Martin and his oldest son, Baxter, came forward to hold the box steady on the stool while Mr. Summers stirred up the papers inside it.

The original paraphernalia for the lottery had been lost long ago, and the black box now resting on the stool had been put into use even before Old Man Warner, the oldest man in town, was born. Mr. Summers spoke frequently to the villagers about making a new box, but no one liked to upset even as much tradition as was represented by the black box. There was a story that the present box had been made with some pieces of the box that had preceded it, the one that had been constructed when the first people settled down to make a village here. Every year, after the lottery, Mr. Summers began talking again about a new box, but every year the subject was allowed to fade off without anything's being done. The black box grew shabbier each year; by now it was no longer completely black but splintered badly along one side to show the original wood color, and in some places faded or stained.

Mr. Martin and his oldest son, Baxter, held the black box securely on the stool until Mr. Summers had stirred the papers thoroughly with his hand. Because so much of the ritual had been forgotten or discarded, Mr. Summers had been successful in having slips of paper substituted for the chips of wood that had been used for generations. Chips of wood, Mr. Summers had argued, had been all very well when the village was tiny, but now that the population was more than three hundred and likely to keep on growing, it was necessary to use something that would fit more easily into the black box. The night before the lottery, Mr. Summers and Mr. Graves made up the slips of paper and put them in the box, and it was then taken to the safe of Mr. Summers' coal company and locked up until Mr. Summers was ready to take it to the square next morning. The rest of the year, the box was put away, sometimes one place, sometimes another: it had spent one year in Mr. Graves's barn and another year underfoot in the post office, and sometimes it was set on a shelf in the Martin grocery and left there.

There was a great deal of fussing to be done before Mr. Summers declared the lottery open. There were the lists to make up—of heads of families, heads of households in each family, members of each household in each family. There was the proper swearing-in of Mr. Summers by the postmaster, as the official of the lottery; at one time, some people remembered, there had been a recital of some sort, performed by the official of the lottery, a perfunctory, tuneless chant that had been rattled off duly each year; some people believed that the official of the lottery used to stand just so when he said or sang it, others believed that he was supposed to walk among the people, but years and years ago this part of the ritual had been allowed to lapse. There had been, also, a ritual salute, which the official of the lottery had had to use in addressing each person who came up to draw from the box, but this also changed with time, until now it was felt necessary only for the official to speak to each person approaching. Mr. Summers was very good at all this; in his clean white shirt and blue jeans, with one hand resting carelessly on the black box, he seemed very proper and important as he talked interminably to Mr. Graves and the Martins.

Just as Mr. Summers finally left off talking and turned to the assembled villagers, Mrs. Hutchinson came hurriedly along the path to the square, her sweater thrown over her shoulders, and slid into place in the back of the crowd. "Clean forgot what day it was," she said to Mrs. Delacroix, who stood next to her, and they both laughed softly. "Thought my old man was out back stacking wood," Mrs. Hutchinson went on, "and then I looked out the window and the kids was gone, and then I remembered it was the twenty-seventh and came a-running." She dried her hands on her apron, and Mrs. Delacroix said, "You're in time though. They're still talking away up there."

Mrs. Hutchinson craned her neck to see through the crowd and found her husband and children standing near the front. She tapped Mrs. Delacroix on the arm as a farewell and began to make her way through the crowd. The people separated good-humoredly to let her through; two or three people said, in voices just loud enough to be heard across the crowd, "Here comes your Missus, Hutchinson," and "Bill, she made it after all." Mrs. Hutchinson reached her husband, and Mr. Summers, who had been waiting, said cheerfully, "Thought we were going to have to get on without you, Tessie." Mrs. Hutchinson said, grinning, "Wouldn't have me leave m'dishes in the sink, now, would you, Joe?," and soft laughter ran through the crowd as the people stirred back into position after Mrs. Hutchinson's arrival.

"Well, now," Mr. Summers said soberly, "guess we better get started, get this over with, so's we can go back to work. Anybody ain't here?"

"Dunbar," several people said. "Dunbar, Dunbar."

Mr. Summers consulted his list. "Clyde Dunbar," he said. "That's right. He's broke his leg, hasn't he. Who's drawing for him?"

"Me, I guess," a woman said, and Mr. Summers turned to look at her. "Wife draws for her husband," Mr. Summers said. "Don't you have a grown boy to do it for you, Janey?" Although Mr. Summers and everyone else in the village knew the answer perfectly well, it was the business of the official of the lottery to ask such questions formally. Mr. Summers waited with an expression of polite interest while Mrs. Dunbar answered.

"Horace's not but sixteen yet," Mrs. Dunbar said regretfully. "Guess I gotta fill in for the old man this year."

"Right," Mr. Summers said. He made a note on the list he was holding. Then he asked, "Watson boy drawing this year?"

A tall boy in the crowd raised his hand. "Here," he said. "I'm drawing for m'mother and me." He blinked his eyes nervously and ducked his head as several voices in the crowd said things like "Good fellow, Jack," and "Glad to see your mother's got a man to do it."

"Well," Mr. Summers said, "guess that's everyone. Old Man Warner make it?"

"Here," a voice said, and Mr. Summers nodded.

A sudden hush fell on the crowd as Mr. Summers cleared his throat and looked at the list. "All ready?" he called. "Now, I'll read the names—heads of families first—and the men come up and take a paper out of the box. Keep the paper folded in your hand without looking at it until everyone has had a turn. Everything clear?"

The people had done it so many times that they only half listened to the directions; most of them were quiet, wetting their lips, not looking around. Then Mr. Summers raised one hand high and said, "Adams." A man disengaged himself from the crowd and came forward. "Hi, Steve," Mr. Summers said, and Mr. Adams said, "Hi, Joe." They grinned at one another humorlessly and nervously. Then Mr. Adams reached into the black box and took out a folded paper. He held it firmly by one corner as he turned and went hastily back to his place in the crowd, where he stood a little apart from his family, not looking down at his hand.

"Allen," Mr. Summers said. "Anderson . . . Bentham."

"Seems like there's no time at all between lotteries any more," Mrs. Delacroix said to Mrs. Graves in the back row. "Seems like we got through with the last one only last week."

"Time sure goes fast," Mrs. Graves said.

"Clark. . . . Delacroix."

"There goes my old man," Mrs. Delacroix said. She held her breath while her husband went forward.

"Dunbar," Mr. Summers said, and Mrs. Dunbar went steadily to the box while one of the women said, "Go on, Janey," and another said, "There she goes."

"We're next," Mrs. Graves said. She watched while Mr. Graves came around from the side of the box, greeted Mr. Summers gravely, and selected a slip of paper from the box. By now, all through the crowd there were men holding the small folded papers in their large hands, turning them over and over nervously. Mrs. Dunbar and her two sons stood together, Mrs. Dunbar holding the slip of paper.

"Harburt. . . . Hutchinson."

"Get up there, Bill," Mrs. Hutchinson said, and the people near her laughed.

"Jones."

"They do say," Mr. Adams said to Old Man Warner, who stood next to him, "that over in the north village they're talking of giving up the lottery."

Old Man Warner snorted. "Pack of crazy fools," he said. "Listening to the young folks, nothing's good enough for *them*. Next thing you know, they'll be wanting to go back to living in caves, nobody work any more, live *that* way for a while. Used to be a saying about 'Lottery in June, corn be heavy soon.' First thing you know, we'd all be eating stewed chickweed and acorns. There's *always* been a lottery," he added petulantly. "Bad enough to see young Joe Summers up there joking with everybody."

"Some places have already quit lotteries," Mrs. Adams said.

"Nothing but trouble in *that*," Old Man Warner said stoutly. "Pack of young fools."

"Martin." And Bobby Martin watched his father go forward. "Overdyke. . . . Percy."

"I wish they'd hurry," Mrs. Dunbar said to her older son. "I wish they'd hurry."

"They're almost through," her son said.

"You get ready to run tell Dad," Mrs. Dunbar said.

Mr. Summers called his own name and then stepped forward precisely and selected a slip from the box. Then he called, "Warner."

"Seventy-seventh year I been in the lottery," Old Man Warner said as he went through the crowd. "Seventy-seventh time."

"Watson." The tall boy came awkwardly through the crowd. Someone said, "Don't be nervous, Jack," and Mr. Summers said, "Take your time, son."

"Zanini."

After that, there was a long pause, a breathless pause, until Mr. Summers, holding his slip of paper in the air, said, "All right, fellows." For a minute, no one moved, and then all the slips of paper were opened. Suddenly, all the women began to speak at once, saying, "Who is it?," "Who's got it?," "Is it the Dunbars?" "Is it the Watsons?" Then the voices began to say, "It's Hutchinson. It's Bill," "Bill Hutchinson's got it."

"Go tell your father," Mrs. Dunbar said to her older son.

People began to look around to see the Hutchinsons. Bill Hutchinson was standing quiet, staring down at the paper in his hand. Suddenly, Tessie Hutchinson shouted to Mr. Summers, "You didn't give him time enough to take any paper he wanted. I saw you. It wasn't fair!"

"Be a good sport, Tessie," Mrs. Delacroix called, and Mrs. Graves said, "All of us took the same chance."

"Shut up, Tessie," Bill Hutchinson said.

"Well, everyone," Mr. Summers said, "that was done pretty fast, and now we've got to be hurrying a little more to get done in time." He consulted his next list. "Bill," he said, "you draw for the Hutchinson family. You got any other households in the Hutchinsons?"

"There's Don and Eva," Mrs. Hutchinson yelled. "Make *them* take their chance!"

"Daughters draw with their husbands' families, Tessie," Mr. Summers said gently. "You know that as well as anyone else."

"It wasn't *fair*," Tessie said.

"I guess not, Joe," Bill Hutchinson said regretfully. "My daughter draws with her husband's family, that's only fair. And I've got no other family except the kids."

"Then, as far as drawing for families is concerned, it's you," Mr. Summers said in explanation, "and as far as drawing for households is concerned, that's you, too. Right?"

"Right," Bill Hutchinson said.

"How many kids, Bill?" Mr. Summers asked formally.

"Three," Bill Hutchinson said. "There's Bill, Jr., and Nancy, and little Dave. And Tessie and me."

"All right, then," Mr. Summers said. "Harry, you got their tickets back?"

Mr. Graves nodded and held up the slips of paper. "Put them in the box, then," Mr. Summers directed. "Take Bill's and put it in."

"I think we ought to start over," Mrs. Hutchinson said, as quietly as she could. "I tell you it wasn't *fair*. You didn't give him time enough to choose. Everybody saw that."

Mr. Graves had selected the five slips and put them in the box, and he dropped all the papers but those onto the ground, where the breeze caught them and lifted them off.

"Listen, everybody," Mrs. Hutchinson was saying to the people around her.

"Ready, Bill?" Mr. Summers asked, and Bill Hutchinson, with one quick glance around at his wife and children, nodded.

"Remember," Mr. Summers said, "take the slips and keep them folded until each person has taken one. Harry, you help little Dave." Mr. Graves took the hand of the little boy, who came willingly with him up to the box. "Take a paper out of the box, Davy," Mr. Summers said. Davy put his hand into the box and laughed. "Take just *one* paper," Mr. Summers said. "Harry, you hold it for him." Mr. Graves took the child's hand and removed the folded paper from the tight fist and held it while little Dave stood next to him and looked up at him wonderingly.

"Nancy next," Mr. Summers said. Nancy was twelve, and her school friends breathed heavily as she went forward, switching her skirt, and took a slip daintily from the box. "Bill, Jr.," Mr. Summers said, and Billy, his face red and his feet overlarge, nearly knocked the box over as he got a paper out. "Tessie," Mr. Summers said. She hesitated for a minute, looking around defiantly, and then set her lips and went up to the box. She snatched a paper out and held it behind her.

"Bill," Mr. Summers said, and Bill Hutchinson reached into the box and felt around, bringing his hand out at last with the slip of paper in it.

The crowd was quiet. A girl whispered, "I hope it's not Nancy," and the sound of the whisper reached the edges of the crowd.

"It's not the way it used to be," Old Man Warner said clearly. "People ain't the way they used to be."

"All right," Mr. Summers said. "Open the papers. Harry, you open little Dave's."

Mr. Graves opened the slip of paper and there was a general sigh through the crowd as he held it up and everyone could see that it was blank. Nancy and Bill, Jr., opened theirs at the same time, and both beamed and laughed, turning around to the crowd and holding their slips of paper above their heads.

"Tessie," Mr. Summers said. There was a pause, and then Mr. Summers looked at Bill Hutchinson, and Bill unfolded his paper and showed it. It was blank.

"It's Tessie," Mr. Summers said, and his voice was hushed. "Show us her paper, Bill."

Bill Hutchinson went over to his wife and forced the slip of paper out of her hand. It had a black spot on it, the black spot Mr. Summers had made the night before with the heavy pencil in the coal-company office. Bill Hutchinson held it up, and there was a stir in the crowd.

"All right, folks," Mr. Summers said. "Let's finish quickly."

Although the villagers had forgotten the ritual and lost the original black box, they still remembered to use stones. The pile of stones the boys had made earlier was ready; there were stones on the ground with the blowing scraps of paper that had come out of the box. Mrs. Delacroix selected a stone so large she had to pick it up with both hands and turned to Mrs. Dunbar. "Come on," she said. "Hurry up."

Mrs. Dunbar had small stones in both hands, and she said, gasping for breath, "I can't run at all. You'll have to go ahead and I'll catch up with you."

The children had stones already, and someone gave little Davy Hutchinson a few pebbles.

Tessie Hutchinson was in the center of a cleared space by now, and she held her hands out desperately as the villagers moved in on her. "It isn't fair," she said. A stone hit her on the side of the head.

Old Man Warner was saying, "Come on, come on, everyone." Steve Adams was in the front of the crowd of villagers, with Mrs. Graves beside him.

"It isn't fair, it isn't right," Mrs. Hutchinson screamed, and then they were upon her.

INTERPRETATION

This story certainly differs very sharply from both of the stories that precede it. The plot is so simple that to some readers it may seem to lack sufficient complication to be interesting. The story seems to do no more than recount the drawing of lots to determine which citizen of the village shall be stoned to death. There is no conflict—at least of the kind that occurs between tangible forces—no decision to be arrived at, no choice between two goods or two evils. There is no development of plot through human struggle and effort: the issue of life and death turns upon pure chance. The suspense secured is the simplest kind possible: which unlucky person will chance determine to be the victim?

Even this suspense is largely undercut by the fact that character interest in the story is also at a minimum. We are not brought close up to any of the characters. We learn little about their inner natures. There is nothing to distinguish them from ten thousand other people and indeed it becomes clear that they represent no more than the typical inhabitants of a New England village. The author seems deliberately to have played down any distinguishing traits. The victim herself, it is made very clear, is simply the typical small-town housewife.

Yet the story makes a very powerful impact, and the handling of plot and character must finally be judged, in terms of the story's development, to be very skillful. Obviously this story, unlike "The Man Who Would Be King," and "The Secret Life of Walter Mitty," has been sharply tilted toward theme. The reaction of most readers, as a matter of fact, tends to center on this problem: what does the story—granted its power—mean? It is not really a story about the victim, Mrs. Hutchinson. It is not literally about life in an American village, since the events portrayed are fantastic events. What then is the story "about"?

Before trying to answer the question specifically, one ought to say that this story is a kind of *fable* (see Glossary). The general flatness of characterization—the fact that the characters are all simply variants of the ordinary human being, and the fantastic nature of the plot make this rather clear. The most famous early fables, Aesop's fables, for example, give us fantastic situations in which animals are actuated by human motivations, speak like human beings, and reveal themselves as rather transparent instances of certain human types. But Aesop's fables usually express a fairly explicit comment on life which can be expressed as a moral. For example, a popular translation of the fable of the fox and the grapes concludes with the moral tag: "It is easy to despise what you cannot get."

The family resemblance of "The Lottery" to the fable is concealed in part by the fact that "The Lottery" does not end with a neat moral tag and indeed avoids focusing upon a particular meaning. This latter point, however, we shall consider a little later.

The general pattern of this story may also be said to resemble that of the *parable* (see Glossary). In a parable the idea or truth is presented by a simple narrative in which the events, persons, and the like, of the narrative are understood as being directly equivalent to terms involved in the statement of the truth. For example, let us look at the parable of the sower, in the Gospel according to Saint Mark:

Hearken; Behold, there went out a sower to sow:
And it came to pass, as he sowed, some fell by the way side, and the fowls of the air came and devoured it up.
And some fell on stony ground, where it had not much earth; and immediately it sprang up, because it had no depth of earth:
But when the sun was up, it was scorched; and because it had no root, it withered away.
And some fell among thorns, and the thorns grew up, and choked it, and it yielded no fruit.
And other fell on good ground, and did yield fruit that sprang up and increased; and brought forth, some thirty, and some sixty, and some an hundred.

Later, Jesus explains and interprets the parable to his disciples:

The sower soweth the word.
And these are they by the way side, where the word is sown; but when they have heard, Satan cometh immediately, and taketh away the word that was sown in their hearts.
And these are they likewise which are sown on stony ground; who, when they have heard the word, immediately receive it with gladness;
And have no root in themselves, and so endure but for a time: afterward, when affliction or persecution ariseth for the word's sake, immediately they are offended.
And these are they which are sown among thorns; such as hear the word,

And the cares of this world, and the deceitfulness of riches, and the lusts of other things entering in, choke the word, and it becometh unfruitful.

And these are they which are sown on good ground; such as hear the word, and receive it, and bring forth fruit, some thirtyfold, some sixty, and some an hundred.

In a parable, it is plain, characterization is reduced to a minimum: the *sower* is any sower. And the action is reduced to a minimum too. We need only so much of narrative as will make the point that the speaker wishes to make. But if "The Lottery" in its relative thinness of characterization and its relative simplicity of narration resembles the parable, it is obviously not a naked parable. The author has taken pains to supply a great deal of concrete detail to make us "believe" in her village, in its goings on this morning of June 27th. It is also obvious that she has preferred to give no key to her parable but to leave its meaning to our inference. One may summarize by saying that "The Lottery" is a normal piece of fiction, even if tilted over toward the fable and the parable form. Yet the comparison with these two forms may be useful in indicating the nature of the story.*

What of its meaning? We had best not try to restrict the meaning to some simple dogmatic statement. The author herself has been rather careful to allow a good deal of flexibility in our interpretation of the meaning. Yet surely a general meaning does emerge. This story comments upon the all-too-human tendency to seize upon a scapegoat and to visit upon the scapegoat the cruelties that most of us seem to have dammed up within us. An example out of our own time might be the case in which some sensational happening occurs in a family—a child is kidnapped, or a youthful

---

* Since we have used the terms *fable* and *parable* in connection with this story, it may be well at this point to relate it also to the more general term *symbol*, which we will often have occasion to use in this book. We have used the term *symbol* earlier (p. 24) in saying that the *Titanic* itself could be considered as a symbol, the ship standing for certain human attitudes such as pride and confidence, and, with reference to "The Man Who Would Be King" (p. 56) in referring to the crown as a symbol of kingship.

Here we need to distinguish between two kinds of symbols. The crown, like the cross and the flag, is a *conventional* symbol. That is, men *have agreed* that the figure of the cross should stand for Christianity, that a flag of a certain design should stand for the United States of America, and that the circlet of gold should stand for the power and authority of kingship. Such conventional symbols occur in literature just as they occur in our daily speech, but the symbolism with which we are characteristically concerned as we read poems and stories is not conventional. It is special and it is related to a particular context. Thus ships do not conventionally stand for human pride, but the *Titanic*, as treated by Hanson Baldwin, is invested with some such meaning (see p. 10). Or consider "The Lottery" itself, where an incident is so handled as to express an interpretation of human life. In literature, objects and events often become symbolic, possessing a wider significance and thus becoming expressive of the author's meaning. Since fiction is concrete and dramatic in its presentation, the author must necessarily make use of symbols at some level; for he does not "state" his meanings abstractly but renders them through the presentation of concrete particulars.

member of the family is implicated in a weird crime. The newspapers sometimes hound the family past all decency, and we good citizens, who support those newspapers, batten upon their misery with a cruelty that would shock us if we ever could realize what we were doing. Or to take another case, a man's patriotism is impugned quite falsely; or, whether the charge against him is false or true, let us say that his wife is completely guiltless. Yet she is "stoned" by her self-righteous neighbors who are acting, of course, out of pure virtue and fervent patriotism. These two instances are merely suggestive. Neither would answer fully to the terms of the story, but they may indicate that the issues with which the story is concerned are thoroughly live issues in our time.

But the author has been wise not to confine the meaning to any precise happening of the sort we have suggested. For evidently she is concerned with the more general psychological basis for such cruelty as a community tends to manifest. "The Lottery" makes such points as these: the cruel stoning is carried out by "decent" citizens who in many other respects show themselves kind and thoughtful. The cruel act is kept from seeming the cruel thing it is by the fact that it has been sanctioned by custom and long tradition. When Mrs. Adams remarks that "Some places have already quit lotteries," Old Man Warner says, "Nothing but trouble in *that*. Pack of young fools." A further point is this: human beings find it difficult to become exercised over ills not their own. Once a family group sees that the victim is not to be selected from among themselves, they proceed to observe matters with a certain callous disinterest. Moreover, even the individual members of the Hutchinson family are themselves relatively unconcerned once each discovers that he is not the victim chosen. Thus, "Nancy and Bill, Jr., opened theirs at the same time, and both beamed and laughed, turning round to the crowd and holding their slips of paper above their heads." The French moralist Rochefoucald ruefully observed that we obtain a certain pleasure from news of misfortune to friends. There is truth in this, and our story savagely makes a related point. Only the victim protests "It isn't fair," and she makes her protest only after she has chosen a slip of paper marked with the black spot. We remember that earlier Mrs. Hutchinson had said to Mrs. Delacroix in neighborly good humor, "Clean forgot what day it was," and both had "laughed softly" together.

"The Lottery," then, deals indeed with live issues and issues relevant to our time. If we hesitate to specify a particular "point" that the story makes, it is not because the story is vague and fuzzy, but rather because its web of observations about human nature is too subtle and too complex to be stated in one or two brief maxims.

What requires a little further attention is a problem of a quite different sort: how does this story differ from a tract or a treatise on human nature? Are we actually justified in calling it a piece of fiction?

An answer to these questions might run like this: This is obviously not a tract or merely an essay. The village is made to exist for us; the characters of Old Man Warner and Mr. Summers and Mrs. Hutchinson do come alive. They are not fully developed, to be sure, and there is a sense in which even the personality of the victim is finally subservient to the "point" to be made and is not developed in its own right and for its own sake. But, as we have said, this is not a "naked parable"—and the fact that we get an impression of a real village and real people gives the sense of grim terror.

The fictional form thus justifies itself by making vivid and forceful what would otherwise have to be given prosaically and undramatically. But it does something else that is very important: it provides a special shaping of the reader's attitude toward the climactic event and toward that from which the climactic event stems. The reader's attitude has been moulded very carefully from the very beginning. Everything in the story has been devised to let us know how we are to "take" the final events in the story. (In this general connection, see the discussion of *tone* on pp. 63–64.)

The very fact that an innocent woman is going to be stoned to death by her friends and neighbors and that this is to happen in an American small town during our own present day of enlightenment requires a special preparation. The apparently fantastic nature of the happening means that everything else in the story must be made plausible, down-to-earth, sensible, commonplace, everyday. We must be made to feel that what is happening on this June morning is perfectly credible. Making it seem credible will do two things: it will increase the sense of shock when we suddenly discover what is really going on, but it will ultimately help us to believe that what the story asserts does come to pass. In general, then, the horror of the ending is counter-balanced by the dry, even cheery, atmosphere of the scene. This contrast between the matter-of-factness and the cheery atmosphere, on one side, and the grim terror, on the other, gives us a dramatic shock. But it also indicates that the author's point in general has to do with the awful doubleness of the human spirit—a doubleness that expresses itself in the blended good neighborliness and cruelty of the community's action. The fictional form, therefore, does not simply "dress up" a specific comment on human nature. The fictional form actually gives point and definition to the social commentary.

1. Attempt to characterize the tone of this story.
2. Why does the author hold up any information about the purpose of the lottery until late in the story? What is gained by her doing so?
3. What is gained by having Mrs. Delacroix select the first stone?

How Plot Reveals

■ BIT by bit, in various places (com-
pare our discussion of "The Attack on the Fort," "R. M. S. *Titanic*," and
"The Man Who Would Be King"), we have discussed the nature of plot.
Now we can try to make a more systematic statement. We may begin
with the most off-hand notion: Plot may be said to be what happens in a
story. It is the string of events *thought of* as different from the persons involved in the events and different from the meaning of the events. We
make such a distinction even though we know that, in fact, we cannot
very well separate an act from the person who commits it, or from its
meaning as an act. The distinction is one we make in our heads and do not
find ready-made for us in fiction. In order better to understand the nature
of a story itself, we analyze the unity which is the story and which is what
we actually experience before the process of analysis begins.

Plot is what happens in a story—that is a good rough-and-ready way
to put the matter. But let us go a step farther. Plot, we may say, is the
structure of an action as presented in a piece of fiction. It is not, we shall
note, the structure of an action as we happen to find it out in the world,
but the structure within a story. It is, in other words, what the teller of
the story has done to the action in order to present it to us. Let us hang
on to this distinction between a "raw" action—action as it occurs out in
the world—and an action in a story, that is, action manipulated by the teller
of the story.

Here we are using the word *action* (see Glossary) in a special way. We
do not mean a single event—John struck Jim with a stone, Mary put the book

on the shelf. We mean a series of events, a movement through time, exhibiting unity and significance. It is a series of connected events moving through three logical stages—the beginning, the middle, and the end.

The beginning of an action always presents us with a situation in which there is some element of instability, some conflict; in the middle of an action there is a period of readjustment of forces in the process of seeking a new kind of stability; in the end of an action, some point of stability is reached, the forces that have been brought into play have been resolved. At the dawn of the day of Waterloo, the fate of Europe hung in the balance; at sunset Napoleon was a broken man. On June 7, 1776, Richard Henry Lee, of Virginia, presented to the Continental Congress a resolution declaring that "these United States are, and of right ought to be, free and independent States"; on July 4 the Declaration of Independence was signed. When Tom Smith met Evelyn Pembroke, he immediately recognized her vain and frivolous nature, but that recognition could not overcome the attraction she exerted over him; and he was the only person in Morristown not surprised when T. P. Smith, the wealthy, middle-aged banker, the very pillar of respectability, was arrested for embezzlement. In each of these actions, two of them historical and one made up, we recognize a movement toward a point of rest, of resolution.

In these actions we recognize, too, unity and significance. That is, these actions move toward an end, and the end settles something. We shall postpone for a page or two our fuller discussion of unity and significance in relation to action (and to plot), and for the moment content ourselves with saying that what constitutes an action always depends upon the perspective in which we view the events involved. The Battle of Waterloo may be regarded as an action, but it may also be regarded as merely an event in the broader action of Napoleon's career, or even as one event in a very different broader action, say the rise of the British Empire or the growth of the theory of free trade. Or to refer to our imaginary action above, the account of the banker and the vain, frivolous Evelyn Pembroke with whom he falls in love, though we may think of this as a complete action, we may, in another perspective, regard it as merely an episode in the life of one of the two persons concerned, or even in the life of, say, Smith's son.

The unity and significance of an action must, however, be felt really to inhere in the action. They cannot be regarded as being merely arbitrary fabrications imposed by us upon the action—even if their nature changes according to the perspective in which we place an action, and according to our interest in the facts and our interpretation of them. The patterns giving unity and significance must be grounded in the facts themselves.

We have just used the word *facts*—speaking of the facts that constitute an action. But we must hasten to say that we do not necessarily mean historical facts, actual happenings. As we have already implied by our reference to Tom Smith and Evelyn Pembroke, the "facts" may be imaginary ones, which in their turn can be placed in some special perspective of interest and interpretation so as to constitute an action. And this brings us to the relation between an action and the manipulation necessary in order to turn an action into a plot.

Let us begin this discussion by thinking of some action—it doesn't matter whether it is real or imaginary—in its full and massive array of facts, all disposed in their chronological order. The teller of a story, whether in idle conversation or in the serious business of writing a thousand-page novel, could not possibly use all the facts involved in the situation. He has to *select* the facts that seem to him useful for his particular purpose.

There are two kinds of usefulness, we may say. A fact is useful if it is vivid, that is, if it stirs the imagination to accept the story. One vivid fact may, suddenly, make a whole passage of narrative seem real to us. And a fact is also useful if it indicates, directly or indirectly, the line of development a story is pursuing, that is, if it indicates how one thing leads to another, or what is the meaning of the movement of events. Vividness and significance—these are the tests of usefulness in selection. But the two tend to merge. The vivid detail that catches the imagination helps to create the special quality, the "feel" of a story, and this "feel", this *atmosphere* (see Glossary) is an element of the meaning.

So if we examine fiction we are continually faced with the questions: Why was this particular thing selected? What has led the writer to use these facts and reject others? How would the choice of other available facts have made this a very different story?

The answers to such questions are always complicated, but the questions are worth pondering. They may lead us toward the full meaning of a story.

After a writer has selected his facts, there comes the question of order. Thus far we have thought of the action as existing in all of its intricate detail out in the world, with all of its components disposed in their strict chronological order. Yet many stories—indeed, in a strict sense, all stories —violate in one way or another the strict chronological sequence of an action as thought of in the actual world. To take an example, no writer can give simultaneously in his narrative two things that occur simultaneously in the action. His order of narration is bound to be artificial. To take another example, the beginning of a story may, or may not, happen to pick up the beginning of the action which it presents. The plot may plunge us into the very middle of things, and then, stage by stage, take us back to the beginning of the action, as in "Old Red," by Caroline Gordon, which we shall soon read. Or there may be a complicated interweaving of times. A little chart of a hypothetical story may indicate this notion:

Sequence of Action: a b c d e f g h i j k l m n o p q r s t u v w x y z

SEQUENCE OF PLOT: F A B H I J E R S T V Y Z

We see, in our chart, that the plot does not use all of the facts of the action, and that the chronological order has been scrambled. The plot, then, is the structure of the action *as presented* in a piece of fiction. It represents the treatment the story-teller makes of the events of his action.

In discussing the nature of an action we have necessarily touched on unity and significance. Let us now return to these topics with more special reference to plot.

When we say "*a* novel," "*a* story," or "*a* plot," we instinctively imply the idea of a unity. We imply that the parts, the various individual events, hang together. There is the matter of cause and effect. In any story we expect to find one thing bringing on another. If we can detect no reasonable connection between them, if there is no "logic" whatever, we lose interest. Every story must indicate some basis for the relation among its parts, for the story itself is a *particular writer's way of saying how you can make sense of human experience.*

Cause and effect constitute one of the ways of saying this. In works of fiction, however, we cannot think of cause as a mechanical thing—as though one event were one domino knocking over the next in the series. The events are human events; that is, they involve human responses to changing situations, including the possibility of action taken to change existing situations. Many nonhuman things may enter into the logic of a story—the weather that ruins a crop, the iceberg that sinks a ship, the explosion that wrecks a mine, the nail lost from the shoe of the horse of the king's messenger—but in the end the central logic we are concerned with is the logic of human motivation. How do human needs work themselves out? Plot, then, is character in action.

Logic, including the logic of motivation, binds the events of a plot together into a unity. This unity is, of course, a dynamic unity. It is a unity involving change: no change, no story. At the beginning of a story we find a situation with some element of instability in it. At the end of the story, we find that things have become stable once more. Something has been settled: Jim Beckworth has captured the Blackfoot fort; the unsinkable *Titanic* has been sunk; Dravot has discovered the true meaning of kingship and godhood through manhood; Walter Mitty, we have come to know, will never wake from his dream. This movement from instability toward stability involves, as we have said, certain natural stages—the beginning, the middle, and the end.

When we come to consider how these natural stages are treated in terms of plot, we find that we need some special terms. The beginning of a plot action is called the *exposition* (see Glossary)—the "setting forth" of the assumptions from which the story will develop. The middle is called the *complication* (see Glossary), for it presents the increasing difficulty encountered in the movement toward stability. If, for example, a character moves easily toward his triumph, or his ruin, there is really no story. It is no story to tell how a barrel rolls downhill. The story interest inheres in the resistances encountered and overcome, or not overcome—in the logic by which resistance evokes responses which, in their turn, encounter or create new resistances to be dealt with. The complication moves toward a moment, an event, when something has to happen, when something has to crack. This moment is the point of highest tension, the moment when the story turns toward its solution. This is called the *climax* (see Glossary). The story, then, is the story of *conflict* developing logically through the stages of the complication.

The end—the *denouement* (see Glossary)—gives us the outcome of the conflict, the solution to the problem, the basis of a new stability. We realize, of course, that the basis of stability now reached may be only provisional and temporary, that something may come along to upset the hard-won stability. If, for example, we have the story of a stormy courtship and "boy gets girl" in the end, we know that, except in the fairy-tale formula of "they lived happily ever after," no promise is made of an end to all conflict, all struggle, all problems. The denouement simply gives us the settling of a particular action, which is the story that the author has elected to tell.

The denouement, as we have just said, gives us the settling of the particular action. But the meaning of the settlement always reaches out beyond the particular action. And this idea takes us back to the question of significance in plot. In so far, of course, as the development of a plot exhibits logic, it is already exhibiting significance—it is telling us, or showing us, something about human nature and human conduct. The conclusion which stems from this logic aims to give us not only an evaluation of the particular experience which is the story, but a *generalized* evaluation. Always the end of a successful story leaves us with an attitude to take toward things in general. The story embodies a comment on human values—on what is good or bad in human nature and human conduct, on what attitude one may take, finally, toward life and the business of living. That is, any particular story will always appear, in our imagination and feelings, as an image, however shadowy, of the meaning of experience.

The way in which the meaning is presented may vary from instance to instance. There may be a perfectly explicit general statement, more or less complete—as in the epigraph of "The Man Who Would Be King." Or a story may, again like "The Man Who Would Be King," use symbolism which can be read back into statement, as we have done in our comment on the end of the story. Even when the denouement may seem merely to wind up events and avoid interpretation, we shall find that the story, if it is a successful one, will turn us back toward some basic quality in the story itself; and we shall find that that quality may have subtly modified our feelings and attitudes. It may have enlarged our sympathies—as with "The Lament," by Chekhov—so that we may now more readily regard other people with charity and humility. Or it may have given us a liberating sense of the comedy of experience—as with "The Drunkard," by Frank O'Connor, or "The Secret Life of Walter Mitty," by James Thurber. Or the story may conclude on a note of savage satire or chilling irony. Always, however, we expect in fiction an idea about, some stance toward, experience, and if we do not get it we are dissatisfied. We feel cheated. We don't know what the shooting has been about. We feel, in other words, that the story is incoherent—the plot has not fulfilled itself, even though stage by stage the logic of motivation, and the like, may have been seeming to work itself out. We do not like to be preached at, but we do demand a sense of meaningfulness.

So our discussion of plot brings us back to theme, just as it has already led us, in discussing motivation, to the question of character. And that is only natural, for a good story is, after all, a unity. It is consistent within itself. The world of imagination that it presents is—to repeat a term we have already used—*coherent*.

We have tried to indicate something of the function of the parts of a plot, and something of the relation among them. Let us ask the next question: Are we to be concerned with any particular *proportion* among the parts? The answer is no. In some pieces of fiction—whether novels or stories—a great deal of exposition is required; there is a great weight of the past behind the moment in which the story comes to crisis and if we are to understand the story we must understand what lies behind it. Or sometimes to understand a story we must know something of a special world that may be unfamiliar to us.

Or to consider the denouement, sometimes a story needs a long and elaborate treatment in this part. In one sense "The Man Who Would Be King" ends when Dravot walks boldly out on the bridge and yells, "Cut, you beggars!" But a good deal of space, and a good deal of narrative, is required before we have the full implications of that moment. Think, however, how little is required to end "The Lottery." Of course, one story is longer than the other, and more complicated, but even so, there is a fundamental difference that has little to do with the question of length as such. "The Man Who Would Be King" is a story giving the development of a character and when the development is over it requires some time and some elaboration for its full weight to be felt. "The Lottery," however, is concerned with a shocking contrast, the contrast between thinking yourself in one position, thinking yourself at one with society, accepting its values and habits, and then suddenly finding yourself in another position, the victim of the values and habits of that society. The shock is the point. If we were to spin out the denouement, we should lose the sense of shock, and add nothing significant. The story does have weighty implications, but they do not need to be elaborated; their force depends on the shock.

What all this amounts to is simple: Proportion is not mechanically determined. It depends on the materials of the particular story and the kind of story the writer is trying to make of those materials. As we read, we must try to sense the needs of the situation, and try to understand the intention of the writer.

One more question presents itself in regard to the divisions of a plot. Are we to expect to find a sharp line between exposition and complication, or between complication and denouement? There may, of course, be sharp division, and sometimes the sharpness contributes greatly to the effect—as in "The Lottery." But, as we have indicated on our little chart distinguishing between action and plot, there is sometimes considerable interpenetration between one part and another, and especially between exposition and complication. There may be certain advantages, for example, in presenting an element of complication very early, at the very start perhaps, to catch the reader's attention, even before he can get the full import of the event before him. And sometimes a piece of exposition may be withheld until fairly late until the reader feels the need for it and it will come with dramatic force. Our principle here, again, is one of tact, of flexibility. There is no hard and fast rule. As readers, we must try to see how sharp separations or intricate interpenetrations among the parts of a plot are related to the final effect.

In this section we shall not confine ourselves to reading and discussing stories in which the element of plot is strongly marked—stories, for example, like "The Man Who Would Be King." We shall, in fact, read some stories in which the plot is seemingly slight. This is a reasonable procedure, for we are concerned here to see how the element of plot, whether strongly marked or recessive, works in relation to other aspects of fiction.

Furthermore, we shall not confine ourselves to stories in which the plot fulfills the requirements of a good plot, that is, exhibits significant order. We shall look at some instances in which the events are not in significant order, in which they do not adequately embody human values— instances, in short, in which the plot is incoherent. Of all the stories we read in this book we shall be asking ourselves: Is the plot coherent? Does it makes sense? If it does not make sense, in what particular way does it fail? We must, in other words, constantly consider the relation of plot to character and theme.

But not only to character and theme. Stories and novels are composed in words, and so we shall have to think a little about the relation of plot to the resources of language which the writer uses well or badly. Problems of coherence, as we shall see, arise here too.

IRWIN SHAW

The Girls in Their Summer Dresses

FIFTH Avenue was shining in the sun when they left the Brevoort. The sun was warm, even though it was February, and everything looked like Sunday morning—the buses and the well-dressed people walking slowly in couples and the quiet buildings with the windows closed.

Michael held Frances' arm tightly as they walked toward Washington Square in the sunlight. They walked lightly, almost smiling, because they had slept late and had a good breakfast and it was Sunday. Michael unbuttoned his coat and let it flap around him in the mild wind.

"Look out," Frances said as they crossed Eighth Street. "You'll break your neck." Michael laughed and Frances laughed with him.

"She's not so pretty," Frances said. "Anyway, not pretty enough to take a chance of breaking your neck."

Michael laughed again. "How did you know I was looking at her?"

Frances cocked her head to one side and smiled at her husband under the brim of her hat. "Mike, darling," she said.

"O.K.," he said. "Excuse me."

Frances patted his arm lightly and pulled him along a little faster toward Washington Square. "Let's not see anybody all day," she said. "Let's just hang around with each other. You and me. We're always up to our neck in people, drinking their Scotch or drinking our Scotch; we only see each other in bed. I want to go out with my husband all day long. I want him to talk only to me and listen only to me."

"What's to stop us?" Michael asked.

"The Stevensons. They want us to drop by around one o'clock and they'll drive us into the country."

"The cunning Stevensons," Mike said. "Transparent. They can whistle. They can go driving in the country by themselves."

"Is it a date?"

"It's a date."

Frances leaned over and kissed him on the tip of the ear.

"Darling," Michael said, "this is Fifth Avenue."

"Let me arrange a program," Frances said. "A planned Sunday in New York for a young couple with money to throw away."

"Go easy."

"First let's go to the Metropolitan Museum of Art," Frances suggested, because Michael had said during the week he wanted to go. "I haven't been there in three years and there're at least ten pictures I want to see again. Then we can take the bus down to Radio City and watch them skate. And later we'll go down to Cavanagh's and get a steak as big as a blacksmith's apron, with a bottle of wine, and after that there's a French picture at the Filmarte that everybody says—say, are you listening to me?"

"Sure," he said. He took his eyes off the hatless girl with the dark hair, cut dancer-style like a helmet, who was walking past him.

"That's the program for the day," Frances said flatly. "Or maybe you'd just rather walk up and down Fifth Avenue."

"No," Michael said. "Not at all."

"You always look at other women," Frances said. "Everywhere. Every damned place we go."

"No, darling," Michael said, "I look at everything. God gave me eyes and I look at women and men in subway excavations and moving pictures and the little flowers of the field. I casually inspect the universe."

"You ought to see the look in your eye," Frances said, "as you casually inspect the universe on Fifth Avenue."

"I'm a happily married man." Michael pressed her elbow tenderly. "Example for the whole twentieth century—Mr. and Mrs. Mike Loomis. Hey, let's have a drink," he said, stopping.

"We just had breakfast."

"Now listen, darling," Mike said, choosing his words with care, "it's a nice day and we both felt good and there's no reason why we have to break it up. Let's have a nice Sunday."

"All right. I don't know why I started this. Let's drop it. Let's have a good time."

They joined hands consciously and walked without talking among the baby carriages and the old Italian men in their Sunday clothes and the young women with Scotties in Washington Square Park.

"At least once a year everyone should go to the Metropolitan Museum of Art," Frances said after a while, her tone a good imitation of the tone she had used at breakfast and at the beginning of their walk. "And it's nice on Sunday. There're a lot of people looking at the pictures and you get the feeling maybe Art isn't on the decline in New York City, after all—"

"I want to tell you something," Michael said very seriously. "I have not touched another woman. Not once. In all the five years."

"All right," Frances said.

"You believe that, don't you?"

"All right."

They walked between the crowded benches, under the scrubby city-park trees.

"I try not to notice it," Frances said, "but I feel rotten inside, in my stomach, when we pass a woman and you look at her and I see that look in your eye and that's the way you looked at me the first time. In Alice Maxwell's house. Standing there in the living room, next to the radio, with a green hat on and all those people."

"I remember the hat," Michael said.

"The same look," Frances said. "And it makes me feel bad. It makes me feel terrible."

"Sh-h-h, please, darling, sh-h-h."

"I think I would like a drink now," Frances said.

They walked over to a bar on Eighth Street, not saying anything. Michael automatically helping her over curbstones and guiding her past automobiles. They sat near a window in the bar and the sun streamed in and there was a small, cheerful fire in the fireplace. A little Japanese waiter came over and put down some pretzels and smiled happily at them.

"What do you order after breakfast?" Michael asked.

"Brandy, I suppose," Frances said.

"Courvoisier," Michael told the waiter, "Two Courvoisiers."

The waiter came with the glasses and they sat drinking the brandy in the sunlight. Michael finished half his and drank a little water.

"I look at women," he said. "Correct. I don't say it's wrong or right. I look at them. If I pass them on the street and I don't look at them, I'm fooling you, I'm fooling myself."

"You look at them as though you want them," Frances said, playing with her brandy glass. "Every one of them."

"In a way," Michael said, speaking softly and not to his wife, "in a way that's true. I don't do anything about it, but it's true."

"I know it. That's why I feel bad."

"Another brandy," Michael called. "Waiter, two more brandies."

He sighed and closed his eyes and rubbed them gently with his finger-tips. "I love the way women look. One of the things I like best about New York is the battalions of women. When I first came to New York from Ohio that was the first thing I noticed, the million wonderful women, all over the city. I walked around with my heart in my throat."

"A kid," Frances said. "That's a kid's feeling."

"Guess again," Michael said. "Guess again. I'm older now. I'm a man getting near middle age, putting on a little fat, and I still love to walk along

Fifth Avenue at three o'clock on the east side of the street between Fiftieth and the Fifty-seventh Streets. They're all out then, shopping, in their furs and their crazy hats, everything all concentrated from all over the world into seven blocks—the best furs, the best clothes, the handsomest women, out to spend money and feeling good about it."

The Japanese waiter put the two drinks down, smiling with great happiness.

"Everything is all right?" he asked.

"Everything is wonderful," Michael said.

"If it's just a couple of fur coats," Frances said, "and forty-five dollar hats—"

"It's not the fur coats. Or the hats. That's just the scenery for that particular kind of women. Understand," he said, "you don't have to listen to this."

"I want to listen."

"I like the girls in the offices. Neat, with their eyeglasses, smart, chipper, knowing what everything is about. I like the girls on Forty-fourth Street at lunchtime, the actresses, all dressed up on nothing a week. I like the salesgirls in the stores, paying attention to you first because you're a man, leaving lady customers waiting. I got all this stuff accumulated in me because I've been thinking about it for ten years and now you've asked for it and here it is."

"Go ahead," Frances said.

"When I think of New York City, I think of all the girls on parade in the city. I don't know whether it's something special with me or whether every man in the city walks around with the same feeling inside him, but I feel as though I'm at a picnic in this city. I like to sit near the women in the theatres, the famous beauties who've taken six hours to get ready and look it. And the young girls at the football games, with the red cheeks, and when the warm weather comes, the girls in their summer dresses." He finished his drink. "That's the story."

Frances finished her drink and swallowed two or three times extra. "You say you love me?"

"I love you."

"I'm pretty, too," Frances said. "As pretty as any of them."

"You're beautiful," Michael said.

"I'm good for you," Frances said, pleading. "I've made a good wife, a good housekeeper, a good friend. I'd do any damn thing for you."

"I know," Michael said. He put his hand out and grasped hers.

"You'd like to be free to—" Frances said.

"Sh-h-h."

"Tell the truth." She took her hand away from under his.

Michael flicked the edge of his glass with his finger. "O.K.," he said gently. "Sometimes I feel I would like to be free."

"Well," Frances said, "any time you say."

"Don't be foolish." Michael swung his chair around to her side of the table and patted her thigh.

She began to cry silently into her handkerchief, bent over just enough so that nobody else in the bar would notice. "Someday," she said, crying, "you're going to make a move."

Michael didn't say anything. He sat watching the bartender slowly peel a lemon.

"Aren't you?" Frances asked harshly. "Come on, tell me. Talk. Aren't you?"

"Maybe," Michael said. He moved his chair back again. "How the hell do I know?"

"You know," Frances persisted. "Don't you know?"

"Yes," Michael said after a while, "I know."

Frances stopped crying then. Two or three snuffles into the handkerchief and she put it away and her face didn't tell anything to anybody. "At least do me one favor," she said.

"Sure."

"Stop talking about how pretty this woman is or that one. Nice eyes, nice breasts, a pretty figure, good voice." She mimicked his voice. "Keep it to yourself. I'm not interested."

Michael waved to the waiter. "I'll keep it to myself," he said.

Frances flicked the corners of her eyes. "Another brandy," she told the waiter.

"Two," Michael said.

"Yes, Ma'am, yes, sir," said the waiter, backing away.

Frances regarded Michael coolly across the table. "Do you want me to call the Stevensons?" she asked. "It'll be nice in the country."

"Sure," Michael said. "Call them."

She got up from the table and walked across the room toward the telephone. Michael watched her walk, thinking what a pretty girl, what nice legs.

INTERPRETATION

The plot structure of this story is quite simple. The exposition gives us a young couple out for a Sunday morning walk, planning on a happy private day together. By the time Michael asks, "What's to stop us?" we know a good deal about them—enough anyway for the limited purposes of the story. We have even had the first element of the complication, when Michael turns around to look at the first girl. It comes in lightly, as a joke, but the germ of instability in the happy situation has been isolated.

It comes in, we have said, as a joke, and this is as it should be. The story is very short, and one of the problems of the author is to give it a sense of rising interest, increasing tension, growing suspense. If much were to be made of Michael's first look, the story would sacrifice something of its development, the suspense. The episode comes in quite casually, but something signals: *This is it, watch now!*

Frances continues her planning of the day, gaily and affectionately, but before long Michael has noticed another girl. Now Frances strikes out at him, and the complication begins in dead earnest. With this repetition, the look at the second girl to pass—we may comment on another principle of plot, the principle of *pattern* (see Glossary). A pattern implies repetition, and pattern in plot is significant repetition. We know that the fact of Michael's looking at the passing girls is now what the story will hinge on, and we know that this will give the key to our understanding of the relationship.

Let us interrupt ourselves for a moment to ask what was the pattern in "The Man Who Would Be King." There is, of course, the series of efforts to gain a kingdom, a series of events pointing toward the same end. But there is a deeper and more significant pattern. As Dravot moves toward power, toward kingship and godhood, he discovers, step by step, the inner meaning of power. He has started out as a simple looter to grab a kingdom and live on the fat of the land. Bit by bit, his acts assume a pattern; he is moving toward a sense of responsibility in power, toward a depersonalizing of power, toward pride in his people, toward a desire to bring order and peace, toward the ambition, not merely to loot and indulge his appetites, but to enter history, to achieve something worthwhile and memorable. This movement is not over when Dravot does achieve full manhood. It continues with Peachey's return, after Dravot's death, and the symbolic presentation, by Peachey's delirium in the mountains, of Dravot as now somehow godlike, able to hold up the mountains. And it is this movement, the pattern of recognitions in ascending order, a pattern that continues after the progress toward practical success is finished, that constitutes the pattern of the plot.

To return to "The Girls in Their Summer Dresses," we can see how the recurrence of the topic of Michael's glances at the passing girls will lead, in the end, to the sad recognition—and the bitter acceptance—of the fact that the couple really mean nothing to each other. Each is, as it were, merely a convenience to the other. This is, of course, especially true of Michael's attitude toward Frances. Despite his actual faithfulness, Frances is just another girl, the one he "happens" to have married. They have now stumbled on the recognition of their plight, and Frances does not, somehow, do more than bitterly accept it. She hasn't the idealism, after all, to struggle for more. She will go and call the Stevensons, for she and her husband have nothing more to say to each other. The last line, as Frances moves toward the telephone, sums up the whole thing: Frances is just another pretty girl worth Michael's attention, and she might be anybody.

This story is a very good example of the compact, well-made short story. The method is about as simple as possible, and a simple method is all that the material requires. Not much of the past needs to be told. We need only a minimum of individualization. The conflict between the two characters progresses in an obvious pattern of repetitions. The main movement is carried by dialogue, as though we were actually unseen eavesdroppers, hearing the pair speak for themselves. The conclusion is quick and sharp. The point is clear and carries with its little ironic turn a serious idea—the failure of love through the failure to recognize the beloved as a person, as more than a convenience.

Many stories, however, use subject matter and express ideas and attitudes that cannot be treated this simply and directly. We must, then, expect other effects, more complicated and indirect methods. But we may use this story as a sort of measuring stick against which to test and define others.

1. What are the stages in the exposition of "The Man Who Would Be King"? In the denouement?

2. What principle of pattern is used in "The Secret Life of Walter Mitty"?

3. Try to imagine a story by James Thurber about Frances and Michael on their Sunday morning walk. What differences in treatment, feeling, and meaning can you imagine between his version and the present one?

O. HENRY

The Furnished Room

RESTLESS, shifting, fugacious as time itself is a certain vast bulk of the population of the red brick district of the lower West Side. Homeless, they have a hundred homes. They flit from furnished room to furnished room, transients forever—transients in abode, transients in heart and mind. They sing "Home, Sweet Home" in ragtime; they carry their *lares et penates* in a bandbox; their vine is entwined about a picture hat; a rubber plant is their fig tree.

Hence the houses of this district, having had a thousand dwellers, should have a thousand tales to tell, mostly dull ones, no doubt; but it would be strange if there could not be found a ghost or two in the wake of all these vagrant guests.

One evening after dark a young man prowled among these crumbling red mansions, ringing their bells. At the twelfth he rested his lean hand baggage upon the step and wiped the dust from his hatband and forehead. The bell sounded faint and far away in some remote, hollow depths.

To the door of this, the twelfth house whose bell he had rung, came a housekeeper who made him think of an unwholesome, surfeited worm that had eaten its nut to a hollow shell and now sought to fill the vacancy with edible lodgers.

He asked if there was a room to let.

"Come in," said the housekeeper. Her voice came from her throat; her throat seemed lined with fur. "I have the third floor, back, vacant since a week back. Should you wish to look at it?"

The young man followed her up the stairs. A faint light from no particular source mitigated the shadows of the halls. They trod noiselessly upon a stair carpet that its own loom would have foresworn. It seemed to have become vegetable; to have degenerated in that rank, sunless air to lush lichen or spreading moss that grew in patches to the staircase and was viscid under the foot like organic matter. At each turn of the stairs were vacant niches in the wall. Perhaps plants had once been set within them. If so, they had died in that foul and tainted air. It may be that statues of the saints had stood there, but it was not difficult to conceive that imps and devils had dragged them forth in the darkness and down to the unholy depths of some furnished pit below.

"This is the room," said the housekeeper, from her furry throat. "It's a nice room. It ain't often vacant. I had some most elegant people in it last summer—no trouble at all, and paid in advance to the minute. The water's at the end of the hall. Sprowls and Mooney kept it three months. They done a vaudeville sketch. Miss B'retta Sprowls—you may have heard of her—oh, that was just the stage names—right there over the dresser is where the marriage certificate hung, framed. The gas is here, and you see there is plenty of closet room. It's a room everybody likes. It never stays idle long."

"Do you have many theatrical people rooming here?" asked the young man.

"They comes and goes. A good proportion of my lodgers is connected with the theaters. Yes, sir, this is the theatrical district. Actor people never stays long anywhere. I get my share. Yes, they comes and they goes."

He engaged the room, paying for a week in advance. He was tired, he said, and would take possession at once. He counted out the money. The room had been made ready, she said, even to towels and water. As the housekeeper moved away he put, for the thousandth time, the question that he carried at the end of his tongue.

"A young girl—Miss Vashner—Miss Eloise Vashner—do you remember such a one among your lodgers? She would be singing on the stage, most likely. A fair girl, of medium height and slender, with reddish, gold hair and a dark mole near her left eyebrow."

"No, I don't remember the name. Them stage people has names they change as often as their rooms. They comes and they goes. No, I can't call that one to mind."

No. Always no. Five months of ceaseless interrogation and the inevitable negative. So much time spent by day in questioning managers, agents, schools, and choruses; by night among the audiences of theaters from all-star casts down to music halls so low that he dreaded to find what he most hoped for. He who had loved her best had tried to find her. He was sure that since her disappearance from home this great, water-girt city held her somewhere, but it was like a monstrous quicksand, shifting its particles constantly, with no foundation, its upper granules of today buried tomorrow in ooze and slime.

The furnished room received its latest guest with a first glow of pseudo-hospitality, a hectic, haggard, perfunctory welcome like the specious smile of a demirep. The sophistical comfort came in reflected gleams from the decayed furniture, the ragged brocade upholstery of a couch and two chairs, a foot-wide cheap pier glass between the two windows, from one or two gilt picture frames and a brass bedstead in a corner.

The guest reclined, inert, upon a chair, while the room, confused in speech as though it were an apartment in Babel, tried to discourse to him of its divers tenantry.

A polychromatic rug like some brilliant-flowered rectangular, tropical islet lay surrounded by a billowy sea of soiled matting. Upon the gay-papered wall were those pictures that pursue the homeless one from house to house—The Huguenot Lovers, The First Quarrel, The Wedding Breakfast, Psyche at the Fountain. The mantel's chastely severe outline was ingloriously veiled behind some pert drapery drawn rakishly askew like the sashes of the Amazonian ballet. Upon it was some desolate flotsam cast aside by the room's marooned when a lucky sail had borne them to a fresh port—a trifling vase or two, pictures of actresses, a medicine bottle, some stray cards out of a deck.

One by one, as the characters of a cryptograph become explicit, the little signs left by the furnished room's procession of guests developed a significance. The threadbare space in the rug in front of the dresser told that lovely women had marched in the throng. The tiny finger prints on the wall spoke of little prisoners trying to feel their way to sun and air. A splattered stain, raying like the shadow of a bursting bomb, witnessed where a hurled glass or bottle had splintered with its contents against the wall. Across the pier glass had been scrawled with a diamond in staggering letters the name "Marie." It seemed that the succession of dwellers in the furnished room had turned in fury—perhaps tempted beyond forbearance by its garish coldness—and wreaked upon it their passions. The furniture was chipped and bruised; the couch, distorted by bursting springs, seemed a horrible monster that had been slain during the stress of some grotesque convulsion. Some more potent upheaval had cloven a great slice from the marble mantel. Each plank in the floor owned its particular cant and shriek as from a separate and individual agony. It seemed incredible that all this malice and injury had been wrought upon the room by those who had called it for a time their home; and yet it may have been the cheated home instinct surviving blindly, the resentful rage at false household gods that had kindled their wrath. A hut that is our own we can sweep and adorn and cherish.

The young tenant in the chair allowed these thoughts to file, softshod, through his mind, while there drifted into the room furnished sounds and furnished scents. He heard in one room a tittering and incontinent, slack laughter; in others the monologue of a scold, the rattling of dice, a lullaby, and one crying dully; above him a banjo tinkled with spirit. Doors banged somewhere; the elevated trains roared intermittently; a cat yowled miserably upon a back fence. And he breathed the breath of the house— a dank savor rather than a smell—a cold, musty effluvium as from underground vaults mingled with the reeking exhalations of linoleum and mildewed and rotten woodwork.

Then, suddenly, as he rested there, the room was filled with the strong, sweet odor of mignonette. It came as upon a single buffet of wind with such sureness and fragrance and emphasis that it almost seemed a living visitant. And the man cried aloud: "What, dear?" as if he had been called, and sprang up and faced about. The rich odor clung to him and wrapped him around. He reached out his arms for it, all his senses for the time confused and commingled. How could one be peremptorily called by an odor? Surely it must have been a sound. But, was it not the sound that had touched, that had caressed him?

"She has been in this room," he cried, and he sprang to wrest from it a token, for he knew he would recognize the smallest thing that had belonged to her or that she had touched. This enveloping scent of mignonette, the odor that she had loved and made her own—whence came it?

The room had been but carelessly set in order. Scattered upon the flimsy dresser scarf were half a dozen hairpins—those discreet, indistinguishable friends of womankind, feminine of gender, infinite of mood and uncommunicative of tense. These he ignored, conscious of their triumphant lack of identity. Ransacking the drawers of the dresser, he came upon a discarded, tiny, ragged handkerchief. He pressed it to his face. It was racy and insolent with heliotrope; he hurled it to the floor. In another drawer he found odd buttons, a theater program, a pawnbroker's card, two lost marshmallows, a book on the divination of dreams. In the last was a woman's black satin hair bow, which halted him, poised between ice and fire. But the black satin hair bow also is femininity's demure, impersonal, common ornament and tells no tales.

And then he traversed the room like a hound on the scent, skimming the walls, considering the corners of the bulging matting on his hands and knees, rummaging mantel and tables, the curtains and hangings, the drunken cabinet in the corner, for a visible sign, unable to perceive that she was there beside, around, against, within, above him, clinging to him, wooing him, calling him so poignantly through the finer senses that even his grosser ones became cognizant of the call. Once again he answered loudly: "Yes, dear!" and turned, wildeyed, to gaze on vacancy, for he could not yet discern form and color and love and outstretched arms in the odor of mignonette. Oh, God! whence that odor, and since when have odors had a voice to call? Thus he groped.

He burrowed in crevices and corners, and found corks and cigarettes. These he passed in passive contempt. But once he found in a fold of the matting a half-smoked cigar, and this he ground beneath his heel with a green and trenchant oath. He sifted the room from end to end. He found dreary and ignoble small records of many a peripatetic tenant; but of her whom he sought, and who may have lodged there, and whose spirit seemed to hover there, he found no trace.

And then he thought of the housekeeper.

He ran from the haunted room downstairs and to a door that showed a crack of light. She came out to his knock. He smothered his excitement as best he could.

"Will you tell me, madam," he besought her, "who occupied the room I have before I came?"

"Yes, sir. I can tell you again. 'Twas Sprowls and Mooney, as I said. Miss B'retta Sprowls it was in the theaters, but Missis Mooney she was. My house is well known for respectability. The marriage certificate hung, framed, on a nail over—"

"What kind of a lady was Miss Sprowls—in looks, I mean?"

"Why, black-haired, sir, short, and stout, with a comical face. They left a week ago Tuesday."

"And before they occupied it?"

"Why, there was a single gentleman connected with the draying business. He left owing me a week. Before him was Missis Crowder and her two children that stayed four months; and back of them was old Mr. Doyle, whose sons paid for him. He kept the room six months. That goes back a year, sir, and further I do not remember."

He thanked her and crept back to his room. The room was dead. The essence that had vivified it was gone. The perfume of mignonette had departed. In its place was the old, stale odor of moldy house furniture, of atmosphere in storage.

The ebbing of his hope drained his faith. He sat staring at the yellow, singing gaslight. Soon he walked to the bed and began to tear the sheets into strips. With the blade of his knife he drove them tightly into every crevice around windows and door. When all was snug and taut, he turned out the light, turned the gas full on again, and laid himself gratefully upon the bed.

*   *   *   *

It was Mrs. McCool's night to go with the can'for beer. So she fetched it and sat with Mrs. Purdy in one of those subterranean retreats where housekeepers foregather and the worm dieth seldom.

"I rented out my third floor, back, this evening," said Mrs. Purdy, across a fine circle of foam. "A young man took it. He went up to bed two hours ago."

"Now, did ye, Mrs. Purdy, ma'am?" said Mrs. McCool, with intense admiration. "You do be a wonder for rentin' rooms of that kind. And did ye tell him, then?" she concluded in a husky whisper laden with mystery.

"Rooms," said Mrs. Purdy, in her furriest tones, "are furnished for to rent. I did not tell him, Mrs. McCool."

" 'Tis right ye are, ma'am; 'tis by rentin' rooms we kape alive. Ye have the rale sense for business, ma'am. There be many people will rayjict the rentin' of a room if they be tould a suicide has been after dyin' in the bed of it."

"As you say, we has our living to be making," remarked Mrs. Purdy.

"Yis, ma'am; 'tis true. 'Tis just one wake ago this day I helped ye lay out the third floor, back. A pretty slip of a colleen she was to be killin' herself wid the gas—a swate little face she had, Mrs. Purdy, ma'am."

"She'd a-been called handsome, as you say," said Mrs. Purdy, assenting but critical, "but for that mole she had a-growin' by her left eyebrow. Do fill up your glass again, Mrs. McCool."

INTERPRETATION

This story is obviously divided into two parts. The first part, which ends with the death of the lodger, concerns his failure in the search for his sweetheart and the motivation of his suicide; the second part concerns the revelation, by the landlady to her crony, that his sweetheart had, a week earlier, committed suicide in the same room. What accounts for the fact that O. Henry felt it necessary to treat the story in this fashion? What holds the two parts of the story together?

The most interesting question has to do with the young man's motivation. In one sense, O. Henry has deliberately made the problem of his motivation more difficult by withholding the information that the sweetheart is dead. The young man does not know that she is dead; indeed, in the room, he gets, with the scent of mignonette, a renewed hope. Why then, under these circumstances, does he commit suicide? Presumably, the explanation is this: he has been searching fruitlessly for five months; he is, we are told, tired—and, we assume, not only momentarily tired physically, but spiritually weary. Indeed, we are told: "He was sure that since her disappearance from home this great water-girt city held her somewhere, but it was like a monstrous quicksand, shifting its particles constantly, with no foundation, its upper granules of today buried tomorrow in ooze and slime." But we are not 'supposed to believe, even so, that he would have necessarily turned on the gas this particular evening, except as a despairing reaction from the hope which has been raised by the scent of mignonette. This is the author's account of the motivation of the suicide.

But is the motivation, as presented, really convincing? That will depend on the character of the man. What sort of man is he? Actually, O. Henry has told us very little about him except that he is young, has searched for his sweetheart for five months, and is tired. Especially does the question of the man's character, and state of mind, come up in the incident in which he notices the odor of mignonette. Did he really smell it? Did he merely imagine that he smelled it? "And he breathed the breath of the house . . . a cold, musty effluvium . . . mingled with the reeking exhalations of linoleum and mildewed and rotten woodwork. . . . Then, suddenly, as he rested there, the room was filled with the strong, sweet odor of mignonette. It came as upon a single buffet of wind. . . . The rich odor clung to him and wrapped him around."

The suddenness with which he notices the odor, the power of the odor, the fact that he can find no source for the odor, and finally the complete disappearance of the odor, all tend to imply that he merely imagines it. But over against this view, we have the testimony of the landlady that the sweetheart had actually occupied the room. This question is important, for it is crucial for the young man's lapse into acute despair. If the odor is real, the author must convince his reader that it exists; if it is imaginary, the author must convince his reader that the psychological condition of the young man will account for its apparent existence. These are the tests which the reader must apply to the situation. We have already pointed out that there is some evidence on both sides of the question. The reader must, of course, decide for himself which explanation must be taken, and more importantly, whether the explanation is convincing, and renders the action credible. The author, however, seems to weight the evidence toward the presence of the real odor. If this is the case, how are we to account for the fact that the search reveals no source of it, especially since the odor is so overpoweringly strong? Or, perhaps the author has in mind some idea that the odor provokes a mystical communion between the two lovers. But this does not relieve the fiction writer from the necessity for furnishing some sort of specific clue to his meaning. (Morever, if we are to take the whole experience as an hallucination, the author is certainly not relieved from providing some clear motivation for the event.)

To sum up: it is obvious enough, from the detailed description of the room, that O. Henry is trying to suggest a ground for the man's experience in the nature of the room itself. That is, the room in its disorder, its squalor, its musty smell, its rubbish and debris of nameless lives, reflects the great city, or the world, in which his sweetheart has been lost, and in which all humanity seems to become degraded and brutalized. It is easy enough to see why O. Henry should want to suggest the contrast between what the sordid surroundings mean to the hero and what the odor of mignonette means to him. As the girl is lost somewhere in the great city, so the odor is lost somewhere in the room. After the young man is told that the girl has not been there, and after he has been unable to find the source of the odor, the room itself is supposed to become a sort of overwhelming symbol for the futility of his effort. This intention on the part of the author may be sound enough, but the fact that we see what the intention is does not mean that the intention has been carried out. The whole effect of the story depends on the incident of the odor, and we have seen that the handling of this detail is confused.

Assuming that this objection is valid, the basic remedy suggests itself at once. The author needed to go back and fill in the character of the young man much more fully. The reader might then have been able to follow the processes of his mind as he goes through his crucial experience, and the specific nature of his response to the odor would have been clarified. But O. Henry chooses an easier solution. Resting upon his rather thin and sketchy characterization of the young man, the author chooses to give a turn to the plot by a last-minute surprise. In the second part of the story the landlady tells her crony that she has lied to the young man about the girl.

What is the effect of this revelation? It is intended, obviously, to underline the "irony of fate," to illustrate the hard-heartedness of the city in which the young man finds himself, to justify the young man's overwhelming sense that the girl has been in the room, and, all in all, to pull the story together. For the sympathetic reader this conclusion is supposed to suggest that the bonds of love stretch across the confusion and squalor of the great city, and that, in a sense, the young man has finally succeeded in his search, for the lovers are at last united in death. The young man finds, as it were, the proper room in the great city in which to die.

But is the story really pulled together? The end of the story depends on the lie. But are the lives of the lovers altered by the lie? Does the lie cause the death of the young man? It is conceivable that, had the landlady told the truth, the shock of the information might have saved the young man from suicide, but this is the merest speculation. The character, as given in the story, commits suicide in despair when the landlady tells him that the girl has not been there; the landlady's telling him that the girl is irretrievably lost, is dead, would presumably have had the same effect.

Actually, is there any point in the lie except to trick the reader—to provide the illusion of a meaningful ending? Whatever irony lies in the ending is based on a far-fetched coincidence, and does not depend on the fact that the woman said one thing rather than another. (Readers who are inclined to accept the conclusion of the story as meaningful might try reconstructing the story with the young man's calling at the door, finding with horror that his sweetheart has committed suicide there a week before, renting the room, and turning on the gas. We would then still have the ironical coincidence and a sort of union of the lovers, but the story would seem very tame and flat.) O. Henry, by withholding certain information and thus surprising us with it at the end, has simply tried to give the reader the illusion that the information was meaningful. The irony, in the story as we have it, simply resides in a trick played on the reader rather than in a trick which fate has played on the young man.

Readers who feel that the end of this story is a shabby trick will be able to point out other symptoms of cheapness: the general thinness of characterization, the cluttered and sometimes mawkish description, the wheedling tone taken by the author, and the obvious play for emotional sympathy in such writing as the following: "Oh, God! whence that odor, and since when have odors had a voice to call?" In other words, we can readily surmise that the trickery involved in the surprise ending may be an attempt to compensate for defects within the body of the story itself. The straining to stir the emotions of the reader, the mawkish and wheedling tone—all are attempts to make up for a lack of logic, a lack of coherence, in the story itself. *Sentimentality* (see Glossary) often springs from such a lack of coherence—emotionalism without reference to a reasonable occasion for it.

A trick of plot does not make a story. A surprise ending may appear in a very good story, but only if the surprise has been prepared for so that, upon second thought, the reader realizes that it is, after all, a logical and meaningful development from what has gone before, and not merely a device employed by the author to give him an easy way out of his difficulties. The same principle applies to *coincidence* (see Glossary) in general. Coincidences do occur in real life, sometimes quite startling ones, and in one sense every story is based on a coincidence—namely, that the particular events happen to occur together, that such and such characters happen to meet, for example. But since fiction is concerned with a logic of character and action, coincidence, in so far as it is purely illogical, has little place in fiction. Truth can afford to be stranger than fiction, because truth is "true"—is acceptable on its own merits—but the happenings of fiction, as we have seen, must justify themselves in terms of logical connection with other elements in fiction and in terms of meaningfulness. Certainly coincidence is never acceptable when it is used to solve the problem of a story—to bail the author out of his difficulties. (See pp. 26–28.)

JOHN COLLIER

De Mortuis

DR. Rankin was a large and raw-boned man on whom the newest suit at once appeared outdated, like a suit in a photograph of twenty years ago. This was due to the squareness and flatness of his torso, which might have been put together by a manufacturer of packing cases. His face also had a wooden and a roughly constructed look; his hair was wiglike and resentful of the comb. He had those huge and clumsy hands which can be an asset to a doctor in a small upstate town where people still retain a rural relish for paradox, thinking that the more apelike the paw, the more precise it can be in the delicate business of a tonsillectomy.

This conclusion was perfectly justified in the case of Dr. Rankin. For example, on this particular fine morning, though his task was nothing more ticklish than the cementing over of a large patch on his cellar floor, he managed those large and clumsy hands with all the unflurried certainty of one who would never leave a sponge within or create an unsightly scar without.

The doctor surveyed his handiwork from all angles. He added a touch here and a touch there till he had achieved a smoothness altogether professional. He swept up a few last crumbs of soil and dropped them into the furnace. He paused before putting away the pick and shovel he had been using, and found occasion for yet another artistic sweep of his trowel, which made the new surface precisely flush with the surrounding floor. At this moment of supreme concentration the porch door upstairs slammed with the report of a minor piece of artillery, which, appropriately enough, caused Dr. Rankin to jump as if he had been shot.

The Doctor lifted a frowning face and an attentive ear. He heard two pairs of heavy feet clump across the resonant floor of the porch. He heard the house door opened and the visitors enter the hall, with which his cellar communicated by a short flight of steps. He heard whistling and then the voices of Buck and Bud crying, "Doc! Hi, Doc! They're biting!"

Whether the Doctor was not inclined for fishing that day, or whether, like others of his large and heavy type, he experienced an especially sharp, unsociable reaction on being suddenly startled, or whether he was merely anxious to finish undisturbed the job in hand and proceed to more im-

99

portant duties, he did not respond immediately to the inviting outcry of his friends. Instead, he listened while it ran its natural course, dying down at last into a puzzled and fretful dialogue.

"I guess he's out."

"I'll write a note—say we're at the creek to come on down."

"We could tell Irene."

"But she's not here, either. You'd think *she'd* be around."

"Ought to be, by the look of the place."

"You said it, Bud. Just look at this table. You could write your name—"

"Sh-h-h! Look!"

Evidently the last speaker had noticed that the cellar door was ajar and that a light was shining below. Next moment the door was pushed wide open and Bud and Buck looked down.

"Why, Doc! There you are!"

"Didn't you hear us yelling?"

The Doctor, not too pleased at what he had overheard, nevertheless smiled his rather wooden smile as his two friends made their way down the steps. "I thought I heard someone," he said.

"We were bawling our heads off," Buck said. "Thought nobody was home. Where's Irene?"

"Visiting," said the Doctor. "She's gone visiting."

"Hey, what goes on?" said Bud. "What are you doing? Burying one of your patients, or what?"

"Oh, there's been water seeping up through the floor," said the Doctor. "I figured it might be some spring opened up or something."

"You don't say!" said Bud, assuming instantly the high ethical standpoint of the realtor. "Gee, Doc, I sold you this property. Don't say I fixed you up with a dump where there's an underground spring."

"There was water," said the Doctor.

"Yes, but, Doc, you can look on that geological map the Kiwanis Club got up. There's not a better section of subsoil in the town."

"Looks like he sold you a pup," said Buck, grinning.

"No," said Bud. "Look. When the Doc came here he was green. You'll admit he was green. The things he didn't know!"

"He bought Ted Webber's jalopy," said Buck.

"He'd have bought the Jessop place if I'd let him," said Bud. "But I wouldn't give him a bum steer."

"Not the poor, simple city slicker from Poughkeepsie," said Buck.

"Some people would have taken him," said Bud. "Maybe some people did. Not me. I recommended this property. He and Irene moved straight in as soon as they were married. I wouldn't have put the Doc on to a dump where there'd be a spring under the foundations."

"Oh, forget it," said the Doctor, embarrassed by this conscientiousness. "I guess it was just the heavy rains."

"By gosh!" Buck said, glancing at the besmeared point of the pick-axe. "You certainly went deep enough. Right down into the clay, huh?"

"That's four feet down, the clay," Bud said.

"Eighteen inches," said the Doctor.

"Four feet," said Bud. "I can show you on the map."

"Come on. No arguments," said Buck. "How's about it, Doc? An hour or two at the creek, eh? They're biting."

"Can't do it, boys," said the Doctor. "I've got to see a patient or two."

"Aw, live and let live, Doc," Bud said. "Give 'em a chance to get better. Are you going to depopulate the whole darn town?"

The Doctor looked down, smiled, and muttered, as he always did when this particular jest was trotted out. "Sorry, boys," he said. "I can't make it."

"Well," said Bud, disappointed, "I suppose we'd better get along. How's Irene?"

"Irene?" asked the Doctor. "Never better. She's gone visiting. Albany. Got the eleven o'clock train."

"Eleven o'clock?" said Buck. "For Albany?"

"Did I say Albany?" said the Doctor. "Watertown, I meant."

"Friends in Watertown?" Buck asked.

"Mrs. Slater," said the Doctor. "Mr. and Mrs. Slater. Lived next door to 'em when she was a kid, Irene said, over on Sycamore Street."

"Slater?" said Bud. "Next door to Irene. Not in *this* town."

"Oh, yes," said the Doctor. "She was telling me all about them last night. She got a letter. Seems this Mrs. Slater looked after her when her mother was in the hospital one time."

"No," said Bud.

"That's what she told me," said the Doctor. "Of course, it was a good many years ago."

"Look, Doc," said Buck. "Bud and I were raised in this town. We've known Irene's folks all our lives. We were in and out of their house all the time. There was never anybody next door called Slater."

"Perhaps," said the Doctor, "she married again, this woman. Perhaps it was a different name."

Bud shook his head.

"What time did Irene go to the station?" Buck asked.

"Oh, about a quarter of an hour ago," said the Doctor.

"You didn't drive her?" said Buck.

"She walked," said the Doctor.

"We came down Main Street," Buck said. "We didn't meet her."

"Maybe she walked across the pasture," said the Doctor.

"That's a tough walk with a suitcase," said Buck.

"She just had a couple of things in a little bag," said the Doctor.

Bud was still shaking his head.

Buck looked at Bud, and then at the pick, at the new, damp cement on the floor. "Jesus Christ!" he said.

"Oh, God, Doc!" Bud said. "A guy like you!"

"What in the name of heaven are you two bloody fools thinking?" asked the Doctor. "What are you trying to say?"

"A spring!" said Bud. "I ought to have known right away it wasn't any spring."

The Doctor looked at his cement-work, at the pick, at the large worried faces of his two friends. His own face turned livid. "Am I crazy?" he said. "Or are you? You suggest that I've—that Irene—my wife—oh, go on! Get out! Yes, go and get the sheriff. Tell him to come here and start digging. You—get out!"

Bud and Buck looked at each other, shifted their feet, and stood still again.

"Go on," said the Doctor.

"I don't know," said Bud.

"It's not as if he didn't have the provocation," Buck said.

"God knows," Bud said.

"God knows," Buck said. "You know. I know. The whole town knows. But try telling it to a jury."

The Doctor put his hand to his head. "What's that?" he said. "What is it? Now what are you saying? What do you mean?"

"If this ain't being on the spot!" said Buck. "Doc, you can see how it is. It takes some thinking. We've been friends right from the start. Damn good friends."

"But we've got to think," said Bud. "It's serious. Provocation or not, there's a law in the land. There's such a thing as being an accomplice."

"You were talking about provocation," said the Doctor.

"You're right," said Buck. "And you're our friend. And if ever it could be called justified—"

"We've got to fix this somehow," said Bud.

"Justified?" said the Doctor.

"You were bound to get wised up sooner or later," said Buck.

"We could have told you," said Bud. "Only—what the hell?"

"We could," said Buck. "And we nearly did. Five years ago. Before ever you married her. You hadn't been here six months, but we sort of cottoned to you. Thought of giving you a hint. Spoke about it. Remember, Bud?"

Bud nodded. "Funny," he said. "I came right out in the open about that Jessop property. I wouldn't let you buy that, Doc. But getting married, that's something else again. We could have told you."

"We're that much responsible," Buck said.

"I'm fifty," said the Doctor. "I suppose it's pretty old for Irene."

"If you was Johnny Weissmuller at the age of twenty-one, it wouldn't make any difference," said Buck.

"I know a lot of people think she's not exactly a perfect wife," said the Doctor. "Maybe she's not. She's young. She's full of life."

"Oh, skip it!" said Buck sharply, looking at the raw cement. "Skip it, Doc, for God's sake."

The Doctor brushed his hand across his face. "Not everybody wants the same thing," he said. "I'm a sort of dry fellow. I don't open up very easily. Irene—you'd call her gay."

"You said it," said Buck.

"She's no housekeeper," said the Doctor. "I know it. But that's not the only thing a man wants. She's enjoyed herself."

"Yeah," said Buck. "She did."

"That's what I love," said the Doctor. "Because I'm not that way myself. She's not very deep, mentally. All right. Say she's stupid. I don't care. Lazy. No system. Well, I've got plenty of system. She's enjoyed herself. It's beautiful. It's innocent. Like a child."

"Yes. If that was all," Buck said.

"But," said the Doctor, turning his eyes full on him, "You seem to know there was more."

"Everybody knows it," said Buck.

"A decent, straightforward guy comes to a place like this and marries the town floozy," Bud said bitterly. "And nobody'll tell him. Everybody just watches."

"And laughs," said Buck. "You and me, Bud, as well as the rest."

"We told her to watch her step," said Bud. "We warned her."

"Everybody warned her," said Buck. "But people get fed up. When it got to truck-drivers—"

"It was never us, Doc," said Bud, earnestly. "Not after you came along, anyway."

"The town'll be on your side," said Buck.

"That won't mean much when the case comes to trial in the county seat," said Bud.

"Oh!" cried the Doctor, suddenly. "What shall I do? What shall I do?"

"It's up to you, Bud," said Buck. "I can't turn him in."

"Take it easy, Doc," said Bud. "Calm down. Look, Buck. When we came in here the street was empty, wasn't it?"

"I guess so," said Buck. "Anyway, nobody saw us come down cellar."

"And we haven't been down," Bud said, addressing himself forcefully to the Doctor. "Get that, Doc? We shouted upstairs, hung around a minute or two, and cleared out. But we never came down into this cellar."

"I wish you hadn't," the Doctor said heavily.

"All you have to do is say Irene went out for a walk and never came back," said Buck. "Bud and I can swear we saw her headed out of town with a fellow in a—well, say in a Buick sedan. Everybody'll believe that, all right. We'll fix it. But later. Now we'd better scram."

"And remember, now. Stick to it. We never came down here and we haven't seen you today," said Bud. "So long!"

Buck and Bud ascended the steps, moving with a rather absurd degree of caution. "You'd better get that . . . that thing covered up," Buck said over his shoulder.

Left alone, the Doctor sat down on an empty box, holding his head with both hands. He was still sitting like this when the porch door slammed again. This time he did not start. He listened. The house door opened and closed. A voice cried, "Yoo-hoo! Yoo-hoo! I'm back."

The Doctor rose slowly to his feet. "I'm down here, Irene!" he called.

The cellar door opened. A young woman stood at the head of the steps. "Can you beat it?" she said. "I missed the damn train."

"Oh!" said the Doctor. "Did you come back across the field?"

"Yes, like a fool," she said. "I could have hitched a ride and caught the train up the line. Only I didn't think. If you'd run me over to the junction, I could still make it."

"Maybe," said the Doctor. "Did you meet anyone coming back?"

"Not a soul," she said. "Aren't you finished with that old job yet?"

"I'm afraid I'll have to take it all up again," said the Doctor. "Come down here, my dear, and I'll show you."

INTERPRETATION

This story, like "The Furnished Room," involves coincidence and has a trick ending. But are those two things more acceptable here than in "The Furnished Room"? Perhaps we can best answer the question by considering the difference between the pretensions of the two stories.

"The Furnished Room" aspires to be a serious story. O. Henry wants us to feel the pathos and irony of life, the brutality and anonymity of the great city in contrast with the loves and hopes of the lost individuals. The story aims to stir our emotions and evoke our sympathies.

"De Mortuis," on the other hand, is a kind of extended joke. It deals with serious materials, the betrayal of a simple, decent man by an immoral wife, and his murder of her, but the emphasis is not on the human passions and suffering. The treatment is the treatment to be found in a joke, and the point, in a way, lies in the contrast between the potentially serious, even tragic, human situation, on the one hand, and the reversal and punch of the joke, on the other. It's a great joke on Irene. Just wait till she gets downstairs! Won't she be surprised! Well, she had it coming. She stepped into it that time. We have the comic effect—the liberation from the demands of sympathy and seriousness.

As a matter of fact, the joke isn't merely on Irene. There is a joke on everybody, on Buck and Bud, who unwittingly get the thing worked up, and on the doctor himself. Life has some rather grim little jokes, the story implies, but the best thing to do is to recognize them as jokes and laugh at them. Even the fact of coincidence—Bud and Buck just happen to drop in at the right time, Irene just happens to miss the train and come back, unseen, across the pasture—are consistent with the comic effect. We accept the coincidences as the machinery of the joke life is playing—for the illogic of life, not the logic, is what gives us the comedy. Poor Irene, and the others, are caught in the improbable coincidences and the unexpected turn, and we laugh at the fact. No appeal has been made to our sympathies. The tone is one of calm detachment, coolly reportorial. We are not involved in the human situation. The fact of the seriousness and the suffering merely gives a grim little edge to the comedy.

To sum up, it is the particular comic tone which makes us accept the coincidences and the trick ending. By tone, as we have already suggested (p. 63–64), we mean the impression that the author gives of his attitude toward his subject and his reader. Collier here takes life as a sardonic joke, full of traps and tricks. Careful, Irene, dear, watch that banana peel. It's right there before your eyes.

1. It may help us in developing some of the principles involved here, if we make a comparison with "The Lottery." That story, too, depends on coincidence and on a trick ending, again a grim joke. But the tone is certainly different. Try to describe the basic difference. Which story is, in its basic intention, more serious? Which do you like better? Why?

2. Try to distinguish between exposition and complication in "De Mortuis." Can you point out any elements of exposition that are withheld until complication has begun?

3. Suppose Collier had interpolated toward the end of the story a passage in which the doctor remembers his loneliness before his marriage, dwells on certain moments of tenderness of which Irene had been capable, shudders at the horror of the impulse that seizes him, then steels himself to the act. How would this change the effect of the story? What would be the effect on the tone? Would the story still be coherent?

4. What value for the story does the first paragraph have?

GUY DE MAUPASSANT

The Necklace

SHE was one of those pretty and charming girls who are sometimes, as if by a mistake of destiny, born in a family of clerks. She had no dowry, no expectations, no means of being known, understood, loved, wedded by any rich and distinguished man; and she let herself be married to a little clerk at the Ministry of Public Instruction.

She dressed plainly because she could not dress well, but she was as unhappy as though she had really fallen from her proper station, since with women there is neither caste nor rank: and beauty, grace, and charm act instead of family and birth. Natural fineness, instinct for what is elegant, suppleness of wit, are the sole hierarchy, and make from women of the people the equals of the very greatest ladies.

She suffered ceaselessly, feeling herself born for all the delicacies and all the luxuries. She suffered from the poverty of her dwelling, from the wretched look of the walls, from the worn-out chairs, from the ugliness of the curtains. All those things, of which another woman of her rank would never even have been conscious, tortured her and made her angry. The sight of the little Breton peasant who did her humble housework aroused in her regrets which were despairing, and distracted dreams. She thought of the silent antechambers hung with Oriental tapestry, lit by tall bronze candelabra, and of the two great footmen in knee breeches who sleep in the big armchairs, made drowsy by the heavy warmth of the hot-air stove. She thought of the long *salons* fitted up with ancient silk, of the delicate furniture carrying priceless curiosities, and of the coquettish perfumed boudoirs made for talks at five o'clock with intimate friends, with men famous and sought after, whom all women envy and whose attention they all desire.

When she sat down to dinner, before the round table covered with a tablecloth three days old, opposite her husband, who uncovered the soup tureen and declared with an enchanted air, "Ah, the good *pot-au-feu!* I don't know anything better than that," she thought of dainty dinners, of shining silverware, of tapestry which peopled the walls with ancient personages and with strange birds flying in the midst of a fairy forest; and she thought of delicious dishes served on marvelous plates, and of the whispered

106

gallantries which you listen to with a sphinxlike smile, while you are eating the pink flesh of a trout or the wings of a quail.

She had no dresses, no jewels, nothing. And she loved nothing but that; she felt made for that. She would so have liked to please, to be envied, to be charming, to be sought after.

She had a friend, a former schoolmate at the convent, who was rich, and whom she did not like to go and see any more, because she suffered so much when she came back.

But one evening, her husband returned home with a triumphant air, and holding a large envelope in his hand.

"There," said he. "Here is something for you."

She tore the paper sharply, and drew out a printed card which bore these words:

"The Minister of Public Instruction and Mme. Georges Ramponneau request the honor of M. and Mme. Loisel's company at the palace of the Ministry on Monday evening, January eighteenth."

Instead of being delighted, as her husband hoped, she threw the invitation on the table with disdain, murmuring:

"What do you want me to do with that?"

"But, my dear, I thought you would be glad. You never go out, and this is such a fine opportunity. I had awful trouble to get it. Everyone wants to go; it is very select, and they are not giving many invitations to clerks. The whole official world will be there."

She looked at him with an irritated glance, and said, impatiently:

"And what do you want me to put on my back?"

He had not thought of that; he stammered:

"Why, the dress you go to the theater in. It looks very well, to me."

He stopped, distracted, seeing his wife was crying. Two great tears descended slowly from the corners of her eyes toward the corners of her mouth. He stuttered:

"What's the matter? What's the matter?"

But, by violent effort, she had conquered her grief, and she replied, with a calm voice, while she wiped her wet cheeks:

"Nothing. Only I have no dress and therefore I can't go to this ball. Give your card to some colleague whose wife is better equipped than I."

He was in despair. He resumed:

"Come, let us see, Mathilde. How much would it cost, a suitable dress, which you could use on other occasions, something very simple?"

She reflected several seconds, making her calculations and wondering also what sum she could ask without drawing on herself an immediate refusal and a frightened exclamation from the economical clerk.

Finally, she replied, hesitatingly:

"I don't know exactly, but I think I could manage it with four hundred francs."

He had grown a little pale, because he was laying aside just that amount to buy a gun and treat himself to a little shooting next summer on the plain of Nanterre, with several friends who went to shoot larks down there, of a Sunday.

But he said:

"All right. I will give you four hundred francs. And try to have a pretty dress."

The day of the ball drew near, and Mme. Loisel seemed sad, uneasy, anxious. Her dress was ready, however. Her husband said to her one evening:

"What is the matter? Come, you've been so queer these last three days."

And she answered:

"It annoys me not to have a single jewel, not a single stone, nothing to put on. I shall look like distress. I should almost rather not go at all."

He resumed:

"You might wear natural flowers. It's very stylish at this time of the year. For ten francs you can get two or three magnificent roses."

She was not convinced.

"No; there's nothing more humiliating than to look poor among other women who are rich."

But her husband cried:

"How stupid you are! Go look up your friend Mme. Forestier, and ask her to lend you some jewels. You're quite thick enough with her to do that."

She uttered a cry of joy:

"It's true. I never thought of it."

The next day she went to her friend and told of her distress.

Mme. Forestier went to a wardrobe with a glass door, took out a large jewel-box, brought it back, opened it, and said to Mme. Loisel:

"Choose, my dear."

She saw first of all some bracelets, then a pearl necklace, then a Venetian cross, gold and precious stones of admirable workmanship. She tried on the ornaments before the glass, hesitated, could not make up her mind to part with them, to give them back. She kept asking:

"Haven't you any more?"

"Why, yes. Look. I don't know what you like."

All of a sudden she discovered, in a black satin box, a superb necklace of diamonds, and her heart began to beat with an immoderate desire. Her hands trembled as she took it. She fastened it around her throat, outside her high-necked dress, and remained lost in ecstasy at the sight of herself.

Then she asked, hesitating, filled with anguish:

"Can you lend me that, only that?"

"Why, yes, certainly."

She sprang upon the neck of her friend, kissed her passionately, then fled with her treasure.

The day of the ball arrived. Mme. Loisel made a great success. She was prettier than them all, elegant, gracious, smiling, and crazy with joy. All the men looked at her, asked her name, endeavored to be introduced. All the attachés of the Cabinet wanted to waltz with her. She was remarked by the minister himself.

She danced with intoxication, with passion, made drunk by pleasure, forgetting all, in the triumph of her beauty, in the glory of her success, in a sort of cloud of happiness composed of all this homage, of all this admiration, of all these awakened desires, and of that sense of complete victory which is so sweet to a woman's heart.

She went away about four o'clock in the morning. Her husband had been sleeping since midnight, in a little deserted anteroom, with three other gentlemen whose wives were having a very good time. He threw over her shoulders the wraps which he had brought, modest wraps of common life, whose poverty contrasted with the elegance of the ball dress. She felt this, and wanted to escape so as not to be remarked by the other women, who were enveloping themselves in costly furs.

Loisel held her back.

"Wait a bit. You will catch cold outside. I will go and call a cab."

But she did not listen to him, and rapidly descended the stairs. When they were in the street they did not find a carriage; and they began to look for one, shouting after the cabmen whom they saw passing by at a distance.

They went down toward the Seine, in despair, shivering with cold. At last they found on the quay one of those ancient noctambulant coupés which, exactly as if they were ashamed to show their misery during the day, are never seen round Paris until after nightfall.

It took them to their door in the Rue des Martyrs, and once more, sadly, they climbed up homeward. All was ended, for her. And as to him, he reflected that he must be at the Ministry at ten o'clock.

She removed the wraps which covered her shoulders, before the glass, so as once more to see herself in all her glory. But suddenly she uttered a cry. She no longer had the necklace around her neck!

Her husband, already half undressed, demanded:

"What is the matter with you?"

She turned madly towards him:

"I have—I have—I've lost Mme. Forestier's necklace."

He stood up, distracted.

"What!—how?—impossible!"

And they looked in the folds of her dress, in the folds of her cloak, in her pockets, everywhere. They did not find it.

He asked:

"You're sure you had it on when you left the ball?"

"Yes, I felt it in the vestibule of the palace."

"But if you had lost it in the street we should have heard it fall. It must be in the cab."

"Yes. Probably. Did you take his number?"

"No. And you, didn't you notice it?"

"No."

They looked, thunderstruck, at one another. At last Loisel put on his clothes.

"I shall go back on foot," said he, "over the whole route which we have taken to see if I can find it."

And he went out. She sat waiting on a chair in her ball dress, without strength to go to bed, overwhelmed, without fire, without a thought.

Her husband came back about seven o'clock. He had found nothing.

He went to Police Headquarters, to the newspaper offices, to offer a reward; he went to the cab companies—everywhere, in fact, whither he was urged by the least suspicion of hope.

She waited all day, in the same condition of mad fear before this terrible calamity.

Loisel returned at night with a hollow, pale face; he had discovered nothing.

"You must write to your friend," said he, "that you have broken the clasp of her necklace and that you are having it mended. That will give us time to turn round."

She wrote at his dictation.

At the end of a week they had lost all hope.

And Loisel, who had aged five years, declared:

"We must consider how to replace that ornament."

The next day they took the box which had contained it, and they went to the jeweler whose name was found within. He consulted his books.

"It was not I, madame, who sold that necklace; I must simply have furnished the case."

Then they went from jeweler to jeweler, searching for a necklace like the other, consulting their memories, sick both of them with chagrin and anguish.

They found, in a shop at the Palais Royal, a string of diamonds which seemed to them exactly like the one they looked for. It was worth forty thousand francs. They could have it for thirty-six.

So they begged the jeweler not to sell it for three days yet. And they made a bargain that he should buy it back for thirty-four thousand francs, in case they found the other one before the end of February.

Loisel possessed eighteen thousand francs which his father had left him. He would borrow the rest.

He did borrow, asking a thousand francs of one, five hundred of another, five louis here, three louis there. He gave notes, took up ruinous obligations, dealt with usurers and all the race of lenders. He compromised all the rest of his life, risked his signature without even knowing if he could meet it; and, frightened by the pains yet to come, by the black misery which was about to fall upon him, by the prospect of all the physical privation and of all the moral tortures which he was to suffer, he went to get the new necklace, putting down upon the merchant's counter thirty-six thousand francs.

When Mme. Loisel took back the necklace, Mme. Forestier said to her, with a chilly manner:

"You should have returned it sooner; I might have needed it."

She did not open the case, as her friend had so much feared. If she had detected the substitution, what would she have thought, what would she have said? Would she not have taken Mme. Loisel for a thief?

Mme. Loisel now knew the horrible existence of the needy. She took her part, moreover, all of a sudden, with heroism. That dreadful debt must be paid. She would pay it. They dismissed their servant; they changed their lodgings; they rented a garret under the roof.

She came to know what heavy housework meant and the odious cares of the kitchen. She washed the dishes, using her rosy nails on the greasy pots and pans. She washed the dirty linen, the shirts, and the dishcloths, which she dried upon a line; she carried the slops down to the street every morning, and carried up the water, stopping for breath at every landing. And, dressed like a woman of the people, she went to the fruiterer, the grocer, the butcher, her basket on her arm, bargaining, insulted, defending her miserable money sou by sou.

Each month they had to meet some notes, renew others, obtain more time.

Her husband worked in the evening making a fair copy of some tradesman's accounts, and late at night he often copied manuscript for five sous a page.

And this life lasted for ten years.

At the end of ten years, they had paid everything, everything, with the rates of usury, and the accumulations of the compound interest.

Mme. Loisel looked old now. She had become the woman of improverished households—strong and hard and rough. With frowsy hair, skirts askew, and red hands, she talked loud while washing the floor with great swishes of water. But sometimes, when her husband was at the office, she sat down near the window, and she thought of that gay evening of long ago, of that ball where she had been so beautiful and so fêted.

What would have happened if she had not lost that necklace? Who knows? Who knows? How life is strange and changeful! How little a thing is needed for us to be lost or to be saved!

But, one Sunday, having gone to take a walk in the Champs Elysées to refresh herself from the labor of the week, she suddenly perceived a woman who was leading a child. It was Mme. Forestier, still young, still beautiful, still charming.

Mme. Loisel felt moved. Was she going to speak to her? Yes, certainly. And now that she had paid, she was going to tell her all about it. Why not?

She went up.

"Good-day, Jeanne."

The other, astonished to be familiarly addressed by this plain goodwife, did not recognize her at all, and stammered:

"But—madam!—I do not know— You must be mistaken."

"No. I am Mathilde Loisel."

Her friend uttered a cry.

"Oh, my poor Mathilde! How you are changed!"

"Yes, I have had days hard enough, since I have seen you, days wretched enough—and that because of you!"

"Of me! How so?"

"Do you remember that diamond necklace which you lent me to wear at the ministerial ball?"

"Yes. Well?"

"Well, I lost it."

"What do you mean? You brought it back."

"I brought you back another just like it. And for this we have been ten years paying. You can understand that it was not easy for us, us who had nothing. At last it is ended, and I am very glad."

Mme. Forestier had stopped.

"You say that you bought a necklace of diamonds to replace mine?"

"Yes. You never noticed it, then! They were very like."

And she smiled with a joy which was proud and naïve at once.

Mme. Forestier, strongly moved, took her two hands.

"Oh, my poor Mathilde! Why, my necklace was paste. It was worth at most five hundred francs!"

INTERPRETATION

This story ends with a surprising turn. The heroine, after years of privation and struggle caused by the loss of the borrowed necklace, learns that the jewels had, after all, been valueless. At first glance this revelation may seem to be a trick, just as the conclusion of "The Furnished Room" is a trick. To determine whether or not the conclusion of "The Necklace" is a trick, one should investigate the following questions:

1. Has Maupassant made use of the fact that the jewels are paste as a starting point from which to develop his story, or has he used it as merely a piece of trickery to provide a surprise ending? In other words, is there a really important difference between the fundamental fact that the jewels are paste, and the fact that the heroine eventually discovers them to be paste? Would there be an irony in the story even if the woman had never discovered the true nature of the jewels?

2. Waiving the question of the nature of the jewels: some people, having lost them, would have made a clean breast of the situation at once. Is the heroine's refusal to do so adequately motivated? Is the pride from which this refusal springs a true and admirable pride or merely a false pride? Or is it an ironical mixture of the two? The heroine's actions subsequent to the loss of the jewels are presumably conditioned by her character. Are these two elements logically related in the story?

3. Finally, does the fundamental meaning of the story depend on the fact of the loss of the jewels, whether paste or real? In other words, is not this the sort of woman who, in one way or another, would have wasted her life on some sort of vanity? (In this connection read the first paragraph of the story.) Does Maupassant not use the accident of the loss of the jewels as a means to speed up and intensify a process which is already inherent in the woman's character? If this can be maintained, then does not the falsity of the jewels become a kind of symbol for the root situation of the story? That is, does not the "falsity" of the jewels stand as a symbol for the falsity of the values by which the woman once lived?

4. Have we any evidence that the author intended to indicate a regeneration of the heroine? If so, what are we to make of the fact that the heroine discovers in the end that she has now paid for "real" jewels?

5. We may say that the irony of "De Mortuis" is based on a general view of life, the surprising and comic way in which things happen, and that the irony of "The Lottery" is based on a general view of human nature, the doubleness of human nature. The irony of "The Necklace" is based on something more specific. How would you describe it?

6. We have said that Madame Forestier's revelation that the original necklace was paste carries to us, the readers, the point of the story. What does it carry to Madame Loisel?

This story gives us a good chance to consider the problem of the treatment of time in fiction. The story takes Madame Loisel from youth to middle age. Her girlhood is passed over in one sentence in the first paragraph, and the early years of marriage are treated in the second to the fifth paragraphs. Then the time of the ball is treated at considerable length in five direct scenes, the conversation about the dress, the conversation about the jewels, the visit to Madame Forestier, the ball itself, the search for the lost necklace. Then the time of deprivation and payment, ten years, occupies a page or so. Then comes the denouement, the encounter with Madame Forestier in the park.

There is, we see, a sort of balance between the long periods of time treated by summary, and the short periods, treated more or less dramatically by direct rendering. In treating the long periods, in which the eye sweeps, as it were, over a panorama, the writer needs to hit on the important fact, or the essential feeling of the period. He needs to distill out the thing fundamental to the story—the character of the young Madame Loisel, or the way she lived through the ten years of deprivation. In the dramatic—or scenic—treatment the need, however, is to show the process of the movement through the time involved, how there is, step by step, a development; how, for example, Madame Loisel decides to speak to her old friend in the park, how she accosts her, how she discovers the unexpected joy in the thought that the necklace she had bought had successfully deceived Madame Forestier, how Madame Forestier makes the revelation which, for us, will carry the burden of meaning. The scene, in other words, gives the "close-ups" of time, and the summary gives the "long shots."

Often in a summary a writer must give more than mere summary. After all, he is writing fiction, and fiction wants to give the feeling of life, not merely the bare facts. Let us notice how even in the relatively bare summary in which Maupassant presents the years of hardship, he manages by a few specific touches to make us sense the quality of the life of the Loisels. Madame Loisel scraped "her rosy nails on the greasy pots and pans." When she carried up her household water every morning, she had to stop "for breath at every landing." She had become, Maupassant tells us, strong, hard, and rough. Then he writes: "With frowsy hair, skirts askew, and red hands, she talked loud while washing the floor with great swishes of water." It all comes alive with the phrase "great swishes of water." We *see* that.

Some pieces of fiction, even some novels, can proceed almost entirely by scenes, by direct presentation. For instance, "De Mortuis" gives us a single little segment of time, as does "The Girls in Their Summer Dresses," with only a minimum of summarized exposition from the past. In fact, both of these stories, in treating the present time, depend almost entirely on conversation and direct action—more so, for instance, than even "The Lottery," which, also, occupies a single short section of continuing time.

Many stories and almost all novels, however, must swing back and forth between more or less direct treatments and narrative summary with more or less of description and analysis thrown in. It is well to begin to notice how these two basic kinds of treatment (with the various shadings and combinations) are related. We must ask ourselves how much the feeling of a particular story, the logic of its telling, the effect it has on us, are related to the writer's handling of this question of time. Again, there is no rule. We must try to inspect our own reactions as carefully and candidly as possible, and try to imagine what would be the effect, in instance after instance, if a different method were used.

AMBROSE BIERCE

An Occurrence at Owl Creek Bridge

A MAN stood upon a railroad bridge in northern Alabama, looking down into the swift water twenty feet below. The man's hands were behind his back, the wrists bound with a cord. A rope closely encircled his neck. It was attached to a stout cross-timber above his head and the slack fell to the level of his knees. Some loose boards laid upon the sleepers supporting the metals of the railway supplied a footing for him and his executioners—two private soldiers of the Federal army, directed by a sergeant who in civil life may have been a deputy sheriff. At a short remove upon the same temporary platform was an officer in the uniform of his rank, armed. He was a captain. A sentinel at each end of the bridge stood with his rifle in the position known as "support," that is to say, vertical in front of the left shoulder, the hammer resting on the forearm thrown straight across the chest—a formal and unnatural position, enforcing an erect carriage of the body. It did not appear to be the duty of these two men to know what was occurring at the center of the bridge; they merely blockaded the two ends of the foot planking that traversed it.

Beyond one of the sentinels nobody was in sight; the railroad ran straight away into a forest for a hundred yards, then, curving, was lost to view. Doubtless there was an outpost farther along. The other bank of the stream was open ground—a gentle acclivity topped with a stockade of vertical tree trunks, loopholed for rifles, with a single embrasure through which protruded the muzzle of a brass cannon commanding the bridge.

Midway of the slope between the bridge and fort were the spectators—a single company of infantry in line, at "parade rest," the butts of the rifles on the ground, the barrels inclining slightly backward against the right shoulder, the hands crossed upon the stock. A lieutenant stood at the right of the line, the point of his sword upon the ground, his left hand resting upon his right. Excepting the group of four at the center of the bridge, not a man moved. The company faced the bridge, staring stonily, motionless. The sentinels, facing the banks of the stream, might have been statues to adorn the bridge. The captain stood with folded arms, silent, observing the work of his subordinates, but making no sign. Death is a dignitary who when he comes announced is to be received with formal manifestations of respect, even by those most familiar with him. In the code of military etiquette silence and fixity are forms of deference.

The man who was engaged in being hanged was apparently about thirty-five years of age. He was a civilian, if one might judge from his habit, which was that of a planter. His features were good—a straight nose, firm mouth, broad forehead, from which his long, dark hair was combed straight back, falling behind his ears to the collar of his well-fitting frock coat. He wore a mustache and pointed beard, but no whiskers; his eyes were large and dark gray, and had a kindly expression which one would hardly have expected in one whose neck was in the hemp. Evidently this was no vulgar assassin. The liberal military code makes provision for hanging many kinds of persons, and gentlemen are not excluded.

The preparations being complete, the two private soldiers stepped aside and each drew away the plank upon which he had been standing. The sergeant turned to the captain, saluted and placed himself immediately behind that officer, who in turn moved apart one pace. These movements left the condemned man and the sergeant standing on the two ends of the same plank, which spanned three of the crossties of the bridge. The end upon which the civilian stood almost, but not quite, reached a fourth. This plank had been held in place by the weight of the captain; it was now held by that of the sergeant. At a signal from the former the latter would step aside, the plank would tilt and the condemned man go down between two ties. The arrangement commended itself to his judgment as simple and effective. His face had not been covered nor his eyes bandaged. He looked a moment at his "unsteadfast footing," then let his gaze wander to the swirling water of the stream racing madly beneath his feet. A piece of dancing driftwood caught his attention and his eyes followed it down the current. How slowly it appeared to move! What a sluggish stream!

He closed his eyes in order to fix his last thoughts upon his wife and children. The water, touched to gold by the early sun, the brooding mists under the banks at some distance down the stream, the fort, the soldiers, the piece of drift—all had distracted him. And now he became conscious of a new disturbance. Striking through the thought of his dear ones was a sound which he could neither ignore nor understand, a sharp, distinct, metallic percussion like the stroke of a blacksmith's hammer upon the anvil; it had the same ringing quality. He wondered what it was, and whether immeasurably distant or near by—it seemed both. Its recurrence was regular, but as slow as the tolling of a death knell. He awaited each stroke with impatience and—he knew not why—apprehension. The intervals of silence grew progressively longer; the delays became maddening. With their greater infrequency the sounds increased in strength and sharpness. They hurt his ear like the thrust of a knife; he feared he would shriek. What he heard was the ticking of his watch.

He unclosed his eyes and saw again the water below him. "If I could free my hands," he thought, "I might throw off the noose and spring into the stream. By diving I could evade the bullets and, swimming vigorously, reach the bank, take to the woods and get away home. My home, thank God, is as yet outside their lines; my wife and little ones are still beyond the invader's farthest advance."

As these thoughts, which have here to be set down in words, were flashed into the doomed man's brain rather than evolved from it the captain nodded to the sergeant. The sergeant stepped aside.

Peyton Farquhar was a well-to-do planter, of an old and highly respected Alabama family. Being a slave owner and like other slave owners a politician, he was naturally an original secessionist and ardently devoted to the Southern cause. Circumstances of an imperious nature, which it is unnecessary to relate here, had prevented him from taking service with the gallant army that had fought the disastrous campaigns ending with the fall of Corinth, and he chafed under the inglorious restraint, longing for the release of his energies, the larger life of the soldier, the opportunity for distinction. That opportunity, he felt, would come, as it comes to all in war time. Meanwhile he did what he could. No service was too humble for him to perform in aid of the South, no adventure too perilous for him to undertake if consistent with the character of a civilian who was at heart a soldier, and who in good faith and without too much qualification assented to at least a part of the frankly villainous dictum that all is fair in love and war.

One evening while Farquhar and his wife were sitting on a rustic bench near the entrance to his grounds, a gray-clad soldier rode up to the gate and asked for a drink of water. Mrs. Farquhar was only too happy to serve him with her own white hands. While she was fetching the water her husband approached the dusty horseman and inquired eagerly for news from the front.

"The Yanks are repairing the railroads," said the man, "and are getting ready for another advance. They have reached the Owl Creek bridge, put it in order and built a stockade on the north bank. The commandant has issued an order, which is posted everywhere, declaring that any civilian caught interfering with the railroad, its bridges, tunnels or trains will be summarily hanged. I saw the order."

"How far is it to the Owl Creek bridge?" Farquhar asked.

"About thirty miles."

"Is there no force on this side of the creek?"

"Only a picket post half a mile out, on the railroad, and a single sentinel at this end of the bridge."

"Suppose a man—a civilian and student of hanging—should elude the picket post and perhaps get the better of the sentinel," said Farquhar, smiling, "what could he accomplish?"

The soldier reflected. "I was there a month ago," he replied. "I observed that the flood of last winter had lodged a great quantity of driftwood against the wooden pier at this end of the bridge. It is now dry and would burn like tow."

The lady had now brought the water, which the soldier drank. He thanked her ceremoniously, bowed to her husband and rode away. An hour later, after nightfall, he re-passed the plantation, going northward in the direction from which he had come. He was a Federal scout.

As Peyton Farquhar fell straight downward through the bridge he lost consciousness and was as one already dead. From this state he was awakened—ages later, it seemed to him—by the pain of a sharp pressure up his throat, followed by a sense of suffocation. Keen, poignant agonies seemed to shoot from his neck downward through every fiber of his body and limbs. These pains appeared to flash along well-defined lines of ramification and to beat with an inconceivably rapid periodicity. They seemed like streams of pulsating fire heating him to an intolerable temperature. As to his head, he was conscious of nothing but a feeling of fullness—of congestion. These sensations were unaccompanied by thought. The intellectual part of his nature was already effaced; he had power only to feel, and feeling was torment. He was conscious of motion. Encompassed in a luminous cloud, of which he was now merely the fiery heart, without material substance, he swung through unthinkable arcs of oscillation, like a vast pendulum. Then all at once, with terrible suddenness, the light about him shot upward with the noise of a loud splash; a frightful roaring was in his ears, and all was cold and dark. The power of thought was restored; he knew that the rope had broken and he had fallen into the stream. There was no additional strangulation; the noose about his neck was already suffocating him and kept the water from his lungs. To die of hanging at the bottom of a river!—the idea seemed to him ludicrous. He opened his eyes in the darkness and saw above him a gleam of light, but how distant, how inaccessible! He was still sinking, for the light became fainter and fainter until it was a mere glimmer. Then it began to grow and brighten, and he knew that he was rising toward the surface—knew it with reluctance, for he was now very comfortable. "To be hanged and drowned," he thought, "that is not so bad; but I do not wish to be shot. No; I will not be shot; that is not fair."

He was not conscious of an effort, but a sharp pain in his wrist apprised him that he was trying to free his hands. He gave the struggle his attention, as an idler might observe the feat of a juggler, without interest in the outcome. What splendid effort! What magnificent, what superhuman strength! Ah, that was a fine endeavor! Bravo! The cord fell away; his arms parted and floated upward, the hands dimly seen on each side in the growing light. He watched them with a new interest as first one and then the other pounced upon the noose at his neck. They tore it away and thrust it fiercely aside, its undulations resembling those of a water snake. "Put it back, put it back!" He thought he shouted these words to his hands, for the undoing of the noose had been succeeded by the direst pang that he had yet experienced. His neck ached horribly; his brain was on fire; his heart, which had been fluttering faintly, gave a great leap, trying to force itself out at his mouth. His whole body was racked and wrenched with an insupportable anguish! But his disobedient hands gave no heed to the command. They beat the water vigorously with quick, downward strokes, forcing him to the surface. He felt his head emerge; his eyes were blinded by the sunlight; his chest expanded convulsively, and with a supreme and crowning agony his lungs engulfed a great draught of air, which instantly he expelled in a shriek!

He was now in full possession of his physical senses. They were, indeed, preternaturally keen and alert. Something in the awful disturbance of his organic system had so exalted and refined them that they made record of things never before perceived. He felt the ripples upon his face and heard their separate sounds as they struck. He looked at the forest on the bank of the stream, saw the individual trees, the leaves and the veining of each leaf—saw the very insects upon them: the locusts, the brilliant-bodied flies, the gray spiders stretching their webs from twig to twig. He noted the prismatic colors in all the dew-drops upon a million blades of grass. The humming of the gnats that danced above the eddies of the stream, the beating of the dragonflies' wings, the strokes of the water spiders' legs, like oars which had lifted their boat—all these made audible music. A fish slid along beneath his eyes and he heard the rush of its body parting the water.

He had come to the surface facing down the stream; in a moment the visible world seemed to wheel slowly round, himself the pivotal point, and he saw the bridge, the fort, the soldiers upon the bridge, the captain, the sergeant, the two privates, his executioners. They were in silhouette against the blue sky. They shouted and gesticulated, pointing at him. The captain had drawn his pistol, but did not fire; the others were unarmed. Their movements were grotesque and horrible, their forms gigantic.

Suddenly he heard a sharp report and something struck the water smartly within a few inches of his head, spattering his face with spray. He heard a second report, and saw one of the sentinels with his rifle at his shoulder, a light cloud of blue smoke rising from the muzzle. The man in the water saw the eye of the man on the bridge gazing into his own through the sights of the rifle. He observed that it was a gray eye and remembered having read that gray eyes were keenest, and that all famous marksmen had them. Nevertheless, this one had missed.

A counter-swirl had caught Farquhar and turned him half round; he was again looking into the forest on the bank opposite the fort. The sound of a clear, high voice in a monotonous singsong now rang out behind him and came across the water with a distinctness that pierced and subdued all other sounds, even the beating of the ripples in his ears. Although no soldier, he had frequented camps enough to know the dread significance of that deliberate, drawling, aspirated chant, the lieutenant on shore was taking a part in the morning's work. How coldly and pitilessly—with what an even, calm intonation, presaging, and enforcing tranquillity in the men—with what accurately measured intervals fell those cruel words:

"Attention, company! . . . Shoulder arms! . . . Ready! . . . Aim! . . . Fire!"

Farquhar dived—dived as deeply as he could. The water roared in his ears like the voice of Niagara, yet he heard the dulled thunder of the volley and, rising again toward the surface, met shining bits of metal, singularly flattened, oscillating slowly downward. Some of them touched him on the face and hands, then fell away, continuing their descent. One lodged between his collar and neck; it was uncomfortably warm and he snatched it out.

As he rose to the surface, gasping for breath, he saw that he had been a long time under water; he was perceptibly farther down stream—nearer to safety. The soldiers had almost finished reloading; the metal ramrods flashed all at once in the sunshine as they were drawn from the barrels, turned in the air, and thrust into their sockets. The two sentinels fired again, independently and ineffectually.

The hunted man saw all this over his shoulder; he was now swimming vigorously with the current. His brain was as energetic as his arms and legs; he thought with the rapidity of lightning.

"The officer," he reasoned, "will not make that martinet's error a second time. It is as easy to dodge a volley as a single shot. He has probably already given the command to fire at will. God help me, I cannot dodge them all!"

An appalling splash within two yards of him was followed by a loud, rushing sound, *diminuendo*, which seemed to travel back through the air to the fort and died in an explosion which stirred the very river to its deeps! A rising sheet of water curved over him, fell down upon him.

blinded him, strangled him! The cannon had taken a hand in the game. As he shook his head free from the commotion of the smitten water he heard the deflected shot humming through the air ahead, and in an instant it was cracking and smashing the branches in the forest beyond.

"They will not do that again," he thought; "the next time they will use a charge of grape. I must keep my eye upon the gun; the smoke will apprise me—the report arrives too late; it lags behind the missile. That is a good gun."

Suddenly he felt himself whirled round and round—spinning like a top. The water, the banks, the forests, the now distant bridge, fort and men —all were commingled and blurred. Objects were represented by their colors only; circular horizontal streaks of color—that was all he saw. He had been caught in a vortex and was being whirled on with a velocity of advance and gyration that made him giddy and sick. In a few moments he was flung upon the gravel at the foot of the left bank of the stream— the southern bank—and behind a projecting point which concealed him from his enemies. The sudden arrest of his motion, the abrasion of one of his hands on the gravel, restored him, and he wept with delight. He dug his fingers into the sand, threw it over himself in handfuls and audibly blessed it. It looked like diamonds, rubies, emeralds; he could think of nothing beautiful which it did not resemble. The trees upon the bank were giant garden plants; he noted a definite order in their arrangement, in- haled the fragrance of their blooms. A strange, roseate light shone through the spaces among their trunks and the wind made in their branches the music of Aeolian harps. He had no wish to perfect his escape—was content to remain in that enchanting spot until retaken.

A whiz and rattle of grapeshot among the branches high above his head roused him from his dream. The baffled cannoneer had fired him a random farewell. He sprang to his feet, rushed up the sloping bank, and plunged into the forest.

All that day he traveled, laying his course by the rounding sun. The forest seemed interminable; nowhere did he discover a break in it, not even a woodman's road. He had not known that he lived in so wild a region. There was something uncanny in the revelation.

By nightfall he was fatigued, footsore, famishing. The thought of his wife and children urged him on. At last he found a road which led him in what he knew to be the right direction. It was as wide and straight as a city street, yet it seemed untraveled. No fields bordered it, no dwelling any- where. Not so much as the barking of a dog suggested human habitation. The black bodies of the trees forced a straight wall on both sides, termi- nating on the horizon in a point, like a diagram in a lesson in perspective. Overhead, as he looked up through this rift in the wood, shone great golden stars looking unfamiliar and grouped in strange constellations. He was sure they were arranged in some order which had a secret and malign sig-

nificance. The wood on either side was full of singular noises, among which
—once, twice, and again—he distinctly heard whispers in an unknown
tongue.

His neck was in pain and lifting his hand to it he found it horribly
swollen. He knew that it had a circle of black where the rope had bruised
it. His eyes felt congested; he could no longer close them. His tongue was
swollen with thirst; he relieved its fever by thrusting it forward from between his teeth into the cold air. How softly the turf had carpeted the untraveled avenue—he could no longer feel the roadway beneath his feet!

Doubtless, despite his suffering, he had fallen asleep while walking,
for now he sees another scene—perhaps he has merely recovered from a
delirium. He stands at the gate of his own home. All is as he left it, and
all bright and beautiful in the morning sunshine. He must have traveled
the entire night. As he pushes open the gate and passes up the wide white
walk, he sees a flutter of female garments; his wife, looking fresh and cool
and sweet, steps down from the veranda to meet him. At the bottom of
the steps she stands waiting, with a smile of ineffable joy, an attitude of
matchless grace and dignity. Ah, how beautiful she is! He springs forward
with extended arms. As he is about to clasp her he feels a stunning blow
upon the back of the neck; a blinding white light blazes all about him with
a sound like the shock of a cannon—then all is darkness and silence!

Peyton Farquhar was dead; his body, with a broken neck, swung
gently from side to side beneath the timbers of the Owl Creek bridge.

INTERPRETATION

This story, like "The Necklace" and "The Furnished Room," involves a surprise ending, an ironical turn. The basic question, then, which
the story raises is this: Is the surprise ending justified; is it validated by the
body of the story; is it, in other words, a mere trick, or is it expressive and
functional?

Perhaps the best way to clear the ground for a consideration of this
basic question is to raise another question which no doubt will occur to
many readers of the story. Is it possible for a man in the last moment of
his life to have a vision of the sort which Farquhar has as he falls from the
bridge? Many people may be inclined to judge the story in terms of their
acceptance or rejection of the psychological realism of this incident. But
is it possible to have absolutely convincing evidence on this point? Isn't
the fact of the vision something which, in itself, can be accepted without
too much strain on the reader's credulity? But there is a much more important consideration to be taken into account. Even if we could arrive at
a completely satisfying decision about the psychological realism of the
incident, would this fact actually determine the nature of our judgment
concerning the story? For reasons to be suggested below, it would not

determine our judgment, and therefore preoccupation with this question is likely to prove a red herring—is likely to distract us from the real problem.

Suppose that we assume for the moment that the incident is psychologically valid; there remain these questions to be answered:

1. Why does the author withhold from the reader the knowledge that the dying man's vision is merely a vision?
2. Is any revelation of character accomplished thereby?
3. Does the withholding of this information throw any light on the development of a theme for the story?
4. There is an irony generated by the end of the story, but is it a meaningful irony?

What we are leading up to by means of these questions is this:

Fiction is concerned with people, and one of the interests we take in it arises from the presentation of human character and human experience as merely human. Both the common and the uncommon human character or experience interest us, the common because we share in it, and the uncommon because it wakes us to marvel at new possibilities. But it is a great—and not uncommon—error to equate the presentation of character as such, or experience as such, with the specific meaning of fiction. Fiction, as we have tried to indicate in our first section, involves a theme, an idea, an interpretation, an attitude toward life developed and embodied in the piece of fiction. Directly or indirectly, through the experience of the characters in the piece of fiction, an evaluation is made—an evaluation which is assumed to have some claim to a general validity.

The plot that depends on some peculiarity of human psychology—as does "An Occurrence at Owl Creek Bridge"—may give as a shock of surprise, but it does not carry a fictional meaning. The peculiar quirk of psychology—the "case study"—must also involve some significant human evaluation, some broadening or deepening of our human attitudes, if it is to be acceptable as fiction. Fiction involves all kinds of human characters and human experiences, common and uncommon, but it is concerned to do more than make a clinical report, medical or psychological. We must keep this firmly in mind.

EUDORA WELTY

A Piece of News

SHE had been out in the rain. She
stood in front of the cabin fireplace, her legs wide apart, bending over,
shaking her wet yellow head crossly, like a cat reproaching itself for not
knowing better. She was talking to herself—only a small fluttering sound,
hard to lay hold of in the sparsity of the room.

"The pouring-down rain, the pouring-down rain"—was that what she
was saying over and over, like a song? She stood turning in little quarter
turns to dry herself, her head bent forward and the yellow hair hanging
out streaming and tangled. She was holding her skirt primly out to draw
the warmth in.

Then, quite rosy, she walked over to the table and picked up a little
bundle. It was a sack of coffee, marked "sample" in red letters, which she
unwrapped from a wet newspaper. But she handled it tenderly.

"Why, how come he wrapped it in a newspaper!" she said, catching
her breath, looking from one hand to the other. She must have been lonesome and slow all her life, the way things would take her by surprise.

She set the coffee on the table, just in the center. Then she dragged
the newspaper by one corner in a dreamy walk across the floor, spread it
all out, and lay down full length on top of it in front of the fire. Her little
song about the rain, her cries of surprise, had been only a preliminary,
only playful pouting with which she amused herself when she was alone.
She was pleased with herself now. As she sprawled close to the fire, her
hair began to slide out of its damp tangles and hung all displayed down her
back like a piece of bargain silk. She closed her eyes. Her mouth fell into
a deepness, into a look of unconscious cunning. Yet in her very stillness
and pleasure she seemed to be hiding there, all alone. And at moments
when the fire stirred and tumbled in the grate, she would tremble, and her
hand would start out as if in impatience or despair.

Presently she stirred and reached under her back for the newspaper.
Then she squatted there, touching the printed page as if it were fragile.
She did not merely look at it—she watched it, as if it were unpredictable,
like a young girl watching a baby. The paper was still wet in places where
her body had lain. Crouching tensely and patting the creases away with
small cracked red fingers, she frowned now and then at the blotched draw-

ing of something and big letters that spelled a word underneath. Her lips trembled, as if looking and spelling so slowly had stirred her heart.

All at once she laughed.

She looked up.

"Ruby Fisher!" she whispered.

An expression of utter timidity came over her flat blue eyes and her soft mouth. Then a look of fright. She stared about. . . . What eye in the world did she feel looking in on her? She pulled her dress down tightly and began to spell through a dozen words in the newspaper.

The little item said:

"Mrs. Ruby Fisher had the misfortune to be shot in the leg by her husband this week."

As she passed from one word to the next she only whispered; she left the long word, "misfortune," until the last, and came back to it, then she said it all over out loud, like conversation.

"That's me," she said softly, with deference, very formally.

The fire slipped and suddenly roared in the house already deafening with the rain which beat upon the roof and hung full of lightning and thunder outside.

"You Clyde!" screamed Ruby Fisher at last, jumping to her feet. "Where are you, Clyde Fisher?"

She ran straight to the door and pulled it open. A shudder of cold brushed over her in the heat, and she seemed striped with anger and bewilderment. There was a flash of lightning, and she stood waiting, as if she half thought that would bring him in, a gun leveled in his hands.

She said nothing more and, backing against the door, pushed it closed with her hip. Her anger passed like a remote flare of elation. Neatly avoiding the table where the bag of coffee stood, she began to walk nervously about the room, as if a teasing indecision, an untouched mystery, led her by the hand. There was one window, and she paused now and then, waiting, looking out at the rain. When she was still, there was a passivity about her, or a deception of passivity, that was not really passive at all. There was something in her that never stopped.

At last she flung herself onto the floor, back across the newspaper, and looked at length into the fire. It might have been a mirror in the cabin, into which she could look deeper and deeper as she pulled her fingers through her hair, trying to see herself and Clyde coming up behind her.

"Clyde?"

But of course her husband, Clyde, was still in the woods. He kept a thick brushwood roof over his whisky still, and he was mortally afraid of lightning like this, and would never go out in it for anything.

And then, almost in amazement, she began to comprehend her predicament: it was unlike Clyde to take up a gun and shoot her.

She bowed her head toward the heat, onto her rosy arms, and began to talk and talk to herself. She grew voluble. Even if he heard about the coffee man, with a Pontiac car, she did not think he would shoot her. When Clyde would make her blue, she would go out onto the road, some car would slow down, and if it had a Tennessee license, the lucky kind, the chances were that she would spend the afternoon in the shed of the empty gin. (Here she rolled her head about on her arms and stretched her legs tiredly behind her, like a cat.) And if Clyde got word, he would slap her. But the account in the paper was wrong. Clyde had never shot her, even once. There had been a mistake made.

A spark flew out and nearly caught the paper on fire. Almost in fright she beat it out with her fingers. Then she murmured and lay back more firmly upon the pages.

There she stretched, growing warmer and warmer, sleepier and sleepier. She began to wonder out loud how it would be if Clyde shot her in the leg. . . . If he were truly angry, might he shoot her through the heart?

At once she was imagining herself dying. She would have a nightgown to lie in, and a bullet in her heart. Anyone could tell, to see her lying there with that deep expression about her mouth, how strange and terrible that would be. Underneath a brand-new nightgown her heart would be hurting with every beat, many times more than her toughened skin when Clyde slapped at her. Ruby began to cry softly, the way she would be crying from the extremity of pain; tears would run down in a little stream over the quilt. Clyde would be standing there above her, as he once looked, with his wild black hair hanging to his shoulders. He used to be very handsome and strong!

He would say, "Ruby, I done this to you."

She would say—only a whisper—"That is the truth, Clyde—you done this to me."

Then she would die; her life would stop right there.

She lay silently for a moment, composing her face into a look which would be beautiful, desirable, and dead.

Clyde would have to buy her a dress to bury her in. He would have to dig a deep hole behind the house, under the cedar, a grave. He would have to nail her up a pine coffin and lay her inside. Then he would have to carry her to the grave, lay her down and cover her up. All the time he would be wild, shouting, and all distracted, to think he could never touch her one more time.

She moved slightly, and her eyes turned toward the window. The white rain splashed down. She could hardly breathe, for thinking that this was the way it was to fall on her grave, where Clyde would come and stand, looking down in the tears of some repentance.

A whole tree of lightning stood in the sky. She kept looking out the window, suffused with the warmth from the fire and with the pity and beauty and power of her death. The thunder rolled.

Then Clyde was standing there, with dark streams flowing over the floor where he had walked. He poked at Ruby with the butt of his gun, as if she were asleep.

"What's keepin' supper?" he growled.

She jumped up and darted away from him. Then, quicker than lightning, she put away the paper. The room was dark, except for the firelight. From the long shadow of his steamy presence she spoke to him glibly and lighted the lamp.

He stood there with a stunned, yet rather good-humored look of delay and patience in his face, and kept on standing there. He stamped his mud-red boots, and his enormous hands seemed weighted with the rain that fell from him and dripped down the barrel of the gun. Presently he sat down with dignity in the chair at the table, making a little tumult of his rightful wetness and hunger. Small streams began to flow from him everywhere.

Ruby was going through the preparations for the meal gently. She stood almost on tiptoe in her bare, warm feet. Once as she knelt at the safe, getting out the biscuits, she saw Clyde looking at her and she smiled and bent her head tenderly. There was some way she began to move her arms that was mysteriously sweet and yet abrupt and tentative, a delicate and vulnerable manner, as though her breasts gave her pain. She made many unnecessary trips back and forth across the floor, circling Clyde where he sat in his steamy silence, a knife and fork in his fists.

"Well, where you been, anyway?" he grumbled at last, as she set the first dish on the table.

"Nowheres special."

"Don't you talk back to me. You been hitchhikin' again, ain't you?" He almost chuckled.

She gave him a quick look straight into his eyes. She had not even heard him. She was filled with happiness. Her hand trembled when she poured the coffee. Some of it splashed on his wrist.

At that he let his hand drop heavily down upon the table and made the plates jump.

"Some day I'm goin' to smack the livin' devil outa you," he said.

Ruby dodged mechanically. She let him eat. Then, when he had crossed his knife and fork over his plate, she brought him the newspaper. Again she looked at him in delight. It excited her even to touch the paper with her hand, to hear its quiet secret noise when she carried it, the rustle of surprise.

"A newspaper!" Clyde snatched it roughly and with a grabbing disparagement. "Where'd you git that? Hussy."

"Look at this-here," said Ruby in her small singsong voice. She opened the paper while he held it and pointed gravely to the paragraph.

Reluctantly, Clyde began to read it. She watched his damp bald head slowly bend and turn.

Then he made a sound in his throat and said, "It's a lie."

"That's what's in the newspaper about me," said Ruby, standing up straight. She took up his plate and gave him that look of joy.

He put his big crooked finger on the paragraph and poked at it.

"Well, I'd just like to see the place I shot you!" he cried explosively. He looked up, his face blank and bold.

But she drew herself in, still holding the empty plate, faced him straightened and hard, and they looked at each other. The moment filled full with their helplessness. Slowly they both flushed, as though with a double shame and a double pleasure. It was as though Clyde might really have killed Ruby, and as though Ruby might really have been dead at his hand. Rare and wavering, some possibility stood timidly like a stranger between them and made them hang their heads.

Then Clyde walked over in his water-soaked boots and laid the paper on the dying fire. It floated there a moment and then burst into flame. They stood still and watched it burn. The whole room was bright.

"Look," said Clyde suddenly. "It's a Tennessee paper. See 'Tennessee'? That wasn't none of you it wrote about." He laughed, to show that he had been right all the time.

"It was Ruby Fisher!" cried Ruby. "My name is Ruby Fisher!" she declared passionately to Clyde.

"Oho, it was another Ruby Fisher—in Tennessee," cried her husband. "Fool me, huh? Where'd you get that paper?" He spanked her good-humoredly across her backside.

Ruby folded her still trembling hands into her skirt. She stood stooping by the window until everything, outside and in, was quieted before she went to her supper.

It was dark and vague outside. The storm had rolled away to faintness like a wagon crossing a bridge.

INTERPRETATION

At first glance this story may seem to be no story at all—merely a trivial incident, which is meaningless except as it may provoke our amuse-ment: an all but illiterate girl happens, quite by accident, to come upon a newspaper story in which a girl with the same name as hers is shot by her husband. She goes off into a reverie in which she imagines that she has been shot by her own husband—imagines that she is really the girl of the newspaper story. This reverie is interrupted by the return of her husband, who reads the account, is for his own part momentarily shocked by the coincidence of names, but with an overriding common sense, throws the newspaper into the fire, and dismisses the incident.

Even the reader who tries to deal with the story sympathetically, who knows, for instance, the authority which the written word carries for many simple people, and who is willing to believe that the coincidence of names might really provoke in the simple girl the action ascribed to her in this story—even such a reader might feel that the story was finally pointless. That is, even if we feel that the motivation of the characters in the story is sound, we still may not be convinced that the story has a "meaning" apart from its humorous commentary on the psychology of simple and primitive folk.

The story does have a meaning, but the author has been careful to dramatize it for us in terms of the action. Perhaps the most fruitful approach to a discussion of the meaning will take into account the dramatic, though gradual, presentation of this meaning.

In the first place, the girl and her husband, Ruby and Clyde, are isolated from the world which we know. Clyde Fisher keeps a still. He is an outlaw, and is properly suspicious of strangers. He and his wife live in a world which reverses most of the conventions of the ordinary world: it is a world in which, for example, guns are common and newspapers uncommon—mention in newspapers, least common of all.

Ruby, as the story opens, has just made a visit to that outside world, to get the sack of coffee. She comes back with the chance-acquired newspaper. Now that she is back inside her own house, the storm builds up the sense of her isolation. The storm has soaked her, and thus accounts for her idling over the newspaper before the fire; with its lightning and thunder, the storm supplies a background for the excited imaginings that possess her. But Miss Welty's use of the natural background is modest, probable, and subdued: the background remains background, yet contributes to the story.

The background helps to create the atmosphere of the story, by which we mean the general feeling that seems inherent in the materials themselves or in the way they are treated. For instance, in Poe's celebrated story, "The Fall of the House of Usher," we speak of the atmosphere of horror, as we may speak of the sunny, cheerful atmosphere of another story. Our general words for describing the atmosphere of a story are relatively few, and often metaphorical, as though we had to appeal to metaphor to make up for the poverty of the language available to us for this purpose. We say horrible, terrible, gay, sunny, cheerful, depressing, morbid, dank, dreamy, mysterious, cold, and so on, but we recognize how inadequate such terms are to describe and discriminate among the great variety and the subtle variations of atmosphere which we find in fiction. The good story is apt to carry with it a certain "feel" which eludes our general descriptions but which we recognize as being essential and meaningful in the story. It is the atmosphere, we may say metaphorically, in which the story can breathe and live.

Though background, feeling, and atmosphere are important in varying degrees in all fiction (no story can exist in a vacuum) this element is more important in some stories than others. In "A Piece of News," we realize that the world in which Ruby Fisher lives is, as we have said, immediately important for the story—much more immediately important, for instance, than the world in which Michael and Frances encounter their dilemma in "The Girls in Their Summer Dresses." Factually, as we have said, it is a world where the newspaper has some magical significance. It is an isolated world, isolated by Clyde's outlawry, by ignorance, by poverty, by distance from the ordinary world. It is also a world in which Ruby moves in a dream divorced from ordinary reality, from ordinary moral standards, locked in her loneliness, humming her little songs to herself, in the monotony of her life breaking out, now and then, to the highway and the sordid adventures of the gin house, or into her dreamy musings, both the adventures of the gin house and those of the musings being somehow innocent, or merely childish—as even Clyde, who might slap her good and hard, but would never shoot her, instinctively recognizes. It is a world of dreaminess, of the mysterious confusions of dreams. How does the writer create this atmosphere for us?

The writer does, as a matter of fact, give us the words *dreamy, mystery, mysteriously*. A cruder writer might have insisted on such words, and have exhorted us, by the their use, to notice and appreciate the effect being created. But here the words are casually absorbed into the body of the story. Ruby drags the newspaper "by one corner in a dreamy walk across the floor," and the dreaminess appears as natural to the specific act, the childish handling of the newspaper, the drifting aimlessness of the walk, and not as a direct comment on the atmosphere. It does, of course, do its work in helping to create the atmosphere, but primarily because it is an accurate description of the act, and not by definition of the atmosphere as such.

To take another example, later in the story, after Clyde has come home and Ruby is getting supper ready, we find the sentence: "There was some way she began to move her arms that was mysteriously sweet and yet abrupt and tentative, a delicate and vulnerable manner, as though her breasts gave her pain." A mysterious thing is indeed happening here: we may say that the daydream Ruby has had of herself as caught in a violent, dramatic, and pitifully sweet experience now overlaps back on real life and she feels the ordinary events and her old relation with Clyde touched by sweetness and romance. Because of the daydream, actuality has become mysteriously rich, full, and sweet. But here again we see that the writer has used the general word as tied to a specific moment; in the end it may also work toward a comment and an interpretation, but it does not come directly to us at that level.

We have seen that the words generally descriptive of the atmosphere are absorbed into the story itself. We could, in fact, dispense entirely with them, so strongly and subtly has the writer created her atmosphere. The girl's talking to herself with the little rhythmic sing-song, her shaking her yellow wet hair crossly "like a cat reproaching itself for not knowing better" than to get wet, her "playful pouting with which she amused herself when . . . alone," the "deepness" of her mouth, the impersonal crashes and flashes of the storm and the rain "hung full of lightning and thunder," the cat-like stretching as she thinks of the gin house, her sweet, sensual self-pitying sleepiness as she thinks of being shot and dying and of Clyde weeping over her grave in the rain—all these things *are* the world, are the atmosphere, of the story. We don't need to describe it, for it exists and does its work upon us by the vividness with which the writer has realized them. And so we begin to understand that that story itself, the events, the very plot, could not exist except in this world, in this atmosphere, for, as we shall see, the story is about an adventure in dream and the return to reality. That is the plot.

To return to the sequence of events in the story itself, we find that Ruby, who "must have been lonesome and slow all her life," is first surprised when she sees her name, surprised and even delighted as a child is delighted. But her next reaction is fright: "What eye in the world did she feel looking in on her?" The isolation has been penetrated. She "pulled her dress down tightly"—as if her modesty were being violated.

The reader soon guesses the common-sense explanation of the matter —the explanation which after a few moments occurs to the husband Clyde when he comes in: the newspaper is referring to another Mrs. Ruby Fisher. But this is not the explanation which occurs in her bewilderment to the girl. The author, however, is not anxious to convince us of the strained and improbable psychology involved in the girl's belief that the newspaper account is true. The girl knows really that it is not true. She even reasons out to herself the impossibility of its being true; Clyde wouldn't do that. Indeed, there had been occasions which might have provoked a husband to shoot his wife, but Clyde had never shot her. Even if she told him about the coffee salesman, Clyde would only strike her—he wouldn't shoot her. But the line which the author has Ruby take in arguing against the impossibility of the action suggests another motive which works against her making a realistic and common-sense dismissal of the newspaper story. It is exciting to imagine herself shot by Clyde—to imagine a Clyde who would shoot her. And after he had shot her, what would she be like, and what would he say, and do? The coincidence of names has stirred her imagination. It allows her—indeed, has seemed to force upon her—a new focus of attention in terms of which both she and Clyde take on new perspectives to each other. By being seen in a new role—reading about "herself" in the newspaper—she takes on the new role; she becomes somehow a stranger to her husband. Even her own body becomes something strange and new to her: "There was some way she began to move her arms that was mysteriously sweet and yet abrupt and tentative. . . ." Throughout the reverie she thinks of herself in a nightgown ("She would have a nightgown to lie in . . .") like a bride.

This sense of illumination in which old and familiar things, by acquiring an altered focus, become mysterious and strange, is a recurrent theme in fiction as it is a basic fact in human existence. A shocking and surprising incident, an emotional crisis, may very well force on us such an alteration of focus. For a person who lives in a surburban world, say, where newspapers and electrical toastmakers are familiar, and guns and whisky stills unfamiliar, such an alteration would hardly be effected by the coincidence of names in a scrap of newspaper. But the fact of the experience is universal. In this story, it comes about in terms consonant with the characters depicted in the story and with their situation, and the accident which brings it about for them is a—to us, ironically—trivial incident.

Ruby's reverie is broken by Clyde's prodding her with the gun. His act is the impingement of common sense, the return to reality. But, ironically, the fact that Clyde stands there with the gun in his hand ties the reverie to the reality. For a moment, to the girl, it almost seems that the imagined situation will become real.

We have seen how concretely—and delicately—the theme is developed. Equally noteworthy is the way the author has played down the ending of the story. The effect of the revelation on both Clyde and Ruby is given quietly, almost by suggestion.

1. Analyze the character of Clyde in relation to the ending of the story.

2. How is coincidence used in this story: is it used to set up the problem of the story or to solve the problem of the story?

3. In this story there is a good deal of interpenetration of exposition and complication. Indicate some of this. Has this fluid blurring of the line between exposition and complication any relation to the general atmosphere of the story and the character of Ruby?

4. Compare the different ways used to create atmosphere here with those used in "The Furnished Room." Is there, furthermore, any difference in the purposes for which the atmosphere is used?

5. In the middle of "A Piece of News" (the paragraph beginning, "She said nothing more, and backing against the door . . . ."), we find the third use of a general word descriptive of the atmosphere of the story, in the sentence: "Neatly avoiding the table where the bag of coffee stood, she began to walk nervously about the room, as if a teasing indecision, an untouched mystery, led her by the hand." Is this instance as thoroughly

"absorbed" (see p. 130 above) as the other two discussed. Do you consider this instance justifiable?

6. Suppose John Collier had written a story about Ruby and the newspaper. On the basis of his story "De Mortuis," how do you imagine he might have ended it? What differences, then, would you expect in the atmosphere of the story?

7. "The Secret Life of Walter Mitty" is about the relation of dream and reality. What differences do you detect between that story and this. Both have comic, or humorous, elements, but is there a difference between them?

RAY BRADBURY

I See You Never

THE soft knock came at the kitchen door, and when Mrs. O'Brian opened it, there on the back porch were her best tenant, Mr. Ramirez, and two police officers, one on each side of him. Mr. Ramirez just stood there, walled in and small.

"Why, Mr. Ramirez!" said Mrs. O'Brian.

Mr. Ramirez was overcome. He did not seem to have words to explain.

He had arrived at Mrs. O'Brian's rooming house more than two years earlier and had lived there ever since. He had come by bus from Mexico City to San Diego and had then gone up to Los Angeles. There he had found the clean little room, with glossy blue linoleum, and pictures and calendars on the flowered walls, and Mrs. O'Brian as the strict but kindly landlady. During the war he had worked at the airplane factory and made parts for the planes that flew off somewhere, and even now, after the war, he still held his job. From the first he had made big money. He saved some of it, and he got drunk only once a week—a privilege that, to Mrs. O'Brian's way of thinking, every good workingman deserved, unquestioned and unreprimanded.

Inside Mrs. O'Brian's kitchen, pies were baking in the oven. Soon the pies would come out with complexions like Mr. Ramirez'—brown and shiny and crisp, with slits in them for the air almost like the slits of Mr. Ramirez' dark eyes. The kitchen smelled good. The policemen leaned forward, lured by the odor. Mr. Ramirez gazed at his feet, as if they had carried him into all this trouble.

"What happened, Mr. Ramirez?" asked Mrs. O'Brian.

Behind Mrs. O'Brian, as he lifted his eyes, Mr. Ramirez saw the long table laid with clean white linen and set with a platter, cool, shining glasses, a water pitcher with ice cubes floating inside it, a bowl of fresh potato salad and one of bananas and oranges, cubed and sugared. At this table sat Mrs. O'Brian's children—her three grown sons, eating and conversing, and her two younger daughters, who were staring at the policemen as they ate.

"I have been here thirty months," said Mr. Ramirez quietly, looking at Mrs. O'Brian's plump hands.

"That's six months too long," said one policeman. "He only had a temporary visa. We've just got around to looking for him."

Soon after Mr. Ramirez had arrived he bought a radio for his little room; evenings, he turned it up very loud and enjoyed it. And he bought a wrist watch and enjoyed that too. And on many nights he had walked silent streets and seen the bright clothes in the windows and bought some of them, and he had seen the jewels and bought some of them for his few lady friends. And he had gone to pictures shows five nights a week for a while. Then, also, he had ridden the streetcars—all night some nights—smelling the electricity, his dark eyes moving over the advertisements, feeling the wheels rumble under him, watching the little sleeping houses and big hotels slip by. Besides that, he had gone to large restaurants, where he had eaten many-course dinners, and to the opera and the theater. And he had bought a car, which later, when he forgot to pay for it, the dealer had driven off angrily from in front of the rooming house.

"So here I am," said Mr. Ramirez now, "to tell you I must give up my room, Mrs. O'Brian. I come to get my baggage and clothes and go with these men."

"Back to Mexico?"

"Yes. To Lagos. That is a little town north of Mexico City."

"I'm sorry, Mr. Ramirez."

"I'm packed," said Mr. Ramirez hoarsely, blinking his dark eyes rapidly and moving his hands helplessly before him. The policemen did not touch him. There was no necessity for that.

"Here is the key, Mrs. O'Brian," Mr. Ramirez said. "I have my bag already."

Mrs. O'Brian, for the first time, noticed a suitcase standing behind him on the porch.

Mr. Ramirez looked in again at the huge kitchen, at the bright silver cutlery and the young people eating and the shining waxed floor. He turned and looked for a long moment at the apartment house next door, rising up three stories, high and beautiful. He looked at the balconies and fire escapes and back-porch stairs, at the lines of laundry snapping in the wind.

"You've been a good tenant," said Mrs. O'Brian.

"Thank you, thank you, Mrs. O'Brian," he said softly. He closed his eyes.

Mrs. O'Brian stood holding the door half open. One of her sons, behind her, said that her dinner was getting cold, but she shook her head at him and turned back to Mr. Ramirez. She remembered a visit she had once made to some Mexican border towns—the hot days, the endless crickets leaping and falling or lying dead and brittle like the small cigars in the shopwindows, and the canals taking river water out to the farms, the dirt roads, the scorched landscape. She remembered the silent towns, the warm beer, the hot, thick foods each day. She remembered the slow, dragging horses and the parched jack rabbits on the road. She remembered the iron mountains and the dusty valleys and the ocean beaches that spread hundreds of miles with no sound but the waves—no cars, no buildings, nothing.

"I'm sure sorry, Mr. Ramirez," she said.

"I don't want to go back, Mrs. O'Brian," he said weakly. "I like it here, I want to stay here. I've worked, I've got money. I look all right, don't I? And I don't want to go back!"

"I'm sorry, Mr. Ramirez," she said. "I wish there was something I could do."

"Mrs. O'Brian!" he cried suddenly, tears rolling out from under his eyelids. He reached out his hands and took her hand fervently, shaking it, wringing it, holding to it. "Mrs. O'Brian, I see you never, I see you never!"

The policemen smiled at this, but Mr. Ramirez did not notice it, and they stopped smiling very soon.

"Good-by, Mrs. O'Brian. You have been good to me. Oh, good-by, Mrs. O'Brian. I see you never!"

The policemen waited for Mr. Ramirez to turn, pick up his suitcase, and walk away. Then they followed him, tipping their caps to Mrs. O'Brian. She watched them go down the porch steps. Then she shut the door quietly and went slowly back to her chair at the table. She pulled the chair out and sat down. She picked up the shining knife and fork and started once more upon her steak.

"Hurry up, Mom," said one of the sons. "It'll be cold."

Mrs. O'Brian took one bite and chewed on it for a long, slow time; then she stared at the closed door. She laid down her knife and fork.

"What's wrong, Ma?" asked her son.

"I just realized," said Mrs. O'Brian—she put her hand to her face—"I'll never see Mr. Ramirez again."

INTERPRETATION

1. This story, like "A Piece of News," has very little action, only a minimal plot. In fact, some readers might argue that it is not a story at all, a mere episode. One way to think of this problem would be to ask what is the point, the theme? Can you state it?

In thinking about this you should remember that "what happens" in a story may be only the growth of an awareness—a realization. It does not have to be an event out in the physical world. It is also well to remember that the awareness may be what comes both to a person in the story and to the reader, or merely to the reader, who, to speak metaphorically, sees over and beyond the characters in the story. For example, we see more of the meaning of Dravot's experience than does Peachey, who tells about it. (But do we see more than the newspaperman who tells about Peachey?) In the present story, "I See You Never," Mrs. O'Brian "realizes" something —and through her realization we come to the meaning of the story.

2. Let us suppose that Mrs. O'Brian were alone in her kitchen when the police bring Mr. Ramirez, and that as soon as he says, "I see you never," she bursts into tears and stands there watching him go away with the policemen. What difference would that make for the story? Would it make the story less of a story? Would there be less sense of conflict? If so, what is the nature of the conflict in the present version?

3. What kind of pattern, if any, do you detect in the complication here?

RING LARDNER

Haircut

I GOT another barber that comes over from Carterville and helps me out Saturdays, but the rest of the time I can get along all right alone. You can see for yourself that this ain't no New York City and besides that, the most of the boys works all day and don't have no leisure to drop in here and get themselves prettied up.

You're a newcomer, ain't you? I thought I hadn't seen you round before. I hope you like it good enough to stay. As I say, we ain't no New York City or Chicago, but we have pretty good times. Not as good, though, since Jim Kendall got killed. When he was alive, him and Hod Meyers used to keep this town in an uproar. I bet they was more laughin' done here than any town its size in America.

Jim was comical, and Hod was pretty near a match for him. Since Jim's gone, Hod tries to hold his end up just the same as ever, but it's tough goin' when you ain't got nobody to kind of work with.

They used to be plenty fun in here Saturdays. This place is jam-packed Saturdays, from four o'clock on. Jim and Hod would show up right after their supper round six o'clock. Jim would set himself down in that big chair, nearest the blue spitoon. Whoever had been settin' in that chair, why, they'd get up when Jim come in and give it to him.

You'd of thought it was a reserved seat like they have sometimes in a theaytre. Hod would generally always stand or walk up and down or some Saturdays, of course, he'd be settin' in this chair part of the time, gettin' a haircut.

Well, Jim would set there a w'ile without openin' his mouth only to spit, and then finally he'd say to me, "Whitey,"—my right name, that is, my right first name, is Dick, but everybody round here calls me Whitey—Jim would say, "Whitey, your nose looks like a rosebud tonight. You must of been drinkin' some of your aw de cologne."

So I'd say, "No, Jim, but you look like you'd been drinkin' somethin' of that kind or somethin' worse."

Jim would have to laugh at that, but then he'd speak up and say, "No, I ain't had nothin' to drink, but that ain't sayin' I wouldn't like somethin'. I wouldn't even mind if it was wood alcohol."

Then Hod Meyers would say, "Neither would your wife." That would set everybody to laughin' because Jim and his wife wasn't on very good terms. She'd of divorced him only they wasn't no chance to get alimony and she didn't have no way to take care of herself and the kids. She couldn't never understand Jim. He *was* kind of rough, but a good fella at heart.

Him and Hod had all kinds of sport with Milt Sheppard. I don't suppose you've seen Milt. Well, he's got an Adam's apple that looks more like a mushmelon. So I'd been shavin' Milt and when I'd start to shave down here on his neck, Hod would holler, "Hey, Whitey, wait a minute! Before you cut into it, let's make up a pool and see who can guess closest to the number of seeds."

And Jim would say, "If Milt hadn't of been so hoggish, he'd of ordered a half a cantaloupe instead of a whole one and it might not of stuck in his throat."

All the boys would roar at this and Milt himself would force a smile, though the joke was on him. Jim certainly was a card!

There's his shavin' mug, setting on the shelf, right next to Charley Vail's. "Charles M. Vail." That's the druggist. He comes in regular for his shave three times a week. And Jim's is the cup next to Charley's. "James H. Kendall." Jim won't need no shavin' mug no more, but I'll leave it there just the same for old time's sake. Jim certainly was a character!

Years ago, Jim used to travel for a canned goods concern over in Carterville. They sold canned goods. Jim had the whole northern half of the State and was on the road five days out of every week. He'd drop in here Saturdays and tell his experiences for that week. It was rich.

I guess he paid more attention to playin' jokes than makin' sales. Finally the concern let him out and he come right home here and told everybody he'd been fired instead of sayin' he'd resigned like most fellas would of

It was a Saturday and the shop was full and Jim got up out of that chair and says, "Gentlemen, I got an important announcement to make. I been fired from my job."

Well, they asked him if he was in earnest and he said he was and nobody could think of nothin' to say till Jim finally broke the ice himself. He says, "I been sellin' canned goods and now I'm canned goods myself."

You see, the concern he'd been workin' for was a factory that made canned goods. Over in Carterville. And now Jim said he was canned himself. He was certainly a card!

Jim had a great trick that he used to play w'ile he was travelin'. For instance, he'd be ridin' on a train and they'd come to some little town like, well, like, well, like, we'll say, like Benton. Jim would look out the train window and read the signs on the stores.

For instance, they'd be a sign, "Henry Smith, Dry Goods." Well, Jim would write down the name and the name of the town and when he got to wherever he was goin' he'd mail back a postal card to Henry Smith at Benton and not sign no name to it, but he'd write on the card, well, somethin' like "Ask your wife about that book agent that spent the afternoon last week," or "Ask your Missus who kept her from gettin' lonesome the last time you was in Carterville." And he'd sign the card, "A Friend."

Of course, he never knew what really come of none of these jokes, but he could picture what *probably* happened and that was enough.

Jim didn't work very steady after he lost his position with the Carterville people. What he did earn, doin' odd jobs round town, why, he spent pretty near all of it on gin, and his family might of starved if the stores hadn't of carried them along. Jim's wife tried her hand at dressmakin', but they ain't nobody goin' to get rich makin' dresses in this town.

As I say, she'd of divorced Jim, only she seen that she couldn't support herself and the kids and she was always hopin' that some day Jim would cut out his habits and give her more than two or three dollars a week.

They was a time when she would go to whoever he was workin' for and ask them to give her his wages, but after she done this once or twice, he beat her to it by borrowin' most of his pay in advance. He told it all round town, how he had outfoxed his Missus. He certainly was a caution!

But he wasn't satisfied with just outwittin' her. He was sore the way she had acted, tryin' to grab off his pay. And he made up his mind he'd get even. Well, he waited till Evans's Circus was advertised to come to town. Then he told his wife and two kiddies that he was goin' to take them to the circus. The day of the circus, he told them he would get the tickets and meet them outside the entrance to the tent.

Well, he didn't have no intentions of bein' there or buyin' tickets or nothin'. He got full of gin and laid round Wright's poolroom all day. His wife and the kids waited and waited and of course he didn't show up. His wife didn't have a dime with her, or nowhere else, I guess. So she finally had to tell the kids it was all off and they cried like they wasn't never goin' to stop.

Well, it seems, w'ile they was cryin', Doc Stair come along and he asked what was the matter, but Mrs. Kendall was stubborn and wouldn't tell him, but the kids told him and he insisted on takin' them and their mother in the show. Jim found this out afterwards and it was one reason why he had it in for Doc Stair.

Doc Stair come here about a year and a half ago. He's a mighty handsome young fella and his clothes always look like he has them made to order. He goes to Detroit two or three times a year and w'ile he's there must have a tailor take his measure and then make him a suit to order. They cost pretty near twice as much, but they fit a whole lot better than if you just bought them in a store.

For a w'ile everybody was wonderin' why a young doctor like Doc Stair should come to a town like this where we already got old Doc Gamble and Doc Foote that's both been here for years and all the practice in town was always divided between the two of them.

Then they was a story got round that Doc Stair's gal had throwed him over, a gal up in the Northern Peninsula somewhere, and the reason he come here was to hide himself away and forget it. He said himself that he thought they wasn't nothin' like general practice in a place like ours to fit a man to be a good all round doctor. And that's why he'd came.

Anyways, it wasn't long before he was makin' enough to live on, though they tell me that he never dunned nobody for what they owed him, and the folks here certainly has got the owin' habit, even in my business. If I had all that was comin' to me for just shaves alone, I could go to Carterville and put up at the Mercer for a week and see a different picture every night. For instance, they's old George Purdy—but I guess I shouldn't ought to be gossipin'.

Well, last year, our coroner died, died of the flu. Ken Beatty, that was his name. He was the coroner. So they had to choose another man to be coroner in his place and they picked Doc Stair. He laughed at first and said he didn't want it, but they made him take it. It ain't no job that anybody would fight for and what a man makes out of it in a year would just about buy seeds for their garden. Doc's the kind, though, that can't say no to nothin' if you keep at him long enough.

But I was goin' to tell you about a poor boy we got here in town—Paul Dickson. He fell out of a tree when he was about ten years old. Lit on his head and it done somethin' to him and he ain't never been right. No harm in him, but just silly. Jim Kendall used to call him cuckoo; that's a name Jim had for anybody that was off their head, only he called people's head their bean. That was another of his gags, callin' head bean and callin' crazy people cuckoo. Only poor Paul ain't crazy, but just silly.

You can imagine that Jim used to have all kinds of fun with Paul. He'd send him to the White Front Garage for a left-handed monkey wrench. Of course they ain't no such thing as a left-handed monkey wrench.

And once we had a kind of a fair here and they was a baseball game between the fats and the leans and before the game started Jim called Paul over and sent him away down to Schrader's hardware store to get a key for the pitcher's box.

They wasn't nothin' in the way of gags that Jim couldn't think up, when he put his mind to it.

Poor Paul was always kind of suspicious of people, maybe on account of how Jim had kept foolin' him. Paul wouldn't have much to do with anybody only his own mother and Doc Stair and a girl here in town named Julie Gregg. That is, she ain't a girl no more, but pretty near thirty or over.

When Doc first came to town, Paul seemed to feel like here was a real friend and he hung round Doc's office most of the w'ile; the only time he wasn't there was when he'd go home to eat or sleep or when he seen Julie Gregg doin' her shoppin'.

When he looked out Doc's window and seen her, he'd run downstairs and join her and tag along with her to the different stores. The poor boy was crazy about Julie and she always treated him mighty nice and made him feel like he was welcome, though of course it wasn't nothin' but pity on her side.

Doc done all he could to improve Paul's mind and he told me once that he really thought the boy was getting better, that they was times when he was as bright and sensible as anybody else.

But I was goin' to tell you about Julie Gregg. Old man Gregg was in the lumber business, but got to drinkin' and lost the most of his money and when he died, he didn't leave nothin' but the house and just enough insurance for the girl to skimp along on.

Her mother was a kind of a half invalid and didn't hardly ever leave the house. Julie wanted to sell the place and move somewheres else after the old man died, but the mother said she was born here and would die here. It was tough on Julie as the young people round this town—well, she's too good for them.

She'd been away to school and Chicago and New York and different places and they ain't no subject she can't talk on, where you take the rest of the young folks here and you mention anything to them outside of Gloria Swanson or Tommy Meighan and they think you're delirious. Did you see Gloria in *Wages of Virtue?* You missed somethin'!

Well, Doc Stair hadn't been here more than a week when he come in one day to get shaved and I recognized who he was, as he had been pointed out to me, so I told him about my old lady. She's been ailin' for a couple years and either Doc Gamble or Doc Foote, neither one, seemed to be helpin' her. So he said he would come out and see her, but if she was able to get out herself, it would be better to bring her to his office where he could make a completer examination.

So I took her to his office and w'ile I was waitin' for her in the reception room, in come Julie Gregg. When somebody comes in Doc Stair's office, they's a bell that rings in his inside office so as he can tell they's somebody to see him.

So he left my old lady inside and come out to the front office and that's the first time him and Julie met and I guess it was what they call love at first sight. But it wasn't fifty-fifty. This young fella was the slickest lookin' fella she'd ever seen in this town and she went wild over him. To him she was just a lady that wanted to see the doctor.

She'd came on about the same business I had. Her mother had been doctorin' for years with Doc Gamble and Doc Foote and without no results. So she'd heard they was a new doc in town and decided to give him a try. He promised to call and see her mother that same day.

I said a minute ago that it was love at first sight on her part. I'm not only judgin' by how she acted afterwards but how she looked at him that first day in his office. I ain't no mind reader, but it was wrote all over her face that she was gone.

Now Jim Kendall, besides bein' a jokesmith and a pretty good drinker, well, Jim was quite a lady-killer. I guess he run pretty wild durin' the time he was on the road for them Carterville people, and besides that, he'd had a couple little affairs of the heart right here in town. As I say, his wife would have divorced him, only she couldn't.

But Jim was like the majority of men, and women, too, I guess. He wanted what he couldn't get. He wanted Julie Gregg and worked his head off tryin' to land her. Only he'd of said bean instead of head.

Well, Jim's habits and his jokes didn't appeal to Julie and of course he was a married man, so he didn't have no more chance than, well, than a rabbit. That's an expression of Jim's himself. When somebody didn't have no chance to get elected or somethin', Jim would always say they didn't have no more chance than a rabbit.

He didn't make no bones about how he felt. Right in here, more than once, in front of the whole crowd, he said he was stuck on Julie and anybody that could get her for him was welcome to his house and his wife and kids included. But she wouldn't have nothin' to do with him; wouldn't even speak to him on the street. He finally seen he wasn't gettin' nowheres with his usual line so he decided to try the rough stuff. He went right up to her house one evenin' and when she opened the door he forced his way in and grabbed her. But she broke loose and before he could stop her, she run in the next room and locked the door and phoned to Joe Barnes. Joe's the marshal. Jim could hear who she was phonin' to and he beat it before Joe got there.

Joe was an old friend of Julie's pa. Joe went to Jim the next day and told him what would happen if he ever done it again.

I don't know how the news of this little affair leaked out. Chances is that Joe Barnes told his wife and she told somebody else's wife and they told their husband. Anyways, it did leak out and Hod Meyers had the nerve to kid Jim about it, right here in this shop. Jim didn't deny nothin' and kind of laughed it off and said for us all to wait; that lots of people had tried to make a monkey out of him, but he always got even.

Meanw'ile everybody in town was wise to Julie's bein' wild mad over the Doc. I don't suppose she had any idear how her face changed when him and her was together; of course she couldn't of, or she'd of kept away from him. And she didn't know that we was all noticin' how many times she made excuses to go up to his office or pass it on the other side of the street and look up in his window to see if he was there. I felt sorry for her and so did most other people.

Hod Meyers kept rubbin' it into Jim about how the Doc had cut him out. Jim didn't pay no attention to the kiddin' and you could see he was plannin' one of his jokes.

One trick Jim had was the knack of changin' his voice. He could make you think he was a girl talkin' and he could mimic any man's voice. To show you how good he was along this line, I'll tell you the joke he played on me once.

You know, in most towns of any size, when a man is dead and needs a shave, why, the barber that shaves him soaks him five dollars for the job; that is, he don't soak *him*, but whoever ordered the shave. I just charge three dollars because personally I don't mind much shavin' a dead person. They lay a whole lot stiller than live customers. The only thing is that you don't feel like talkin' to them and you get kind of lonesome.

Well, about the coldest day we ever had here, two years ago last winter, the phone rung at the house w'ile I was home to dinner and I answered the phone and it was a woman's voice and she said she was Mrs. John Scott and her husband was dead and would I come out and shave him.

Old John had always been a good customer of mine. But they live seven miles out in the country, on the Streeter road. Still I didn't see how I could say no.

So I said I would be there, but would have to come in a jitney and it might cost three or four dollars besides the price of the shave. So she, or the voice, it said that was all right, so I got Frank Abbott to drive me out to the place and when I got there, who should open the door but old John himself! He wasn't no more dead than, well, than a rabbit.

It didn't take no private detective to figure out who had played me this little joke. Nobody could of thought it up but Jim Kendall. He certainly was a card!

I tell you this incident just to show you how he could disguise his voice

and make you believe it was somebody else talkin'. I'd of swore it was
Mrs. Scott had called me. Anyways, some woman.

Well, Jim waited till he had Doc Stair's voice down pat; then he went
after revenge.

He called Julie up on a night when he knew Doc was over in Carterville. She never questioned but what it was Doc's voice. Jim said he must
see her that night; he couldn't wait no longer to tell her somethin'. She
was all excited and told him to come to the house. But he said he was
expectin' an important long distance call and wouldn't she please forget
her manners for once and come to his office. He said they couldn't nothin'
hurt her and nobody would see her and he just *must* talk to her a little
w'ile. Well, poor Julie fell for it.

Doc always keeps a night light in his office, so it looked to Julie like
they was somebody there.

Meanw'ile Jim Kendall had went to Wright's poolroom, where they
was a whole gang amusin' themselves. The most of them had drank plenty
of gin, and they was a rough bunch when sober. They was always strong
for Jim's jokes and when he told them to come with him and see some fun
they give up their card games and pool games and followed along.

Doc's office is on the second floor. Right outside his door they's a
flight of stairs leadin' to the floor above. Jim and his gang hid in the dark
behind these stairs.

Well, Julie come up to Doc's door and rung the bell and they was
nothin' doin'. She rung it again and she rung it seven or eight times. Then
she tried the door and found it locked. Then Jim made some kind of a
noise and she heard it and waited a minute, and then she says, "Is that you,
Ralph?" Ralph is Doc's first name.

They was no answer and it must of came to her all of a sudden that
she'd been bunked. She pretty near fell downstairs and the whole gang
after her. They chased her all the way home, hollerin', "Is that you, Ralph?"
and "Oh, Ralphie, dear, is that you?" Jim says he couldn't holler it himself,
as he was laughin' too hard.

Poor Julie! She didn't show up here on Main Street for a long, long
time afterward.

And of course Jim and his gang told everybody in town, everybody
but Doc Stair. They was scared to tell him, and he might of never knowed
only for Paul Dickson. The poor cuckoo, as Jim called him, he was here
in the shop one night when Jim was still gloatin' yet over what he'd done
to Julie. And Paul took in as much of it as he could understand and he run
to Doc with the story.

It's a cinch Doc went up in the air and swore he'd make Jim suffer.
But it was a kind of a delicate thing, because if it got out that he had beat
Jim up, Julie was bound to hear of it and then she'd know that Doc knew

and of course knowin' that he knew would make it worse for her than ever. He was goin' to do somethin', but it took a lot of figurin'.

Well, it was a couple days later when Jim was here in the shop again, and so was the cuckoo. Jim was goin' duck-shootin' the next day and had came in lookin' for Hod Meyers to go with him. I happened to know that Hod had went over to Carterville and wouldn't be home till the end of the week. So Jim said he hated to go alone and he guessed he would call it off. Then poor Paul spoke up and said if Jim would take him he would go along. Jim thought a w'ile and then he said, well, he guessed a half-wit was better than nothin'.

I suppose he was plottin' to get Paul out in the boat and play some joke on him, like pushin' him in the water. Anyways, he said Paul could go. He asked him had he ever shot a duck and Paul said no, he'd never even had a gun in his hands. So Jim said he could set in the boat and watch him and if he behaved himself, he might lend him his gun for a couple of shots. They made a date to meet in the mornin' and that's the last I seen of Jim alive.

Next mornin', I hadn't been open more than ten minutes when Doc Stair come in. He looked kind of nervous. He asked me had I seen Paul Dickson. I said no, but I knew where he was, out duck-shootin' with Jim Kendall. So Doc says that's what he had heard, and he couldn't understand it because Paul had told him he wouldn't never have no more to do with Jim as long as he lived.

He said Paul had told him about the joke Jim had played on Julie. He said Paul had asked him what he thought of the joke and the Doc told him that anybody that would do a thing like that ought not to be let live.

I said it had been a kind of a raw thing, but Jim just couldn't resist no kind of a joke, no matter how raw. I said I thought he was all right at heart, but just bubblin' over with mischief. Doc turned and walked out.

At noon he got a phone call from old John Scott. The lake where Jim and Paul had went shootin' is on John's place. Paul had came runnin' up to the house a few minutes before and said they'd been an accident. Jim had shot a few ducks and then give the gun to Paul and told him to try his luck. Paul hadn't never handled a gun and he was nervous. He was shakin' so hard that he couldn't control the gun. He let fire and Jim sunk back in the boat, dead.

Doc Stair, bein' the coroner, jumped in Frank Abbott's flivver and rushed out to Scott's farm. Paul and old John was down on the shore of the lake. Paul had rowed the boat to shore, but they'd left the body in it, waiting for Doc to come.

Doc examined the body and said they might as well fetch it back to town. They was no use leavin' it there or callin' a jury, as it was a plain case of accidental shootin'.

Personally I wouldn't never leave a person shoot a gun in the same boat I was in unless I was sure they knew somethin' about guns. Jim was a sucker to leave a new beginner have his gun, let alone a half-wit. It probably served Jim right, what he got. But still we miss him round here. He certainly was a card! Comb it wet or dry?

INTERPRETATION

The main action here is the story of the "card," the practical joker. He has no shred of human perception or feeling, and his jokes are, naturally, brutal and stupid, only a way of inflating his own ego. In the end, one of his jokes backfires, and we have the moral satisfaction of seeing the biter bit, the joker caught in the destructive consequences of a joke whose destructive nature for other people he could never have understood or cared about. Assuming that the card is adequately characterized, that the setting of the small town is adequately rendered for us, and that the plot is logically worked out, we might still feel that this main action, taken by itself, is somewhat over-simple and predictable, even too moralistic and too obviously an illustration of brutal arrogance being paid off. Anyway, it would seem that Ring Lardner must have felt some dissatisfaction with a naked presentation of the main action, such as we might have if it were told on the author's own responsibility; for he provides a narrator, the barber, who gives us his version of the business.

The use of the narrator does make the story seem less bare and simple, but, of course, complication for the mere sake of complication would scarcely justify itself. What positive values is Ring Lardner aiming at in the use of the barber? To answer this we may well begin by asking another question: What is the barber like? More specifically, what is his attitude toward the story he tells?

The barber, we quickly discover, admires the card, and thinks that life is pretty dull around town now that the card is gone. The barber has accepted the card at his own evaluation, has vicariously participated in the brutal jokes, and is, therefore, a kind of accomplice. So we have a deepening of the originally simple action—a sense that brutality and evil thrive by a kind of connivance on the part of those who do not directly participate in it, a sense of the spreading ripples of complicity always around the evil act.

There is, also, another kind of deepening, not in content this time but in the way of presentation. Let us suppose that the narrator of the story had merely told us about people like the barber, people who had some tacit complicity with the card's jokes, and that he himself, the narrator, found such people reprehensible. Given this treatment, we would find ourselves in immediate agreement with his attitude. There would be no shock of the collision between the narrator's attitude and our own. But as things actually stand, there is a shock of collision between the narrator's attitude and our own, a growing need to reassess things and repudiate his attitude. In other words, Lardner has used an inverted and ironical method. The narrator does not represent the author's view, nor our own. The barber is put there to belie, as it were, the meaning of the story, and by so doing to heighten our own feelings—even to irritate us to a fuller awareness of what is at stake in the story.

If the story were told directly, or told by a narrator whose attitudes were congenial with our own, we should be inclined to say: Of course, the card is a brute, a louse, and got just what he deserved. But we might say it too quickly, too easily, and we might be inclined to dismiss the whole business. As it is, we are compelled, in a greater or lesser degree, to take issue with the barber, and in taking issue we are drawn more deeply into the story.

The use of this kind of narrator is, then, a fairly simple device for provoking what we may call "reader participation"—for making the reader do some of the interpreting himself, for drawing him into the inside of the story by making him invert an apparent meaning (here the barber's valuations) or develop meaning beyond the point where the story actually comes to rest. Irony, *understatement* (see Glossary), withholding—these are ways to provoke the reader to reassess things, to reassess his own feelings, and thus enter more deeply into the process of the piece of fiction.

Here it might be well to consider the general problem of the *point of view* or the *focus of narration* (see Glossary). We have just seen how important it is that "Haircut" is presented through the mentality of the barber, and have seen how the use of this point of view affects the whole story and our reception of the story. The point of view—the choice of the teller of the story—is a question of the greatest importance for any piece of fiction. The action has to come to us through words, but through whose words? On the answer to that question, all else may often hinge. So we have such subsidiary questions as these:

1. What does the narrator know of the total action lying beyond the story? What can he tell?

2. Does he tell all he knows? If not, why not? What accounts for his withholding any information or narrative? If there is withholding, is it reasonable and justifiable, or merely trickery and mystification?

3. Why does he tell what he does tell? What is his motivation as narrator?

4. What is the narrator's attitude toward what he tells?

5. Assuming that the narrator is not the author himself, as he is not in "Haircut," is the narrator's attitude toward what he tells the same as the attitude of the author?

6. Is the narrator's attitude supposed to be the same as that of the reader? If not, why not? If the narrator's attitude is supposed to be a sort

of guide to the reader's reaction, does the narrator go all the way in interpretation, or does he stop short, withhold, or understate the meaning of the story?

Though there are many other important questions that may develop around the point of view of a piece of fiction, we can see from these that the point of view bears most important relations to the structure and meaning of fiction. Before we go into such relations, however, we should sort out what points of view are possible in fiction.

There is, obviously, the first person—the story told, as in "Haircut," by an "I," speaking in his own person and in his own language, telling only what he himself can be reasonably supposed to know and what he is interested in telling. We are immediately aware that the relation of such a narrator varies from case to case. The "I" may be the main character, or one of the main characters, telling of his own experience, as in Sherwood Anderson's "I Want To Know Why," a story which we shall come to later; or, to take the other extreme, the "I" may be a mere observer who sees the action of the story but has no stake in it beyond curiosity, as for example the newspaper man who is supposed to narrate "The Man Who Would Be King." In between these two extremes, there may be all sorts of shadings of relationships, from the narrator who is not central but who is deeply involved, like Peachey in "The Man Who Would Be King," through the narrator like the barber, who is not involved in any direct sense but has some moral connection with the action, or a narrator who is an observer but who is affected in some significant way, for better or worse, by what he observes.

The other general point of view from which a story may be told is the third person, the unidentified author speaking impersonally. But there are many variations and shadings possible also in this point of view. The narrator may tell only what can be seen or heard from the outside—as though he were a camera and sound machine making the objective record. "The Girls in Their Summer Dresses," except for the last line, when we enter the head of Michael, is such a story. We see the young couple and hear their conversation as though we were eavesdropping or watching a play on the stage. The method is, we may say, dramatic, objective; we never get a glimpse inside anyone's head except by his actions or words, no thoughts, no feelings, directly given. That is, until the last line, when we are admitted into Michael's head: "Michael watched her walk, thinking what a pretty girl, what nice legs." John Collier's "De Mortuis" is another almost perfect example of the dramatic method, the immediate reportorial method, without summary or psychological interpretation or any entering into the heads of characters.

In the third person, however, we find at the other extreme from the objective method, a method which does let us into the thoughts and feel-

ings of one or more characters, sometimes most intimately into them so
that the story is little more than the tracing of their reactions. "Walter
Mitty" is such a story; his dream world is the world of the story, and by
being admitted into it we make a judgment on it. "A Piece of News,"
though not as pure an example of this subjective treatment, gives us the
same kind of intimate knowledge of the inner goings-on of Ruby Fisher.
But we may, of course, enter into a character's head, not to follow more
or less sympathetically the flow of thought and feeling, but to dissect,
analyze, and summarize, as in the subjective moments of "The Necklace."

We may summarize what we have said of kinds of point of view by
the following chart:

	Internal analysis of events	*External observation of events*
Narrator as a character in story	1. Main character tells own story	2. Minor character tells main character's story
Narrator not a character in story	4. Analytic or omnicient author tells story, entering thoughts and feelings	3. Author tells story as external observer

To return to our remarks about the relation of point of view to structure and meaning, we may take a backward glance at "The Man Who
Would Be King." That story has not only one narrator, but two. There is
the newspaper man who gives us the general narration in his own person,
a sort of shadow of Kipling, but within his narration there is the action narrated by Peachey, again in the first person. What is the logic of Kipling's
choice of method?

First, we may observe that by taking a first-person narrator, a certain
naturalness may be gained. This is not to say that the reader is so innocent
that he more readily "believes" a story told in the first person, but it is to
say that certain things can be introduced into a story more informally and
casually, even though we recognize that the first-person itself is a *convention* (see Glossary), a fiction. In this particular story we need to know
something about the strange world of India, and if that information were
given in the third person the burden of mere exposition would be more
apparent. As it is, the newspaperman can more or less casually and incidentally give us a fairly complete notion of his world; he can feed the
expository material in without making us feel that it is labelled, for it is
part of his life.

Second, the presence of a first-person narrator introduces naturally
into a story a device for *selectivity* (see p. 147 and Glossary). Since the

narrator can tell only what he has observed, heard, or reasonably surmised, a considerable body of material from the hypothetical underlying action is not available to him. If for a particular story the narrator is well chosen, then the deletions he must make will seem natural, and the selections significant. We feel that what he has to tell is what he can tell and must tell.

For example, in "The Man Who Would Be King" we are dealing with an action which, taken in itself, is potentially a novel—the conquest of Kafiristan. Kipling is, however, interested in only one thing—the idea of kingship, godhood, and manhood—and he wants to render only so much of the general action as is needed to make vivid and credible the development of Dravot. By the time Dravot's story is filtered through Peachey and the newspaperman only vivid and telling strokes are left. A piece of action that might require pages if given any ordinary development comes down to a sentence or two—for example, the taking of the four mules in the mountains. The scale of treatment can be controlled in terms of the narrator's presence—he tells it in his way, he makes the emphasis. Selection, foreshortening, summary—these things are natural to all fiction, but with the first-person narrator we have, as it were, a built-in device for controlling them. In other words, the plot of a story—that is, the structure of action as it is actually presented to us—depends on the point of view.

Not only does structure depend on point of view. Let us take Peachey again. He is useful in the way we have said, as a narrator of events, the giver of the structure, but he is also a mirror to Dravot's development, a device of interpretation as well as of control. We can ask not merely what he knows of the action, but what he knows of the meaning of the action. We sense immediately that Dravot is the powerful one of the pair, the one with ambition and imagination, the one who starts the great scheme of looting a kingdom. Peachey is content to follow at an admiring distance. This same relationship prevails as Dravot begins his spiritual journey from mere looter up to the point that he achieves in the end. Each new phase of his development is played off against Peachey, the unimaginative follower who if left alone, would be perfectly content to be merely the self-indulgent loafer and looter. It is through Peachey's not entirely comprehending response and blundering account that we sense the depth of experience represented by Dravot. We may say that Peachey, with his blunt lack of sensitivity and his simplicity of mind, is a device of irony and understatement. The fact that the spiritual significance of the theme comes through the man who, except for his association with Dravot, would remain loafer and looter, gives an ironical contrast—though the irony here, as is not the case with the barber, makes us think not worse, but better, of the narrator. The meaning of the story, as filtered to us through Peachey, is understated: the full significance is not offered. Peachey is, as it were, a guide for our response, though a rather limping one; and in the end it is he who, in his delirium in the mountains, presents the image of the godlike Dravot who can hold up the peaks. Peachey's simplicity of mind makes possible the image which we can reasonably accept—we accept the thematic truth of it and at the same time, because it comes from the delirium of Peachey's simple mind, accept the plausibility of it.

This is perhaps enough to indicate something of the importance of point of view for both structure and meaning. Let us glance at some other stories we have already read:

1. Try to think of "The Girls in Their Summer Dresses" as narrated by Frances. What difference do you think this shift in point of view would make to the story? What is our attitude toward the events of the story as it now stands? If she told it would we be more inclined to think her nagging and self-pitying? What would be lost at the very end? All this is not to say that for every story there is an absolutely right way to narrate the action, but it is to say that a shift in point of view creates new considerations and new problems.

2. We have discussed the tone of "De Mortuis." How is the point of view related to the tone of the story?

3. What is the point of view of "The Necklace"? How is this related to questions of scale in the story?

4. How is the point of view related to questions of atmosphere in "A Piece of News"?

ISAAC BABEL

Crossing into Poland

THE Commander of the VI Division reported: Novgorad-Volynsk was taken at dawn today. The Staff had left Krapivno, and our baggage train was spread out in a noisy rearguard over the highroad from Brest to Warsaw built by Nicholas I upon the bones of peasants.

Fields flowered around us, crimson with poppies; a noontide breeze played in the yellowing rye; on the horizon virginal buckwheat rose like the wall of a distant monastery. The Volyn's peaceful stream moved away from us in sinuous curves and was lost in the pearly haze of the birch groves; crawling between flowery slopes, it wound weary arms through a wilderness of hops. The orange sun rolled down the sky like a lopped-off head, and mild light glowed from the cloud gorges. The standards of the sunset flew above our heads. Into the cool of evening dripped the smell of yesterday's blood, of slaughtered horses. The blackened Zbruch roared, twisting itself into foamy knots at the falls. The bridges were down, and we waded across the river. On the waves rested a majestic moon. The horses were in to the cruppers, and the noisy torrent gurgled among hundreds of horses' legs. Somebody sank, loudly defaming the Mother of God. The river was dotted with the square black patches of the wagons, and was full of confused sounds, of whistling and singing, that rose above the gleaming hollows, the serpentine trails of the moon.

Far on in the night we reached Novograd. In the house where I was billeted I found a pregnant woman and two red-haired, scraggy-necked Jews. A third, huddled to the wall with his head covered up, was already asleep. In the room I was given I discovered turned-out wardrobes, scraps of women's fur coats on the floor, human filth, fragments of the occult crockery the Jews use only once a year, at Eastertime.

"Clear this up," I said to the woman. "What a filthy way to live!" The two Jews rose from their places and, hopping on their felt soles, cleared the mess from the floor. They skipped about noiselessly, monkey-fashion, like Japs in a circus act, their necks swelling and twisting. They put down for me a feather bed that had been disemboweled, and I lay down by the wall next to the third Jew, the one who was asleep. Faint-hearted poverty closed in over my couch.

Silence overcame all. Only the moon, clasping in her blue hands her round, bright, carefree face, wandered like a vagrant outside the window.

I kneaded my numbed legs and, lying on the ripped-open mattress, fell asleep. And in my sleep the Commander of the VI Division appeared to me; he was pursuing the Brigade Commander on a heavy stallion, fired at him twice between the eyes. The bullets pierced the Brigade Commander's head, and both his eyes dropped to the ground. "Why did you turn back the brigade?" shouted Savitsky, the Divisional Commander, to the wounded man—and here I woke up, for the pregnant woman was groping over my face with her fingers.

"Good sir," she said, "you're calling out in your sleep and you're tossing to and fro. I'll make you a bed in another corner, for you're pushing my father about."

She raised her thin legs and rounded belly from the floor and removed the blanket from the sleeper. Lying on his back was an old man, a dead old man. His throat had been torn out and his face cleft in two; in his beard blue blood was clotted like a lump of lead.

"Good sir," said the Jewess, shaking up the feather bed, "the Poles cut his throat, and he begging them: 'Kill me in the yard so that my daughter shan't see me die.' But they did as suited them. He passed away in this room, thinking of me.—And now I should wish to know," cried the woman with sudden and terrible violence, "I should wish to know where in the whole world you could find another father like my father?"

INTERPRETATION

This, like "I See You Never," may be regarded by some readers as a mere episode, not a story at all, lacking conflict and complication and any acceptable resolution. What do you think? In considering this question you may find some help in imagining, by way of contrast, the same action told in the third person, very impersonally. Does the fact of a first-person narrator, who, presumably, arrives at the unspecified awareness, give more fictional shape and significance than would be possible otherwise? What is the awareness arrived at?

LUIGI PIRANDELLO

War

THE passengers who had left Rome by the night express had had to stop until dawn at the small station of Fabriano in order to continue their journey by the small old-fashioned local joining the main line with Sulmona.

At dawn, in a stuffy and smoky second-class carriage in which five people had already spent the night, a bulky woman in deep mourning was hoisted in—almost like a shapeless bundle. Behind her, puffing and moaning, followed her husband—a tiny man, thin and weakly, his face death-white, his eyes small and bright and looking shy and uneasy.

Having at last taken a seat he politely thanked the passengers who had helped his wife and who had made room for her; then he turned round to the woman trying to pull down the collar of her coat, and politely inquired:

"Are you all right, dear?"

The wife, instead of answering, pulled up her collar again to her eyes, so as to hide her face.

"Nasty world," muttered the husband with a sad smile.

And he felt it his duty to explain to his traveling companions that the poor woman was to be pitied, for the war was taking away from her her only son, a boy of twenty to whom both had devoted their entire life, even breaking up their home at Sulmona to follow him to Rome, where he had to go as a student, then allowing him to volunteer for war with an assurance, however, that at least for six months he would not be sent to the front and now, all of a sudden, receiving a wire saying that he was due to leave in three days' time and asking them to go and see him off.

The woman under the big coat was twisting and wriggling, at times growling like a wild animal, feeling certain that all those explanations would not have aroused even a shadow of sympathy from those people who—most likely—were in the same plight as herself. One of them, who had been listening with particular attention, said:

"You should thank God that your son is only leaving now for the front. Mine has been sent there the first day of the war. He has already come back twice wounded and been sent back again to the front."

"What about me? I have two sons and three nephews at the front," said another passenger.

"Maybe, but in our case it is our *only* son," ventured the husband.

"What difference can it make? You may spoil your only son with excessive attentions, but you cannot love him more than you would all your other children if you had any. Paternal love is not like bread that can be broken into pieces and split amongst the children in equal shares. A father gives *all* his love to each one of his children without discrimination, whether it be one or ten, and if I am suffering now for my two sons, I am not suffering half for each of them but double . . ."

"True . . . true . . ." sighed the embarrassed husband, "but suppose (of course we all hope it will never be your case) a father has two sons at the front and he loses one of them, there is still one left to console him . . . while . . ."

"Yes," answered the other, getting cross, "a son left to console him but also a son left for whom he must survive, while in the case of the father of an only son if the son dies the father can die too and put an end to his distress. Which of the two positions is the worse? Don't you see how my case would be worse than yours?"

"Nonsense," interrupted another traveler, a fat, red-faced man with bloodshot eyes of the palest gray.

He was panting. From his bulging eyes seemed to spurt inner violence of an uncontrolled vitality which his weakened body could hardly contain.

"Nonsense," he repeated, trying to cover his mouth with his hand so as to hide the two missing front teeth. "Nonsense. Do we give life to our children for our own benefit?"

The other travelers stared at him in distress. The one who had had his son at the front since the first day of the war sighed: "You are right. Our children do not belong to us, they belong to the Country. . . ."

"Bosh," retorted the fat traveler. "Do we think of the Country when we give life to our children? Our sons are born because . . . well, because they must be born and when they come to life they take our own life with them. This is the truth. We belong to them but they never belong to us. And when they reach twenty they are exactly what we were at their age. We too had a father and mother, but there were so many other things as well . . . girls, cigarettes, illusions, new ties . . . and the Country, of course, whose call we would have answered—when we were twenty—even if father and mother had said no. Now at our age, the love of our Country is still great, of course, but stronger than it is the love for our children. Is there any one of us here who wouldn't gladly take his son's place at the front if he could?"

There was a silence all round, everybody nodding as to approve.

"Why then," continued the fat man, "shouldn't we consider the feelings of our children when they are twenty? Isn't it natural that at their age they should consider the love for their Country (I am speaking of decent boys, of course) even greater than the love for us? Isn't it natural that it should be so, as after all they must look upon us as upon old boys who cannot move any more and must stay at home? If Country exists, if Country is a natural necessity, like bread, of which each of us must eat in order not to die of hunger, somebody must go to defend it. And our sons go, when they are twenty, and they don't want tears, because if they die, they die inflamed and happy (I am speaking, of course, of decent boys). Now, if one dies young and happy, without having the ugly sides of life, the boredom of it, the pettiness, the bitterness of disillusion . . . what more can we ask for him? Everyone should stop crying; everyone should laugh, as I do . . . or at least thank God—as I do—because my son, before dying, sent me a message saying that he was dying satisfied at having ended his life in the best way he could have wished. That is why, as you see, I do not even wear mourning. . . ."

He shook his light fawn coat as to show it; his livid lip over his missing teeth was trembling, his eyes were watery and motionless, and soon after he ended with a shrill laugh which might well have been a sob.

"Quite so . . . quite so . . ." agreed the others.

The woman who, bundled in a corner under her coat, had been sitting and listening had—for the last three months—tried to find in the words of her husband and her friends something to console her in her deep sorrow, something that might show her how a mother should resign herself to send her son not even to death but to a probably dangerous life. Yet not a word had she found amongst the many which had been said . . . and her grief had been greater in seeing that nobody—as she thought—could share her feelings.

But now the words of the traveler amazed and almost stunned her. She suddenly realized that it wasn't the others who were wrong and could not understand her but herself who could not rise up to the same height of those fathers and mothers willing to resign themselves, without crying, not only to the departure of their sons but even to their death.

She lifted her head, she bent over from her corner trying to listen with great attention to the details which the fat man was giving to his companions about the way his son had fallen as a hero, for his King and his Country, happy and without regrets. It seemed to her that she had stumbled into a world she had never dreamt of, a world so far unknown to her and she was so pleased to hear everyone joining in congratulating that brave father who could so stoically speak of his child's death.

Then suddenly, just as if she had heard nothing of what had been said and almost as if waking up from a dream, she turned to the old man, asking him:

"Then . . . is your son really dead?"

Everybody stared at her. The old man, too, turned to look at her, fixing his great, bulging, horribly watery light gray eyes, deep in her face. For some little time he tried to answer, but words failed him. He looked and looked at her, almost as if only then—at that silly, incongruous question—he had suddenly realized at last that his son was really dead—gone for ever—for ever. His face contracted, became horribly distorted, then he snatched in haste a handkerchief from his pocket and, to the amazement of everyone, broke into harrowing, heart-rending, uncontrollable sobs.

INTERPRETATION

This story may seem peculiarly lacking in action, if by the term we mean physical action. After the fat woman has been "hoisted" into the compartment and her shy, apologetic husband has climbed in after her, there is no physical movement indicated except the wriggling and twisting of the fat woman under her coat, the attempt of the old man to cover his mouth with his hand when he talks in order to conceal the fact that two of his teeth are missing, his shaking of his fawn-colored overcoat to show that he does not wear mourning, the fat woman's bending forward to listen to the old man, the turning of all eyes upon the woman when she finally asks the old man about his son, and the contortion of the old man's face as he tries to answer. These physical actions are important in the story, but their importance lies in the fact that they are clues to the feelings and attitudes of the persons involved in the story. They do not, in other words, actually constitute the plot.

The plot itself is constituted of the conflicts among the various attitudes held by the characters toward the subject: the giving of children to the country. The form, then, is almost the form of a debate—different points of view are stated and argued, one after another. But this is not a debate for the mere sake of debate. The persons involved are persons for whom the issue is very real; they have sons in the war, and one man, the old man in the fawn-colored overcoat, has already lost his son. That is, the debate is dramatically meaningful for the participants.

The two extreme positions in the debate are held by the fat woman and the old man. The fat woman says nothing, but we know what her position is: "The woman under the big coat was twisting and wriggling, at times growling like a wild animal, feeling certain that all those explanations would not have aroused even a shadow of sympathy from those people who—most likely—were in the same plight as herself." Her grief has a kind of immediacy, like physical pain; it is beyond reasoning or discussion; she can only twist as in pain or utter meaningless animal-like sounds. The other extreme position, that of the old man whose son has been actually killed, is the most fully stated. He argues that one does not, in the first place, have children for one's own benefit; that, in the second place, a son, being young and idealistic, is more drawn by love of country than by love of parents; that if a son dies for his country he dies happy— if he is "decent"; that one who dies young and happy has been spared the ugly side of life, boredom, pettiness, disillusion; that, therefore, a parent whose son has died heroically should be happy and laugh, as he says he does, or should at least thank God. That is, the old man has completely argued away, philosophized away, all of the fundamental sense of loss and grief. Such are the two extremes of attitude.

Now, what may be called the plot pattern of the story depends upon the opposition between these two extreme views. But it is not a static opposition—a mere statement of difference. Both views are modified.

First, the fat woman, who had been unable to take consolation from her husband or her friends, because, as she felt, nobody could share her feelings, begins to take consolation from the words of the stranger. He has actually lost a son, and therefore he must know, must be able to share, her own feelings. He must be wise, because his loss is greater than hers, for her son is yet alive. Furthermore, the very violence of the old man's position, its difference from all the views given her by husband and friends, its absolute denial of grief by its heroic terms, make her feel that she has "stumbled into a world she had never dreamt of." It seems incredible to her that a man whose son is really dead can speak thus of his loss. So "almost as if waking up from a dream" she asks him: "Then . . . is your son really dead?"

Presumably, if the man should say, simply, "Yes, he is dead," she would be prepared to accept, for the moment at least, his position. If the man could assure her once more that the son is "really" dead, then she could try to imitate his heroic attitude. She, too, would be able to face the fact of death.

But her question, which provides the climax, the focal point of the story, reveals something to the old man, just as his previous words have revealed something to her. So, as in the first place, we find her position modified by him, we find now, in the second place, his position modified by her. When she utters the words "really dead" everybody "stares" at her—as though she had said something out of place, something impolite and embarrassing, as though she had divulged some horrible and shocking secret. The old man stares at her too, and cannot answer. For the first time, he realizes that his son is "really dead—gone for ever—for ever." He is caught now in the abject, animal-like, unreasoning misery, in which she had previously been held, and bursts into sobs.

The story, then, depends on a conflict between the basic, personal, unformulable emotion on the one hand, and systems, codes, reason, ideal compensations, and interpretations on the other. There is here an ironical contrast, an irreconcilable contrast—or a contrast, which if reconcilable is reconcilable only by the greatest effort. The equilibrium of the man who has made the reconciliation is upset, we see, by the slightest touch, by the woman's "silly, incongruous question," but a question which is fundamental. Are we to assume, therefore, that the author is simply saying that codes, systems, reason, obligations, ideals do not matter, that the only thing which matters is the fact of personal emotion? It would not seem to be the case. If that were the case, why would he illustrate the powerful appeal which the old man's words make to the woman who is sunk in grief? No, it seems that the author is putting, in dramatic terms, a basic conflict in human experience—is saying that the two terms of the opposition are always in existence and that neither can be ignored. (Compare the author's attitude toward his theme with that of Bradbury toward the theme of "I See You Never," see pp. 133–135).

Let us turn again to the pattern of the story. We have said that we find a movement away from the two extreme positions, a process of mutual modification focused, finally, on the question which the woman asks the old man. In other words, we have, in a sense, two "stories" within a story—the story of the woman's change of attitude and the story of the old man's change of attitude. Each of the two persons seems, when introduced, to be firmly fixed in a special attitude. How are we to account for the changes? Are the changes prepared for and made acceptable in the story?

The author devotes some analysis to the woman's change. It is the novelty, the heroic quality, of the consolation offered by the old man, that attract her. Further, the fact that he has really lost a son makes her feel that he will "understand" her. But we have no such explicit analysis of the change on the part of the old man. His change of attitude comes as a surprise. But does he not overstate his case in the earlier part of the story? Is there not an inkling of the fact that he is trying to argue against himself rather than against other people? Is there not a hint of hysteria? In this connection one might investigate the following sentence, which comes just after he has said that he does not even wear mourning: "He shook his light fawn coat as to show it; his livid lip over his missing teeth was trembling, his eyes were watery and motionless, and soon after he ended with a shrill laugh which might well have been a sob" Then, we may take the attitude of the woman herself as a kind of preparation for the old man's final change. She represents, as it were, the opposite pole of experience, but an undeniable pole.

The foregoing analysis of the story is not complete. Certain other questions are important for a full interpretation and for an understanding of the author's method.

1. What is the importance of the physical actions in the story? We have said that they offer clues to the feelings and attitudes of the characters. How is this true? Take, for instance, the fact that the old man at first tries to cover his mouth but later forgets to do so.

2. What is the significance of the words which are italicized in the following sentence: "The old man, too, turned to look at her, fixing his great, bulging, *horribly* watery light gray eyes, *deep* in her face."

3. The following version of the story would be inferior to the present version: The old man's son is merely at the front. He argues with the other people in the compartment, and persuades them, as in the present version of the story. At a station, he receives a telegram saying that his son has been killed and bursts into "heart-rending, uncontrollable sobs," while they stare at him in amazement. Why would this version be inferior to the story as given?

STEPHEN CRANE

The Bride Comes to Yellow Sky

I

THE great Pullman was whirling onward with such dignity of motion that a glance from the window seemed simply to prove that the plains of Texas were pouring eastward. Vast flats of green grass, dull-hued spaces of mesquit and cactus, little groups of frame houses, woods of light and tender trees, all were sweeping into the east, sweeping over the horizon, a precipice.

A newly married pair had boarded this coach at San Antonio. The man's face was reddened from many days in the wind and sun, and a direct result of his new black clothes was that his brick-coloured hands were constantly performing in a most conscious fashion. From time to time he looked down respectfully at his attire. He sat with a hand on each knee, like a man waiting in a barber's shop. The glances he devoted to other passengers were furtive and shy.

The bride was not pretty, nor was she very young. She wore a dress of blue cashmere, with small reservations of velvet here and there, and with steel buttons abounding. She continually twisted her head to regard her puff sleeves, very stiff, straight, and high. They embarrassed her. It was quite apparent that she had cooked, and that she expected to cook, dutifully. The blushes caused by the careless scrutiny of some passengers as she had entered the car were strange to see upon this plain, under-class countenance, which was drawn in placid, almost emotionless lines.

They were evidently very happy. "Ever been in a parlor-car before?" he asked, smiling with delight.

"No," she answered; "I never was. It's fine, ain't it?"

"Great! And then after a while we'll go forward to the diner, and get a big lay-out. Finest meal in the world. Charge a dollar."

"Oh, do they?" cried the bride. "Charge a dollar? Why, that's too much—for us—ain't it, Jack?"

"Not this trip, anyhow," he answered bravely. "We're going to go the whole thing."

Later he explained to her about the trains. "You see, it's a thousand miles from one end of Texas to the other; and this train runs right across it, and never stops but four times." He had the pride of an owner. He pointed out to her the dazzling fittings of the coach; and in truth her eyes opened wider as she contemplated the sea-green figured velvet, the shining brass, silver, and glass, the wood that gleamed as darkly brilliant as the surface of a pool of oil. At one end a bronze figure sturdily held a support for a separated chamber, and at convenient places on the ceiling were frescos in olive and silver.

To the minds of the pair, their surroundings reflected the glory of their marriage that morning in San Antonio; this was the environment of their new estate; and the man's face in particular beamed with an elation that made him appear ridiculous to the Negro porter. This individual at times surveyed them from afar with an amused and superior grin. On other occasions he bullied them with skill in ways that did not make it exactly plain to them that they were being bullied. He subtly used all the manners of the most unconquerable kind of snobbery. He oppressed them; but on this oppression they had small knowledge, and they speedily forgot that infrequently a number of travellers covered them with stares of derisive enjoyment. Historically there was supposed to be something infinitely humorous in their situation.

"We are due in Yellow Sky at 3:42," he said, looking tenderly into her eyes.

"Oh, are we?" she said, as if she had not been aware of it. To evince surprise at her husband's statement was part of her wifely amiability. She took from a pocket a little silver watch; and as she held it before her, and stared at it with a frown of attention, the new husband's face shone.

"I bought it in San Anton' from a friend of mine," he told her gleefully.

"It's seventeen minutes past twelve," she said, looking up at him with a kind of shy and clumsy coquetry. A passenger. noting this play, grew excessively sardonic, and winked at himself in one of the numerous mirrors.

At last they went to the dining-car. Two rows of Negro waiters, in glowing white suits, surveyed their entrance with the interest, and also the equanimity, of men who had been forewarned. The pair fell to the lot of a waiter who happened to feel pleasure in steering them through their meal. He viewed them with the manner of a fatherly pilot, his countenance radiant with benevolence. The patronage, entwined with the ordinary deference, was not plain to them. And yet, as they returned to their coach, they showed in their faces a sense of escape.

To the left, miles down a long purple slope, was a little ribbon of mist where moved the keening Rio Grande. The train was approaching it at an angle, and the apex was Yellow Sky. Presently it was apparent that, as the distance from Yellow Sky grew shorter, the husband became commensurately restless. His brick-red hands were more insistent in their prominence. Occasionally he was even rather absent-minded and far-away when the bride leaned forward and addressed him.

As a matter of truth, Jack Potter was beginning to find the shadow of a deed weigh upon him like a leaden slab. He, the town marshal of Yellow Sky, a man known, liked, and feared in his corner, a prominent person, had gone to San Antonio to meet a girl he believed he loved, and there, after the usual prayers, had actually induced her to marry him, without consulting Yellow Sky for any part of the transaction. He was now bringing his bride before an innocent and unsuspecting community.

Of course people in Yellow Sky married as it pleased them, in accordance with a general custom; but such was Potter's thought of his duty to his friends, or of their idea of his duty, or of an unspoken form which does not control men in these matters, that he felt he was heinous. He had committed an extraordinary crime. Face to face with this girl in San Antonio, and spurred by his sharp impulse, he had gone headlong over all the social hedges. At San Antonio he was like a man hidden in the dark. A knife to sever any friendly duty, any form, was easy to his hand in that remote city. But the hour of Yellow Sky—the hour of daylight—was approaching.

He knew full well that his marriage was an important thing to his town. It could only be exceeded by the burning of the new hotel. His friends could not forgive him. Frequently he had reflected on the advisability of telling them by telegraph, but a new cowardice had been upon him. He feared to do it. And now the train was hurrying him toward a scene of amazement, glee, and reproach. He glanced out of the window at the line of haze swinging slowly in toward the train.

Yellow Sky had a kind of brass band, which played painfully, to the delight of the populace. He laughed without heart as he thought of it. If the citizens could dream of his prospective arrival with his bride, they would parade the band at the station and escort them, amid cheers and laughing congratulations to his adobe home.

He resolved that he would use all the devices of speed and plainscraft in making the journey from the station to his house. Once within that safe citadel, he could issue some sort of vocal bulletin, and then not go among the citizens until they had time to wear off a little of their enthusiasm.

The bride looked anxiously at him. "What's worrying you, Jack?"

He laughed again. "I'm not worrying, girl; I'm only thinking of Yellow Sky."

She flushed in comprehension.

A sense of mutual guilt invaded their minds and developed a finer tenderness. They looked at each other with eyes softly aglow. But Potter often laughed the same nervous laugh; the flush upon the bride's face seemed quite permanent.

The traitor to the feelings of Yellow Sky narrowly watched the speeding landscape. "We're nearly there," he said.

Presently the porter came and announced the proximity of Potter's home. He held a brush in his hand, and, with all his airy superiority gone, he brushed Potter's new clothes as the latter slowly turned this way and that way. Potter fumbled out a coin and gave it to the porter, as he had seen others do. It was a heavy and muscle-bound business, as that of a man shoeing his first horse.

The porter took their bag, and as the train began to slow they moved forward to the hooded platform of the car. Presently the two engines and their long string of coaches rushed into the station of Yellow Sky.

"They have to take water here," said Potter, from a constricted throat and in mournful cadence, as one announcing death. Before the train stopped his eyes had swept the length of the platform, and he was glad and astonished to see there was none upon it but the station-agent, who, with a slightly hurried and anxious air, was walking toward the water-tanks. When the train had halted, the porter alighted first, and placed in position a little temporary step.

"Come on, girl," said Potter, hoarsely. As he helped her down they each laughed on a false note. He took the bag from the Negro, and bade his wife cling to his arm. As they slunk rapidly away, his hang-dog glance perceived that they were unloading the two trunks, and also that the station-agent, far ahead near the baggage-car, had turned and was running toward him, making gestures. He laughed, and groaned as he laughed, when he noted the first effect of his marital bliss upon Yellow Sky. He gripped his wife's arm firmly to his side, and they fled. Behind them the porter stood, chuckling fatuously.

II

The California express on the Southern Railway was due at Yellow Sky in twenty-one minutes. There were six men at the bar of the Weary Gentleman saloon. One was a drummer who talked a great deal and rapidly; three were Texans who did not care to talk at that time; and two were Mexican sheepherders, who did not talk as a general practice in the Weary Gentleman saloon. The barkeeper's dog lay on the board walk that crossed in front of the door. His head was on his paws, and he glanced drowsily here and there with the constant vigilance of a dog that is kicked on occasion. Across the sandy street were some vivid green grass-plots, so wonderful in appearance, amid the sands that burned near them in a blazing sun, that they caused a doubt in the mind. They exactly resembled the grass mats used to represent lawns on the stage. At the cooler end of the railway station, a man without a coat sat in a tilted chair and smoked his pipe. The fresh-cut bank of the Rio Grande circled near the town, and there could be seen beyond it a great plum-coloured plain of mesquit.

Save for the busy drummer and his companions in the saloon, Yellow Sky was dozing. The new-comer leaned gracefully upon the bar, and recited many tales with the confidence of a bard who has come upon a new field.

"—and at the moment that the old man fell downstairs with the bureau in his arms, the old woman was coming up with two scuttles of coal, and of course—"

The drummer's tale was interrupted by a young man who suddenly appeared in the open door. He cried: "Scratchy Wilson's drunk, and has turned loose with both hands." The two Mexicans at once set down their glasses and faded out of the rear entrance of the saloon.

The drummer, innocent and jocular, answered: "All right, old man. S'pose he has? Come in and have a drink, anyhow."

But the information had made such an obvious cleft in every skull in the room that the drummer was obliged to see its importance. All had become instantly solemn. "Say," said he, mystified, "what is this?" His three companions made the introductory gesture of eloquent speech; but the young man at the door forestalled them.

"It means, my friend," he answered, as he came into the saloon, "that for the next two hours this town won't be a health resort."

The barkeeper went to the door, and locked and barred it; reaching out of the window, he pulled in heavy wooden shutters, and barred them. Immediately a solemn, chapel-like gloom was upon the place. The drummer was looking from one to another.

"But say," he cried, "what is this, anyhow? You don't mean there is going to be a gun-fight?"

"Don't know whether there'll be a fight or not," answered one man, grimly; "but there'll be some shootin'—some good shootin'."

The young man who had warned them waved his hand. "Oh, there'll be a fight fast enough, if any one wants it. Anybody can get a fight out there in the street. There's a fight just waiting."

The drummer seemed to be swayed between the interest of a foreigner and a perception of personal danger.

"What did you say his name was?" he asked.

"Scratchy Wilson," they answered in chorus.

"And will he kill anybody? What are you going to do? Does this happen often? Does he rampage around like this once a week or so? Can he break in that door?"

"No; he can't break down that door," replied the barkeeper. "He's tried it three times. But when he comes you'd better lay down on the floor, stranger. He's dead sure to shoot at it, and a bullet may come through."

Thereafter the drummer kept a strict eye upon the door. The time had not yet been called for him to hug the floor, but, as a minor precaution, he sidled near to the wall. "Will he kill anybody?" he said again.

The man laughed low and scornfully at the question.

"He's out to shoot, and he's out for trouble. Don't see any good in experimentin' with him."

"But what do you do in a case like this? What do you do?"

A man responded: "Why, he and Jack Potter—"

"But," in chorus the other men interrupted, "Jack Potter's in San Anton'."

"Well, who is he? What's he got to do with it?"

"Oh, he's the town marshal. He goes out and fights Scratchy when he gets on one of these tears."

"Wow!" said the drummer, mopping his brow. "Nice job he's got."

The voices had toned away to mere whisperings. The drummer wished to ask further questions, which were born of an increasing anxiety and bewilderment; but when he attempted them, the men merely looked at him in irritation and motioned him to remain silent. A tense waiting hush was upon them. In the deep shadows of the room their eyes shone as they listened for sounds from the street. One man made three gestures at the barkeeper; and the latter, moving like a ghost, handed him a glass and a bottle. The man poured a full glass of whisky, and set down the bottle noiselessly. He gulped the whisky in a swallow, and turned again toward the door in immovable silence. The drummer saw that the barkeeper, without a sound, had taken a Winchester from beneath the bar. Later he saw this individual beckoning to him, so he tiptoed across the room.

"You better come with me back of the bar."

"No, thanks," said the drummer, perspiring; "I'd rather be where I can make a break for the back door."

Whereupon the man of bottles made a kindly but peremptory gesture. The drummer obeyed it, and, finding himself seated on a box with his head below the level of the bar, balm was laid upon his soul at sight of various zinc and copper fittings that bore a resemblance to armour-plate. The barkeeper took a seat comfortably upon an adjacent box.

"You see," he whispered, "this here Scratchy Wilson is a wonder with a gun—a perfect wonder; and when he goes on the war-trail, we hunt our holes—naturally. He's about the last one of the old gang that used to hang out along the river here. He's a terror when he's drunk. When he's sober he's all right—kind of simple—wouldn't hurt a fly—nicest fellow in town. But when he's drunk—whoo!"

There were periods of stillness. "I wish Jack Potter was back from San Anton'," said the barkeeper. "He shot Wilson up once—in the leg— and he would sail in and pull out the kinks in this thing."

Presently they heard from a distance the sound of a shot, followed by three wild yowls. It instantly removed a bond from the men in the darkened saloon. There was a shuffling of feet. They looked at each other. "Here he comes," they said.

III

A man in a maroon-colored flannel shirt, which had been purchased for purposes of decoration, and made principally by some Jewish women on the East Side of New York, rounded a corner and walked into the middle of the main street of Yellow Sky. In either hand the man held a long, heavy, blue-black revolver. Often he yelled, and these cries rang through a semblance of a deserted village, shrilly flying over the roofs in a volume that seemed to have no relation to the ordinary vocal strength of a man. It was as if the surrounding stillness formed the arch of a tomb over him. These cries of ferocious challenge rang against walls of silence. And his boots had red tops with gilded imprints, of the kind beloved in winter by little sledding boys on the hillsides of New England.

The man's face flamed in a rage begot of whisky. His eyes, rolling, and yet keen for ambush, hunted the still doorways and windows. He walked with the creeping movement of the midnight cat. As it occurred to him, he roared menacing information. The long revolvers in his hands were as easy as straws; they were moved with an electric swiftness. The little fingers of each hand played sometimes in a musician's way. Plain from the low collar of the shirt, the cords of his neck straightened and sank, straightened and sank, as passion moved him. The only sounds were his terrible invitations. The calm adobes preserved their demeanour at the passing of this small thing in the middle of the street.

There was no offer of fight—no offer of fight. The man called to the sky. There were no attractions. He bellowed and fumed and swayed his revolvers here and everywhere.

The dog of the barkeeper of the Weary Gentleman saloon had not appreciated the advance of events. He yet lay dozing in front of his master's door. At sight of the dog, the man paused and raised his revolver humorously. At sight of the man, the dog sprang up and walked diagonally away, with a sullen head, and growling. The man yelled, and the dog broke into a gallop. As it was about to enter an alley, there was a loud noise, a whistling, and something spat the ground directly before it. The dog screamed, and, wheeling in terror, galloped headlong in a new direction. Again there was a noise, a whistling, and sand was kicked viciously before it. Fear-stricken, the dog turned and flurried like an animal in a pen. The man stood laughing, his weapons at his hips.

Ultimately the man was attracted by the closed door of the Weary Gentleman saloon. He went to it and, hammering with a revolver, demanded drink.

The door remaining imperturbable, he picked a bit of paper from the walk, and nailed it to the framework with a knife. He then turned his back contemptuously upon this popular resort and, walking to the opposite side of the street and spinning there on his heel quickly and lithely, fired at the bit of paper. He missed it by a half-inch. He swore at himself, and went away. Later he comfortably fusilladed the windows of his most intimate friend. The man was playing with this town; it was a toy for him.

But still there was no offer of fight. The name of Jack Potter, his ancient antagonist, entered his mind, and he concluded that it would be a glad thing if he should go to Potter's house, and by bombardment induce him to come out and fight. He moved in the direction of his desire, chanting Apache scalp-music.

When he arrived at it, Potter's house presented the same still front as had the other adobes. Taking up a strategic position, the man howled a challenge. But this house regarded him as might a great stone god. It gave no sign. After a decent wait, the man howled further challenges, mingling with them wonderful epithets.

Presently there came the spectacle of a man churning himself into deepest rage over the immobility of a house. He fumed at it as the winter wind attacks a prairie cabin in the North. To the distance there should have gone the sound of a tumult like the fighting of two hundred Mexicans. As necessity bade him, he paused for breath or to reload his revolvers.

IV

Potter and his bride walked sheepishly and with speed. Sometimes they laughed together shamefacedly and low.

"Next corner, dear," he said finally.

They put forth the efforts of a pair walking bowed against a strong wind. Potter was about to raise a finger to point the first appearance of the new home when, as they circled the corner, they came face to face with a man in a maroon-colored shirt, who was feverishly pushing cartridges into a large revolver. Upon the instant the man dropped his revolver to the ground and, like lightning, whipped another from its holster. The second weapon was aimed at the bridegroom's chest.

There was a silence. Potter's mouth seemed to be merely a grave for his tongue. He exhibited an instinct to at once loosen his arm from the woman's grip, and he dropped the bag to the sand. As for the bride, her face had gone as yellow as old cloth. She was a slave to hideous rites, gazing at the apparitional snake.

The two men faced each other at a distance of three paces. He of the revolver smiled with a new and quiet ferocity.

"Tried to sneak up on me," he said. "Tried to sneak up on me!" His eyes grew more baleful. As Potter made a slight movement, the man thrust his revolver venomously forward. "No; don't you do it, Jack Potter. Don't you move a finger toward a gun just yet. Don't you move an eyelash. The time has come for me to settle with you, and I'm goin' to do it my own way, and loaf along with no interferin'. So if you don't want a gun bent on you, just mind what I tell you."

Potter looked at his enemy. "I ain't got a gun on me, Scratchy," he said. "Honest, I ain't." He was stiffening and steadying, but yet somewhere at the back of his mind a vision of the Pullman floated: the sea-green figured velvet, the shining brass, silver, and glass, the wood that gleamed as darkly brilliant as the surface of a pool of oil—all the glory of the marriage, the environment of the new estate. "You know I fight when it comes to fighting, Scratchy Wilson; but I ain't got a gun on me. You'll have to do all the shootin' yourself."

His enemy's face went livid. He stepped forward, and lashed his weapon to and fro before Potter's chest. "Don't you tell me you ain't got no gun on you, you whelp. Don't tell me no lie like that. There ain't a man in Texas ever seen you without no gun. Don't take me for no kid." His eyes blazed with light, and his throat worked like a pump.

"I ain't takin' you for no kid," answered Potter. His heels had not moved an inch backward. "I'm takin' you for a damn fool. I tell you I ain't got a gun, and I ain't. If you're goin' to shoot me up, you better begin now; you'll never get a chance like this again."

So much enforced reasoning had told on Wilson's rage; he was calmer. "If you ain't got a gun, why ain't you got a gun?" he sneered. "Been to Sunday-school?"

"I ain't got a gun because I've just come from San Anton' with my wife. I'm married," said Potter. "And if I'd thought there was going to be any galoots like you prowling around when I brought my wife home, I'd had a gun, and don't you forget it."

"Married!" said Scratchy, not at all comprehending.

"Yes, married. I'm married," said Potter, distinctly.

"Married?" said Scratchy. Seemingly for the first time, he saw the drooping, drowning woman at the other man's side. "No!" he said. He was like a creature allowed a glimpse of another world. He moved a pace backward, and his arm, with the revolver, dropped to his side. "Is this the lady?" he asked.

"Yes; this is the lady," answered Potter.

There was another period of silence.

"Well," said Wilson at last, slowly, "I s'pose it's all off now."

"It's all off if you say so, Scratchy. You know I didn't make the trouble." Potter lifted his valise.

"Well, I 'low it's off, Jack," said Wilson. He was looking at the ground. "Married!" He was not a student of chivalry; it was merely that in the presence of this foreign condition he was a simple child of the earlier plains. He picked up his starboard revolver, and, placing both weapons in their holsters, he went away. His feet made funnel-shaped tracks in the heavy sand.

INTERPRETATION

1. What pattern, or patterns, do you discover in the plot of this story? Does the kind of patterning used have any relation to the fact that the story is divided into parts? What relation does the patterning have to suspense?

2. What is the attitude of the narrator toward his characters? How would you describe the tone of the story?

3. What do you take to be the theme of the story? What relation does the theme of the story have to the last line: "His feet made funnel-shaped tracks in the heavy sand"? Why doesn't Crane write: "The high heels of his boots made funnel-shaped tracks in the heavy sand"?

What Character Reveals

THE stories in this section can be usefully considered with a special view to the problem of character in fiction. But as we have had occasion to observe several times before this, fiction never deals with character in isolation, for what a man is determines what he does, and it is primarily through what he does that we who observe him know what he is.

The proof of the inextricable interweaving of character and action may be most readily seen by a glance back at the stories in the preceding section. Though our attention was focused there upon problems of plot, we found that we could not discuss these stories without going into the problems of character. We had constantly to ask whether the actions performed were "in character"; that is, whether they were psychologically credible. We had to ask too whether the actions performed were significant in terms of character.

Though plot and character interpenetrate each other, there is some justification for stressing one problem at a time: let us consider here some of the problems of characterization. One may begin with the problem of exposition. In some fundamental sense, every character in fiction must resemble ourselves; that is, he must be recognizably human even as we are human. But some characters are obviously much more special than others, and require much fuller descriptive characterization. In "The Lottery" the characters are simple village types. Though the modern American suburbanite may consider these people a bit archaic, still he will have no real difficulty in understanding them. They are ordinary and typical, rather than special, and the author needs no elaborate techniques in presenting them. But Dravot in "The Man Who Would Be King" is a man quite outside the average reader's common acquaintance—in many ways a most unusual man—and if he is to seem real, he must be convincingly presented. The fact that Dravot is a man of action, not a meditative and introspective man, makes the author's task easier. If the character's inward life is more complicated and significant than his outer, more special problems of presentation may arise. Walter Mitty is a fairly simple instance of this kind of introverted character. Or, consider Ruby Fisher, the heroine of "A Piece of News," who would be regarded by most people as a rather simple character. Certainly she is an unsophisticated and even primitive character. Yet the "action" of this story has to do almost entirely with her interior life, and part of the charm of this story is its revelation of the unsuspected introspective depths of a "simple" person.

How shall the author present his character? Directly, with a summary of his traits and characteristics; or dramatically, through dialogue and action? The very nature of fiction suggests that the latter is its characteristic means and yet a more direct presentation is constantly used in fiction, and frequently effectively used. Much depends upon the underlying purpose of the story and much depends upon matters of scope and scale. If the author made every presentation of character indirect, insisting that each character gradually unfold himself through natural talk and gesture and action, the procedure might become intolerably boring. "The Necklace" will indicate how direct presentation—and even summary presentation—may be properly and effectively used. (Look back at the first three paragraphs of this story, p. 106). But when he comes to the significant scenes of the story, the author of "The Necklace" discards summary in favor of dramatic presentation.

The danger of a direct presentation is that it tends to forfeit the vividness of drama and the reader's imaginative participation. Direct presentation works best, therefore, with rather flat and typical characters, or as a means to get rapidly over more perfunctory materials. When the direct presentation of character becomes also a direct commentary on the character, the author may find himself "telling" us what to feel and think rather than "rendering" a scene for our imaginative participation. O. Henry's "The Furnished Room" will illustrate. The author tends to "editorialize" on the hero's motives and beliefs, and the author's constant plucking at the reader's sleeve and nudging him to sympathize with the hero's plight may become so irritating that the whole scene seems falsified. Yet a story later to be read in this section, D. H. Lawrence's "Tickets, Please," will indicate how direct commentary—and even explicit interpretation of the characters' motives—may on occasion be effectively used by the author.

The contrast between rather ordinary characters and out-of-the-way characters can be used to suggest the opposing extremes that bound the domain of fiction. The ordinary and typical characters tend to be secondary in a story. If they are its most prominent characters, then the story is probably tilted toward the fable or the parable. (*Completely* flat characters, mere types, of course, would probably take us out of fiction altogether: even if every hero does at some level represent all of us, still no story can be about that pure abstraction, common humanity as such.)

At the opposite extreme, we find the fictional character who is so eccentric, so much out of the way, so perverse, that he ceases to be humanly credible. Fiction at this point passes off imperceptibly into the psychiatrist's case study. This is not to put narrow limits upon what the artist can do. If one looks deep enough, any character reveals complexities and eccentricities. The great and interesting personalities are indeed in a sense unique and unpredictable. Even madness is not to be automatically ruled out of the subject matter of fiction. In a story to be read later in this text, William Faulkner's "A Rose for Emily," the author tells us the story of a character perverted to the point of madness, and yet many people will feel that the story has a large human significance, and is not merely a clincian's report. (See also the comments on "An Occurrence at Owl Creek Bridge, pp. 122–123, and "A Good Man is Hard to Find," p. 355.)

The domain of fiction is, then, the world of credible human beings, admittedly an amazingly diverse and varied world. Since it is the world of human beings, it can be presented concretely and dramatically. What it excludes at either end is the world of pure abstraction: economic man, Mrs. Average Housewife, the typical American, *homo sapiens;* and at the other extreme, the mere freak, the psychological monster, the report from the psychiatrist's casebook. (But of course an artist may be able to put Mrs. Average Housewife or the young man with the classic Oedipus complex into a successful story. To do so, of course, he must satisfy more than a scientific and statistical interest: the abstraction must be made credible and significant, which means it ceases to be a mere abstraction.)

From what has been said already, it is plain that the author's selection of modes of character presentation will depend upon a number of things. His decision on when to summarize traits or events, on when to describe directly, and on when to allow the character to express his feelings through dialogue and action, will depend upon the general end of the story and upon the way in which the action of the story is to be developed from a beginning, through a complicating middle, to an inevitable end.

One of the most important modes for character revelation is of course the way in which characters talk. The laconic soldier, the querulous charwoman, the shy convent-school girl, the garrulous barkeep, the pedantic professor—all have their own vocabularies and their ways of putting words together. The artist in order to be convincing must have his characters speak "in character," and his normal way of presenting the unusual character is to give us the flavor of his peculiar dialect and idiom.

This use of speech is a rich resource for dramatic presentation. But again, if used incessantly it might kill the story by making it too talky. Indirect discourse, like character summary and character description, is a quicker way of getting over the ground, and in fiction has its very important uses. Notice, for example, in "War" (pp. 152–153) that the husband's speech in which he explains why his wife and he are to be pitied is very properly put into indirect discourse: "And he felt it his duty to explain . . . that the poor woman was to be pitied, for the war was taking away her only son, . . ." But the speeches of the "fat, red-faced man" who argues for the sublimity of sacrificing one's son for one's country have to be given as direct discourse. The importance of those speeches to the story, the need for dramatic vividness, the very pace of the story—all call for direct discourse. Thus we have: " 'Nonsense,' interrupted another traveler," etc. (p. 153).

So important is character to fiction that one way in which to approach the basic pattern of a story is to ask: "Whose story is this?" In other words, it usually is of first importance to see whose fortunes are at stake—whose situation is settled by the events that are described. Sometimes the answer is quite obvious. In "The Secret Life of Walter Mitty," for example, it is very easy to see that this is Mr. Mitty's story and not Mrs. Mitty's. Her only function is to throw light upon her husband's situation. Mrs. Mitty undoubtedly has a story—who of us has not?—and James Thurber might have elected to tell it. But he has not done so here. It is easy to see that this is Mr. Mitty's story, but it is not so easy to see whose story it is that is related in "The Man Who Would Be King." One is inclined to say that it is Dravot's story. He is pictured as the dominant member of the pair; it is he who rises to the heroic gesture at the end and who dies like a king. Yet one could at least argue that this is Peachey's story since he too learns the nature of kingship through witnessing Dravot's heroic action, and since, magnificently loyal to the memory of Dravot, he acts out a heroic role himself. But even when it is not easy to say—or even important to determine—precisely whose story it is, the question is usually worth putting. For to entertain the question is to throw light upon the relation of character with character.

One further word about the Dravot-Peachey relationship: we shall encounter in this text stories in which the story primarily belongs to "Peachey"—that is, to the observer of the action rather than to the most prominent actor himself (see p. 147). For what "happens" in the story is not necessarily some external thing. An internal thing—a shifted relationship, a change of heart—may decisively change the life of a man.

When we ask of "The Lottery" whose story this is, we find ourselves in real difficulties. For if we say that it is Mrs. Hutchinson's story because it is Mrs. Hutchinson who draws the black spot and is stoned to death, we realize that in the terms of the story itself, it might just as easily have been one of a hundred other people. One is driven finally to say that this is the story of the community itself, or to put the same thing in a slightly different way, this is the story of Man—of any human being living in a community—its supporter and its victim. But this kind of answer simply draws attention again to the fact that "The Lottery" is a rather special kind of story, tilted over toward parable.

In our earlier discussion of plot we had a good deal to say about conflict in fiction. Conflict has the closest relation to character, for we cannot remain long interested in conflicts between impersonal forces. If conflicts between animals are more interesting, that is because we can rather easily project ourselves into them. We actually make some such projection even in the instance of a man's conflict with the elements or with some other inanimate force. A man who is fighting a fire or trying to beat his way through a great storm, or who is trying to hold out against hunger and pain is likely to treat the impersonal force as if it were another being—the Enemy.

Man's contest with external forces is the simplest kind of struggle and finally the least interesting. Few stories deal with it in purity. The great and typical human conflict is one human being's conflict with other human beings. This is the material out of which most of our fiction is made. Here we find the typical story of the hero defeating the villain, of the true lover winning out over the wealthy roué, of the amateur detective outwitting the Machiavellian murderer. These are the standard contests of our more popular fiction. But in this general category of one human being against another, we also find stories of greater sensitivity and depth and penetration. For human beings, being the mixture of good and bad that they are, frequently find themselves at cross purposes and in conflict—not only with outsiders but with aspects of their own natures. Indeed, the more mature examples of conflict between character and character shade off into the third category which has to do with man's conflict with himself.

One can illustrate this last statement by referring to some of the stories that we have already read. "The Man Who Would Be King" is an "action" story and we think of the conflict as primarily a conflict between Dravot and the wild tribesmen upon whom he means to impose his will. But even in this story, a more important and significant conflict occurs within Dravot himself. The conflict between his appetites and his sense of statesmanship costs Dravot his kingdom. But it is through another inward event, Dravot's conquest of himself, that his final spiritual victory comes. One can also illustrate the importance of inward conflict from Pirandello's story "War." Ostensibly the conflict is between the fervent old man's attitude toward dying for one's country and the attitudes of his frightened and apprehensive, all-too-human companions in the railway compartment. The old man's passionate arguments prevail over the minds of the others; but in convincing them, he discovers for the first time that he has never really convinced himself.

Earlier in this book we argued for the importance of the truth of coherence as distinguished from the truth of correspondence. Since a work of literature does not pretend to be a factual document of actual events, but a typical and representative "action," the demands of truth of correspondence tend to be limited to correspondence to human nature and to the human norms. Within the story or poem itself we are primarily and unremittingly concerned with truth of coherence—with how the parts cohere into a total meaningful pattern. (In this connection the student may want to reread pp. 26–28.)

Nowhere are the claims for coherence asserted more plainly than in the matter of character presentation. A character must be credible—must make sense, must be able to command our belief. True, the character in question may be an eccentric; he may be brutally criminal; he may even be mad. But his thoughts and actions must ultimately be coherent. If the characters in a story simply don't make sense, we have to reject the story. But we must remember that the kind of sense a character must make is his own kind, not our kind. For example, a more sensible, less proud woman than Madame Loisel in "The Necklace" (p. 106) might have made a clean breast of things to her friend and been spared the terrible and unnecessary consequences, but it is the coherence of Madame Loisel's character that Maupassant must convince us of. If he does not convince us that his Madame Loisel is really capable of accepting, and persisting through, the life of hardship that comes with the loss of the necklace, then the story itself is incredible. Unless Eudora Welty has convinced us that Ruby Fisher is capable of entertaining the fantasy which the chance-read newspaper suggests to her, then her story makes no sense. An obvious test of fiction then is that the motives and actions of its characters are rendered coherent. It is the glory of fiction that the great artists have been able to render coherent so many strange and out-of-the-way, often apparently self-contradictory, examples of human nature.

BRET HARTE

Tennessee's Partner

I DO not think that we ever knew his real name. Our ignorance of it certainly never gave us any social inconvenience, for at Sandy Bar in 1854 most men were christened anew. Sometimes these appellatives were derived from some distinctiveness of dress, as in the case of "Dungaree Jack"; or from some peculiarity of habit, as shown in "Saleratus Bill," so called from an undue proportion of that chemical in his daily bread; or from some unlucky slip, as exhibited in "The Iron Pirate," a mild, inoffensive man, who earned that baleful title by his unfortunate mispronunciation of the term "iron pyrites." Perhaps this may have been the beginning of a rude heraldry; but I am constrained to think that it was because a man's real name in that day rested solely upon his own unsupported statement. "Call yourself Clifford, do you?" said Boston, addressing a timid newcomer with infinite scorn; "hell is full of such Cliffords!" He then introduced the unfortunate man, whose name happened to be really Clifford, as "Jay-bird Charley"—an unhallowed inspiration of the moment that clung to him ever after.

But to return to Tennessee's Partner, whom we never knew by any other than this relative title. That he had ever existed as a separate and distinct individuality we only learned later. It seems that in 1853 he left Poker Flat to go to San Francisco, ostensibly to procure a wife. He never got any farther than Stockton. At that place he was attracted by a young person who waited upon the table at the hotel where he took his meals. One morning he said something to her which caused her to smile not unkindly, to somewhat coquettishly break a plate of toast over his upturned, serious, simple face, and to retreat to the kitchen. He followed her, and emerged a few moments later, covered with more toast and victory. That day week they were married by a justice of the peace, and returned to Poker Flat. I am aware that something more might be made of this episode, but I prefer to tell it as it was current at Sandy Bar—in the gulches and barrooms—where all sentiment was modified by a strong sense of humor.

Of their married felicity but little is known, perhaps for the reason that Tennessee, then living with his partner, one day took occasion to say something to the bride on his own account, at which, it is said, she smiled not unkindly and chastely retreated—this time as far as Marysville, where

174

Tennessee followed her, and where they went to housekeeping without the aid of a justice of the peace. Tennessee's Partner took the loss of his wife simply and seriously, as was his fashion. But to everybody's surprise, when Tennessee one day returned from Marysville, without his partner's wife—she having smiled and retreated with somebody else—Tennessee's Partner was the first man to shake his hand and greet him with affection. The boys who had gathered in the cañon to see the shooting were naturally indignant. Their indignation might have found vent in sarcasm but for a certain look in Tennessee's Partner's eye that indicated a lack of humorous appreciation. In fact, he was a grave man, with a steady application to practical detail which was unpleasant in a difficulty.

Meanwhile a popular feeling against Tennessee had grown up on the Bar. He was known to be a gambler; he was suspected to be a thief. In these suspicions Tennessee's Partner was equally compromised; his continued intimacy with Tennessee after the affair above quoted could only be accounted for on the hypothesis of a copartnership of crime. At last Tennessee's guilt became flagrant. One day he overtook a stranger on his way to Red Dog. The stranger afterward related that Tennessee beguiled the time with interesting anecdote and reminiscence, but illogically concluded the interview in the following words: "And now, young man, I'll trouble you for your knife, your pistols, and your money. You see your weppings might get you into trouble at Red Dog, and your money's a temptation to the evilly disposed. I think you said your address was San Francisco. I shall endeavor to call." It may be stated here that Tennessee had a fine flow of humor, which no business preoccupation could wholly subdue.

This exploit was his last. Red Dog and Sandy Bar made common cause against the highwayman. Tennessee was hunted in very much the same fashion as his prototype, the grizzly. As the toils closed around him, he made a desperate dash through the Bar, emptying his revolver at the crowd before the Arcade Saloon, and so on up Grizzly Cañon; but at its farther extremity he was stopped by a small man on a gray horse. The men looked at each other a moment in silence. Both were fearless, both self-possessed and independent; and both types of a civilization that in the seventeenth century would have been called heroic, but in the nineteenth simply "reckless."

"What have you got there?—I call," said Tennessee, quietly.

"Two bowers and an ace," said the stranger, as quietly, showing two revolvers and a bowie knife.

"That takes me," returned Tennessee; and, with this gambler's epigram, he threw away his useless pistol, and rode back with his captor.

It was a warm night. The cool breeze which usually sprang up with the going down of the sun behind the chaparral-crested mountain was that evening withheld from Sandy Bar. The little cañon was stifling with heated resinous odors, and the decaying driftwood on the Bar sent forth faint, sickening exhalations. The feverishness of day and its fierce passions still filled the camp. Lights moved restlessly along the bank of the river, striking no answering reflection from its tawny current. Against the blackness of the pines the windows of the old loft above the express office stood out staringly bright; and through their curtainless panes the loungers below could see the forms of those who were even then deciding the fate of Tennessee. And above all this, etched on the dark firmament, rose the Sierra, remote and passionless, crowned with remoter passionless stars.

The trial of Tennessee was conducted as fairly as was consistent with a judge and jury who felt themselves to some extent obliged to justify, in their verdict, the previous irregularities of arrest and indictment. The law of Sandy Bar was implacable, but not vengeful. The excitement and personal feeling of the chase were over; with Tennessee safe in their hands, they were ready to listen patiently to any defense, which they were already satisfied was insufficient. There being no doubt in their own minds, they were willing to give the prisoner the benefit of any that might exist. Secure in the hypothesis that he ought to be hanged on general principles, they indulged him with more latitude of defense than his reckless hardihood seemed to ask. The judge appeared to be more anxious than the prisoner, who, otherwise unconcerned, evidently took a grim pleasure in the responsibility he had created. "I don't take any hand in this yer game," had been his invariable, but good-humored reply to all questions. The judge—who was also his captor—for a moment vaguely regretted that he had not shot him "on sight" that morning, but presently dismissed this human weakness as unworthy of the judicial mind. Nevertheless, when there was a tap at the door, and it was said that Tennessee's Partner was there on behalf of the prisoner, he was admitted at once without question. Perhaps the younger members of the jury, to whom the proceedings were becoming irksomely thoughtful, hailed him as a relief.

For he was not, certainly, an imposing figure. Short and stout, with a square face, sunburned into a preternatural redness, clad in a loose duck "jumper" and trousers streaked and splashed with red soil, his aspect under any circumstances would have been quaint, and was now even ridiculous. As he stooped to deposit at his feet a heavy carpetbag he was carrying, it became obvious, from partially developed legends and inscriptions, that the material with which his trousers had been patched had been originally intended for a less ambitious covering. Yet he advanced with great gravity, and after having shaken the hand of each person in the room with labored cordiality, he wiped his serious perplexed face on a red bandana handkerchief, a shade lighter than his complexion, laid his powerful hand upon the table to steady himself, and thus addressed the judge:

"I was passin' by," he began, by way of apology, "and I thought I'd just step in and see how things was gittin' on with Tennessee thar—my pardner. It's a hot night. I disremember any sich weather before on the Bar."

He paused a moment, but nobody volunteering any other meteorological recollection, he again had recourse to his pocket handkerchief, and for some moments mopped his face diligently.

"Have you anything to say on behalf of the prisoner?" said the judge finally.

"Thet's it," said Tennessee's Partner, in a tone of relief. "I come yar as Tennessee's pardner—knowing him nigh on four year, off and on, wet and dry, in luck and out o' luck. His ways ain't aller my ways, but thar ain't any p'ints in that young man, thar ain't any liveliness as he's been up to, as I don't know. And you sez to me, sez you—confidential-like, and between man and man—sez you, 'Do you know anything in his behalf?' and I sez to you, sez I—confidential-like, as between man and man—'What should a man know of his pardner?'"

"Is this all you have to say?" asked the judge impatiently, feeling, perhaps, that a dangerous sympathy of humor was beginning to humanize the court.

"Thet's so," continued Tennessee's Partner. "It ain't for me to say anything agin' him. And now, what's the case? Here's Tennessee wants money, wants it bad, and doesn't like to ask it of his old pardner. Well, what does Tennessee do? He lays for a stranger, and he fetches that stranger; and you lays for *him*, and you fetches *him*; and the honors is easy. And I put it to you, bein' a fa'r-minded man, and to you, gentlemen all, as fa'r-minded men, ef this isn't so."

"Prisoner," said the judge, interrupting, "have you any questions to ask this man?"

"No! no!" continued Tennessee's Partner, hastily. "I play this yer hand alone. To come down to the bedrock, it's just this: Tennessee, thar, has played it pretty rough and expensive-like on a stranger, and on this yer camp. And now, what's the fair thing? Some would say more, some would say less. Here's seventeen hundred dollars in coarse gold and a watch,—it's about all my pile,—and call it square!" And before a hand could be raised to prevent him, he had emptied the contents of the carpetbag upon the table.

For a moment his life was in jeopardy. One or two men sprang to their feet, several hands groped for hidden weapons, and a suggestion to "throw him from the window" was only overridden by a gesture from the judge. Tennessee laughed. And apparently oblivious of the excitement, Tennessee's Partner improved the opportunity to mop his face again with his handkerchief.

When order was restored, and the man was made to understand, by the use of forcible figures and rhetoric, that Tennessee's offense could not be condoned by money, his face took a more serious and sanguinary hue, and those who were nearest to him noticed that his rough hand trembled slightly on the table. He hesitated a moment as he slowly returned the gold to the carpetbag, as if he had not yet entirely caught the elevated sense of justice which swayed the tribunal, and was perplexed with the belief that he had not offered enough. Then he turned to the judge, and saying, "This yer is a lone hand, played alone, and without my pardner," he bowed to the jury and was about to withdraw, when the judge called him back:

"If you have anything to say to Tennessee, you had better say it now."

For the first time that evening the eyes of the prisoner and his strange advocate met. Tennessee smiled, showed his white teeth, and saying, "Euchred, old man!" held out his hand. Tennessee's Partner took it in his own, and saying, "I just dropped in as I was passin' to see how things was gettin' on," let the hand passively fall, and adding that "it was a warm night," again mopped his face with his handkerchief, and without another word withdrew.

The two men never again met each other alive. For the unparalleled insult of a bribe offered to Judge Lynch—who, whether bigoted, weak, or narrow, was at least incorruptible—firmly fixed in the mind of that mythical personage any wavering determination of Tennessee's fate; and at the break of day he was marched, closely guarded, to meet it at the top of Marley's Hill.

How he met it, how cool he was, how he refused to say anything, how perfect were the arrangements of the committee, were all duly reported, with the addition of a warning moral and example to all future evil-doers, in the *Red Dog Clarion*, by its editor, who was present, and to whose vigorous English I cheerfully refer the reader. But the beauty of that midsummer morning, the blessed amity of earth and air and sky, the awakened life of the free woods and hills, the joyous renewal and promise of Nature, and above all, the infinite serenity that thrilled through each, was not reported, as not being a part of the social lesson. And yet, when the weak and foolish deed was done, and a life, with its possibilities and responsibilities, had passed out of the misshapen thing that dangled between earth and sky, the birds sang, the flowers bloomed, the sun shone, as cheerily as before; and possibly the *Red Dog Clarion* was right.

Tennessee's Partner was not in the group that surrounded the ominous tree. But as they turned to disperse, attention was drawn to the singular appearance of a motionless donkey cart halted at the side of the road. As they approached, they at once recognized the venerable Jenny and the two-wheeled cart as the property of Tennessee's Partner, used by him in carrying dirt from his claim; and a few paces distant the owner of the equipage himself, sitting under a buckeye tree, wiping the perspiration from his glowing face. In answer to an inquiry, he said he had come for the body of the "diseased," "if it was all the same to the committee." He didn't wish to "hurry anything"; he could "wait." He was not working that day; and when the gentlemen were done with the "diseased," he would take him. "Ef thar is any present," he added, in his simple, serious way, "as would care to jine in the fun'l, they kin come." Perhaps it was from a sense of humor, which I have already intimated was a feature of Sandy Bar—perhaps it was from something even better than that, but two thirds of the loungers accepted the invitation at once.

It was noon when the body of Tennessee was delivered into the hands of his partner. As the cart drew up to the fatal tree, we noticed that it contained a rough oblong box,—apparently made from a section of sluicing,—and half filled with bark and the tassels of pine. The cart was further decorated with slips of willow, and made fragrant with buckeye blossoms. When the body was deposited in the box, Tennessee's Partner drew over it a piece of tarred canvas, and gravely mounting the narrow seat in front, with his feet upon the shafts, urged the little donkey forward. The equipage moved slowly on, at that decorous pace which was habitual with Jenny even under less solemn circumstances. The men—half curiously, half jestingly, but all good-humoredly—strolled along beside the cart, some in advance, some a little in the rear of the homely catafalque. But whether from the narrowing of the road or some present sense of decorum, as the cart passed on, the company fell to the rear in couples, keeping step, and otherwise assuming the external show of a formal procession. Jack Folinsbee, who had at the outset played a funeral march in dumb show upon an imaginary trombone, desisted from a lack of sympathy and appreciation—not having, perhaps, your true humorist's capacity to be content with the enjoyment of his own fun.

The way led through Grizzly Cañon, by this time clothed in funereal drapery and shadows. The redwoods, burying their moccasined feet in the red soil, stood in Indian file along the track, trailing an uncouth benediction from their bending boughs upon the passing bier. A hare, surprised into helpless inactivity, sat upright and pulsating in the ferns by the roadside, as the cortège went by. Squirrels hastened to gain a secure outlook from higher boughs; and the bluejays, spreading their wings, fluttered before them like outriders, until the outskirts of Sandy Bar were reached, and the solitary cabin of Tennessee's Partner.

Viewed under more favorable circumstances, it would not have been a cheerful place. The unpicturesque site, the rude and unlovely outlines, the unsavory details, which distinguish the nest-building of the California miner, were all here, with the dreariness of decay superadded. A few paces from the cabin there was a rough enclosure, which, in the brief days of Tennessee's Partner's matrimonial felicity, had been used as a garden, but was now overgrown with fern. As we approached it, we were surprised to find that what we had taken for a recent attempt at cultivation was the broken soil about an open grave.

The cart was halted before the enclosure, and rejecting the offers of assistance with the same air of simple self-reliance he had displayed throughout, Tennessee's Partner lifted the rough coffin on his back, and deposited it unaided within the shallow grave. He then nailed down the board which served as a lid, and mounting the little mound of earth beside it, took off his hat and slowly mopped his face with his handkerchief. This the crowd felt was a preliminary to speech, and they disposed themselves variously on stumps and boulders, and sat expectant.

"When a man," began Tennessee's Partner slowly, "has been running free all day, what's the natural thing for him to do? Why, to come home. And if he ain't in a condition to go home, what can his best friend do? Why, bring him home. And here's Tennessee has been running free, and we brings him home from his wandering." He paused and picked up a fragment of quartz, rubbed it thoughtfully on his sleeve and went on: "It ain't the first time I've packed him on my back, as you see'd me now. It ain't the first time that I brought him to this yer cabin when he couldn't help himself; it ain't the first time that I and Jinny have waited for him on yon hill, and picked him up and so fetched him home, when he couldn't speak and didn't know me. And now that it's the last time, why"—he paused, and rubbed the quartz gently on his sleeve—"you see it's sort of rough on his pardner. And now, gentlemen," he added abruptly, picking up his long-handled shovel, "the fun'l's over; and my thanks, and Tennessee's thanks, to you for your trouble."

Resisting any proffers of assistance, he began to fill in the grave, turning his back upon the crowd, that after a few moments' hesitation gradually withdrew. As they crossed the little ridge that hid Sandy Bar from view, some, looking back, thought they could see Tennessee's Partner, his work done, sitting upon the grave, his shovel between his knees, and his face buried in his red bandana handkerchief. But it was argued by others that you couldn't tell his face from his handkerchief at that distance, and this point remained undecided.

In the reaction that followed the feverish excitement of that day, Tennessee's Partner was not forgotten. A secret investigation had cleared him of any complicity in Tennessee's guilt, and left only a suspicion of his general sanity. Sandy Bar made a point of calling on him, and proffering various uncouth but well-meant kindnesses. But from that day his rude health and great strength seemed visibly to decline; and when the rainy season fairly set in, and the tiny grass blades were beginning to peep from the rocky mound above Tennessee's grave, he took to his bed.

One night, when the pines beside the cabin were swaying in the storm and trailing their slender fingers over the roof, and the roar and rush of the swollen river were heard below, Tennessee's Partner lifted his head from the pillow, saying, "It is time to go for Tennessee; I must put Jinny in the cart"; and would have risen from his bed but for the restraint of his attendant. Struggling, he still pursued his singular fancy: "There, now, steady, Jinny—steady, old girl. How dark it is! Look out for the ruts—and look out for him, too, old gal. Sometimes, you know, when he's blind drunk, he drops down right in the trail. Keep on straight up to the pine on the top of the hill. Thar! I told you so!—thar he is—coming this way, too—all by himself, sober, and his face a-shining. Tennessee! Pardner!"

And so they met.

INTERPRETATION

This is the story of a man's intense loyalty to his friend. The man Tennessee actually steals his partner's wife, but the friendship of the men survives even this severe test: they become reconciled, and later after Tennessee has been executed for highway robbery, his partner claims the body, buries it with such rites of decency as he can contrive, and soon himself wastes away and dies. What makes this display of loyalty even more remarkable, and perhaps, therefore, all the more moving, is that Tennessee's partner is not a man to whom we would ordinarily ascribe much delicacy of feeling. Not that this latter point invalidates the story. Other writers have remarked upon the intensity and rightness of the feelings of simple and "unliterary" persons. William Wordsworth makes this point over and over again in poetry. Or, to take an instance from a contemporary writer, Ernest Hemingway frequently allows his "tough" and "hard-boiled" characters to reveal a sensitivity that belies their apparent callousness (see p. 310).

The difficulty with this story has to do with the credibility of the actions of Tennessee's partner. Do we really believe that he would act so magnanimously? That will depend upon our understanding of his character; and that in turn will have to do with Bret Harte's presentation of the psychological steps by which Tennessee's partner arrives at the actions in question. In any case, the episode of the wife-stealing will be the hardest to accept.

The community in this instance certainly expected trouble: according to the primitive code the loss of honor that Tennessee's partner has suffered definitely demands blood-letting. Moreover, the partner is a man who evidently sees everything in very concrete and personal terms—witness his conduct at the trial in which he shows that he has no conception of abstract justice, and the relation of a man to his wife is a very personal and concrete relation. How could this man forgive Tennessee? (If, of course, he regarded his wife as a mere chattel, then the whole meaning of his act of forgiveness is lost, for the conflict—between affection for his friend on the one hand and affection for his wife on the other—disappears from the situation.)

The problems that we raise are not insuperable. A skillful writer of fiction could presumably make thoroughly credible the reconciliation between Tennessee and his partner. But Bret Harte has really dodged this psychological problem. Even though it is plain that for Bret Harte it is the burial scene and not the wife-stealing episode that is the climax of the story, we still have a right to ask that the wife-stealing episode be credibly developed. In fact, if it is not made credible, the whole story loses its point.

We have said that the burial scene is the climax of the story. What else does Bret Harte give us in preparation for this climax? He gives us the scene of the attempted bribery. The purpose of this scene seems to be to indicate the partner's naïveté with regard to the conventions of society, to the nature of law, and even to the concept of abstract justice itself. Apparently, he honestly sees the situation into which Tennessee has fallen as one which can be settled by a money payment. The stranger will be compensated for his losses and will be given something for his trouble. Perhaps there is the implication that he is attempting to bribe the court; certainly, the violent reaction of the bystanders would support this assumption, though the judge apparently realizes the childlike nature of the man's mind. Indeed, the judge proceeds to give the man a lecture on the nature of law: "the man was made to understand . . . that Tennessee's offense could not be condoned by money." But another purpose of the scene is to develop the idea of the partner's dog-like devotion: he is willing to sacrifice his "pile" for his friend.

For what, after all, does this court incident intend to prepare us? It is, of course, not merely for the incident of the burial, as such. For someone among the rough citizenry would have buried the hanged man in any case, and perhaps with a kind of elemental pity. (Tennessee, has, for instance, certain qualities which would extort special admiration in this primitive community—a courage and coolness, which are dramatized several times in the story.) The intended high point in the story is the funeral oration, which Tennessee's partner delivers to the camp. It is here that our full sense of the pathos is supposed to emerge.

But if such pathos is to emerge to the full, and is to be meaningful, the author must have convinced us (1) that it is logical for this particular character to deliver the oration under the circumstances and (2) that this oration brings to focus elements of interpretation and meaning implicit in previous incidents.

But there are more difficulties. First, would the partner, as his character has been prepared for in earlier pages of the story, have made such a speech to the members of the community who had turned out, purely from curiosity, to see what he would do? A man whose life had been dominated by a merely personal attachment to his friend and who had been completely incapable of understanding why his friend had to be hanged (as indicated by the bribery scene), would more probably have felt a sullen resentment against the men who had done his friend to death for, in his eyes, no good reason. At least, he would probably have wanted privacy for his sorrow. (He can be under no illusion that the spectators have come out of love for Tennessee.)

Second, assuming that the partner would have delivered the oration, would he have said what Bret Harte makes him say? For example, would he have apologized to the spectators and have thanked them for their trouble? (Notice that Bret Harte does not intend for us to take this as the bitter irony of a hurt man, but as a manifestation of a kind of Christlike forgiveness. The partner is almost too good to be true.) And notice, further, in this connection, what Bret Harte has the partner say in his delirium as he dies of a broken heart. Here, even the language becomes unrealistic; it is entirely out of the partner's idiom. For example, would he have said: "There, now, steady, Jinny—steady, old girl. How dark it is!" Isn't it more likely that he would have said: "It's dark as hell." Or: "God-a-mighty, it's dark!" Why does Bret Harte break out of the partner's idiom? Because Bret Harte is straining for a highly emotional effect, and feeling that the realistic language is not good enough, he resorts to "poeticizing" the character. In other words, he is not willing to let the case rest on its own merits. The same thing is true of the symbolic reference, in the dying speech, to the pine tree on the top of the hill.

But other examples of such strain are to be found earlier in the story— take, for example, the description of nature as the partner carries the body to the place of burial: "The way led through Grizzly Cañon, by this time clothed in funereal drapery and shadows. The redwoods, burying their moccasined feet in the red soil, stood in Indian file along the track, trailing an uncouth benediction from their bending boughs upon the passing bier." Nature, apparently, is sympathetic with the partner's grief. Like him, it can give only an "uncouth benediction," but it expresses its brooding sympathy as best it can. One recognizes that a writer may legitimately use description of nature as a device for defining the atmosphere of a piece of fiction, or may even use it as specific symbolism. But it should be quite clear that Bret Harte here is not using it legitimately. It is used here to give a false heightening to the pathos of the scene, and the language in which the description is couched is as "poeticized" as is the language of the partner's dying speech. For example, the description of the redwoods "burying their moccasined feet in the red soil" is completely irrelevant and represents an attempt at fanciful decoration; it is another instance of the author's straining for effects which, he seems to feel, are not adequately supported by the situation in itself.*

The presence of this straining for an emotional effect is one of the surest symptoms that one is dealing with a case of sentimentality. In its

---

* Compare Bret Harte's use of nature here with the use made of the references to the storm in "A Piece of News," p. 129, or to the use of nature made by Chekhov in "The Lament," pp. 207–208.

general sense, as we have seen, sentimentality may be defined as an emotional response in excess of the occasion. We speak of a person who weeps at some trivial occurrence as being sentimental. Such a person lacks a sense of proportion and gets a morbid enjoyment from an emotional debauch for its own sake. When we apply the term to a piece of literature, a story, for instance, we usually mean that the author intends for the reader to experience an intense emotion which is actually not justified by the materials of the story.

One symptom of sentimentality is, as we have said, the author's straining to heighten and prettify and poeticize his language quite apart from the dramatic issues involved in the story.

A second symptom frequently to be found is "editorializing" on the part of the author—pointing out to the reader what he should feel, nudging the reader to respond—devices which would not be necessary if the story could make its own case. (For example, Bret Harte comments on the hanging of Tennessee as follows: "And yet, when the weak and foolish deed was done, and a life, with its possibilities and responsibilities, had passed out of the misshapen thing that dangled between earth and sky, the birds sang, the flowers bloomed, the sun shone, as cheerily as before. . . .")

A third symptom is the tendency to dodge the real issues which should prepare for the final effect of a story. That is, an author who is primarily concerned with giving the emotional effect may not be too scrupulous about the means adopted to that end. For example, in this story Bret Harte is so thoroughly obsessed with the pathos of the partner's loyalty that he has devoted no thought to the precise nature of the basis of that loyalty. As has already been pointed out, he does not bring the wife-stealing episode into real focus. Psychologically and dramatically, the wife-stealing scene, as material, is the most interesting thing in the story. By skimping it and moving away from it toward the final effort at pathos, Bret Harte has made the whole story seem anticlimactic and illogical. Either he was so little interested in the psychology of the situation that he did not investigate it, or he was aware that the issues involved were too complicated for him to handle.

The reading of this story raises such questions as this: Has not Bret Harte taken a theme which, perhaps, he had seen successfully employed for pathetic effects in other fiction, and attempted to trick it out with a new romantic setting, touches of local color (such as descriptions of the community and bits of dialect), and poeticized writing, without ever grounding the story in a presentation of the real psychological issues involved—without, in other words, trying to understand his main character?

1. Compare the relation of Tennessee and his partner with that of Dravot and Peachey in "The Man Who Would Be King." How does Kipling avoid sentimentality?

2. Is O. Henry's "The Furnished Room" guilty of sentimentality? Compare the "editorializing" of O. Henry with that of Bret Harte. What is the function of the "editorializing" in each case?

JAMES JOYCE

Araby

NORTH Richmond Street, being blind, was a quiet street except at the hour when the Christian Brothers' School set the boys free. An uninhabited house of two stories stood at the blind end, detached from its neighbors in a square ground. The other houses of the street, conscious of decent lives within them, gazed at one another with brown imperturbable faces.

The former tenant of our house, a priest, had died in the back drawing room. Air, musty from having been long enclosed, hung in all the rooms, and the waste room behind the kitchen was littered with old useless papers. Among these I found a few paper-covered books, the pages of which were curled and damp: *The Abbot,* by Walter Scott, *The Devout Communicant,* and *The Memoirs of Vidocq.* I liked the last best because its leaves were yellow. The wild garden behind the house contained a central apple tree and a few straggling bushes under one of which I found the late tenant's rusty bicycle pump. He had been a very charitable priest; in his will he had left all his money to institutions and the furniture of his house to his sister.

When the short days of winter came dusk fell before we had well eaten our dinners. When we met in the street the houses had grown somber. The space of sky above us was the color of ever-changing violet and towards it the lamps of the street lifted their feeble lanterns. The cold air stung us and we played till our bodies glowed. Our shouts echoed in the silent street. The career of our play brought us through the dark muddy lanes behind the houses where we ran the gauntlet of the rough tribes from the cottages, to the back doors of the dark dripping gardens where odors arose from the ashpits, to the dark odorous stables where a coachman smoothed and combed the horse or shook music from the buckled harness. When we returned to the street, light from the kitchen windows had filled the areas. If my uncle was seen turning the corner we hid in the shadow until we had seen him safely housed. Or if Mangan's sister came out on the doorstep to call her brother in to his tea we watched her from our shadow peer up and down the street. We waited to see whether she would remain or go in and, if she remained, we left our shadow and walked up to Mangan's steps resignedly. She was waiting for us, her figure defined by the light from the half-opened door. Her brother always teased her before he obeyed and I stood by the railings looking at her. Her dress swung as she moved her body and the soft rope of her hair tossed from side to side.

Every morning I lay on the floor in the front parlor watching her door. The blind was pulled down to within an inch of the sash so that I could not be seen. When she came out on the doorstep my heart leaped. I ran to the hall, seized my books and followed her. I kept her brown figure always in my eye and, when we came near the point at which our ways diverged, I quickened my pace and passed her. This happened morning after morning. I had never spoken to her, except for a few casual words, and yet her name was like a summons to all my foolish blood.

Her image accompanied me even in places the most hostile to romance. On Saturday evenings when my aunt went marketing I had to go to carry some of the parcels. We walked through the flaring streets, jostled by drunken men and bargaining women, amid the curses of laborers, the shrill litanies of shop boys who stood on guard by the barrels of pigs' cheeks, the nasal chanting of street singers, who sang a *come-all-you* about O'Donovan Rossa, or a ballad about the troubles in our native land. These noises converged in a single sensation of life for me: I imagined that I bore my chalice safely through a throng of foes. Her name sprang to my lips at moments in strange prayers and praises which I myself did not understand. My eyes were often full of tears (I could not tell why) and at times a flood from my heart seemed to pour itself out into my bosom. I thought little of the future. I did not know whether I would ever speak to her or not or, if I spoke to her, how I could tell her of my confused adoration. But my body was like a harp and her words and gestures were like fingers running upon the wires.

One evening I went into the back drawing room in which the priest had died. It was a dark rainy evening and there was no sound in the house. Through one of the broken panes I heard the rain impinge upon the earth, the fine incessant needles of water playing in the sodden beds. Some distant lamp or lighted window gleamed below me. I was thankful that I could see so little. All my senses seemed to desire to veil themselves and, feeling that I was about to slip from them, I pressed the palms of my hands together until they trembled, murmuring: "*O love! O love!*" many times.

At last she spoke to me. When she addressed the first words to me I was so confused that I did not know what to answer. She asked me was I going to *Araby*. I forgot whether I answered yes or no. It would be a splendid bazaar, she said; she would love to go.

"And why can't you?" I asked.

While she spoke she turned a silver bracelet round and round her wrist. She could not go, she said, because there would be a retreat that week in her convent. Her brother and two other boys were fighting for their caps and I was alone at the railings. She held one of the spikes, bowing her head towards me. The light from the lamp opposite our door caught the white curve of her neck, lit up her hair that rested there and, falling, lit up the hand upon the railing. It fell over one side of her dress and caught the white border of a petticoat, just visible as she stood at ease.

"It's well for you," she said.

"If I go," I said, "I will bring you something."

What innumerable follies laid waste my waking and sleeping thoughts after that evening! I wished to annihilate the tedious intervening days. I chafed against the work of school. At night in my bedroom and by day in the classroom her image came between me and the page I strove to read. The syllables of the word *Araby* were called to me through the silence in which my soul luxuriated and cast an Eastern enchantment over me. I asked for leave to go to the bazaar on Saturday night. My aunt was surprised and hoped it was not some Freemason affair. I answered few questions in class. I watched my master's face pass from amiability to sternness; he hoped I was not beginning to idle. I could not call my wandering thoughts together. I had hardly any patience with the serious work of life which, now that it stood between me and my desire, seemed to me child's play, ugly monotonous child's play.

On Saturday morning I reminded my uncle that I wished to go to the bazaar in the evening. He was fussing at the hall stand, looking for the hat brush, and answered me curtly:

"Yes, boy, I know."

As he was in the hall I could not go into the front parlor and lie at the window. I left the house in bad humor and walked slowly towards the school. The air was pitilessly raw and already my heart misgave me.

When I came home to dinner my uncle had not yet been home. Still it was early. I sat staring at the clock for some time and, when its ticking began to irritate me, I left the room. I mounted the staircase and gained the upper part of the house. The high cold empty gloomy rooms liberated me and I went from room to room singing. From the front window I saw my companions playing below in the street. Their cries reached me weakened and indistinct and, leaning my forehead against the cool glass, I looked over at the dark house where she lived. I may have stood there for an hour, seeing nothing but the brown-clad figure cast by my imagination, touched discreetly by the lamplight at the curved neck, at the hand upon he railings and at the border below the dress.

When I came downstairs again I found Mrs. Mercer sitting at the fire. She was an old garrulous woman, a pawnbroker's widow, who collected used stamps for some pious purpose. I had to endure the gossip of the tea table. The meal was prolonged beyond an hour and still my uncle did not come. Mrs. Mercer stood up to go: she was sorry she couldn't wait any longer, but it was after eight o'clock and she did not like to be out late, as the night air was bad for her. When she had gone I began to walk up and down the room, clenching my fists. My aunt said:

"I'm afraid you may put off your bazaar for this night of Our Lord."

At nine o'clock I heard my uncle's latchkey in the hall door. I heard him talking to himself and heard the hall stand rocking when it had received the weight of his overcoat. I could interpret these signs. When he was midway through his dinner I asked him to give me the money to go to the bazaar. He had forgotten.

"The people are in bed and after their first sleep now," he said.

I did not smile. My aunt said to him energetically:

"Can't you give him the money and let him go? You've kept him late enough as it is."

My uncle said he was very sorry he had forgotten. He said he believed in the old saying: "All work and no play makes Jack a dull boy." He asked me where I was going and, when I had told him a second time he asked me did I know *The Arab's Farewell to His Steed*. When I left the kitchen he was about to recite the opening lines of the piece to my aunt.

I held a florin tightly in my hand as I strode down Buckingham Street towards the station. The sight of the streets thronged with buyers and glaring with gas recalled to me the purpose of my journey. I took my seat in a third-class carriage of a deserted train. After an intolerable delay the train moved out of the station slowly. It crept onward among ruinous houses and over the twinkling river. At Westland Row Station a crowd of people pressed to the carriage doors; but the porters moved them back, saying that it was a special train for the bazaar. I remained alone in the bare carriage. In a few minutes the train drew up beside an improvised wooden platform. I passed out on to the road and saw by the lighted dial of a clock that it was ten minutes to ten. In front of me was a large building which displayed the magical name.

I could not find any sixpenny entrance and, fearing that the bazaar would be closed, I passed in quickly through a turnstile, handing a shilling to a weary-looking man. I found myself in a big hall girdled at half its height by a gallery. Nearly all the stalls were closed and the greater part of the hall was in darkness. I recognized a silence like that which pervades a church after a service. I walked into the center of the bazaar timidly. A few people were gathered about the stalls which were still open. Before a curtain, over which the words *Café Chantant* were written in colored lamps, two men were counting money on a salver. I listened to the fall of the coins.

Remembering with difficulty why I had come I went over to one of stalls and examined porcelain vases and flowered tea sets. At the door of the stall a young lady was talking and laughing with two young gentlemen. I remarked their English accents and listened vaguely to their conversation.

"O, I never said such a thing!"

"O, but you did!"

"O, but I didn't!"

"Didn't she say that?"

"Yes. I heard her."

"O, there's a . . . fib!"

Observing me, the young lady came over and asked me did I wish to buy anything. The tone of her voice was not encouraging; she seemed to have spoken to me out of a sense of duty. I looked humbly at the great jars that stood like eastern guards at either side of the dark entrance to the stall and murmured:

"No, thank you."

The young lady changed the position of one of the vases and went back to the two young men. They began to talk of the same subject. Once or twice the young lady glanced at me over her shoulder.

I lingered before her stall, though I knew my stay was useless, to make my interest in her wares seem the more real. Then I turned away slowly and walked down the middle of the bazaar. I allowed the two pennies to fall against the sixpence in my pocket. I heard a voice call from one end of the gallery that the light was out. The upper part of the hall was now completely dark.

Gazing up into the darkness I saw myself as a creature driven and derided by vanity; and my eyes burned with anguish and anger.

INTERPRETATION

On what may be called the simplest level this is a story of a boy's disappointment. A great part of the story, however, does not directly concern itself with the boy's love affair, but with the world in which he lives—the description of his street, the information about the dead priest and the priest's abandoned belongings, the relations with the aunt and uncle. These matters seem to come very naturally into the story; that is, they may be justified individually in the story on realistic grounds. But if such elements *merely* serve as "setting" or as mere atmosphere, then the story is obviously overloaded with nonfunctional material. Obviously, for any reader except the most casual, these items do have a function. If we find in what way these apparently irrelevant items in "Araby" are related to each other and to the disappointment of the boy, we shall have defined the theme of the story.

What, then, is the relation of the boy's disappointment to such matters as the belongings of the dead priest, the fact that he stands apart talking to the girl while his friends are quarreling over the cap, the gossip over the tea table, the uncle's lateness, and so on? One thing that is immediately suggested by the mention of these things is the boy's growing sense of isolation, the lack of sympathy between him and his friends, teachers, and family. He says, "I imagined that I bore my chalice safely through a throng of foes." For instance, when the uncle is standing in the hall, the boy could not go into the front parlor and lie at the window; or at school his ordinary occupations began to seem "ugly monotonous child's play." But this sense of isolation has, also, moments which are almost triumphant, as for example, is implied when the porters at the station wave the crowds back, "saying that it was a special train for the bazaar" and was not for them. The boy is left alone in the bare carriage, but he is going to "Araby," moving triumphantly toward some romantic and exotic fulfillment. The metaphor of the chalice implies the same kind of precious secret triumph. It is not only the ordinary surrounding world, however, from which he is cruelly or triumphantly isolated. He is also isolated from the girl herself. He talks to her only once, and then is so confused that he does not know how to answer her. But the present which he hopes to bring her from Araby would somehow serve as a means of communicating his feelings to her, a symbol for their relationship in the midst of the inimical world.

In the last scene at the bazaar, there is a systematic, though subtle, preparation for the final realization on the part of the boy. There is the "improvised wooden platform" in contrast with the "magical name" displayed above the building. Inside, most of the stalls are closed. The young lady and young men who talk together are important in the preparation. They pay the boy no mind, except in so far as the young lady is compelled by her position as clerk to ask him what he wants. But her tone is not "encouraging." She, too, belongs to the inimical world. But she, also, belongs to a world into which he is trying to penetrate: she and her admirers are on terms of easy intimacy—an intimacy in contrast to his relation to Mangan's sister. It is an exotic, rich world into which he cannot penetrate: he can only look "humbly at the great jars that stood like eastern guards at either side of the dark entrance to the stall. . . ." But, ironically, the young lady and her admirers, far from realizing that they are on holy, guarded ground, indulge in a trivial, easy banter, which seems to defile and cheapen the secret world from which the boy is barred. How do we know this? It is not stated, but the contrast between the conversation of the young lady and her admirers, and the tone of the sentence quoted just above indicates such an interpretation.

This scene, then, helps to point up and particularize the general sense of isolation suggested by the earlier descriptive materials, and thereby to prepare for the last sentence of the story, in which, under the sudden darkness of the cheap and barnlike bazaar, the boy sees himself as "a creature driven and derided by vanity," while his eyes burn with anguish and anger.

We have seen how the apparently casual incidents and items of description do function in the story to build up the boy's sense of intolerable isolation. But this is only part of the function of this material. The careful reader will have noticed how many references, direct or indirect, there are to religion and the ritual of the church. We have the dead priest, the Christian Brothers' School, the aunt's hope that the bazaar is not "some Freemason affair," her remark when the uncle has been delayed, to "this night of Our Lord." At one level, these references merely indicate the type of community in which the impressionable boy is growing up. But there are other, less obvious, references, which relate more intimately to the boy's experience. Even the cries of the shop boys for him are "shrill litanies." He imagines that he bears a "chalice safely through a throng of foes." When he is alone the name of Mangan's sister springs to his lips "in strange prayers and praises." For this reason, when he speaks of his "confused adoration," we see that the love of the girl takes on, for him, something of the nature of a mystic, religious experience. The use of the very word *confused* hints of the fact that romantic love and religious love are mixed up in his mind.

It has been said that the boy is isolated from a world which seems ignorant of, and even hostile to, his love. In a sense he knows that his aunt and uncle are good and kind, but they do not understand him. He had once found satisfaction in the society of his companions and in his school work, but he has become impatient with both. But there is also a sense in which he accepts his isolation and is even proud of it. The world not only does not understand his secret but would cheapen and contaminate it. The metaphor of the chalice borne through a throng of foes, supported as it is by the body of the story, suggests a sort of consecration like that of the religious devotee. The implications of the references to religion, then, help define the boy's attitude and indicate why, for him, so much is staked upon the journey to the bazaar. It is interesting to note, therefore, that the first overt indication of his disillusionment and disappointment is expressed in a metaphor involving a church: "Nearly all the stalls were closed and the greater part of the hall was in darkness. I recognized a silence like that which pervades a church after a service. . . . Two men were counting money on a salver. I listened to the fall of the coins." So, it would seem, here we have the idea that the contamination of the world has invaded the very temple of love—there are, as it were, money-changers in the very temple. (The question may arise as to whether this is not reading too much into the passage. Perhaps it is. But whatever interpretation is to be made of the particular incident, it is by just such suggestion and implication that closely wrought stories, such as this one, are controlled by the author and embody their fundamental meaning.)

Is this a sentimental story? It is about an adolescent love affair, about "calf love," a subject which usually is not to be taken seriously and is often an occasion for amusement. The boy of the story is obviously investing casual incidents with a meaning which they do not deserve; and himself admits, in the end, that he has fallen into self-deception. How does the author avoid the charge that he has taken the matter over-seriously?

The answer to this question would involve a consideration of the point of view from which the story is told. It is told by the hero himself, but after a long lapse of time, after he has reached maturity. This fact, it is true, is not stated in the story, but the style itself is not that of an adolescent boy. It is a formal and complicated style, rich, as has already been observed, in subtle implications. In other words, the man is looking back upon the boy, detached and judicial. For instance, the boy, in the throes of the experience, would never have said of himself: "I had never spoken to her, except for a few casual words, and yet her name was like a summons to all my foolish blood." The man knows, as it were, that the behavior of the boy was, in a sense, foolish. The emotions of the boy are confused, but the person telling the story, the boy grown up, is not confused. He has un-raveled the confusion long after, knows that it existed and why it existed.

If the man has unraveled the confusions of the boy, why is the event still significant to him? Is he merely dwelling on the pathos of adolescent experience? It seems, rather, that he sees in the event, as he looks back on it, a kind of parable of a problem which has run through later experience. The discrepancy between the real and the ideal scarcely exists for the child, but it is a constant problem, in all sorts of terms, for the adult. This story is about a boy's first confrontation of that problem—that is, about his grow-ing up. The man may have made adjustments to this problem, and may have worked out certain provisional solutions, but, looking back, he still recog-nizes it as a problem, and an important one. The sense of isolation and disillusion which, in the boy's experience, may seem to spring from a trivial situation, becomes not less, but more aggravated and fundamental in the adult's experience. So, the story is not merely an account of a stage in the process of growing up—it does not merely represent a clinical interest in the psychology of growing up—but is a symbolic rendering of a central conflict in mature experience.

1. What does the boy have in common with the dead priest? Suppose that the dead man had been a shopkeeper, a lawyer, or anyone else who did not "carry a chalice." Would that have made any difference in the story?

2. Children are supposed to have more imagination than adults. What has happened when, for the boy, his previous occupations seem to be "ugly monotonous child's play"?

3. There is in this story a relatively small amount of dramatically rendered material. Can you say why? Is this fact consistent with the gen-eral tone and meaning of the story?

FRANK O'CONNOR

The Drunkard

IT was a terrible blow to Father when Mr. Dooley on the terrace died. Mr. Dooley was a commercial traveller with two sons in the Dominicans and a car of his own, so socially he was miles ahead of us, but he had no false pride. Mr. Dooley was an intellectual, and, like all intellectuals the thing he loved best was conversation, and in his own limited way Father was a well-read man and could appreciate an intelligent talker. Mr. Dooley was remarkably intelligent. Between business acquaintances and clerical contacts, there was very little he didn't know about what went on in town, and evening after evening he crossed the road to our gate to explain to Father the news behinds the news. He had a low, palavering voice and a knowing smile, and Father would listen in astonishment, giving him a conversational lead now and again, and then stump triumphantly in to Mother with his face aglow and ask: "Do you know what Mr. Dooley is after telling me?" Ever since, when somebody has given me some bit of information off the record I have found myself on the point of asking: "Was it Mr. Dooley told you that?"

Till I actually saw him laid out in his brown shroud with the rosary beads entwined between his waxy fingers I did not take the report of his death seriously. Even then I felt there must be a catch and that some summer evening Mr. Dooley must reappear at our gate to give us the lowdown on the next world. But Father was very upset, partly because Mr. Dooley was about one age with himself, a thing that always gives a distinctly personal turn to another man's demise; partly because now he would have no one to tell him what dirty work was behind the latest scene at the Corporation. You could count on your fingers the number of men in Blarney Lane who read the papers as Mr. Dooley did, and none of these would have overlooked the fact that Father was only a laboring man. Even Sullivan, the carpenter, a mere nobody, thought he was a cut above Father. It was certainly a solemn event.

"Half past two to the Curragh," Father said meditatively, putting down the paper.

"But you're not thinking of going to the funeral?" Mother asked in alarm.

"'Twould be expected," Father said, scenting opposition. "I wouldn't give it to say to them."

"I think," said Mother with suppressed emotion, "it will be as much as anyone will expect if you go to the chapel with him."

("Going to the chapel," of course, was one thing, because the body was removed after work, but going to a funeral meant the loss of a half-day's pay.)

"The people hardly know us," she added.

"God between us and all harm," Father replied with dignity, "we'd be glad if it was our own turn."

To give Father his due, he was always ready to lose a half day for the sake of an old neighbor. It wasn't so much that he liked funerals as that he was a conscientious man who did as he would be done by; and nothing could have consoled him so much for the prospect of his own death as the assurance of a worthy funeral. And, to give Mother her due, it wasn't the half-day's pay she begrudged, badly as we could afford it.

Drink, you see, was Father's great weakness. He could keep steady for months, even for years, at a stretch, and while he did he was as good as gold. He was first up in the morning and brought the mother a cup of tea in bed, stayed at home in the evenings and read the paper; saved money and bought himself a new blue serge suit and bowler hat. He laughed at the folly of men who, week in and week out, left their hard-earned money with the publicans; and sometimes, to pass an idle hour, he took pencil and paper and calculated precisely how much he saved each week through being a teetotaller. Being a natural optimist he sometimes continued this calculation through the whole span of his prospective existence and the total was breathtaking. He would die worth hundreds.

If I had only known it, this was a bad sign; a sign he was becoming stuffed up with spiritual pride and imagining himself better than his neighbors. Sooner or later, the spiritual pride grew till it called for some form of celebration. Then he took a drink—not whisky, of course; nothing like that—just a glass of some harmless drink like lager beer. That was the end of Father. By the time he had taken the first he already realized that he had made a fool of himself, took a second to forget it and a third to forget that he couldn't forget, and at last came home reeling drunk. From this on it was "The Drunkard's Progress," as in the moral prints. Next day he stayed in from work with a sick head while Mother went off to make his excuses at the works, and inside a fortnight he was poor and savage and despondent again. Once he began he drank steadily through everything down to the kitchen clock. Mother and I knew all the phases and dreaded all the dangers. Funerals were one.

"I have to go to Dunphy's to do a half-day's work," said Mother in distress. "Who's to look after Larry?"

"I'll look after Larry," Father said graciously. "The little walk will do him good."

There was no more to be said, though we all knew I didn't need anyone to look after me, and that I could quite well have stayed at home and looked after Sonny, but I was being attached to the party to act as a brake on Father. As a brake I had never achieved anything, but Mother still had great faith in me.

Next day, when I got home from school, Father was there before me and made a cup of tea for both of us. He was very good at tea, but too heavy in the hand for anything else; the way he cut bread was shocking. Afterwards, we went down the hill to the church. Father wearing his best blue serge and a bowler cocked to one side of his head with the least suggestion of the masher. To his great joy he discovered Peter Crowley among the mourners. Peter was another danger signal, as I knew well from certain experiences after Mass on Sunday morning: a mean man, as Mother said, who only went to funerals for the free drinks he could get at them. It turned out that he hadn't even known Mr. Dooley! But Father had a sort of contemptuous regard for him as one of the foolish people who wasted their good money in public-houses when they could be saving it. Very little of his own money Peter Crowley wasted!

It was an excellent funeral from Father's point of view. He had it all well studied before we set off after the hearse in the afternoon sunlight.

"Five carriages!" he exclaimed. "Five carriages and sixteen covered cars! There's one alderman, two councillors and 'tis unknown how many priests. I didn't see a funeral like this from the road since Willie Mack, the publican, died."

"Ah, he was well liked," said Crowley in his husky voice.

"My goodness, don't I know that?" snapped Father. "Wasn't the man my best friend? Two nights before he died—only two nights—he was over telling me the goings-on about the housing contract. Them fellows in the Corporation are night and day robbers. But even I never imagined he was as well connected as that."

Father was stepping out like a boy, pleased with everything: the other mourners, and the fine houses along Sunday's Well. I knew the danger signals were there in full force: a sunny day, a fine funeral, and a distinguished company of clerics and public men were bringing out all the natural vanity and flightiness of Father's character. It was with something like genuine pleasure that he saw his old friend lowered into the grave; with the sense of having performed a duty and the pleasant awareness that however much he would miss poor Mr. Dooley in the long summer evenings, it was he and not poor Mr. Dooley who would do the missing.

"We'll be making tracks before they break up," he whispered to Crowley as the gravediggers tossed in the first shovelfuls of clay, and away he went, hopping like a goat from grassy hump to hump. The drivers, who were probably in the same state as himself, though without months of abstinence to put an edge on it, looked up hopefully.

"Are they nearly finished, Mick?" bawled one.

"All over now bar the last prayers," trumpeted Father in the tone of one who brings news of great rejoicing.

The carriages passed us in a lather of dust several hundred yards from the public-house, and Father, whose feet gave him trouble in hot weather, quickened his pace, looking nervously over his shoulder for any sign of the main body of mourners crossing the hill. In a crowd like that a man might be kept waiting.

When we did reach the pub the carriages were drawn up outside, and solemn men in black ties were cautiously bringing out consolation to mysterious females whose hands reached out modestly from behind the drawn blinds of the coaches. Inside the pub there were only the drivers and a couple of shawly women. I felt if I was to act as a brake at all, this was the time, so I pulled Father by the coattails.

"Dadda, can't we go home now?" I asked.

"Two minutes now," he said, beaming affectionately. "Just a bottle of lemonade and we'll go home."

This was a bribe, and I knew it, but I was always a child of weak character. Father ordered lemonade and two pints. I was thirsty and swallowed my drink at once. But that wasn't Father's way. He had long months of abstinence behind him and an eternity of pleasure before. He took out his pipe, blew through it, filled it, and then lit it with loud pops, his eyes bulging above it. After that he deliberately turned his back on the pint, leaned one elbow on the counter in the attitude of a man who did not know there was a pint behind him, and deliberately brushed the tobacco from his palms. He had settled down for the evening. He was steadily working through all the important funerals he had ever attended. The carriages departed and the minor mourners drifted in till the pub was half full.

"Dadda," I said, pulling his coat again, "can't we go home now?"

"Ah, your mother won't be in for a long time yet," he said benevolently enough. "Run out in the road and play, can't you?"

It struck me as very cool, the way grown-ups assumed that you could play all by yourself on a strange road. I began to get bored as I had so often been bored before. I knew Father was quite capable of lingering there till nightfall. I knew I might have to bring him home, blind drunk, down Blarney Lane, with all the old women at their doors, saying: "Mick Delaney is on it again." I knew that my mother would be half crazy with anxiety; that next day Father wouldn't go out to work; and before the end of the week she would be running down to the pawn with the clock under her shawl. I could never get over the lonesomeness of the kitchen without a clock.

I was still thirsty. I found if I stood on tiptoe I could just reach Father's glass, and the idea occurred to me that it would be interesting to know what the contents were like. He had his back to it and wouldn't notice. I took down the glass and sipped cautiously. It was a terrible disappointment. I was astonished that he could even drink such stuff. It looked as if he had never tried lemonade.

I should have advised him about lemonade but he was holding forth himself in great style. I heard him say that bands were a great addition to a funeral. He put his arms in the position of someone holding a rifle in reverse and hummed a few bars of Chopin's Funeral March. Crowley nodded reverently. I took a longer drink and began to see that porter might have its advantages. I felt pleasantly elevated and philosophic. Father hummed a few bars of the Dead March in *Saul*. It was a nice pub and a very fine funeral, and I felt sure that poor Mr. Dooley in Heaven must be highly gratified. At the same time I thought they might have given him a band. As Father said, bands were a great addition.

But the wonderful thing about porter was the way it made you stand aside, or rather float aloft like a cherub rolling on a cloud, and watch yourself with your legs crossed, leaning against a bar counter, not worrying about trifles but thinking deep, serious, grown-up thoughts about life and death. Looking at yourself like that, you couldn't help thinking after a while how funny you looked, and suddenly you got embarrassed and wanted to giggle. But by the time I had finished the pint, that phase too had passed; I found it hard to put back the glass, the counter seemed to have grown so high. Melancholia was supervening again.

"Well," Father said reverently, reaching behind him for his drink, "God rest the poor man's soul, wherever he is!" He stopped, looked first at the glass, and then at the people round him. "Hello," he said in a fairly good-humoured tone, as if he were just prepared to consider it a joke, even if it was in bad taste, "who was at this?"

There was silence for a moment while the publican and the old women looked first at Father and then at his glass.

"There was no one at it, my good man," one of the women said with an offended air. "Is it robbers you think we are?"

"Ah, there's no one here would do a thing like that, Mick," said the publican in a shocked tone.

"Well, someone did it," said Father, his smile beginning to wear off.

"If they did, they were them that were nearer it," said the woman darkly, giving me a dirty look; and at the same moment the truth began to dawn on Father. I suppose I must have looked a bit starry-eyed. He bent and shook me.

"Are you all right, Larry?" he asked in alarm.

Peter Crowley looked down at me and grinned.

"Could you beat that?" he exclaimed in a husky voice.

I could, and without difficulty. I started to get sick. Father jumped back in holy terror that I might spoil his good suit, and hastily opened the back door.

"Run! run! run!" he shouted.

I saw the sunlit wall outside with the ivy overhanging it, and ran. The intention was good but the performance was exaggerated, because I lurched right into the wall, hurting it badly, as it seemed to me. Being always very polite, I said "Pardon" before the second bout came on me. Father, still concerned for his suit, came up behind and cautiously held me while I got sick.

"That's a good boy!" he said encouragingly. "You'll be grand when you get that up."

Begor, I was not grand! Grand was the last thing I was. I gave one unmerciful wail out of me as he steered me back to the pub and put me sitting on the bench near the shawlies. They drew themselves up with an offended air, still sore at the suggestion that they had drunk his pint.

"God help us!" moaned one, looking pityingly at me, "isn't it the likes of them would be fathers?"

"Mick," said the publican in alarm, spraying sawdust on my tracks, "that child isn't supposed to be in here at all. You'd better take him home quick in case a bobby would see him."

"Merciful God!" whimpered Father, raising his eyes to heaven and clapping his hands silently as he only did when distraught, "what misfortune was on me? Or what will his mother say? . . . If women might stop at home and look after their children themselves!" he added in a snarl for the benefit of the shawlies. "Are them carriages all gone, Bill?"

"The carriages are finished long ago, Mick," replied the publican.

"I'll take him home," Father said despairingly. . . . "I'll never bring you out again," he threatened me. "Here," he added, giving me the clean handkerchief from his breast pocket, "put that over your eyes."

The blood on the handkerchief was the first indication I got that I was cut, and instantly my temple began to throb and I set up another howl.

"Whisht, whisht, whisht!" Father said testily, steering me out the door. "One'd think you were killed. That's nothing. We'll wash it when we get home."

"Steady now, old scout!" Crowley said, taking the other side of me. "You'll be all right in a minute."

I never met two men who knew less about the effects of drink. The first breath of fresh air and the warmth of the sun made me groggier than ever and I pitched and rolled between wind and tide till Father started to whimper again.

"God Almighty, and the whole road out! What misfortune was on me didn't stop at my work! Can't you walk straight?"

I couldn't. I saw plain enough that, coaxed by the sunlight, every woman old and young in Blarney Lane was leaning over her half-door or sitting on her doorstep. They all stopped gabbling to gape at the strange spectacle of two sober, middle-aged men bringing home a drunken small boy with a cut over his eye. Father, torn between the shamefast desire to get me home as quick as he could, and the neighborly need to explain that it wasn't his fault, finally halted outside Mrs. Roche's. There was a gang of old women outside a door at the opposite side of the road. I didn't like the look of them from the first. They seemed altogether too interested in me. I leaned against the wall of Mrs. Roche's cottage with my hands in my trousers pockets, thinking mournfully of poor Mr. Dooley in his cold grave on the Curragh, who would never walk down the road again, and, with great feeling, I began to sing a favorite song of Father's.

> *Though lost to Mononia and cold in the grave*
> *He returns to Kincora no more.*

"Wisha, the poor child!" Mrs. Roche said. "Haven't he a lovely voice, God bless him!"

That was what I thought myself, so I was the more surprised when Father said "Whisht!" and raised a threatening finger at me. He didn't seem to realize the appropriateness of the song, so I sang louder than ever.

"Whisht, I tell you!" he snapped, and then tried to work up a smile for Mrs. Roche's benefit. "We're nearly home now. I'll carry you the rest of the way."

But, drunk and all as I was, I knew better than to be carried home ignominiously like that.

"Now," I said severely, "can't you leave me alone? I can walk all right. 'Tis only my head. All I want is a rest."

"But you can rest at home in bed," he said viciously, trying to pick me up, and I knew by the flush on his face that he was very vexed.

"Ah, Jasus," I said crossly, "what do I want to go home for? Why the hell can't you leave me alone?"

For some reason the gang of old women at the other side of the road thought this very funny. They nearly split their sides over it. A gassy fury began to expand in me at the thought that a fellow couldn't have a drop taken without the whole neighborhood coming out to make game of him.

"Who are ye laughing at?" I shouted, clenching my fists at them. "I'll make ye laugh at the other side of yeer faces if ye don't let me pass."

They seemed to think this funnier still; I had never seen such ill-mannered people.

"Go away, ye bloody bitches!" I said.

"Whisht, whisht, whisht, I tell you!" snarled Father, abandoning all pretence of amusement and dragging me along behind him by the hand. I was maddened by the women's shrieks of laughter. I was maddened by Father's bullying. I tried to dig in my heels but he was too powerful for me, and I could only see the women by looking back over my shoulder

"Take care or I'll come back and show ye!" I shouted. "I'll teach ye to let decent people pass. Fitter for ye to stop at home and wash yeer dirty faces."

" 'Twill be all over the road," whimpered Father. "Never again, never again, not if I lived to be a thousand!"

To this day I don't know whether he was forswearing me or the drink. By way of a song suitable to my heroic mood I bawled "The Boys of Wexford," as he dragged me in home. Crowley, knowing he was not safe, made off and Father undressed me and put me to bed. I couldn't sleep because of the whirling in my head. It was very unpleasant, and I got sick again. Father came in with a wet cloth and mopped up after me. I lay in a fever, listening to him chopping sticks to start a fire. After that I heard him lay the table.

Suddenly the front door banged open and Mother stormed in with Sonny in her arms, not her usual gentle, timid self, but a wild, raging woman. It was clear that she had heard it all from the neighbors.

"Mick Delaney," she cried hysterically, "what did you do to my son?"

"Whisht, woman, whisht, whisht!" he hissed, dancing from one foot to the other. "Do you want the whole road to hear?"

"Ah," she said with a horrifying laugh, "the road knows all about it by this time. The road knows the way you filled your unfortunate innocent child with drink to make sport for you and that other rotten, filthy brute."

"But I gave him no drink," he shouted, aghast at the horrifying interpretation the neighbors had chosen to give his misfortune. "He took it while my back was turned. What the hell do you think I am?"

"Ah," she replied bitterly, "everyone knows what you are now. God forgive you, wasting our hard-earned few ha'pence on drink, and bringing up your child to be a drunken corner-boy like yourself."

Then she swept into the bedroom and threw herself on her knees by the bed. She moaned when she saw the gash over my eye. In the kitchen Sonny set up a loud bawl on his own, and a moment later Father appeared in the bedroom door with his cap over his eyes, wearing an expression of the most intense self-pity.

"That's a nice way to talk to me after all I went through," he whined. "That's a nice accusation, that I was drinking. Not one drop of drink crossed my lips the whole day. How could it when he drank it all? I'm the one that ought to be pitied, with my day ruined on me, and I after being made a show for the whole road."

But next morning, when he got up and went out quietly to work with his dinner-basket, Mother threw herself on me in the bed and kissed me. It seemed it was all my doing, and I was being given a holiday till my eye got better.

"My brave little man!" she said with her eyes shining. "It was God did it you were there. You were his guardian angel."

INTERPRETATION

In this amusing story, there is a reversal of roles: it is not the father who comes reeling down the street, the scandal of the family and the talk of the neighbors, as the appalled little son tries to lead him home and put him mercifully out of sight. It is the little boy who is unsteady on his feet, singing off key, calling the neighbor women "bloody bitches"—to the horror of the appalled father. If the story simply presented us with this topsy-turvy situation and let it go at that, it would amount to no more than a joke that was momentarily amusing. It would not be very much of a story and it would not even wear well as a joke. For even a joke, if it is to continue to seem funny, must be rooted in a true perception of human nature.

The reversal of the roles of father and son in this story is not a momentary trick. If we think back a bit, we shall see that the reversal is assumed throughout the story. On the important matter of his father's weakness for drink, Larry, the little boy, takes his mother's viewpoint. His is the adult concern for an essentially good but childishly weak character who must be protected from himself. Larry is apprehensive and worried. He knows what "signs" are ominous. He knows all too well what the consequences of the first drink will be. His consciousness continues to be suffused with this kind of concern for his father until the beer finally takes effect upon *him*, and for the first time in the story, his apprehensions melt away.

Throughout the story it is the father who has the childlike guilessness —and the charm that frequently accompanies such guilessness. Consider his delight in the funeral: "It was an excellent funeral from Father's point of view." He exclaims that there are "Five carriages and sixteen covered cars!" Later, as Larry remarks, "It was with something like genuine pleasure that he saw his old friend lowered into the grave; with the sense of having performed a duty and the pleasant awareness that however much he would miss poor Mr. Dooley in the long summer evenings, it was he and not Mr. Dooley who would do the missing." Later still, he tells the waiting coachmen that the service at the grave is nearly over: " 'All over now bar the last prayers,' trumpeted Father in the tone of one who brings news of great rejoicing." And how happily a few minutes later he settles down in the pub as he gets ready to break his long drought!

If Larry's father were a more calculating man, or even a more self-conscious man, the special quality of the humor would be lost, for we would have to take a different attitude toward him. If it is his simplicity and his naïveté that cause his troubles, they go far toward relieving him of adult responsibility for them. He is a man more sinned against than sinning —and nowhere more so than when he has to face the protests of the neighborwomen that he has got his own son drunk. The character of the father thus has everything to do with the point of the story and even with the matter of whether or not we find the story genuinely funny. Though "all occasions inform against him," he has the consciousness of outraged innocence.

The most amusing instance of the general reversal of roles occurs on the way home from the pub, when the father does not forcibly shut up the noisy, tipsy little boy, but pleads with him to be reasonable and quiet just as Larry himself might have pleaded with the drunken father—if our normal expectations about this particular expedition had been realized. But this most amusing of the reversals is also rooted in the father's character: a more cruel man, a more brutal man, would have forced the boy to hush. He would thus have eliminated the humorous exchanges, and the suppression of these—and perhaps also the harshness by which they were suppressed—would have deprived the scene of its humor.

The most startling of the reversals (and that which caps the story) is the twist at the end in which the episode of juvenile delinquency becomes Providential and the little boy drunkenly weaving down the street becomes in the mother's grateful eyes a "guardian angel" guiding aright the steps of the weak father. We laugh at the mother—the way in which she has expressed her commendation is almost as startling as the phrasings of Mrs. Malaprop—and yet what she says is, from her point of view, quite right: Larry has been a little "man." He has saved the family one of the usual visits to the pawnbroker.

1. Is the episode in which Larry drinks his father's pint of beer made plausible? Is this the sort of thing that Larry usually does? Is it credible that the father should have neglected his pint long enough for the child to drink it?

2. Are the observations made by Larry upon his father too sophisticated for a child to make? Is this story being told by Larry soon after the events described, or long after, when Larry has become a man?

3. The exposition in this story is managed very skillfully. Comment upon it. What is gained by deferring for over a page the matter of the father's propensity to drink?

4. What is the importance of the fact that Larry gets a little nick over his eye? Does the fact of the blood and the wound help account for certain reactions to the incident?

ANTON CHEKHOV

The Lament

IT is twilight. A thick wet snow is twirling around the newly lighted street lamps, and lying in soft thin layers on roofs, on horses' backs, on people's shoulders and hats. The cabdriver Iona Potapov is quite white, and looks like a phantom; he is bent double as far as a human body can bend double; he is seated on his box; he never makes a move. If a whole snowdrift fell on him, it seems as if he would not find it necessary to shake it off. His little horse is also quite white, and remains motionless; its immobility, its angularity, and its straight wooden-looking legs, even close by, give it the appearance of a ginger-bread horse worth a *kopek*. It is, no doubt, plunged in deep thought. If you were snatched from the plow, from your usual gray surroundings, and were thrown into this slough full of monstrous lights, unceasing noise, and hurrying people, you too would find it difficult not to think.

Iona and his little horse have not moved from their place for a long while. They left their yard before dinner, and up to now, not a fare. The evening mist is descending over the town, the white lights of the lamps replacing brighter rays, and the hubbub of the street getting louder. "Cabby for Viborg way!" suddenly hears Iona. "Cabby!"

Iona jumps, and through his snow-covered eyelashes sees an officer in a greatcoat, with his hood over his head.

"Viborg way!" the officer repeats. "Are you asleep, eh? Viborg way!"

With a nod of assent Iona picks up the reins, in consequence of which layers of snow slip off the horse's back and neck. The officer seats himself in the sleigh, the cabdriver smacks his lips to encourage his horse, stretches out his neck like a swan, sits up, and, more from habit than necessity, brandishes his whip. The little horse also stretches its neck, bends its wooden-looking legs, and makes a move undecidedly.

"What are you doing, werewolf!" is the exclamation Iona hears from the dark mass moving to and fro, as soon as they have started.

"Where the devil are you going? To the r-r-right!"

"You do not know how to drive. Keep to the right!" calls the officer angrily.

A coachman from a private carriage swears at him; a passerby, who has run across the road and rubbed his shoulder against the horse's nose, looks at him furiously as he sweeps the snow from his sleeve. Iona shifts about on his seat as if he were on needles, moves his elbows as if he were trying to keep his equilibrium, and gapes about like someone suffocating, who does not understand why and wherefore he is there.

"What scoundrels they all are!" jokes the officer; "one would think they had all entered into an agreement to jostle you or fall under your horse."

Iona looks round at the officer, and moves his lips. He evidently wants to say something, but the only sound that issues is a snuffle.

"What?" asks the officer.

Iona twists his mouth into a smile, and with an effort says hoarsely: "My son, *barin,* died this week."

"Hm! What did he die of?"

Iona turns with his whole body toward his fare, and says:

"And who knows! They say high fever. He was three days in the hospital, and then died. . . . God's will be done."

"Turn round! The devil!" sounds from the darkness. "Have you popped off, old doggie, eh? Use your eyes!"

"Go on, go on," says the officer, "otherwise we shall not get there by tomorrow. Hurry up a bit!"

The cabdriver again stretches his neck, sits up, and, with a bad grace, brandishes his whip. Several times again he turns to look at his fare, but the latter has closed his eyes, and apparently is not disposed to listen. Having deposited the officer in the Viborg, he stops by the tavern, doubles himself up on his seat, and again remains motionless, while the snow once more begins to cover him and his horse. An hour, and another. . . . Then, along the footpath, with a squeak of galoshes, and quarreling, come three young men, two of them tall and lanky, the third one short and hump-backed.

"Cabby, to the Police Bridge!" in a cracked voice calls the humpback. "The three of us for two *griveniks!*"

Iona picks up his reins, and smacks his lips. Two *griveniks* is not a fair price, but he does not mind whether it is a *rouble* or five *kopeks*—to him it is all the same now, so long as they are fares. The young men, jostling each other and using bad language, approach the sleigh, and all three at once try to get onto the seat; then begins a discussion as to which two shall sit and who shall be the one to stand. After wrangling, abusing each other, and much petulance, it is at last decided that the humpback shall stand, as he is the smallest.

"Now then, hurry up!" says the humpback in a twanging voice, as he takes his place and breathes in Iona's neck. "Old furry! Here, mate, what a cap you have! There is not a worse one to be found in all Petersburg! . . ."

"He-he!—he-he!" giggles Iona. "Such a . . ."

"Now you, 'such a,' hurry up, are you going the whole way at this pace? Are you? . . . Do you want it in the neck?"

"My head feels like bursting," says one of the lanky ones. "Last night at the Donkmasovs, Vaska and I drank the whole of four bottles of cognac."

"I don't understand what you lie for," says the other lanky one angrily; "you lie like a brute."

"God strike me, it's the truth!"

"It's as much the truth as that a louse coughs!"

"He, he," grins Iona, "what gay young gentlemen!"

"Pshaw, go to the devil!" says the humpback indignantly.

"Are you going to get on or not, you old pest? Is that the way to drive? Use the whip a bit! Go on, devil, go on, give it to him well!"

Iona feels at his back the little man wriggling, and the tremble in his voice. He listens to the insults hurled at him, sees the people, and little by little the feeling of loneliness leaves him. The humpback goes on swearing until he gets mixed up in some elaborate six-foot oath, or chokes with coughing. The lankies begin to talk about a certain Nadejda Petrovna. Iona looks round at them several times; he waits for a temporary silence, then, turning round again, he murmurs:

"My son . . . died this week."

"We must all die," sighs the humpback, wiping his lips after an attack of coughing. "Now, hurry up, hurry up! Gentlemen, I really cannot go any farther like this! When will he get us there?"

"Well, just you stimulate him a little in the neck!"

"You old pest, do you hear, I'll bone your neck for you! If one treated the like of you with ceremony one would have to go on foot! Do you hear, old serpent Gorinytch! Or do you not care a spit?"

Iona hears rather than feels the blows they deal him.

"He, he," he laughs. "They are gay young gentlemen, God bless 'em!"

"Cabby, are you married?" asks a lanky one.

"I? He, he, gay young gentlemen! Now I have only a wife and the moist ground. . . . He, ho, ho . . . that is to say, the grave. My son has died, and I am alive. . . . A wonderful thing, death mistook the door . . . instead of coming to me, it went to my son. . . ."

Iona turns round to tell them how his son died, but at this moment, the humpback, giving a little sigh, announces, "Thank God, we have at last reached our destination," and Iona watches them disappear through the dark entrance. Once more he is alone, and again surrounded by silence. . . . His grief, which has abated for a short while, returns and rends his heart with greater force. With an anxious and hurried look, he searches among the crowds passing on either side of the street to find whether there may be just one person who will listen to him. But the crowds hurry by without noticing him or his trouble. Yet it is such an immense, illimitable grief. Should his heart break and the grief pour out, it would flow over the whole earth, so it seems, and yet no one sees it. It has managed to conceal itself in such an insignificant shell that no one can see it even by day and with a light.

Iona sees a hall porter with some sacking, and decides to talk to him. "Friend, what sort of time is it?" he asks.

"Past nine. What are you standing here for? Move on."

Iona moves on a few steps, doubles himself up, and abandons himself to his grief. He sees it is useless to turn to people for help. In less than five minutes he straightens himself, holds up his head as if he felt some sharp pain, and gives a tug at the reins; he can bear it no longer. "The stables," he thinks, and the little horse, as if it understood, starts off at a trot.

About an hour and a half later Iona is seated by a large dirty stove. Around the stove, on the floor, on the benches, people are snoring; the air is thick and suffocatingly hot. Iona looks at the sleepers, scratches himself, and regrets having returned so early.

"I have not even earned my fodder," he thinks. "That's what's my trouble. A man who knows his job, who has had enough to eat, and his horse too, can always sleep peacefully."

A young cabdriver in one of the corners half gets up, grunts sleepily, and stretches towards a bucket of water.

"Do you want a drink?" Iona asks him.

"Don't I want a drink!"

"That's so? Your good health! But listen, mate—you know, my son is dead. . . . Did you hear? This week, in the hospital. . . . It's a long story."

Iona looks to see what effect his words have, but sees none—the young man has hidden his face and is fast asleep again. The old man sighs, and scratches his head. Just as much as the young one wants to drink, the old man wants to talk. It will soon be a week since his son died, and he has not been able to speak about it properly to anyone. One must tell it slowly and carefully; how his son fell ill, how he suffered, what he said before he died, how he died. One must describe every detail of the funeral, and the journey to the hospital to fetch the dead son's clothes. His daughter Anissia has remained in the village—one must talk about her too. Is it nothing he has to tell? Surely the listener would gasp and sigh, and sympathize with him? It is better, too, to talk to women; although they are stupid, two words are enough to make them sob.

"I'll go and look after my horse," thinks Iona; "there's always time to sleep. No fear of that!"

He puts on his coat, and goes to the stables to his horse; he thinks of the corn, the hay, the weather. When he is alone, he dares not think of his son; he can speak about him to anyone, but to think of him, and picture him to himself, is unbearably painful.

"Are you tucking in?" Iona asks his horse, looking at its bright eyes; "go on, tuck in, though we've not earned our corn, we can eat hay. Yes!

I am too old to drive—my son could have, not I. He was a first-rate cab-driver. If only he had lived!"

Iona is silent for a moment, then continues:

"That's how it is, my old horse. There's no more Kuzma Ionitch. He has left us to live, and he went off pop. Now let's say, you had a foal, you were the foal's mother, and suddenly, let's say, that foal went and left you to live after him. It would be sad, wouldn't it?"

The little horse munches, listens, and breathes over its master's hand. . . .

Iona's feelings are too much for him, and he tells the little horse the whole story.

INTERPRETATION

This story, like "Tennessee's Partner," deals with a pathetic situation. An old cabdriver, who has lost his son, can find no one in the world to whom he can confide his grief, and in the end goes out to the stable to tell his horse. In writing this story an author would almost certainly run the risk of sentimentality. In considering this story, particularly after having read "Tennessee's Partner," one is interested in seeing what means Chekhov uses to avoid sentimentalizing his material.

One of the most obvious things which the reader notices in looking back on this story is the objective and neutral presentation. The author seems to be presenting scenes and actions to us without weighting them in favor of one interpretation or another.

For instance, consider his use of nature. In "Tennessee's Partner," as has been pointed out, Bret Harte uses nature to set a mood. But the use here—say in the first paragraph of "The Lament"—is different on two counts. First, Chekhov gives us the picture of the lonely scene on the street corner at evening, with the snow falling on the old cabdriver and the little horse. The fact of isolation is suggested, but there is no appeal to our sympathies either by poeticized language, as is the case in "Tennessee's Partner," or by editorial comment. Indeed, when Chekhov does depart from the straight, neutral, objective description, the effect is to play down the appeal to our sympathy rather than to insist upon it. For example, the suggestion is that the scene is scarcely real: "The cabdriver . . . is quite white, and looks like a phantom." And the "little horse is also quite white, and remains motionless; its immobility, its angularity, and its straight wooden-looking legs, even close by, give it the appearance of a gingerbread horse worth a *kopek*." The comparisons to the phantom and to the ginger-bread horse serve to make the scene vivid and particular. But phantoms and gingerbread horses are fantastic things which do not feel or suffer and can make no appeal to sympathy. In other words, the scene, though it does give a sense of isolation, an effect which is important in the story of the cab-driver, is ostensibly pointed *away* from the appeal for sympathy and not *toward* it; Chekhov seems to say that he will be willing to rest his case on its own merits. The second way in which Chekhov's use of nature differs from that of Bret Harte in "Tennessee's Partner" is this: the function of the scene in "The Lament" is purely preparatory; the function in "Tennessee's Partner" is to seduce the reader into a proper response when he comes to the crucial point in the story.

The objective and neutral presentation, of which we have spoken in connection with the first paragraph of the story, continues through the various incidents which constitute the action.

The cabman picks up a fare who seems to be friendly and conversational. Apparently the cabman is sufficiently encouraged by the friendliness of the officer to make a remark that his son has just died. But Chekhov does not indicate at this point the true meaning of the son's death to the cabman. Chekhov merely tells us that he "twists his mouth into a smile, and with an effort says hoarsely" that the boy is dead. This description of how the cabman says the words is our first revelation of his feelings, but we notice that the description is objective, and, indeed, somewhat ambiguous. What does the smile mean? Obviously, we can take it to be, in part, a response of gratitude for the officer's friendliness which comes in contrast to the isolation of the original scene. But the smile, like the comparisons to the phantom and the gingerbread horse in the first scene, tends to play down, rather than up, any direct appeal to our sympathy with the cabman as a grief-stricken man. At any rate, when the cabman, further encouraged by the officer's perfunctory expression of curiosity, takes his attention from his driving and begins to give some details of the son's death, he is interrupted by an irate protest from the darkness. And the officer then tells him to hurry, and forbids further conversation by leaning back and shutting his eyes.

It is worth noting that such information as we have been given about the cabman's feelings has come to us *dramatically*—that is, we have had it only in terms of his speech and not by commentary. By the same token, our information is incomplete. The basic motivation of the cabman has only been hinted at; it has not been fully revealed. Thus the dramatic presentation and the development of the reader's suspense here go hand in hand.

The motivation is further developed in the next scene, when the cabman tries, with unfriendly and boisterous passengers, to open the same subject. Their attitude toward him, too, emphasizes his own isolation. He tries to humor them in their drunkenness, and flatter them. In part, this behavior, no doubt, may be taken as an effort to get on good terms with his fares and as an indication of his humble position in society: but in part it may be taken as an indication of his willingness to accept any humiliation in order to tell his story. Thus, his behavior dramatically suggests the over-powering necessity which compels him to tell his story. (One should notice how, even here, Chekhov continues to play down the pathos of Iona: the young men are not necessarily cruel, but may be merely drunken and thoughtless.)

After the young men get out and the cabman is again left alone, Chekhov introduces his first explicit statement of the situation: "His grief, which has abated for a short while, returns and rends his heart with greater force. With an anxious and hurried look, he searches among the crowds passing on either side of the street to find if there may be just one person who will listen to him." In other words, Chekhov has been cunning enough to validate the situation dramatically, before he commits himself to the overt statement. Unlike similar statements in the Bret Harte story, which attempt to prod the reader's sympathies, this statement summarizes what the intelligent reader has already been able to infer. But, of course, it is not merely a summary. It analyzes the state of mind of the cabman: as long as he has had any kind of human contact, even an unpleasant one, as with the drunken youths, his grief has abated, but now that he is completely alone, it returns with added force. Now he is even compelled to get out of the cab and seek conversation.

But the attempt to engage the porter in conversation fails, and the cabman finally returns to the stables. There, at least, one would expect him to be able to find some sympathy among his own kind and class. But even here he is forced back upon himself.

This sets the stage for the second piece of analysis of the cabman's state of mind. Chekhov now, for the first time, gives us some of the details of the son's death. But not merely as information. He gives them as preparation for the question which is wrung from the heart of the old man by the realization that no one will listen to him: "Is it nothing he has to tell?"

This seems to be the summary of the old man's feelings—his incom-prehension of the world, and his loneliness in it. If this were all, however, the story could come to a proper close after the old man's next thought: "I'll go and look after my horse . . . there's always time to sleep. No fear of that!"

But the situation is a little more complicated than this. Therefore, we have the last bit of analysis, which is now fully prepared for. Iona tries to think of the corn, the hay, and the weather. Presumably, he is go-ing out to see about his horse, but really, we learn, he thinks of these things and goes out to his horse, simply because he cannot bear to be alone with the thought of his loss. The impulse to go to the stable does not depend on any conscious decision to tell the horse his troubles. He is fulfilling an un-conscious need. This need is unconscious, but it colors even the way in which he begins to talk to the horse: "Are you tucking in?" He talks as if the horse were a child. But the unconscious need is so great that before he has uttered more than a sentence or two, he is back to the subject of his son. And once he has started talking with the horse, he begins to explain to the horse what he had been unable to explain to anyone else. But we may note that not only what he says to the horse is important, but the way in which he speaks: he adopts the careful, patient tone of explanation which a father might take to a young child: "Now, let's say, you had a foal, you were the foal's mother . . ."

This whole episode, though it has been prepared for by all preceding incidents and by the psychological analysis in the story, comes with an *ironical* shock of surprise. It is a surprise because the cabman's decision to go out to the stables is presented, on the surface at least, as a routine matter: the good cabman goes out to look after his horse. It is ironical, because it offers a commentary on a world in which one human being can find human sympathy only from a beast. Furthermore, this irony itself is shocking, for Chekhov has so presented the world of the story that it does not seem entirely vindictive and cruel. Some of the people who do not listen are simply preoccupied with their own affairs, or worn out with their own work. Yet this apparently normal world, in which there is a mixture of attitudes, turns out to be a world which does drive the man, seeking human sympathy, to the beast in the stable. And this turns out to be the theme of the story.

1. Comment on the use of the comparison of the old man to a swan in the fifth paragraph.

2. Comment on the function of these lines in helping supply preparation for the last scene: ". . . he can bear it no longer. 'The stables,' he thinks . . . starts off at a trot" (p. 206).

3. In the last scene, Chekhov gives us Iona, a simple man, speaking in his full simplicity. This is a device for pathetic effect. Bret Harte uses a similar device in the funeral speech and in the dying speech of the partner. Why is the device successful in one instance, and unsuccessful in the other?

D. H. LAWRENCE

Tickets, Please

THERE is in the Midlands a single-line tramway system which boldly leaves the country town and plunges off into the black, industrial countryside, up hill and down dale, through the long, ugly villages of workmen's houses, over canals and railways, past churches perched high and nobly over the smoke and shadows, through stark, grimy, cold little market-places, tilting away in a rush past cinemas and shops down to the hollow where the collieries are, then up again, past a little rural church, under the ash trees, on in a rush to the terminus, the last little ugly place of industry, the cold little town that shivers on the edge of the wild, gloomy country beyond. There the green and creamy colored tram-car seems to pause and purr with curious satisfaction. But in a few minutes—the clock on the turret of the Co-operative Wholesale Society's Shops gives the time—away it starts once more on the adventure. Again there are the reckless swoops downhill, bouncing the loops: again the chilly wait in the hill-top market-place: again the breathless slithering round the precipitous drop under the church: again the patient halts at the loops, waiting for the outcoming car: so on and on, for two long hours, till at last the city looms beyond the fat gas-works, the narrow factories draw near, we are in the sordid streets of the great town, once more we sidle to a standstill at our terminus, abashed by the great crimson and cream-coloured city cars, but still perky, jaunty, somewhat dare-devil, green as a jaunty sprig of parsley out of a black colliery garden.

To ride on these cars is always an adventure. Since we are in war-time, the drivers are men unfit for active service: cripples and hunchbacks. So they have the spirit of the devil in them. The ride becomes a steeple-chase. Hurray! we have leapt in a clear jump over the canal bridges—now for the four-lane corner. With a shriek and a trail of sparks we are clear again. To be sure, a tram often leaps the rails—but what matter! It sits in a ditch till other trams come to haul it out. It is quite common for a car, packed with one solid mass of living people, to come to a dead halt in the midst of unbroken blackness, the heart of nowhere on a dark night, and for the driver and the girl conductor to call, "All get off—car's on fire!" Instead, however, of rushing out in a panic, the passengers stolidly reply: "Get on—get on! We're not coming out. We're stopping where we are. Push on, George." So till flames actually appear.

The reason for this reluctance to dismount is that the nights are howlingly cold, black, and windswept, and a car is a haven of refuge. From village to village the miners travel, for a change of cinema, of girl, of pub. The trams are desperately packed. Who is going to risk himself in the black gulf outside, to wait perhaps an hour for another tram, then to see the forlorn notice "Depot Only," because there is something wrong! or to greet a unit of three bright cars all so tight with people that they sail past with a howl of derision. Trams that pass in the night.

This, the most dangerous tram-service in England, as the authorities themselves declare, with pride, is entirely conducted by girls, and driven by rash young men, a little crippled, or by delicate young men, who creep forward in terror. The girls are fearless young hussies. In their ugly blue uniform, skirts up to their knees, shapeless old peaked caps on their heads, they have all the sang-froid of an old non-commissioned officer. With a tram packed with howling colliers, roaring hymns downstairs and a sort of antiphony of obscenities upstairs, the lasses are perfectly at their ease. They pounce on the youths who try to evade their ticket-machine. They push off the men at the end of their distance. They are not going to be done in the eye—not they. They fear nobody—and everybody fears them.

"Hello, Annie!"

"Hello, Ted!"

"Oh, mind my corn, Miss Stone. It's my belief you've got a heart of stone, for you've trod on it again."

"You should keep it in your pocket," replies Miss Stone, and she goes sturdily upstairs in her high boots.

"Tickets, please."

She is peremptory, suspicious, and ready to hit first. She can hold her own against ten thousand. The step of that tram-car is her Thermopylæ.

Therefore, there is a certain wild romance aboard these cars—and in the sturdy bosom of Annie herself. The time for soft romance is in the morning, between ten o'clock and one, when things are rather slack: that is, except market-day and Saturday. Thus Annie has time to look about her. Then she often hops off her car and into a shop where she has spied something, while the driver chats in the main road. There is very good feeling between the girls and the drivers. Are they not companions in peril, shipments aboard this careering vessel of a tram-car, for ever rocking on the waves of a stormy land.

Then, also, during the easy hours, the inspectors are most in evidence. For some reason, everybody employed in this tram-service is young: there are no grey heads. It would not do. Therefore the inspectors are of the right age, and one, the chief, is also good-looking. See him stand on a wet, gloomy morning, in his long oilskin, his peaked cap well down over his eyes, waiting to board a car. His face is ruddy, his small brown moustache is weathered, he has a faint impudent smile. Fairly tall and agile, even in his waterproof, he springs aboard a car and geets Annie.

"Hello, Annie! Keeping the wet out?"

"Trying to."

There are only two people in the car. Inspecting is soon over. Then for a long and impudent chat on the footboard, a good, easy, twelve-mile chat.

The inspector's name is John Thomas Raynor—always called John Thomas, except sometimes, in malice, Coddy. His face sets in fury when he is addressed, from a distance, with this abbreviation. There is considerable scandal about John Thomas in half a dozen villages. He flirts with the girl conductors in the morning and walks out with them in the dark night, when they leave their tram-car at the depot. Of course, the girls quit the service frequently. Then he flirts and walks out with the newcomer: always providing she is sufficiently attractive, and that she will consent to walk. It is remarkable, however, that most of the girls are quite comely, they are all young, and this roving life aboard the car gives them a sailor's dash and recklessness. What matter how they behave when the ship is in port. Tomorrow they will be aboard again.

Annie, however, was something of a Tartar, and her sharp tongue had kept John Thomas at arm's length for many months. Perhaps, therefore, she liked him all the more: for he always came up smiling, with impudence. She watched him vanquish one girl, then another. She could tell by the movement of his mouth and eyes, when he flirted with her in the morning, that he had been walking out with this lass, or the other, the night before. A fine cock-of-the-walk he was. She could sum him up pretty well.

In this subtle antagonism they knew each other like old friends, they were as shrewd with one another almost as man and wife. But Annie had always kept him sufficiently at arm's length. Besides, she had a boy of her own.

The Statutes fair, however, came in November, at Bestwood. It happened that Annie had the Monday night off. It was a drizzling ugly night, yet she dressed herself up and went to the fair ground. She was alone, but she expected soon to find a pal of some sort.

The roundabouts were veering round and grinding out their music, the side shows were making as much commotion as possible. In the cocoanut shies there were no cocoanuts, but artificial war-time substitutes, which the lad declared were fastened into the irons. There was a sad decline in brilliance and luxury. None the less, the ground was muddy as ever, there was the same crush, the press of faces lighted up by the flares and the electric lights, the same smell of naphtha and a few fried potatoes, and of electricity.

Who should be the first to greet Miss Annie, on the show ground, but John Thomas. He had a black overcoat buttoned up to his chin, and a tweed cap pulled down over his brows, his face between was ruddy and smiling and handy as ever. She knew so well the way his mouth moved.

She was very glad to have a "boy." To be at the Statutes without a fellow was no fun. Instantly, like the gallant he was, he took her on the Dragons, grim-toothed, roundabout switchbacks. It was not nearly so exciting as a tram-car actually. But, then, to be seated in a shaking green dragon, uplifted above the sea of bubble faces, careering in a rickety fashion in the lower heavens, whilst John Thomas leaned over her, his cigarette in his mouth, was after all the right style. She was a plump, quick, alive little creature. So she was quite excited and happy.

John Thomas made her stay on for the next round. And therefore she could hardly for shame repulse him when he put his arm round her and drew her a little nearer to him, in a very warm and cuddly manner. Besides, he was fairly discreet, he kept his movement as hidden as possible. She looked down and saw that his red, clean hand was out of sight of the crowd. And they knew each other so well. So they warmed up to the fair.

After the dragons they went on the horses. John Thomas paid each time, so she could but be complaisant. He, of course, sat astride on the outer horse—named "Black Bess"—and she sat sideways, towards him, on the inner horse—named "Wildfire." But of course John Thomas was not going to sit discreetly on "Black Bess," holding the brass bar. Round they spun and heaved, in the light. And round he swung on his wooden steed, flinging one leg across her mount, and perilously tipping up and down, across the space, half lying back, laughing at her. He was perfectly happy; she was afraid her hat was on one side, but she was excited.

He threw quoits on a table and won for her two large, pale-blue hatpins. And then, hearing the noise of the cinemas, announcing another performance, they climbed the boards and went in.

Of course, during these performances pitch darkness falls from time to time, when the machine goes wrong. Then there is a wild whooping, and a loud smacking of simulated kisses. In these moments John Thomas drew Annie towards him. After all, he had a wonderfully warm, cosy way of holding a girl with his arm, he seemed to make such a nice fit. And after all, it was pleasant to be so held: so very comforting and cosy and nice. He leaned over her and she felt his breath on her hair; she knew he wanted to kiss her on the lips. And after all, he was so warm and she fitted in to him so softly. After all, she wanted him to touch her lips.

But the light sprang up; she also started electrically, and put her hat straight. He left his arm lying nonchalantly behind her. Well, it was fun, it was exciting to be at the Statutes with John Thomas.

When the cinema was over they went for a walk across the dark, damp fields. He had all the arts of love-making. He was especially good at holding a girl, when he sat with her on a stile in the black, drizzling darkness. He seemed to be holding her in space, against his own warmth and gratification. And his kisses were soft and slow and searching.

So Annie walked out with John Thomas, though she kept her own boy dangling in the distance. Some of the tram-girls chose to be huffy. But there, you must take things as you find them, in this life.

There was no mistake about it, Annie liked John Thomas a good deal. She felt so rich and warm in herself whenever he was near. And John Thomas really liked Annie more than usual. The soft, melting way in which she could flow into a fellow, as if she melted into his very bones, was something rare and good. He fully appreciated this.

But with a developing acquaintance there began a developing intimacy. Annie wanted to consider him a person, a man; she wanted to take an intelligent interest in him, and to have an intelligent response. She did not want a mere nocturnal presence, which was what he was so far. And she prided herself that he could not leave her.

Here she made a mistake. John Thomas intended to remain a nocturnal presence; he had no idea of becoming an all-round individual to her. When she started to take an intelligent interest in him and his life and his character, he sheered off. He hated intelligent interest. And he knew that the only way to stop it was to avoid it. The possessive female was aroused in Annie. So he left her.

It is no use saying she was not surprised. She was at first startled, thrown out of her count. For she had been so *very* sure of holding him. For a while she was staggered, and everything became uncertain to her. Then she wept with fury, indignation, desolation, and misery. Then she had a spasm of despair. And then, when he came, still impudently, on to her car, still familiar, but letting her see by the movement of his head that he had gone away to somebody else for the time being and was enjoying pastures new, then she determined to have her own back.

She had a very shrewd idea what girls John Thomas had taken out. She went to Nora Purdy. Nora was a tall, rather pale, but well-built girl, with beautiful yellow hair. She was rather secretive.

"Hey!" said Annie, accosting her; then softly, "Who's John Thomas on with now?"

"I don't know," said Nora.

"Why tha does," said Annie, ironically lapsing into dialect. "Tha knows as well as I do."

"Well, I do, then," said Nora. "It isn't me, so don't bother."

"It's Cissy Meakin, isn't it?"

"It is, for all I know."

"Hasn't he got a face on him!" said Annie. "I don't half like his cheek. I could knock him off the footboard when he comes round at me."

"He'll get dropped-on one of these days," said Nora.

"Ay, he will when somebody makes up their mind to drop it on him. I should like to see him taken down a peg or two, shouldn't you?"

"I shouldn't mind," said Nora.

"You've got quite as much cause to as I have," said Annie. "But we'll drop on him one of these days, my girl. What? Don't you want to?"

"I don't mind," said Nora.

But as a matter of fact, Nora was much more vindictive than Annie.

One by one Annie went the round of the old flames. It so happened that Cissy Meakin left the tramway service in quite a short time. Her mother made her leave. Then John Thomas was on the qui-vive. He cast his eyes over his old flock. And his eyes lighted on Annie. He thought she would be safe now. Besides, he liked her.

She arranged to walk home with him on Sunday night. It so happened that her car would be in the depot at half-past nine: the last car would come in at ten-fifteen. So John Thomas was to wait for her there.

At the depot the girls had a little waiting-room of their own. It was quite rough, but cosy, with a fire and an oven and a mirror, and table and wooden chairs. The half dozen girls who knew John Thomas only too well had arranged to take service this Sunday afternoon. So, as the cars began to come in, early, the girls dropped into the waiting-room. And instead of hurrying off home, they sat around the fire and had a cup of tea. Outside was the darkness and lawlessness of war-time.

John Thomas came on the car after Annie, at about a quarter to ten. He poked his head easily into the girls' waiting-room.

"Prayer-meeting?" he asked.

"Ay," said Laura Sharp. "Ladies only."

"That's me!" said John Thomas. It was one of his favourite exclamations.

"Shut the door, boy," said Muriel Baggaley.

"On which side of me?" said John Thomas.

"Which tha likes," said Polly Birkin.

He had come in and closed the door behind him. The girls moved in their circle, to make a place for him near the fire. He took off his great-coat and pushed back his hat.

"Who handles the teapot?" he said.

Nora Purdy silently poured him out a cup of tea.

"Want a bit o' my bread and drippin'?" said Muriel Baggaley to him.

"Ay, give us a bit."

And he began to eat his piece of bread.

"There's no place like home, girls," he said.

They all looked at him as he uttered this piece of impudence. He seemed to be sunning himself in the presence of so many damsels.

"Especially if you're not afraid to go home in the dark," said Laura Sharp.

"Me! By myself I am."

They sat till they heard the last tram come in. In a few minutes Emma Houselay entered.

"Come on, my old duck!" cried Polly Birkin.

"It *is* perishing," said Emma, holding her fingers to the fire.

"But—I'm afraid to, go home in, the dark," sang Laura Sharp, the tune having got into her mind.

"Who're you going with tonight, John Thomas?" asked Muriel Baggaley, coolly.

"Tonight?" said John Thomas. "Oh, I'm going home by myself tonight—all on my lonely-O."

"That's me!" said Nora Purdy, using his own ejaculation.

The girls laughed shrilly.

"Me as well, Nora," said John Thomas.

"Don't know what you mean," said Laura.

"Yes, I'm toddling," said he, rising and reaching for his overcoat.

"Nay," said Polly. "We're all here waiting for you."

"We've got to be up in good time in the morning," he said in the benevolent official manner.

They all laughed.

"Nay," said Muriel. "Don't leave us all lonely, John Thomas. Take one!"

"I'll take the lot, if you like," he responded gallantly.

"That you won't, either," said Muriel. "Two's company; seven's too much of a good thing."

"Nay—take one," said Laura. "Fair and square, all above board, and say which."

"Ay," cried Annie, speaking for the first time. "Pick, John Thomas; let's hear thee."

"Nay," he said. "I'm going home quiet tonight. Feeling good, for once."

"Whereabouts?" said Annie. "Take a good un, then. But tha's got to take one of us!"

"Nay, how can I take one," he said, laughing uneasily. "I don't want to make enemies."

"You'd only make *one*," said Annie.

"The chosen *one*," added Laura.

"Oh, my! Who said girls!" exclaimed John Thomas, again turning, as if to escape. "Well—good-night."

"Nay, you've got to make your pick," said Muriel. "Turn your face to the wall and say which one touches you. Go on—we shall only just touch your back—one of us. Go on—turn your face to the wall, and don't look, and say which one touches you."

He was uneasy, mistrusting them. Yet he had not the courage to break away. They pushed him to a wall and stood him there with his face to it. Behind his back they all grimaced, tittering. He looked so comical. He looked around uneasily.

"Go on!" he cried.

"You're looking—you're looking!" they shouted.

He turned his head away. And suddenly, with a movement like a swift cat, Annie went forward and fetched him a box on the side of the head that set his cap flying, and himself staggering. He started round.

But at Annie's signal they all flew at him, slapping him, pinching him, pulling his hair, though more in fun than in spite or anger. He, however, saw red. His blue eyes flamed with strange fear as well as fury, and he butted through the girls to the door. It was locked. He wrenched at it. Roused, alert, the girls stood round and looked at him. He faced them, at bay. At that moment they were rather horrifying to him, as they stood in their short uniforms. He was distinctly afraid.

"Come on, John Thomas! Come on! Choose!" said Annie.

"What are you after? Open the door," he said.

"We sha'n't—not till you've chosen!" said Muriel.

"Chosen what?" he said.

"Chosen the one you're going to marry," she replied.

He hesitated a moment.

"Open the blasted door," he said, "and get back to your senses." He spoke with official authority.

"You've got to choose!" cried the girls.

"Come on!" cried Annie, looking him in the eye. "Come on! Come on!"

He went forward, rather vaguely. She had taken off her belt, and swinging it, she fetched him a sharp blow over the head with the buckle end. He sprang and seized her. But immediately the other girls rushed upon him, pulling and tearing and beating him. Their blood was now thoroughly up. He was their sport now. They were going to have their own back, out of him. Strange, wild creatures, they hung on him and rushed at him to bear him down. His tunic was torn right up the back, Nora had hold at the back of his collar, and was actually strangling him. Luckily the button burst. He struggled in a wild frenzy of fury and terror, almost mad terror. His tunic was simply torn off his back, his shirt-sleeves were torn away, his arms were naked. The girls rushed at him, clenched their hands on him and pulled at him: or they rushed at him and pushed him, butted him with all their might: or they struck him wild blows. He ducked and cringed and struck sideways. They became more intense.

At last he was down. They rushed on him, kneeling on him. He had neither breath nor strength to move. His face was bleeding with a long scratch, his brow was bruised.

Annie knelt on him, the other girls knelt and hung on to him. Their faces were flushed, their hair wild, their eyes were all glittering strangely. He lay at last quite still, with face averted, as an animal lies when it is defeated and at the mercy of the captor. Sometimes his eye glanced back at the wild faces of the girls. His breast rose heavily, his wrists were torn.

"Now, then, my fellow!" gasped Annie at length. "Now then—now——"

At the sound of her terrifying, cold triumph, he suddenly started to struggle as an animal might, but the girls threw themselves upon him with unnatural strength and power, forcing him down.

"Yes—now, then!" gasped Annie at length.

And there was a dead silence, in which the thud of heart-beating was to be heard. It was a suspense of pure silence in every soul.

"Now you know where you are," said Annie.

The sight of his white, bare arm maddened the girls. He lay in a kind of trance of fear and antagonism. They felt themselves filled with supernatural strength.

Suddenly Polly started to laugh—to giggle wildly—helplessly—and Emma and Muriel joined in. But Annie and Nora and Laura remained the same, tense, watchful, with gleaming eyes. He winced away from these eyes.

"Yes," said Annie, in a curious low tone, secret and deadly. "Yes! You've got it now! You know what you've done, don't you? You know what you've done."

He made no sound nor sign, but lay with bright, averted eyes, and averted, bleeding face.

"You ought to be *killed*, that's what you ought," said Annie tensely. "You ought to be *killed*." And there was a terrifying lust in her voice.

Polly was ceasing to laugh, and giving long-drawn oh-h-hs and sighs as she came to herself.

"He's got to choose," she said vaguely.

"Oh, yes, he has," said Laura, with vindictive decision.

"Do you hear—do you hear?" said Annie. And with a sharp movement that made him wince, she turned his face to her.

"Do you hear?" she repeated, shaking him.

But he was quite dumb. She fetched him a sharp slap on the face. He started, and his eyes widened. Then his face darkened with defiance, after all.

"Do you hear?" she repeated.

He only looked at her with hostile eyes.

"Speak!" she said, putting her face devilishly near his.

"What?" he said, almost overcome.

"You've got to *choose!*" she cried, as if it were some terrible menace, and as if it hurt her that she could not exact more.

"What?" he said in fear.

"Choose your girl, Coddy. You've got to choose her now. And you'll get your neck broken if you play any more of your tricks, my boy. You're settled now."

There was a pause. Again he averted his face. He was cunning in his overthrow. He did not give in to them really—no, not if they tore him to bits.

"All right, then," he said, "I choose Annie." His voice was strange and full of malice. Annie let go of him as if he had been a hot coal.

"He's chosen Annie!" said the girls in chorus.

"Me!" cried Annie. She was still kneeling, but away from him. He was still lying prostrate, with averted face. The girls grouped uneasily around.

"Me!" repeated Annie, with a terrible bitter accent.

Then she got up, drawing away from him with strange disgust and bitterness.

"I wouldn't touch him," she said.

But her face quivered with a kind of agony, she seemed as if she would fall. The other girls turned aside. He remained lying on the floor, with his torn clothes and bleeding, averted face.

"Oh, if he's chosen——" said Polly.

"I don't want him—he can choose again," said Annie, with the same rather bitter hopelessness.

"Get up," said Polly, lifting his shoulder. "Get up."

He rose slowly, a strange, ragged, dazed creature. The girls eyed him from a distance, curiously, furtively, dangerously.

"Who wants him?" cried Laura roughly.

"Nobody," they answered with contempt. Yet each one of them waited for him to look at her, hoped he would look at her. All except Annie, and something was broken in her.

He, however, kept his face closed and averted from them all. There was a silence of the end. He picked up the torn pieces of his tunic, without knowing what to do with them. The girls stood about uneasily, flushed, panting, tidying their hair and their dress unconsciously, and watching him. He looked at none of them. He espied his cap in a corner and went and picked it up. He put it on his head, and one of the girls burst into a shrill, hysteric laugh at the sight he presented. He, however, took no heed but went straight to where his overcoat hung on a peg. The girls moved away from contact with him as if he had been an electric wire. He put on his coat and buttoned it down. Then he rolled his tunic-rags into a bundle, and stood before the locked door, dumbly.

"Open the door, somebody," said Laura.

"Annie's got the key," said one.

Annie silently offered the key to the girls. Nora unlocked the door.

"Tit for tat, old man," she said. "Show yourself a man, and don't bear a grudge."

But without a word or sign he had opened the door and gone, his face closed, his head dropped.

"That'll learn him," said Laura.

"Coddy!" said Nora.

"Shut up, for God's sake!" cried Annie fiercely, as if in torture.

"Well, I'm about ready to go, Polly. Look sharp!" said Muriel.

The girls were all anxious to be off. They were tidying themselves hurriedly, with mute, stupefied faces.

INTERPRETATION

The plot of this story is quite simple. One of the young inspectors of the tram line, John Thomas, begins to go out with Annie, one of the girl conductors. He drops her when he realizes that she is taking his attentions seriously. Annie plans to revenge herself by having the other girls whom he has treated in this fashion join her in roughing him up. They do not hurt him, though they get in some blows and they tear his tunic. John Thomas leaves, and the girls find themselves nonplussed at what they have done, a little dazed, and even a little frightened.

Though the story presents a good deal of action, even violent action, not very much has been resolved. Presumably John Thomas and Annie will continue to go their separate ways. Indeed, the story ends on a note of uneasy irresolution. The superficial reader may even feel baffled by the ending of the story and so dismiss it.

Other readers, however, may feel that the internal action is important. Indeed, the very debacle of the ending points toward an exciting psychological development. The girls have got in over their depth and find that their emotions toward John Thomas are in excess of, and indeed widely different from, the rather tomboyish triumph of their revenge. As the author tells us in the last sentence, after John Thomas's departure, the girls wear "mute, stupified faces."

The story derives much of its richness from the fact that it succeeds in dramatizing what may be called the "doubleness" of love—its strange mixture of aggressiveness and passivity, of cruelty and tenderness, of possessiveness and surrender. All the characters in the story experience something of these contradictory feelings, but the author has properly kept the focus upon one particular character, Annie, who is more deeply involved than the others, and who therefore not only feels the experience more intensely but is also the more intensely subject to the contradictory impulses within the experience.

What is it that Annie wants from the trick to be played on John Thomas? On the conscious level, presumably no more than the humiliation that he will suffer at the rough handling the girls intend to give him and the taunts that they mean to hurl at him. But unconsciously Annie must have wanted much more—if we are to judge from what actually happens in the latter part of the story. Certainly she must have wanted the specific confrontation with him—including the physical contact. She must also have wanted a chance to pour out some of her feelings of hurt and anger—the prank will afford her a kind of justification for doing so. Secretly, perhaps she wanted to hear him name her as his choice—if only to have the chance to tell him she has no interest in him. But it is plain that neither Annie nor the rest of the girls have really thought out just what they expect the prank to accomplish or to mean.

The last point comes out clearly when we see that nobody knows just how to end the joke. Once they have got into it, their actions are emotional and compulsive. Annie hits John Thomas a box on the side of the head that is probably much harder than she had first meant to strike. At this signal the girls fly at John Thomas "more in fun than in spite or anger." But soon they have their "blood . . . up," and are attacking in frenzy. When John Thomas stops resisting, the girls find themselves waiting for something to happen, not knowing what to do next, and repeating illogically and "vaguely" that he has "got to choose." Indeed, some of the girls, beginning "to giggle wildly," are obviously on the verge of hysteria.

There is, of course, no way for the episode to end satisfactorily for any of the girls—least of all for the leader of the prank, Annie, whose relation to John Thomas is so emotionally ambiguous. The only satisfactory ending for such a mixture of feelings—and of feelings waked to such intensity by the physical struggle—is possession and marriage. But this is the solution that the tomboy prank has made impossible. (To Annie at least it will now *seem* so.) It is as if Annie's revenge has made John Thomas more desirable, and yet that the forcing of his admission that, having to choose, he would indeed choose her, has made that choice in fact impossible. The very frustration of the prank she has engineered has revealed to her things about herself that she had not surmised.

1. Why is it with a "bitter hopelessness" that Annie says "I don't want him"?

2. What is meant by the author's saying of Annie that "something was broken in her"?

3. How would you describe Annie's feelings toward John Thomas at the end of the story?

4. How would you characterize John Thomas's feelings toward Annie?

5. Has the author put too much emphasis upon John Thomas's emotions, particularly in the last half of the story? Or too little emphasis?

6. Note that the author is constantly telling us what the characters think and what certain of their actions mean: for example, "He was un-

easy, mistrusting them," or, "Yet each one of them . . . hoped he would look at her." Even so, the story is vivid in its presentation and remains "dramatic." Why do not the author's comments and interpretations "kill" the immediacy of this story?

JAMES PURDY

Eventide

MAHALA had waited as long as she thought she could; after all, Plumy had left that morning and now here it was going on four o'clock. It was hardly fair if she was loitering, but she knew that certainly Plumy would never loiter on a day like this when Mahala wanted so to hear. It was in a way the biggest day of her whole life, bigger than any day she had ever lived through as a girl or young woman. It was the day that decided whether her son would come back to live with her or not.

And just think, a whole month had rolled past since he left home. Two months ago if anyone would have said that Teeboy would leave home, she would have stopped dead in her tracks, it would have been such a terrible thing even to say, and now here she was, talking over the telephone about how Teeboy had gone.

"My Teeboy is gone," that is what Mahala said for a long time after the departure. These words announced to her mind what had happened, and just as an announcement they gave some mild comfort, like a pain-killer with a fatal disease.

"My Teeboy," she would say, like the mother of a dead son, like the mother of a son who had died in battle, because it hurt as much to have a son missing in peacetime as to have lost him through war.

The room seemed dark even with the summer sunshine outside, and close, although the window was open. There was a darkness all over the city. The fire department had been coming and going all afternoon. There were so many fires in the neighborhood—that is what she was saying to Cora on the telephone, too many fires: the fire chief had just whizzed past again. No, she said to Cora, she didn't know if it was in the white section of town or theirs, she couldn't tell, but oh it was so hot to have a fire.

Talking about the fires seemed to help Mahala more than anything. She called several other old friends and talked about the fires and she mentioned that Teeboy had not come home. The old friends did not say much about Teeboy's not having returned, because, well, what was there to say about a boy who had been practicing to leave home for so long. Everyone had known it but her blind mother love.

"What do you suppose can be keeping my sister Plumy?" Mahala said to herself as she walked up and down the hall and looked out from behind the screen in the window. "She would have to fail me on the most important errand in the world."

Then she thought about how much Plumy hated to go into white neighborhoods, and how the day had been hot and she thought of the fires and how perhaps Plumy had fallen under a fire truck and been crushed. She thought of all the possible disasters and was not happy, and always in the background there was the fresh emotion of having lost Teeboy.

"People don't know," she said, "that I can't live without Teeboy."

She would go in the clothes closet and look at his dirty clothes just as he had left them; she would kiss them and press them to her face, smelling them; the odors were especially dear to her. She held his rayon trousers to her bosom and walked up and down the small parlor. She had not prayed; she was waiting for Plumy to come home first, then maybe they would have prayer.

"I hope I ain't done anything I'll be sorry for," she said.

It was then, though, when she felt the worst, that she heard the steps on the front porch. Yes, those were Plumy's steps, she was coming with the news. But whatever the news was, she suddenly felt, she could not accept it.

As she came up the steps, Plumy did not look at Mahala with any particular kind of meaning on her face. She walked unsteadily, as if the heat had been too much for her.

"Come on in now, Plumy, and I will get you something cool to drink."

Inside, Plumy watched Mahala as if afraid she was going to ask her to begin at once with the story, but Mahala only waited, not saying anything, sensing the seriousness of Plumy's knowledge and knowing that this knowledge could be revealed only when Plumy was ready.

While Mahala waited patiently there in the kitchen, Plumy arranged herself in the easy chair, and when she was once settled, she took up the straw fan which lay on the floor.

"Well, I seen him!" Plumy brought the words out.

This beginning quieted the old mother a little. She closed her mouth and folded her hands, moving now to the middle of the parlor, with an intentness on her face as if she was listening to something high up in the sky, like a plane which is to drop something, perhaps harmless and silver, to the ground.

"I seen him!" Plumy repeated, as if to herself. "And I seen all the white people!" she finished, anger coming into her voice.

"Oh, Plumy," Mahala whined. Then suddenly she made a gesture for her sister to be quiet because she thought she heard the fire department going again, and then when there was no sound, she waited for her to go on, but Plumy did not say anything. In the slow afternoon there was nothing, only a silence a city sometimes has within itself.

Plumy was too faint from the heat to go on at once; her head suddenly shook violently and she slumped in the chair.

"Plumy Jackson!" Mahala said, going over to her. "You didn't *walk* here from the white district! You didn't walk them forty-seven blocks in all this August heat!"

Plumy did not answer immediately. Her hand caressed the worn upholstery of the chair.

"You know how nervous white folks make me," she said at last.

Mahala made a gesture of disgust. "Lord, to think you walked it in this hot sun. Oh, I don't know why God wants to upset me like this. As if I didn't have enough to make me wild already, without havin' you come home in this condition."

Mahala watched her sister's face for a moment with the same figuring expression of the man who comes to read the water meter. She saw everything she really wanted to know there, yet she pretended she didn't know the verdict; she brought the one question out:

"You did see Teeboy, honey?" she said, her voice changed from her tears. She waited a few seconds, and then as Plumy did not answer but only sank deeper into the chair, she continued: "What word did he send?"

"It's the way I told you before," Plumy replied crossly. "Teeboy ain't coming back. I thought you knowed from the way I looked at you that he ain't coming back."

Mahala wept quietly into a small handkerchief.

"Your pain is realer to me sometimes than my own," Plumy said, watching her cry. "That's why I hate to say to you he won't never come back, but it's true as death he won't."

"When you say that to me I got a feeling inside myself like everything had been busted and taken; I got the feeling like I don't have nothing left inside of me."

"Don't I know that feeling!" Plumy said, almost angrily, resting the straw fan on the arm of the chair, and then suddenly fanning herself violently so that the strokes sounded like those of a small angry whip. "Didn't I lose George Watson of sleeping sickness and all 'cause doctor wouldn't come?"

Plumy knew that Mahala had never shown any interest in the death of her own George Watson and that it was an unwelcome subject, especially tonight, when Teeboy's never coming back had become final, yet she could not help mentioning George Watson just the same. In Mahala's eyes there really had never been any son named George Watson; there was only a son named Teeboy and Mahala was the only mother.

"It ain't like there bein' no way out to your troubles: it's the way out that kills you," Mahala said. "If it was good-bye for always like when someone dies, I think I could stand it better. But this kind of parting ain't like the Lord's way!"

Plumy continued fanning herself, just letting Mahala run on.

"So he ain't never coming back!" Mahala began beating her hands together as if she were hearing music for a dance.

Plumy looked away as the sound of the rats downstairs caught her attention; there seemed to be more than usual tonight and she wondered why they were running so much, for it was so hot everywhere.

Her attention strayed back to Mahala standing directly in front of her now, talking about her suffering: "You go through all the suffering and the heartache," she said, "and then they go away. The only time children is nice is when they're babies and you know they can't get away from you. You got them then and your love is all they crave. They don't know who you are exactly, they just know you are the one to give them your love, and they ask you for it until you're worn out giving it."

Mahala's speech set Plumy to thinking of how she had been young and how she had had George Watson, and how he had died of sleeping sickness when he was four.

"My only son died of sleeping sickness," Plumy said aloud, but not really addressing Mahala. "I never had another. My husband said it was funny. He was not a religious man, but he thought it was queer."

"Would you like a cooling drink?" Mahala said absently.

Plumy shook her head and there was a silence of a few minutes in which the full weight of the heat of evening took possession of the small room.

"I can't get used to that idea of him *never* comin' back!" Mahala began again. "I ain't never been able to understand that word *never* anyhow. And now it's like to drive me wild."

There was another long silence, and then, Mahala suddenly rousing herself from drowsiness and the heat of the evening, began eagerly: "How did he look, Plumy? Tell me how he looked, and what he was doing. Just describe."

"He wasn't doin' nothin'!" Plumy said flatly. "He looked kind of older, though, like he had been thinking about new things."

"Don't keep me waiting," Mahala whined. "I been waitin' all day for the news, don't keep me no more, when I tell you I could suicide over it all. I ain't never been through such a hell day. Don't you keep me waitin'."

"Now hush," Plumy said. "Don't go frettin' like this. Your heart won't take a big grief like this if you go fret so."

"It's *so* unkind of you not to tell," she muffled her lips in her handkerchief.

Plumy said: "I told you I talked to him, but I didn't tell you where. It was in a drinking place called the Music Box. He called to me from inside. The minute I looked at him I knew there was something wrong. There was something wrong with his hair."

"With his hair!" Mahala cried.

"Then I noticed he had had it all made straight! That's right," she said looking away from Mahala's eyes. "He had had his hair straightened. 'Why ain't you got in touch with your mother,' I said. 'If you only knowed how she was carryin' on.'

"Then he told me how he had got a tenor sax and how he was playing it in the band at the Music Box and that he had begun a new life, and it was all on account of his having the tenor sax and being a musician. He said the players didn't have time to have homes. He said they were playing all the time, they never went home, and that was why he hadn't been."

Plumy stopped. She saw the tenor sax only in her imagination because he had not shown it to her, she saw it curved and golden and heard it playing far-off melodies. But the real reason she stopped was not on account of the tenor sax but because of the memory of the white woman who had come out just then. The white woman had come out and put her arm around Teeboy. It had made her get creepy all over. It was the first time that Plumy had realized that Teeboy's skin was nearly as light as the white people's.

Both Teeboy and the woman had stood there looking at Plumy, and Plumy had not known how to move away from them. The sun beat down on her in the street but she could not move. She saw the streetcars going by with all the white people pushing one another around and she looked around on the scorched pavements and everyone was white, with Teeboy looking just as white as the rest of them, looking just as white as if he had come out of Mahala's body white, and as if Mahala had been a white woman and not her sister, and as if Mahala's mother and hers had not been black.

Then slowly she had begun walking away from Teeboy and the Music Box, almost without knowing she was going herself, walking right on through the streets without knowing what was happening, through the big August heat, without an umbrella or a hat to keep off the sun; she could see no place to stop, and people could see the circles of sweat that were forming all over her dress. She was afraid to stop and she was afraid to go on walking. She felt she would fall down eventually in the afternoon sun and it would be like the time George Watson had died of sleeping sickness, nobody would help her to an easy place.

Would George Watson know her now? That is what she was thinking as she walked through the heat of that afternoon. Would he know her—

because when she had been his mother she had been young and her skin, she was sure, had been lighter; and now she was older looking than she remembered her own mother ever being, and her skin was very black.

It was Mahala's outcries which brought her back to the parlor, now full of the evening twilight.

"Why can't God call me home?" Mahala was asking. "Why can't He call me to His Throne of Grace?"

Then Mahala got up and wandered off into her own part of the house. One could hear her in her room there, faintly kissing Teeboy's soiled clothes and speaking quietly to herself.

"Until you told me about his having his hair straightened, I thought maybe he would be back," Mahala was saying from the room. "But when you told me that, I knew. He won't never be back."

Plumy could hear Mahala kissing the clothes after she had said this.

"He was so dear to her," Plumy said aloud. It was necessary to speak aloud at that moment because of the terrible feeling of evening in the room. Was it the smell of the four o'clocks, which must have just opened to give out their perfume, or was it the evening itself which made her uneasy? She felt not alone, she felt someone else had come, uninvited and from far away.

Plumy had never noticed before what a strong odor the four o'clocks had, and then she saw the light in the room, growing larger, a light she had not recognized before, and then she turned and saw *him*, George Watson Jackson, standing there before her, large as life. Plumy wanted to call out, she wanted to say *No* in a great voice, she wanted to brush the sight before her all away, which was strange because she was always wanting to see her baby and here he was, although seventeen years had passed since she had laid him away.

She looked at him with unbelieving eyes because really he was the same, the same except she did notice that little boys' suits had changed fashion since his day, and how that everything about him was slightly different from the little children of the neighborhood now.

"Baby!" she said, but the word didn't come out from her mouth, it was only a great winged thought that could not be made into sound. "George Watson, honey!" she said still in her silence.

He stood there, his eyes like they had been before. Their beauty stabbed at her heart like a great knife; the hair looked so like she had just pressed the wet comb to it and perhaps put a little pomade on the sides; and the small face was clean and sad. Yet her arms somehow did not ache to hold him like her heart told her they should. Something too far away and too strong was between her and him; she only saw him as she had always seen resurrection pictures, hidden from us as in a wonderful mist that will not let us see our love complete.

There was this mist between her and George Watson like the dew

that will be on the four o'clocks when you pick one of them off the plant.
It was her baby come home, and at such an hour.

Then as she came slowly to herself, she began to raise herself slightly,
stretching her arms and trying to get the words to come out to him:

"George Watson, baby!"

This time the words did come out, with a terrible loudness, and as
they did so the light began to go from the place where he was standing:
the last thing she saw of him was his bright forehead and hair, then there
was nothing at all, not even the smell of flowers.

Plumy let out a great cry and fell back in the chair. Mahala heard her
and came out of her room to look at her.

"What you got?" Mahala said.

"I seen *him!* I seen *him!* Big as life!"

"Who?" Mahala said.

"George Watson, just like I laid him away seventeen years ago!"

Mahala did not know what to say. She wiped her eyes dry, for she
had quit crying.

"You was exposed too long in the sun," Mahala said vaguely.

As she looked at her sister she felt for the first time the love that Plumy
had borne all these years for a small son Mahala had never seen, George
Watson. For the first time she dimly recognized Plumy as a mother, and
she had suddenly a feeling of intimacy for her that she never had before.

She walked over to the chair where Plumy was and laid her hand
on her. Somehow the idea of George Watson's being dead so long and yet
still being a baby a mother could love had a kind of perfect quality that
she liked. She thought then, quietly and without shame, how nice it would
be if Teeboy could also be perfect in death, so that he would belong to
her in the same perfect way as George Watson belonged to Plumy. There
was comfort in tending the grave of a dead son, whether he was killed in
war or peace, and it was so difficult to tend the memory of a son who just
went away and never came back. Yet somehow she knew as she looked at
Plumy, somehow she would go on with the memory of Teeboy Jordan
even though he still lived in the world.

As she stood there considering the lives of the two sons Teeboy Jordan
and George Watson Jackson, the evening which had for some time been
moving slowly into the house entered now as if in one great wave, bringing
the small parlor into the heavy summer night until you would have believed daylight would never enter there again, the night was so black and
secure.

INTERPRETATION

The most interesting questions about this story may be put as follows:

1. What is the action? (Since it is obviously internal and psychologi-

cal rather than some overt thing "done" by one of the characters, the definition may not be easy.)

2. What are we to make of the vision that appears to Plumy? Can we believe that she would have this particular hallucination and just at this time?

3. What is the meaning of Plumy's vision? For Plumy herself? For Mahala? For the story?

Even a cursory inspection of the questions makes it plain that we need to know a good deal about the characters of the two women and their relationship to each other. The author has nowhere given us full-dress "discussions" of his characters; what we know about them comes largely from their conversation when Plumy returns to Mahala to tell her about having seen Teeboy. The method of character presentation is thus "dramatic": the characters are not "explained" to us abstractly but are revealed through what they do and say—that is, they are made to "act out" their relationship.

The method is effective: before the story ends we have learned a great deal about these sisters. For one thing, there is a very close rapport between them. When Plumy comes in, her sister, in spite of her agony of suspense, waits, "not saying anything, sensing the seriousness of Plumy's knowledge and knowing that this knowledge could be revealed only when Plumy was ready." Later, before Plumy says a word, her sister knows the answer to her question: "She saw everything she really wanted to know" on Plumy's face. Plumy herself is well aware of the fact that she does not need really to tell her sister Teeboy's answer in so many words. She says to Mahala: "I thought you knowed from the way I looked at you that he ain't coming back."

Yet there are other matters in which the sisters are not in rapport at all. Mahala seems to lack full confidence in her sister's sympathy. She has a bad moment when she actually murmurs to herself: "She would have to fail me on the most important errand in the world." Specifically, her inability to believe that Plumy is really able to sympathize with her in her grief stems from the fact that she cannot think of Plumy as ever having had the experience of motherhood. As the author tells us, "In Mahala's eyes there really had never been any son named George Watson; there was only a son named Teeboy and Mahala was the only mother."

This then is in brief the relationship that exists between the sisters as Plumy, exhausted after the long afternoon, recovers herself in Mahala's parlor and tries to tell her sister about Teeboy's refusal to come home. There is a further point that might be added. Plumy, one surmises, has all along been aware of the hopelessness of her mission, for apparently all of

Mahala's friends had known that Teeboy for a long time "had been prac-
tising to leave home." She says at one point to her sister: "It's the way I
told you before" as if this were an old issue about which she has more than
once tried to convince her sister.

With this in mind, we can say that this story is not primarily concerned
with Teeboy's decision. The attentive reader has from the beginning probably been aware that Mahala's son will not return. What "happens" in this
story—if indeed anything happens—must concern some other issue. We
may be sure that it bears upon—perhaps has chiefly to do with—the relation
of the sisters themselves.

As for Plumy, something indeed does "happen": she has a vision of
her four-year old son. The problem is to see whether the vision has been
made plausible to us who are the readers, and if so, what bearing it has upon
the import of the story.

The most important fact, of course, is the obvious one: Plumy has just
talked to Mahala's son, she is worried about Mahala, and she wonders how
her sister will take the news that Teeboy will not come back. What is more
natural than that she should suddenly find herself thinking about her own
son and the way in which she has lost him. Her general emotional state is
also very important. She is a rather primitive and unsophisticated person,
and she is now experiencing the letdown after a period of sustained excitement. She has seen Teeboy, she has made the long journey back through
the white neighborhood that always makes her nervous, and she has gone
through the difficult business of telling her sister the depressing truth.
There is her physical state to be considered too: she has taken a long walk
through the hot sun and she is now very tired. Mahala refers to Plumy's
having "come home in this condition," and a little later, when Plumy cries
out to tell her sister about the vision, Mahala says "You was exposed too
long in the sun."

Perhaps Plumy has experienced a touch of the sun, but the significance
of the experience is not to be measured by what may have been one of its
contributing causes. Plumy has been exposed, we might say, to life as well
as to the sun. So Mahala finds herself at last profoundly moved by her
sister's vision. She goes over to lay her hand upon her sister, and as she does
she feels for the first time that Plumy also has been a mother and with this
realization, there comes "a feeling of intimacy for her that she never
had before."

What happens in the story, then, is a change in the relation between
the two sisters. In the last three paragraphs of the story, Purdy handles
skillfully and very delicately their concordant movement into sympathy
and understanding. The student should ponder these concluding paragraphs carefully. In order to see just what they accomplish and how, he
might consider the following questions:

1. What is the meaning, in this context, of "perfect quality" and "perfect in death" and "perfect way"? Is the adjective *perfect* used vaguely and sentimentally?

2. Is the phrasing of these paragraphs too literary and highfalutin for a description of what is going on in Mahala's mind? If not, why not?

3. Does an appreciation of Plumy's experience help to modify Mahala's own experience of loss? How?

4. What, if anything, is accomplished by the last sentence with its description of the surging into the parlor of the night and darkness? What does darkness usually signify? Is that significance modified here by the phrase "so black and *secure*"?

The student may want to put to himself some further questions that have to do with earlier sections of the story or the story as a whole.

5. Would you agree that exposition is well handled in the opening paragraphs? Is it also mingled with a forward movement—the setting up of expectations in the reader's mind? How specifically is this done?

6. Does Mahala have to be regarded as in reality a selfish, possessive mother? Is there any evidence for this interpretation of her character? If you think that there is evidence for it, how, if at all, is the meaning of the story affected?

7. How is sentimentality avoided in this story as it is *not* avoided in the Bret Harte story?

CAROLINE GORDON

Old Red

I

WHEN the door had closed behind his daughter, Mister Maury went to the window and stood a few moments looking out. The roses that had grown in a riot all along that side of the fence had died or been cleared away, but the sun lay across the garden in the same level lances of light that he remembered. He turned back into the room. The shadows had gathered until it was nearly all in gloom. The top of his minnow bucket just emerging from the duffel bag glinted in the last rays of the sun. He stood looking down at his traps all gathered neatly in a heap at the foot of the bed. He would leave them like that. Even if they came in here sweeping and cleaning up—it was only in hotels that a man was master of his own room—even if they came in here cleaning up, he would tell them to leave all his things exactly as they were. It was reassuring to see them all there together, ready to be taken up in the hand, to be carried down and put into a car, to be driven off to some railroad station at a moment's notice.

As he moved toward the door, he spoke aloud, a habit that was growing on him:

"Anyhow, I won't stay but a week. . . . I ain't going to stay but a week, no matter what they say. . . ."

Downstairs in the dining room they were already gathered at the supper table, his white-haired, shrunken mother-in-law, his tall sister-in-law who had the proud carriage of the head, the aquiline nose, but not the spirit of his dead wife, his lean, blond new son-in-law, his black-eyed daughter who, but that she was thin, looked so much like him, all of them gathered there waiting for him, Alexander Maury. It occurred to him that this was the first time he had sat down in the bosom of the family for some years. They were always writing saying that he must make a visit this summer or certainly next fall. ". . . all had a happy Christmas together but missed you. . . ." They had even made the pretext that he ought to come up to inspect his new son-in-law. As if he hadn't always known exactly the kind of young man Sarah would marry! What was the boy's name? Stephen, yes, Stephen. He must be sure and remember that.

He sat down, and shaking out his napkin spread it over his capacious paunch and tucked it well up under his chin in the way his wife had never allowed him to do. He let his eyes rove over the table and released a long sigh.

"Hot batter bread," he said, "and ham. Merry Point ham. I sure am glad to taste them one more time before I die."

The old lady was sending the little Negro girl scurrying back to the kitchen for a hot plate of batter bread. He pushed aside the cold plate and waited. She had bridled when he spoke of the batter bread and a faint flush had dawned on her withered cheeks. Vain she had always been as a peacock, of her housekeeping, her children, the animals on her place, anything that belonged to her. And she went on, even at her advanced age, making her batter bread, smoking her hams according to that old recipe she was so proud of; but who came here now to this old house to eat or to praise?

He helped himself to a generous slice of batter bread, buttered it, took the first mouthful and chewed it slowly. He shook his head.

"There ain't anything like it," he said. "There ain't anything else like it in this world."

His dark eye roving the table fell on his son-in-law. "You like batter bread?" he inquired.

Stephen nodded, smiling. Mister Maury, still masticating slowly, regarded his face, measured the space between the eyes—his favorite test for man, horse, or dog. Yes, there was room enough for sense between the eyes. But how young the boy looked! And infected already with the fatal germ, the *cacoëthes scribendi.* Well, their children would probably escape. It was like certain diseases of the eyes, skipped every other generation. His own father had had it badly all his life. He could see him now sitting at the head of the table spouting his own poetry—or Shakespeare's—while the children watched the preserve dish to see if it was going around. He, Aleck Maury, had been lucky to be born in the generation he had. He had escaped that at least. A few translations from Heine in his courting days, a few fragments from the Greek, but no, he had kept clear of that on the whole. . . .

The eyes of his sister-in-law were fixed on him. She was smiling faintly. "You don't look much like dying, Aleck. Florida must agree with you."

The old lady spoke from the head of the table. "I can't see what you do with yourself all winter long. Doesn't time hang heavy on your hands?"

Time, he thought, time! They were always mouthing the word and what did they know about it? Nothing in God's world! He saw time suddenly, a dull, leaden-colored fabric depending from the old lady's hands, from the hands of all of them, a blanket that they pulled about, now this way, now that, trying to cover up their nakedness. Or they would cast it on the ground and creep in among the folds, finding one day a little more tightly rolled than another, but all of it everywhere the same dull gray substance. But time was a banner that whipped before him always in the wind. He stood on tiptoe to catch at the bright folds, to strain them to his bosom. They were bright and glittering. But they whipped by so fast and were whipping always ever faster. The tears came into his eyes. Where, for instance, had this year gone? He could swear he had not wasted a minute of it, for no man living, he thought, knew better how to make each day a pleasure to him. Not a minute wasted and yet here it was already May! If he lived to the Biblical three score and ten, which was all he ever allowed himself in his calculations, he had before him only nine more Mays. Only nine more Mays out of all eternity, and they wanted him to waste one of them sitting on the front porch at Merry Point!

The butter plate which had seemed to swim in a glittering mist was coming solidly to rest upon the white tablecloth. He winked his eyes rapidly and laying down his knife and fork squared himself about in his chair to address his mother-in-law:

"Well, ma'am, you know I'm a man that always likes to be learning something. Now this year I learned how to smell out fish." He glanced around the table, holding his head high and allowing his well-cut nostrils to flutter slightly with his indrawn breaths. "Yes, sir," he said, "I'm probably the only white man in this country knows how to smell out feesh."

There was a discreet smile on the faces of the others. Sarah was laughing outright. "Did you have to learn how or did it just come to you?" she asked.

"I learned it from an old nigger woman," her father said. He shook his head reminiscently. "It's wonderful how much you can learn from niggers. But you have to know how to handle them. I was half the winter wooing that old Fanny. . . ."

He waited until their laughter had died down. "We used to start off every morning from the same little cove and we'd drift in there together at night. I noticed how she always brought in a good string, so I says to her, 'Fanny, you just lemme go 'long with you.' But she wouldn't have nothing to do with me. I saw she was going to be a hard nut to crack, but I kept right on. Finally I began giving her presents. . . ."

Laura was regarding him fixedly, a queer look on her face.

"What sort of presents did you give her, Aleck?"

He made his tones hearty in answer. "I give her a fine string of fish one day and I gave her fifty cents. And finally I made her a present of a Barlow knife. That was when she broke down. She took me with her that morning. . . ."

"Could she really smell fish?" the old lady asked curiously.

"You ought to 'a' seen her," Mister Maury said. "She'd sail over that lake like a hound on the scent. She'd row right along and then all of a sudden she'd stop rowing." He bent over, wrinkling his nose and peering into the depths of imaginary water. " 'Thar they are, White Folks, thar they are. Cain't you smell 'em?' "

Stephen was leaning forward, eyeing his father-in-law intently. "Could you?" he asked.

"I got so I could smell feesh," Mister Maury told him. "I could smell out the feesh, but I couldn't tell which kind they were. Now Fanny could row over a bed and tell just by the smell whether it was bass or bream. But she'd been at it all her life." He paused, sighing. "You can't just pick these things up. You have to give yourself to them. Who was it said 'Genius is an infinite capacity for taking pains'?"

Sarah was rising briskly. Her eyes sought her husband's across the table. She was still laughing. "Sir Izaak Walton," she said, "we'd better go in the other room. Mandy wants to clear the table."

The two older ladies remained in the dining room. Mister Maury walked across the hall to the sitting room, accompanied by Steve and Sarah. He lowered himself cautiously into the most solid-looking of the rocking chairs that were drawn up around the fire. Steve was standing on the hearthrug, back to the fire, gazing abstractedly off across the room.

Mister Maury glanced up at him curiously. "What are you thinking about, feller?" he asked.

Steve looked down. He smiled, but his gaze was still contemplative. "I was thinking about the sonnet," he said, "in the form in which it first came to England."

Mister Maury shook his head. "Wyatt and Surrey," he said. "Hey, nonny, nonny. . . . You'll have hardening of the liver long before you're my age." He looked past Steve's shoulder at the picture that hung over the mantel shelf: Cupid and Psyche holding between them a fluttering veil and running along a rocky path toward the beholder. "Old Merry Point," he said; "it don't change much, does it?"

He settled himself more solidly in his chair. His mind veered from the old house to his own wanderings in brighter places. He regarded his daughter and son-in-law affably.

"Yes, sir," he said, "this winter in Florida was valuable to me just for the acquaintances I made. Take my friend, Jim Barbee. Just to live in the same hotel with that man is an education." He paused, smiling reminiscently into the fire. "I'll never forget the first time I saw him. He came up to me there in the lobby of the hotel. 'Professor Maury!' he says, 'You been hearin' about me for twenty years and I been hearin' about you for twenty years. And now we've done met!' "

Sarah had sat down in the little rocking chair by the fire. She leaned toward him now, laughing. "They ought to have put down a cloth of gold for the meeting," she said.

Mister Maury shook his head. "Nature does that in Florida," he said. "I knew right off the reel it was him. There were half a dozen men standing around. I made 'em witness. 'Jim Barbee,' I says, 'Jim Barbee of Maysville or I'll eat my hat!'"

"Why is he so famous?" Sarah asked.

Mister Maury took out his knife and cut a slice from a plug of tobacco. When he had offered a slice to his son-in-law and it had been refused, he put the plug back in his pocket. "He's a man of imagination," he said slowly. "There ain't many in this world."

He took a small tin box out of his pocket and set it on the little table that held the lamp. Removing the top he tilted the box so that they could see its contents: an artificial lure, a bug with a dark body and a red, bulbous head, a hook protruding from what might be considered its vitals.

"Look at her," he said, "ain't she a killer?"

Sarah leaned forward to look and Steve, still standing on the hearth-rug, bent above them. The three heads ringed the light.

Mister Maury disregarded Sarah and addressed himself to Steve. "She takes nine strips of rind," he said, "nine strips just thick enough." He marked off the width of the strips with his two fingers on the table, then picking up the lure and cupping it in his palm he moved it back and forth quickly so that the painted eyes caught the light.

"Look at her," he said, "look at the wicked way she sets forward."

Sarah was poking at the lure with the tip of her finger.

"Wanton," she said, "simply wanton. What does he call her?"

"This is his Devil Bug," Mister Maury said. "He's the only man in this country makes it. I myself had the idea thirty years ago and let it slip by me the way I do with so many of my ideas." He sighed, then elevating his tremendous bulk slightly above the table level and continuing to hold Steve with his gaze he produced from his coat pocket the oilskin book that held his flies. He spread it open on the table and began to turn the pages. His eyes sought his son-in-law's as his hand paused before a gray, rather draggled-looking lure.

"Old Speck," he said. "I've had that fly for twenty years. I reckon she's taken five hundred pounds of fish in her day. . . ."

The fire burned lower. A fiery coal rolled from the grate and fell onto the hearthrug. Sarah scooped it up with a shovel and threw it among the ashes. In the circle of the lamplight the two men still bent over the table looking at the flies. Steve was absorbed in them but he spoke seldom. It was her father's voice that rising and falling filled the room. He talked a great deal, but he had a beautiful speaking voice. He was telling Steve now about Little West Fork, the first stream ever he put a fly in. "My first love," he kept calling it. It sounded rather pretty, she thought, in his mellow voice. "My first love . . ."

II

When Mister Maury came downstairs the next morning the dining room was empty except for his daughter, Sarah, who sat dawdling over a cup of coffee and a cigarette. Mister Maury sat down opposite her. To the little Negro girl who presented herself at his elbow he outlined his wants briefly. "A cup of coffee and some hot batter bread just like we had last night." He turned to his daughter. "Where's Steve?"

"He's working," she said, "he was up at eight and he's been working ever since."

Mister Maury accepted the cup of coffee from the little girl, poured half of it into his saucer, set it aside to cool. "Ain't it wonderful," he said, "the way a man can sit down and work day after day? When I think of all the work I've done in my time. . . . Can he work *every* morning?"

"He sits down at his desk every morning," she said, "but of course he gets more done some mornings than others."

Mister Maury picked up his saucer, found the coffee cool enough for his taste. He sipped it slowly, looking out of the window. His mind was already busy with his day's program. No water—no running water—nearer than West Fork three miles away. He couldn't drive a car and Steve was going to be busy writing all morning. There was nothing for it but a pond. The Willow Sink. It was not much but it was better than nothing. He pushed his chair back and rose.

"Well," he said, "I'd better be starting."

When he came downstairs with his rod a few minutes later the hal¹ was still full of the sound of measured typing. Sarah sat in the dining room in the same position in which he had left her, smoking. Mister Maury paused in the doorway while he slung his canvas bag over his shoulders. "How you ever going to get anything done if you don't take advantage of the morning hours?" he asked. He glanced at the door opposite as if it had been the entrance to a sick chamber.

"What's he writing about?" he inquired in a whisper.

"It's an essay on John Skelton."

Mister Maury looked out at the new green leaves framed in the doorway. "John Skelton," he said. "God Almighty!"

He went through the hall and stepped down off the porch onto the ground that was still moist with spring rains. As he crossed the lower yard he looked up into the branches of the maples. Yes, the leaves were full grown already even on the late trees. The year, how swiftly, how steadily it advanced! He had come to the far corner of the yard. Grown up it was in pokeberry shoots and honeysuckle, but there was a place to get through. The top strand of wire had been pulled down and fastened to the others with a ragged piece of rope. He rested his weight on his good leg and swung himself over onto the game one. It gave him a good, sharp twinge when he came down on it. It was getting worse all the time, that leg, but on the other hand he was learning better all the time how to handle it. His mind flew back to a dark, startled moment, that day when the cramp first came on him. He had been sitting still in the boat all day long and that evening when he had stood up to get out his leg had failed him utterly. He had pitched forward among the reeds, had lain there a second, face downwards, before it came to him what had happened. With the realization came a sharp picture of his faraway youth: Uncle Quent lowering himself ponderously out of the saddle after a hard day's hunting had fallen forward in exactly the same way, into a knot of yowling little Negroes. He had got up and cursed them all out of the lot. It had scared the old boy to death, coming down like that. The black dog he had had on his shoulder all that fall. But he himself had never lost one day's fishing on account of his leg. He had known from the start how to handle it. It meant simply that he was slowed down that much. It hadn't really made much difference in fishing. He didn't do as much wading but he got around just about as well on the whole. Hunting, of course, had had to go. You couldn't walk all day shooting birds, dragging a game leg. He had just given it up right off the reel, though it was a shame when a man was as good a shot as he was.

That day he was out with Tom Kensington last November, the only day he got out during the season. Nine shots he'd had and he'd bagged nine birds. Yes, it was a shame. But a man couldn't do everything. He had to limit himself. . . .

He was up over the little rise now. The field slanted straight down before him to where the pond lay, silver in the morning sun. A Negro cabin was perched halfway up the opposite slope. A woman was hanging out washing on a line stretched between two trees. From the open doorway little Negroes spilled down the path toward the pond. Mister Maury surveyed the scene, spoke aloud:

"Ain't it funny now? Niggers always live in the good places."

He stopped under a wild cherry tree to light his pipe. It had been hot crossing the field, but the sunlight here was agreeably tempered by the branches. And that pond down there was fringed with willows. His eyes sought the bright disk of the water, then rose to where the smoke from the cabin chimney lay in a soft plume along the crest of the hill.

When he stooped to pick up his rod again it was with a feeling of sudden, keen elation. An image had risen in his memory, an image that was familiar but came to him infrequently of late and that only in moments of elation: the wide field in front of his uncle's old house in Albemarle, on one side the dark line of undergrowth that marked the Rivanna River, on the other the blue of Peters' Mountain. They would be waiting there in that broad plain when they had the first sight of the fox. On that little rise by the river, loping steadily, not yet alarmed. The sun would glint on his bright coat, on his quick-turning head as he dove into the dark of the woods. There would be hullabaloo after that and shouting and riding. Sometimes there was the tailing of the fox—that time old Whisky was brought home on a mattress! All of that to come afterward, but none of it ever like that first sight of the fox there on the broad plain between the river and the mountain.

There was one fox, they grew to know him in time, to call him affectionately by name. Old Red it was who showed himself always like that there on the crest of the hill. "There he goes, the damn' impudent scoundrel!" . . . Uncle Quent would shout and slap his thigh and yell himself hoarse at Whisky and Mag and the pups, but they would have already settled to their work. They knew his course, every turn of it by heart. Through the woods and then down across the fields again to the river. Their hope was always to cut him off before he could circle back to the mountain. If he got in there among those old field pines it was all up. But he always made it. Lost 'em every time and then dodged through to his hole in Pinnacle Rock. . . . A smart fox, Old Red. . . .

He descended the slope and paused in the shade of a clump of willows. The little Negroes who squatted, dabbling in the water, watched him out of round eyes as he unslung his canvas bag and laid it on a stump. He looked down at them gravely.

"D'you ever see a white man that could conjure?" he asked.

The oldest boy laid the brick he was fashioning out of mud down on a plank. He ran the tip of his tongue over his lower lip to moisten it before he spoke. "Naw suh."

"I'm the man," Mister Maury told him. "You chillun better quit that playin' and dig me some worms."

He drew his rod out of the case, jointed it up and laid it down on a stump. Taking out his book of flies he turned the pages, considering. "Silver Spinner,'" he said aloud. "They ought to take that . . . in May. Naw, I'll just give Old Speck a chance. It's a long time now since we had her out."

The little Negroes had risen and were stepping quietly off along the path toward the cabin, the two little boys hand in hand, the little girl following, the baby astride her hip. They were pausing now before a dilapidated building that might long ago have been a henhouse. Mister Maury shouted at them. "Look under them old boards. That's the place for worms." The biggest boy was turning around. His treble "Yassuh" quavered over the water. Then their voices died away. There was no sound except the light turning of the willow boughs in the wind.

Mister Maury walked along the bank, rod in hand, humming: "Bangum's gone to the wild boar's den . . . *Bangum's* gone to the wild boar's den . . ." He stopped where a white, peeled log protruded six or seven feet into the water. The pond made a little turn here. Two lines of willows curving in framed the whole surface of the water. He stepped out squarely upon the log, still humming. The line rose smoothly, soared against the blue and curved sweetly back upon the still water. His quick ear caught the little whish that the fly made when it clove the surface, his eye followed the tiny ripples of its flight. He cast again, leaning a little backward as he did sometimes when the mood was on him. Again and again his line soared out over the water. His eye rested now and then on his wrist. He noted with detachment the expert play of the muscles, admired each time the accuracy of his aim. It occurred to him that it was four days now since he had wet a line. Four days. One whole day packing up, parts of two days on the train and yesterday wasted sitting there on that front porch with the family. But the abstinence had done him good. He had never cast better than he was casting this morning.

There was a rustling along the bank, a glimpse of blue through the trees. Mister Maury leaned forward and peered around the clump of willows. A hundred yards away Steve, hatless, in an old blue shirt and khaki pants, stood jointing up a rod.

Mister Maury backed off his log and advanced along the path. He called out cheerfully, "Well, feller, do any good?"

Steve looked up. His face had lightened for a moment, but the abstracted expression stole over it again when he spoke. "Oh, I fiddled with it," he said, "all morning, but I didn't do much good."

Mister Maury nodded sympathetically. "*Minerva invita erat*," he said; "you can do nothing unless Minerva perches on the rooftree. Why, I been castin' here all morning and not a strike. But there's a boat tied up over on the other side. What say we get in it and just drift around?" He paused, looked at the rod Steve had finished jointing up. "I brought another rod along," he said. "You want to use it?"

Steve shook his head. "I'm used to this one."

An expression of relief came over Mister Maury's face. "That's right," he said, "a man always does better with his own rod."

The boat was only a quarter full of water. They heaved her over and dumped it out, then dragged her down to the bank. The little Negroes had come up, bringing a can of worms. Mister Maury threw them each a nickel and set the can in the bottom of the boat. "I always like to have a few worms handy," he told Steve, "ever since I was a boy." He lowered himself ponderously into the bow and Steve pushed off and dropped down behind him.

The little Negroes still stood on the bank staring. When the boat was a little distance out on the water the boldest of them spoke: "You reckon 'at ole jawnboat going to hold you up, Cap'm?"

Mister Maury turned his head to call over his shoulder. "Go 'way, boy, ain't I done tole you I's a conjure?"

The boat dipped ominously. Steve changed his position a little and she settled to the water. Sitting well forward Mister Maury made graceful casts, now to this side, now to that. Steve, in the stern, made occasional casts, but he laid his rod down every now and then to paddle, though there was really no use in it. The boat drifted well enough with the wind. At the end of half an hour seven sizable bass lay on the bottom of the boat. Mister Maury had caught five of them. He reflected that perhaps he really ought to change places with Steve. The man in the bow certainly had the best chance at the fish. "But no," he thought, "it don't make any difference. He don't hardly know where he is now."

He stole a glance over his shoulder at the young man's serious, abstracted face. It was like that of a person submerged. Steve seemed to float up to the surface every now and then, his expression would lighten, he would make some observation that showed he knew where he was, then he would sink again. If you asked him a question he answered punctiliously, two minutes later. Poor boy, dead to the world and would probably be that way the rest of his life! A pang of pity shot through Mister Maury, and on the heels of it a gust of that black fear that occasionally shook him. It was he, not Steve, that was the queer one! The world was full of people like this boy, all of them walking around with their heads so full of this and

that they hardly knew where they were going. There was hardly anybody
—there was *nobody* really in the whole world like him. . . .

Steve, coming out of his abstraction, spoke politely. He had heard
that Mister Maury was a fine shot. Did he like to fish better than hunt?

Mister Maury reflected. "Well," he said, "they's something about a
covey of birds rising up in front of you . . . they's something. And a
good dog. Now they ain't anything in this world that I like better than
a good bird dog." He stopped and sighed. "A man has got to come to himself early in life if he's going to amount to anything. Now I was smart,
even as a boy. I could look around me and see all the men of my family,
Uncle Jeems, Uncle Quent, my father, every one of 'em weighed two
hundred by the time he was fifty. You get as heavy on your feet as all
that and you can't do any good shooting. But a man can fish as long as
he lives. . . . Why, one place I stayed last summer there was an old man
ninety years old had himself carried down to the river every morning.
. . . Yes, sir, a man can fish as long as he can get down to the water's
edge. . . ."

There was a little plop to the right. He turned just in time to see the
fish flash out of the water. He watched Steve take it off the hook and drop
it on top of the pile in the bottom of the boat. Eight bass that made and
two bream. The old lady would be pleased. "Aleck always catches me fish,"
she'd say.

The boat glided on over the still water. There was no wind at all now.
The willows that fringed the bank might have been cut out of paper. The
plume of smoke hung perfectly horizontal over the roof of the Negro
cabin. Mister Maury watched it stream out in little eddies and disappear
into the bright blue.

He spoke softly: "Ain't it wonderful . . . ain't it wonderful now that
a man of my gifts can content himself a whole morning on this here little
old pond?"

III

Mister Maury woke with a start. He realized that he had been sleeping
on his left side again. A bad idea. It always gave him palpitations of the
heart. It must be that that had waked him up. He had gone to sleep almost
immediately after his head hit the pillow. He rolled over, cautiously, as he
always did since that bed in Leesburg had given down with him, and lying
flat on his back stared at the opposite wall.

The moon rose late. It must be at its height now. That patch of light
was so brilliant he could almost discern the pattern of the wall paper. It
hung there, wavering, bitten by the shadows into a semblance of a human
figure, a man striding with bent head and swinging arms. All the shadows
in the room seemed to be moving toward him. The protruding corner of

the washstand was an arrow aimed at his heart, the clumsy old-fashioned dresser was a giant towering above him.

They had put him to sleep in this same room the night after his wife died. In the summer it had been, too, in June, and there must have been a full moon, for the same giant shadows had struggled there with the same towering monsters. It would be like that here on this wall every full moon, for the pieces of furniture would never change their position, had never been changed, probably, since the house was built.

He turned back on his side. The wall before him was dark, but he knew every flower in the pattern of the wall paper, interlacing pink roses with thrusting up between every third cluster the enormous, spreading fronds of ferns. The wall paper in the room across the hall was like that too. The old lady slept there, and in the room next to his own, Laura, his sister-in-law, and in the east bedroom downstairs the young couple. He and Mary had slept there when they were first married, when they were the young couple in the house.

He tried to remember Mary as she must have looked the day he first saw her, the day he arrived from Virginia to open his school in the old office that used to stand in the corner of the yard. He could see Mister Allard plainly, sitting there under the sugar tree with his chair tilted back, could discern the old lady—young she had been then!—hospitably poised in the doorway, could hear her voice: "Well, here are two of your pupils to start with. . . ." He remembered Laura, a shy child of nine hiding her face in her mother's skirts, but Mary was only a shadow in the dark hall. He could not even remember how her voice had sounded. "Professor Maury," she would have said and her mother would have corrected her with "Cousin Aleck. . . ."

That day a year later when she was getting off her horse at the stile blocks. . . . She had turned as she walked across the lawn to look back at him. Her white sunbonnet had fallen back on her shoulders, her eyes meeting his had been wide and startled. He had gone on and had hitched both the horses before he leaped over the stile to join her. But he had known in that moment that she was the woman he was going to have. He could not remember all the rest of it, only that moment stood out. He had won her. She had become his wife, but the woman he had won was not the woman he had sought. It was as if he had had her only in that moment there on the lawn. As if she had paused there only for that one moment, and was ever after retreating before him down a devious, a dark way that he would never have chosen.

The death of the first baby had been the start of it, of course. It had been a relief when she took so definitely to religion. Before that there had been those sudden, unaccountable forays out of some dark lurking place that she had. Guerrilla warfare and trying to the nerves, but that had been only at the first. For many years they had been two enemies contending in the open. . . . Toward the last she had taken mightily to prayer. He would wake often to find her kneeling by the side of the bed in the dark. It had gone on for years. She had never given up hope. . . .

Ah, a stout-hearted one, Mary! She had never given up hope of changing him, of making him over into the man she thought he ought to be. Time and again she almost had him. And there were long periods, of course, during which he had been worn down by the conflict, one spring when he himself said, when she had told all the neighbors that he was too old now to go fishing any more. . . . But he had made a comeback. She had had to resort to stratagem. His lips curved in a smile, remembering the trick.

It had come over him suddenly, a general lassitude, an odd faintness in the mornings, the time when his spirits ordinarily were always at their highest. He had sat there looking out of the window at the woods glistening with spring rain; he had not even taken his gun down to shoot a squirrel.

Remembering Uncle Quent's last days, he had been alarmed, had decided finally that he must tell her so that they might begin preparations for the future—he had shuddered at the thought of eventual confinement, perhaps in some institution. She had looked up from her sewing, unable to repress a smile.

"You think it's your mind, Aleck. . . . It's coffee. . . . I've been giving you a coffee substitute every morning. . . ."

They had laughed together over her cleverness. He had not gone back to coffee, but the lassitude had worn off. She had gone back to the attack with redoubled vigor. In the afternoons she would stand on the porch calling after him as he slipped down to the creek, "Now, don't stay long enough to get that cramp. You remember how you suffered last time. . . ." He would have forgotten all about the cramp until that moment, but it would hang over him then through the whole afternoon's sport, and it would descend upon him inevitably when he left the river and started for the house.

Yes, he thought with pride. She was wearing him down—he didn't believe there was a man living who could withstand her a lifetime!—she was wearing him down and would have had him in another few months, another year certainly. But she had been struck down just as victory was in her grasp. The paralysis had come on her in the night. It was as if a curtain had descended, dividing their life sharply into two parts. In the bewildered year and a half that followed he had found himself forlornly trying to reconstruct the Mary he had known. The pressure she had so constantly exerted upon him had become for him a part of her personality. This new, calm Mary was not the woman he had loved all these years. She had lain there—heroically they all said—waiting for death. And lying there, waiting, all her faculties engaged now in defensive warfare, she had raised as it were her lifelong siege; she had lost interest in his comings and goings, had once even encouraged him to go out for an afternoon's sport. He felt a rush of warm pity. Poor Mary! She must have realized toward the last that she had wasted herself in conflict; she had spent her arms and her strength against an inglorious foe when all the time the real, the invincible adversary waited. . . .

He turned over on his back again. The moonlight was waning, the contending shadows paler now and retreating toward the door. From across the hall came the sound of long, sibilant breaths, ending each one on a little upward groan. The old lady . . . she would maintain till her dying day that she did not snore. He fancied that he could hear from the next room Laura's light, regular breathing, and downstairs were the young couple asleep in each other's arms. . . .

All of them quiet and relaxed now, but they had been lively enough at dinner time! It had started with the talk about Aunt Sally Crenfew's funeral Tuesday. Living as he had for some years away from women of his family he had forgotten the need to be cautious. He had spoken up before he thought:

"But that's the day Steve and I were going to Barker's Mill. . . ."

Sarah had cried out at the idea. "Barker's Mill!" she had said, "right on the Crenfew land . . . well, if not on the very farm in the very next field." It would be a scandal if he, Professor Maury, known by everybody to be in the neighborhood, could not spare one afternoon, one insignificant summer afternoon from his fishing long enough to attend the funeral of his cousin, the cousin of all of them, the oldest lady in the whole family connection. . . .

She had got him rattled; he had fallen back upon technicalities:

"I'm not a Crenfew. I'm a Maury. Aunt Sally Crenfew is no more kin to me than a catfish. . . ."

An unlucky crack, that about the catfish. Glancing around the table he had caught the same look in every eye. He had felt a gust of the same fright that had shaken him there on the pond. That look! Sooner or later you met it in every human eye. The thing was to be up and ready, ready to run for your life at a moment's notice. Yes, it had always been like that. It always would be. His fear of them was shot through suddenly with contempt. It was as if Mary was there laughing at them with him. *She* knew that none of them could have survived what he had survived, could have paid the price for freedom that he had paid. . . .

Sarah had come to a full stop. He had to say something. He shook his head:

"You think we just go fishing to have a good time. The boy and I hold high converse on that pond. . . . I'm starved for intellectual companionship, I tell you. In Florida I never see anybody but niggers. . . ."

They had all laughed out at that. "As if you didn't *prefer* the society of niggers," Sarah said scornfully.

The old lady had been moved to anecdote:

"I remember when Aleck first came out here from Virginia, Cousin Sophy said: 'Professor Maury is so well educated. Now Cousin Cave Maynor is dead, who is there in their neighborhood for him to associate with?' 'Well,' I said, 'I don't know about that. He seems perfectly satisfied now with Ben Hooser. They're off to the creek together every evening soon as school is out.' "

Ben Hooser. . . . He could see now the wrinkled face, overlaid with that ashy pallor of the aged Negro, the shrewd, smiling eyes, the pendulous lower lip that dropping away showed always some of the rotten teeth. A finer nigger, Ben, and on to a lot of tricks, the only man really that he'd ever cared to take fishing with him. . . .

But the first real friend of his bosom had been old Uncle Teague, back in Virginia. Once a week, or more likely every ten days, he fed the hounds on the carcass of a calf that had had time to get pretty high. They would drive the spring wagon out into the lot, he, a boy of ten, beside Uncle Teague on the driver's seat. The hounds would come in a great rush and rear their slobbering jowls against the wagon wheels. Uncle Teague would wield his whip, chuckling while he threw the first hunk of meat to Old Mag, his favorite.

"Dey goin' run on dis," he'd say, "dey goin' run like a shadow. . . ."

He shifted his position again, cautiously. People, he thought . . . people . . . so bone ignorant, all of them. Not one person in a thousand realized that a fox hound remains at heart a wild beast and must kill and gorge, and then when he is ravenous kill and gorge again. . . . Or that the channel cat is a night feeder. . . . Or . . . his daughter had told him once that he ought to set all his knowledges down in a book. "Why?" he had asked. "So everybody else can know as much as I do?"

If he allowed his mind to get active, really active, he would never get any sleep. He was fighting an inclination now to get up and find a cigarette. He relaxed again upon his pillows, deliberately summoned pictures up before his mind's eye. Landscapes—and streams. He observed their outlines, watched one flow into another. The Black River into West Fork, that in turn into Spring Creek and Spring Creek into the Withlicoochee. Then they were all flowing together, merging into one broad plain. He watched it take form slowly: the wide field in front of Hawkwood, the Rivanna River on one side, on the other Peters' Mountain. They would be waiting there till the fox showed himself on that little rise by the river. The young men would hold back till Uncle Quent had wheeled Old Filly, then they would all be off pell-mell across the plain. He himself would be mounted on Jonesboro. Blind as a bat, but she would take anything you put her at. That first thicket on the edge of the woods. They would break there, one half of them going around, the other half streaking it through the woods. He was always of those going around to try to cut the fox off on the other side. No, he was down off his horse. He was coursing with the fox. He could hear the sharp, pointed feet padding on the dead leaves, see the quick head turned now and then over the shoulder.

The trees kept flashing by, one black trunk after another. And now it was a ragged mountain field and the sage grass running before them in waves to where a narrow stream curved in between the ridges. The fox's feet were light in the water. He ran steadily, head down. The hounds' baying was louder now. Old Mag knew the trick. She had stopped to give tongue by the big rock, and now they had all leaped the gulch and were scrambling up through the pines. But the fox's feet were already hard on the mountain path. He ran slowly now, past the big boulder, past the blasted pine to where the shadow of the Pinnacle Rock was black across the path. He ran on and the shadow rose and swayed to meet him. Its cool touch was on his hot tongue, his heaving flanks. He had slipped in under it. He was sinking down, panting, in black dark, on moist earth while the hounds' baying filled the bowl of the valley and reverberated from the mountainside.

INTERPRETATION

"Old Red" may seem to the casual reader devoid of any significant action. Mister Maury comes to his mother-in-law's home for a visit. He has dinner with the family; he exhibits his fishing tackle; next morning he goes fishing; and waking that night in the room in which he had slept on the night of his wife's death, he meditates upon his past life. Since this is all that "happens," the reader may plausibly conclude that the author is interested only in finding occasions for exhibiting Maury's character, and that such little scenes of action as do occur serve merely as convenient pegs on which to hang further character descriptions.

For some readers, therefore, the important question may be whether "Old Red" is not merely a more elaborate portrait of the sort that we looked at in the account of Sir Tatton Sykes (pp. 4–6) and not true fiction at all.

A satisfactory answer to this question will necessarily involve an examination of the whole story. Suppose that we begin by considering certain aspects of Mister Maury's character. We learn that his fishing is his life—the more so now that his crippled leg has forced him to give up hunting. His sport is not merely a passion—it is an art and a philosophy. To it he has given the thought and discipline that other men give to their businesses or their professions. He does not fish merely to kill time or to get away from himself: rather, it is in his sport that he truly finds himself; and, as for wasting time, "Time, he thought, time! They were always mouthing the word and what did they know about it? . . . The tears came into his eyes. Where, for instance, had this year gone? He could swear that he had not wasted a minute of it. . . . Not a minute wasted and yet here it was already May!" He knows the true value of time, he feels, for he enjoys his fishing so much that he covets for it every instant of time allowed to him. Far from being careless of time, he sees with a real poignance the few seasons still left to him slip away. Time, for him, is infinitely precious.

Maury, then, is not the thoughtless man nor the indolent man nor the disappointed man. But it is easy for other people to think him so, and because he is an observant and reflective man, he is acutely aware that they do think him so. His mother-in-law, for example, asks him: "Doesn't time hang heavy on your hands?"—as if he had no vocation! Or, his daughter, who does realize in a sense that his sport is for him an art, suggests that "he ought to set all his knowledges down in a book." For her, his sport would be justified if out it he could publish a book—as if the art had no justification as an end in itself but only as a means to some other end: fame, a reputation for out-of-the-way knowledge, public adulation.

The criticism of Mister Maury by the world and Maury's own counter-criticism of the world become increasingly emphasized as the story develops. We are being given more than an amusing description of a rather picturesque character. We are being given the character's own justification of the way of life which he exemplifies; and, as the story unfolds, we are made aware that the character has had to struggle to hold on to a pattern of living to which the outside world is inimical.

For example, Maury judges his son-in-law with a sort of pity: "If you asked him a question he answered punctiliously, two minutes later. Poor boy, dead to the world and would probably be that way the rest of his life! A pang of pity shot through Mister Maury. . . ." The judgment springs from his own way of living in which life has a purpose, a meaning, a way of expressing itself concretely, and yet meaningfully through a discipline which involves, not only technical skill of wrist and arm, but learning, self-control, and even a sort of ritual. From this point of view, the young man's life is disordered, abstract, and indeed, hardly life at all. Yet, in this same scene, Mister Maury realizes, clearly perhaps for the first time, that it is the young man's way of living that represents the norm, not his own: "It was he, not Steve, that was the queer one! . . . There was hardly anybody—there was *nobody* really in the whole world like him. . . ."

Mister Maury has not only to justify his way of living. As we have remarked above, he has actually had to struggle to maintain it. That struggle, in its most drastic phase, has been a struggle with his wife who had felt that he was wasting his talents, and who had tried through the years to "change" him. This we learn in the long *cutback* (see Glossary) in the last scene of the story when Maury, waking in the night, revolves in memory his life with her. There is humor, and tenderness, and pity in his memories of their contention. "Yes, he thought with pride. She was wearing him down—he didn't believe there was a man living who could withstand her a lifetime!—she was wearing him down and would have had him in another few months, another year certainly. But she had been struck down just as victory was in her grasp."

He has escaped, but the chase is still on. That evening in the conversation he "had felt a gust of the same fright that had shaken him there on the pond. That look! Sooner or later you met it in every human eye. . . . Yes, it had always been like that. It always would be."

What is this freedom which he has tried to preserve? It is difficult to describe. Certainly Mister Maury himself has difficulty in trying to state it, even to his family circle. He had tried to state it to them earlier that evening: "You think that we just go fishing to have a good time. The boy and I hold high converse on that pond. . . . I'm starved for intellectual companionship, I tell you. . . ." The last statement provokes a burst of friendly laughter. Presumably, Mister Maury, too, realizes how inadequate and apparently fantastic his statement sounds.

What is it, then, that he gets from his fishing? Why does he fish, anyway? Mister Maury cannot tell us. But the author has told us, or at least has suggested it in the story itself. May we not summarize it somewhat as follows?

Man craves an activity in which he can participate as a whole man, not merely as a mind, not merely as a body—an activity in which body and mind participate harmoniously. Man also craves some sort of harmony between means and ends: in other words, it is not enough for a man to give himself to some abstract activity in which there is no interest or pleasure in itself merely in order that he may gain money and time to enjoy himself in some other activity. Under such conditions, the pursuit of pleasure tends to become feverish and hysterical, the pursuit of mere excitement and forgetfulness.

The old man feels himself to be in a hostile world, a world which has nothing but criticism for him. "Sooner or later you met it in every human eye," he thinks. Why do people think that he is indolent? Because they feel that his occupation can only be a time-killer, and do not see that it requires its own knowledge and discipline. They tend to feel that anything which gives so much pleasure must be wrong, because they think of pleasure as separate from "work"—important work can't be pleasurable. Why do they think that he is a failure? Because they think that he has nothing "to show" for his life. Important activity, according to their view, gains something, "makes money," or leaves some mark of influence on the world. They cannot understand success that may be measured in terms of inner happiness and not in terms of a bank account and public esteem. Why do people think that Mister Maury is thoughtless? Because they cannot understand that a man may use his mind, or create his own philosophy, for his own pleasure and not to "put into a book." We have already seen how Mister Maury tries to indicate this when he says that he and the boy "hold high converse on that pond," and then gives up at the burst of friendly laughter.

We have said that Mister Maury does not, and perhaps could not, really state his position; but the point toward which the story moves is the realization, by the old man, of the meaning of his own life in relation to the world. This realization, however, does not come in terms of statement. It comes in terms of a symbol, the symbol of the fox.

How is this symbol prepared for? We notice that in the earlier part of the story there are various references to Mister Maury's youth in Virginia, and among them, references to his fox-hunting on the plain between the Rivanna River and Peters' Mountain. One fox, in particular, he remembers, Old Red, the fox they could never catch, the fox that showed himself as if in challenge, and which, because they could never catch him, they came to regard with a certain affection. It is implied that Old Red himself came to regard the chase as a sporting event: the fox staked his life again and again on his knowledge of the course, his cunning, and his speed. "A smart one, Old Red," they said about him.

So, in the last scene, when Mister Maury is lying sleepless in the very bed where he had been put on the night of his wife's death, and when he is thinking back over his past life, he suddenly feels that he himself is like the fox—no, that he *is* the fox, leading the chase to the safety of his lair on Peters' Mountain. But this is not the only preparation which has been given for the final symbol. Incidents in the immediate past have picked up and recapitulated the long struggle which he has had with his wife and with the world: the gentle chiding of the family that evening; memories of his wife's long struggle to "change him"; the attempt that evening to persuade him to go to the funeral; Sarah's remark, "As if you didn't *prefer* the society of niggers"; memories of the Negroes he has liked, of Ben Hooser, and, earlier still, of Uncle Teague and the fox hounds. As he tries to drift off to sleep, the picture of the fox hunt comes before his mind and summarizes the meaning of his whole life. He has always thought of himself as the hunter, but now he finds himself to be the hunted; but, like Old Red, the smart fox, he finds that that, too, may be sport. And he, like Old Red, is safe; he has won his race.

Our first question was: how does this story differ from a mere character sketch, like the portrait of Sir Tatton Sykes? The answer seems to lie in the fact that one finds here a definite progression, a definite movement toward the discovery on the part of the old man of the meaning of his life. This is a psychological progression, it is true; but, as we have seen, it is none the less dramatic for that. Furthermore, we have seen, as in the case of "The Man Who Would Be King," that stories which emphasize action and excitement, if they are good ones, have a similar psychological progression.

Has this story a more general meaning than the one which we have discussed? Is not the story, in one sense, a story about a basic conflict in our civilization—the conflict between man's desire for a harmonious development of all his faculties and a set of social conditions which tend to compartmentalize life and to make "work" and "pleasure" viciously antithetical? The question of importance is not whether or not we feel that Mister Maury's solution is ideal; it is rather whether Mister Maury might not have felt, in a more balanced society, that he did not need to take such drastic measures with his life in order to save himself as a human being.

1. Why does Mister Maury prefer the society of Negroes to that of white people?

2. Why is it significant that Mister Maury is an able and educated man?

3. Why is the conclusion with the symbol of the fox more effective here than a mere statement by Mister Maury of his "philosophy" would have been?

MARY McCARTHY

Cruel and Barbarous Treatment

SHE could not bear to hurt her husband. She impressed this on the Young Man, on her confidantes, and finally on her husband himself. The thought of Telling Him actually made her heart turn over in a sudden and sickening way, she said. This was true, and yet she knew that being a potential divorcee was deeply pleasurable in somewhat the same way that being an engaged girl had been. In both cases, there was at first a subterranean courtship, whose significance it was necessary to conceal from outside observers. The concealment of the original, premarital courtship had, however, been a mere superstitious gesture, briefly sustained. It had also been, on the whole, a private secretiveness, not a partnership of silence. One put one's family and one's friends off the track because one was still afraid that the affair might not come out right, might not lead in a clean, direct line to the altar. To confess one's aspirations might be, in the end, to publicize one's failure. Once a solid understanding had been reached, there followed a short intermission of ritual bashfulness, in which both parties awkwardly participated, and then came the Announcement.

But with the extramarital courtship, the deception was prolonged where it had been ephemeral, necessary where it had been frivolous, conspiratorial where it had been lonely. It was, in short, serious where it had been dilettantish. That it was accompanied by feelings of guilt, by sharp and genuine revulsions, only complicated and deepened its delights, by abrading the sensibilities, and by imposing a sense of outlawry and consequent mutual dependence upon the lovers. But what this interlude of deception gave her, above all, she recognized, was an opportunity, unparalleled in her experience, for exercising feelings of superiority over others. For her husband she had, she believed, only sympathy and compunction. She got no fun, she told the Young Man, out of putting horns on her darling's head, and never for a moment, she said, did he appear to her as the comic figure of the cuckolded husband that one saw on the stage. (The Young Man assured her that his own sentiments were equally delicate, that for the wronged man he felt the most profound respect, tinged with consideration.) It was as if by the mere act of betraying her husband, she had adequately bested him; it was supererogatory for her to gloat, and, if she gloated at all, it was over her fine restraint in not-gloating, over the integrity of her moral sense, which allowed her to preserve even while engaged in sinfulness the acute realization of sin and shame. Her overt superiority feelings she reserved for her friends. Lunches, and teas, which had been time killers, matters of routine, now became perilous and dramatic adventures. The Young Man's name was a bright, highly explosive ball which she bounced casually back and forth in these feminine tête-à-têtes. She would discuss him in his status of friend of the family, speculate on what girls he might have, attack him or defend him, anatomize him, keeping her eyes clear and impersonal, her voice empty of special emphasis, her manner humorously detached. *While all the time . . . !*

Three times a week or oftener, at lunch or tea, she would let herself tremble thus on the exquisite edge of self-betrayal, involving her companions in a momentous game whose rules and whose risks only she herself knew. The Public Appearances were even more satisfactory. To meet at a friend's house by design and to register surprise, to strike just the right note of young-matronly affection at cocktail parties, to treat him formally as "my escort" at the theater during intermissions—these were triumphs of stage management, more difficult of execution, more nerve-racking than the lunches and teas, because *two* actors were involved. His overardent glance must be hastily deflected; his too-self-conscious reading of his lines must be entered in the debit side of her ledger of love, in anticipation of an indulgent accounting in private.

The imperfections of his performance were, indeed, pleasing to her. Not, she thought, because his impetuosities, his gaucheries, demonstrated the sincerity of his passion for her, nor because they proved him a new hand at this game of intrigue, but rather because the high finish of her own acting showed off well in comparison. "I should have gone on the stage," she could tell him gaily, "or been a diplomat's wife or an international spy," while he would admiringly agree. Actually, she doubted whether she could ever have been an actress, acknowledging that she found it more amusing and more gratifying to play herself than to interpret any character conceived by a dramatist. In these private theatricals it was her own many-faceted nature that she put on exhibit, and the audience, in this case unfortunately limited to two, could applaud both her skill of projection and intrinsic variety. Furthermore, this was a play in which the *donnée* was real, and the penalty for a missed cue or an inopportune entrance was, at first anyway, unthinkable.

She loved him, she knew, for being a bad actor, for his docility in accepting her tender, mock-impatient instruction. Those superiority feelings were fattening not only on the gullibility of her friends, but also on the comic flaws of her lover's character, and on the vulnerability of her lover's position. In this particular hive she was undoubtedly queen bee.

The Public Appearances were not exclusively duets. They sometimes took the form of a trio. On these occasions the studied and benevolent carefulness which she always showed for her husband's feelings served a double purpose. She would affect a conspicuous domesticity, an affectionate conjugal demonstrativeness, would sprinkle her conversation with "Darlings," and punctuate it with pats and squeezes till her husband would visibly expand and her lover plainly and painfully shrink. For the Young Man no retaliation was possible. These endearments of hers were sanctioned by law, usage, and habit; they belonged to her role of wife and could not be condemned or paralleled by a young man who was himself unmarried. They were clear provocations, but they could not be called so, and the Young Man preferred not to speak of them. *But she knew.* . . . Though she was aware of the sadistic intention of these displays, she was not ashamed of them, as she was sometimes twistingly ashamed of the hurt she was preparing to inflict on her husband. Partly she felt that they were punishments which the Young Man richly deserved for the wrong he was doing her husband, and that she herself in contriving them was acting, quite fittingly, both as judge and accused. Partly, too, she believed herself justified in playing the fond wife, whatever the damage to her lover's ego, because, in a sense, she actually was a fond wife. She *did* have these feelings, she insisted, whether she was exploiting them or not.

Eventually, however, her reluctance to wound her husband and her solicitude for his pride were overcome by an inner conviction that her love affair must move on to its next preordained stage. The possibilities of subterranean courtship had been exhausted; it was time for the Announcement. She and the Young Man began to tell each other in a rather breathless and literary style that the Situation Was Impossible, and Things Couldn't Go On This Way Any Longer. The ostensible meaning of these flurried laments was that, under present conditions, they were not seeing enough of each other, that their hours together were too short and their periods of separation too dismal, that the whole business of deception had become morally distasteful to them. Perhaps the Young Man really believed these things; she did not. For the first time, she saw that the virtue of marriage as an institution lay in its public character. Private cohabitation, long continued, was, she concluded, a bore. Whatever the coziness of isolation, the warm delights of having a secret, a love affair finally reached the point where it needed the glare of publicity to revive the interest of its protagonists. Hence, she thought, the engagement parties, the showers, the big church weddings, the presents, the receptions. These were simply socially approved devices by which the lovers got themselves talked about. The gossip-value of a divorce and remarriage was obviously far greater than the gossip-value of a mere engagement, and she was now ready, indeed hungry, to hear What People Would Say.

The lunches, the teas, the Public Appearances were getting a little flat. It was not, in the end, enough to be a Woman With A Secret, if to one's friends one appeared to be a woman without a secret. The bliss of having a secret required, in short, the consummation of telling it, and she looked forward to the My-dear-I-had-no-idea's, the I-thought-you-and-Bill-were-so-happy-together's, the How-did-you-keep-it-so-dark's with which her intimates would greet her announcement. The audience of two no longer sufficed her; she required a larger stage. She tried it first, a little nervously, on two or three of her closest friends, swearing them to secrecy. "Bill must hear it first from me," she declared. "It would be too terrible for his pride if he found out afterwards that the whole town knew it before he did. So you mustn't tell, even later on, that I told you about this today. I felt I had to talk to someone." After these lunches she would hurry to a phone booth to give the Young Man the gist of the conversation, just as a reporter, sent to cover a fire, telephones in to the city desk. "She certainly was surprised," she could always say with a little gush of triumph. "But she thinks it's fine." *But did they actually?* She could not be sure. Was it possible that she sensed in these luncheon companions, her dearest friends, a certain reserve, a certain unexpressed judgment?

It was a pity, she reflected, that she was so sensitive to public opinion. "I couldn't really love a man," she murmured to herself once, "if everybody didn't think he was wonderful." Everyone seemed to like the Young Man, of course. *But still. . . .* She was getting panicky, she thought. Surely it was only common sense that nobody is admired by everybody. And even if a man were universally despised, would there not be a kind of defiant nobility in loving him in the teeth of the whole world? There would, certainly, but it was a type of heroism that she would scarcely be called upon to practice, for the Young Man was popular, he was invited everywhere, he danced well, his manners were ingratiating, he kept up intellectually.

But was he not perhaps *too* amiable, *too* accommodating? Was it for this that her friends seemed silently to criticize him?

At this time a touch of acridity entered into her relations with the Young Man. Her indulgent scoldings had an edge to them now, and it grew increasingly difficult for her to keep her make-believe impatience from becoming real. She would look for dark spots in his character and drill away at them as relentlessly as a dentist at a cavity. A compulsive didacticism possessed her: no truism of his, no cliché, no ineffectual joke could pass the rigidity of her censorship. And, hard as she tried to maintain the character of charming schoolmistress, the Young Man, she saw, was taking alarm. She suspected that, frightened and puzzled, he contemplated flight. She found herself watching him with scientific interest, speculating as to what course he would take, and she was relieved but faintly disappointed when it became clear that he ascribed her sharpness to the tension of the situation and had decided to stick it out.

The moment had come for her to tell her husband. By this single, cathartic act, she would, she believed, rid herself of the doubts and anxieties that beset her. If her husband were to impugn the Young Man's character, she could answer his accusations and at the same time discount them as arising from jealousy. From her husband, at least, she might expect the favor of an open attack to which she could respond with the prepared defense that she carried, unspoken, about with her. Further, she had an intense, childlike curiosity as to How Her Husband Would Take It, a curiosity which she disguised for decency's sake as justifiable apprehension. The confidences already imparted to her friends seemed like pale dress rehearsals of the supreme confidence she was about to make. Perhaps it was toward this moment that the whole affair had been tending, for this moment that the whole affair had been designed. This would be the ultimate testing of her husband's love, its final, rounded, quintessential expression. Never, she thought, when you live with a man do you feel the full force of his love. It is gradually rationed out to you in an impure state, compounded with all the other elements of daily existence, so that you are hardly sensible of receiving it. There is no single point at which it is concentrated; it spreads out into the past and the future until it appears as a nearly imperceptible film over the surface of your life. Only face to face with its own annihilation could it show itself wholly, and, once shown, drop into the category of completed experiences.

She was not disappointed. She told him at breakfast in a fashionable restaurant, because, she said, he would be better able to control his feelings in public. When he called at once for the check, she had a spasm of alarm lest in an access of brutality or grief he leave her there alone, conspicuous, and, as it were, unfulfilled. But they walked out of the restaurant together and through the streets, hand in hand, tears streaming, "unchecked," she whispered to herself, down their faces. Later they were in the Park, by an artificial lake, watching the ducks swim. The sun was very bright, and she felt a kind of superb pathos in the careful and irrelevant attention they gave to the pastoral scene. This was, she knew, the most profound, the most subtle, the most idyllic experience of her life. All the strings of her nature were, at last, vibrant. She was both doer and sufferer: she inflicted pain and participated in it. And she was, at the same time, physician, for, as she was the weapon that dealt the wound, she was also the balm that could assuage it. Only she could know the hurt that engrossed him, and it was to her that he turned for the sympathy she had ready for him. Finally, though she offered him his discharge slip with one hand, with the other she beckoned him to approach. She was wooing him all over again, but wooing him to a deeper attachment than he had previously experienced, to an unconditional surrender. She was demanding his total understanding of her, his compassion, and his forgiveness. When at last he answered her repeated and agonized I-love-you's by grasping her hand more tightly and saying gently, "I know," she saw that she had won him over. She had drawn him into a truly mystical union. Their marriage was complete.

Afterwards everything was more prosaic. The Young Man had to be telephoned and summoned to a conference à trois, a conference, she said, of civilized, intelligent people. The Young Man was a little awkward, even dropped a tear or two, which embarrassed everyone else, but what after all, she thought, could you expect? He was in a difficult position; his was a thankless part. With her husband behaving so well, indeed, so gallantly, the Young Man could not fail to look a trifle inadequate. The Young Man would have preferred it, of course, if her husband had made a scene, had bullied or threatened her, so that he himself might have acted the chivalrous protector. She, however, did not hold her husband's heroic courtesy against him: in some way, it reflected credit on herself. The Young Man, apparently, was expecting to Carry Her Off, but this she would not allow. "It would be too heartless," she whispered when they were alone for a moment. "We must all go somewhere together."

So the three went out for a drink, and she watched with a sort of desperation her husband's growing abstraction, the more and more perfunctory attention he accorded the conversation she was so bravely sustaining. "He is bored," she thought. "He is going to leave." The prospect of being left alone with the Young Man seemed suddenly unendurable. If her husband were to go now, he would take with him the third dimension that had given the affair depth, and abandon her to a flat and vulgar love scene. Terrified, she wondered whether she had not already prolonged the drama beyond its natural limits, whether the confession in the restaurant and the absolution in the Park had not rounded off the artistic whole, whether the sequel of divorce and remarriage would not, in fact, constitute an anticlimax. Already she sensed that behind her husband's good manners an ironical attitude toward herself had sprung up. Was it possible that he had believed that they would return from the Park and all would continue as before? It was conceivable that her protestations of love had been misleading, and that his enormous tenderness toward her had been based, not on the idea that he was giving her up, but rather on the idea that he was taking her back—with no questions asked. If that were the case, the telephone call, the conference, and the excursion had in his eyes been a monstrous *gaffe*, a breach of sensibility and good taste, for which he would never forgive her. She blushed violently. Looking at him again, she thought he was watching her with an expression which declared: I have found you out: now I know what you are like. For the first time, she felt him utterly alienated.

When he left them she experienced the letdown she had feared but also a kind of relief. She told herself that it was as well that he had cut himself off from her: it made her decision simpler. There was now nothing for her to do but to push the love affair to its conclusion, whatever that might be, and this was probably what she most deeply desired. Had the poignant intimacy of the Park persisted, she might have been tempted to drop the adventure she had begun and return to her routine. But that was, looked at coldly, unthinkable. For if the adventure would seem a little flat after the scene in the Park, the resumption of her marriage would seem even flatter. If the drama of the triangle had been amputated by her confession, the curtain had been brought down with a smack on the drama of wedlock.

And, as it turned out, the drama of the triangle was not quite ended by the superficial rupture of her marriage. Though she had left her husband's apartment and been offered shelter by a confidante, it was still necessary for her to see him every day. There were clothes to be packed, and possessions to be divided, love letters to be reread and mementoes to be wept over in common. There were occasional passionate, unconsummated embraces; there were endearments and promises. And though her husband's irony remained, it was frequently vulnerable. It was not, as she had at first thought, an armor against her, but merely a sword, out of *Tristan and Isolde*, which lay permanently between them and enforced discretion.

They met often, also, at the houses of friends, for, as she said, "What can I do? I know it's not tactful, but we all know the same people. You can't expect me to give up my friends." These Public Appearances were heightened in interest by the fact that these audiences, unlike the earlier ones, had, as it were, purchased librettos, and were in full possession of the intricacies of the plot. She preferred, she decided, the evening parties to the cocktail parties, for there she could dance alternately with her lover and her husband to the accompaniment of subdued gasps on the part of the bystanders.

This interlude was at the same time festive and heartrending: her only dull moments were the evenings she spent alone with the Young Man. Unfortunately, the Post-Announcement period was only too plainly an interlude and its very nature demanded that it be followed by something else. She could not preserve her anomalous status indefinitely. It was not decent and, besides, people would be bored. From the point of view of one's friends, it was all very well to entertain a Triangle as a novelty; to cope with it as a permanent problem was a different matter. Once they had all three gotten drunk, and there was a scene, and, though everyone talked about it afterwards, her friends were, she thought, a little colder, a little more critical. People began to ask her when she was going to Reno. Furthermore, she noticed that her husband was getting a slight edge in popularity over the Young Man. It was natural, of course, that everyone should feel sorry for him, and be especially nice. *But yet.* . . .

When she learned from her husband that he was receiving invitations from members of her own circle, invitations in which she and the Young Man were unaccountably not included, she went at once to the station and bought her ticket. Her good-by to her husband, which she had privately allocated to her last hours in town, took place prematurely, two days before she was to leave. He was rushing off to what she inwardly feared was a Gay Weekend in the country; he had only a few minutes; he wished her a pleasant trip; and he would write, of course. His highball was drained while her glass still stood half full; he sat forward nervously on his chair; and she knew herself to be acting the Ancient Mariner, but her dignity would not allow her to hurry. She hoped that he would miss his train for her, but he did not. He left her sitting in the bar, and that night the Young Man could not, as he put it, do a thing with her. There was nowhere, absolutely nowhere, she said passionately, that she wanted to go, nobody she wanted to see, nothing she wanted to do. "You need a drink," he said with the air of a diagnostician. "A drink," she answered bitterly. "I'm sick of the drinks we've been having. Gin, whisky, rum, what else is there?" He took her into a bar, and she cried, but he bought her a fancy mixed drink, something called a Ramos gin fizz, and she was a little appeased because she had never had one before. Then some friends came in, and they all had another drink together, and she felt better. "There," said the Young Man, on the way home, "don't I know what's good for you? Don't I know how to handle you?" "Yes," she answered in her most humble and feminine tones, but she knew that they had suddenly dropped into a new pattern, that they were no longer the cynosure of a social group, but merely another young couple with an evening to pass, another young couple looking desperately for entertainment, wondering whether to call on a married couple or to drop in somewhere for a drink. This time the Young Man's prescription had worked, but it was pure luck that they had chanced to meet someone they knew. A second or a third time they would scan the faces of the other drinkers in vain, would order a second drink and surreptitiously watch the door, and finally go out alone, with a quite detectable air of being unwanted.

When, a day and a half later, the Young Man came late to take her to the train, and they had to run down the platform to catch it, she found him all at once detestable. He would ride to 125th Street with her, he declared in a burst of gallantry, but she was angry all the way because she was afraid there would be trouble with the conductor. At 125th Street, he stood on the platform blowing kisses to her and shouting something that she could not hear through the glass. She made a gesture of repugnance, but, seeing him flinch, seeing him weak and charming and incompetent, she brought her hand reluctantly to her lips and blew a kiss back. The other passengers were watching, she was aware, and though their looks were doting and not derisive, she felt herself to be humiliated and somehow vulgarized. When the train began to move, and the Young Man began to run down the platform after it, still blowing kisses and shouting alternately, she got up, turned sharply away from the window and walked back to the club car. There she sat down and ordered a whisky and soda.

There were a number of men in the car, who looked up in unison as she gave her order, but, observing that they were all the middle-aged, small-business-men who "belonged" as inevitably to the club car as the white-coated porter and the leather-bound *Saturday Evening Post*, she paid them no heed. She was now suddenly overcome by a sense of depression and loss that was unprecedented for being in no way dramatic or pleasurable. In the last half hour she had seen clearly that she would never marry the Young Man, and she found herself looking into an insubstantial future with no signpost to guide her. Almost all women, she thought, when they are girls never believe that they will get married. The terror of spinsterhood hangs over them from adolescence on. Even if they are popular they think that no one really interesting will want them enough to marry them. Even if they get engaged they are afraid that something will go wrong, something will intervene. When they do get married it seems to them a sort of miracle, and, after they have been married for a time, though in retrospect the whole process looks perfectly natural and inevitable, they retain a certain unarticulated pride in the wonder they have performed. Finally, however, the terror of spinsterhood has been so thoroughly exorcised that they forget ever having been haunted by it, and it is at this stage that they contemplate divorce. "How could I have forgotten?" she said to herself and began to wonder what she would do.

She could take an apartment by herself in the Village. She would meet new people. She would entertain. But, she thought, if I have people in for cocktails, there will always come the moment when they have to leave, and I will be alone and have to pretend to have another engagement in order to save embarrassment. If I have them to dinner, it will be the same thing, but at least I will not have to pretend to have an engagement. I shall give dinners. Then, she thought, there will be the cocktail parties, and, if I go alone, I shall always stay a little too late, hoping that a young man or even a party of people will ask me to dinner. And if I fail, if no one asks me, I shall have the ignominy of walking out alone, trying to look as if I had somewhere to go. Then there will be the evenings at home with a good book when there will be no reason at all for going to bed, and I shall perhaps sit up all night. And the mornings when there will be no point in getting up, and I shall perhaps stay in bed till dinnertime. There will be the dinners in tearooms with other unmarried women, tearooms because women alone look conspicuous and forlorn in good restaurants. And then, she thought, I shall get older.

She would never, she reflected angrily, have taken this step, had she felt that she was burning her bridges behind her. She would never have left one man unless she had had another to take his place. But the Young Man, she now saw, was merely a sort of mirage which she had allowed herself to mistake for an oasis. "If the Man," she muttered, "did not exist, the Moment would create him." This was what had happened to her. She had made herself the victim of an imposture. But, she argued, with an access of cheerfulness, if this were true, if out of the need of a second, a new, husband she had conjured up the figure of one, she had possibly been impelled by unconscious forces to behave more intelligently than appearances would indicate. She was perhaps acting out in a sort of hypnotic trance a ritual whose meaning had not yet been revealed to her, a ritual which required that, first of all, the Husband be eliminated from the cast of characters. Conceivably, she was designed for the role of *femme fatale*, and for such a personage considerations of safety, provisions against loneliness and old age, were not only philistine but irrelevant. She might marry a second, a third, a fourth time, or she might never marry again. But, in any case, for the thrifty bourgeois love-insurance, with its daily payments of patience, forbearance, and resignation, she was no longer eligible. She would be, she told herself delightedly, a bad risk.

She was, or soon would be, a Young Divorcee, and the term still carried glamor. Her divorce decree would be a passport conferring on her the status of citizeness of the world. She felt gratitude toward the Young Man for having unwittingly effected her transit into a new life. She looked about her at the other passengers. Later she would talk to them. They would ask, of course, where she was bound for; that was the regulation opening move of train conversations. But it was a delicate question what her reply should be. To say "Reno" straight out would be vulgar; it would smack of confidences too cheaply given. Yet to lie, to say "San Francisco" for instance, would be to cheat herself, to minimize her importance, to mislead her interlocutor into believing her an ordinary traveler with a commonplace destination. There must be some middle course which would give information without appearing to do so, which would hint at a *vie galante* yet indicate a barrier of impeccable reserve. It would probably be best, she decided, to say "West" at first, with an air of vagueness and hesitation. Then, when pressed, she might go so far as to say "Nevada." But no farther.

INTERPRETATION

In this story we never learn the name of the heroine and yet we come to know a great deal about her. Indeed it could be said that her little self-conscious soul is quite pitilessly stripped naked. But if the exposure of her follies and limitations is pitiless, it is not heavy handed and it does not smack of any sour moralism. The author's treatment seems detached and objective. In fact, though the author does not have the heroine tell her story, the story affects to follow the very play of the heroine's thoughts. And so we have the sense that the exposure of the heroine is a self-exposure.

One may illustrate from the very first sentence in the story: "She could not bear to hurt her husband." As we learn, there is a sense in which this is true, or at least the heroine quite clearly believes it to be true. If later, we come to realize that the heroine can bear to hurt her husband, and indeed needs to hurt him for her own titillation, the realization does not seem to be one imposed from without. We accept it as part of our developing knowledge of the woman.

This story is, then, in a sense, a rather brilliant character story, but it is more than a character sketch. We are not "told" about the young woman. Her character is presented dramatically: we come to know it through what she does and says, and her thoughts and actions are presented so expertly that the author never needs to summarize her traits.

There is another obvious way in which we can look at the story. It presents not only a particular character, but a particular kind of society with its manners, ethical standards, implied values, and so on. The young woman is necessarily presented against this social background. Her character can be understood only in relation to such a society, for only in terms of such a society is she conceivable. We may even say that she is far more responsive to the claims of this society than she is either to her husband or to the Young Man. Her self-consciousness is exceeded only by her unconscious deference to what her friends and acquaintances may think of her. Thus she is not only self-centered, but she is a snob as well.

1. What is the tone of this story? The story is obviously a kind of social satire, but the reader should try to find a more specific characterization of the tone. Notice that the author is never sarcastic. If she is ironic, the irony is never bitter nor localized in a particular sentence or phrase. If you find it difficult to describe the tone of the whole story, then try first to characterize the tone of the first two paragraphs.

2. What is the basic character of the young divorcee-to-be? Is she a monster of self-conceit and self-deceit, or is she really capable of human warmth and passion? Is her self-consciousness—her awareness of her feelings—her attempts to analyze them—wholly a bad thing? How insincere is she? How calculating?

3. What kind of people are the husband and the Young Man? Characterize them. In this story they obviously play subordinate roles, but are they sufficiently credible?

4. Does the "plot" supply a rising tide of interest, a climax, and a change in the course of the heroine's life? This plot is, in a sense, simply the stages of the love affair and the movement toward the divorce; that is, it is conventional and thoroughly predictable. Yet does it serve the necessary functions of a plot? If so, how has the author managed the matter?

5. In a story of this sort it is hard to find an effective ending. Is the ending actually effective? If you believe that it is, try to indicate why.

6. Compare and contrast the heroine of this story in her introspective reveries with Ruby in "A Piece of News."

CARSON McCULLERS

A Domestic Dilemma

ON Thursday Martin Meadows left the office early enough to make the first express bus home. It was the hour when the evening lilac glow was fading in the slushy streets, but by the time the bus had left the Mid-town terminal the bright city night had come. On Thursdays the maid had a half-day off and Martin liked to get home as soon as possible, since for the past year his wife had not been—well. This Thursday he was very tired and, hoping that no regular commuter would single him out for conversation, he fastened his attention to the newspaper until the bus had crossed the George Washington Bridge. Once on 9-W Highway Martin always felt that the trip was halfway done, he breathed deeply, even in cold weather when only ribbons of draught cut through the smoky air of the bus, confident that he was breathing country air. It used to be that at this point he would relax and begin to think with pleasure of his home. But in this last year nearness brought only a sense of tension and he did not anticipate the journey's end. This evening Martin kept his face close to the window and watched the barren fields and lonely lights of passing townships. There was a moon, pale on the dark earth and areas of late, porous snow; to Martin the countryside seemed vast and somehow desolate that evening. He took his hat from the rack and put his folded newspaper in the pocket of his overcoat a few minutes before time to pull the cord.

The cottage was a block from the bus stop, near the river but not directly on the shore; from the living-room window you could look across the street and opposite yard and see the Hudson. The cottage was modern, almost too white and new on the narrow plot of yard. In summer the grass was soft and bright and Martin carefully tended a flower border and a rose trellis. But during the cold, fallow months the yard was bleak and the cottage seemed naked. Lights were on that evening in all the rooms in the little house and Martin hurried up the front walk. Before the steps he stopped to move a wagon out of the way.

The children were in the living room, so intent on play that the opening of the front door was at first unnoticed. Martin stood looking at his safe, lovely children. They had opened the bottom drawer of the secretary and taken out the Christmas decorations., Andy had managed to plug in the Christmas tree lights and the green and red bulbs glowed with out-of-season festivity on the rug of the living room. At the moment he was trying to trail the bright cord over Marianne's rocking horse. Marianne sat on the floor pulling off an angel's wings. The children wailed a startling welcome. Martin swung the fat little baby girl up to his shoulder and Andy threw himself against his father's legs.

"Daddy, Daddy, Daddy!"

Martin sat down the little girl carefully and swung Andy a few times like a pendulum. Then he picked up the Christmas tree cord.

"What's all this stuff doing out? Help me put it back in the drawer. You're not to fool with the light socket. Remember I told you that before. I mean it, Andy."

The six-year-old child nodded and shut the secretary drawer. Martin stroked his fair soft hair and his hand lingered tenderly on the nape of the child's frail neck.

"Had supper yet, Bumpkin?"

"It hurt. The toast was hot."

The baby girl stumbled on the rug and, after the first surprise of the fall, began to cry; Martin picked her up and carried her in his arms back to the kitchen.

"See, Daddy," said Andy. "The toast——"

Emily had laid the children's supper on the uncovered porcelain table. There were two plates with the remains of cream-of-wheat and eggs and silver mugs that had held milk. There was also a platter of cinnamon toast, untouched, except for one tooth-marked bite. Martin sniffed the bitten piece and nibbled gingerly. Then he put the toast into the garbage pail.

"Hoo—phui—What on earth!"

Emily had mistaken the tin of cayenne for the cinnamon.

"I like to have burnt up," Andy said. "Drank water and ran outdoors and opened my mouth. Marianne didn't eat none."

"Any," corrected Martin. He stood helpless, looking around the walls of the kitchen. "Well, that's that, I guess," he said finally. "Where is your mother now?"

"She's up in you alls' room."

Martin left the children in the kitchen and went up to his wife. Outside the door he waited for a moment to still his anger. He did not knock and once inside the room he closed the door behind him.

Emily sat in the rocking chair by the window of the pleasant room. She had been drinking something from a tumbler and as he entered she put the glass hurriedly on the floor behind the chair. In her attitude there was confusion and guilt which she tried to hide by a show of spurious vivacity.

"Oh, Marty! You home already? The time slipped up on me. I was just going down——" She lurched to him and her kiss was strong with sherry. When he stood unresponsive she stepped back a pace and giggled nervously.

"What's the matter with you? Standing there like a barber pole. Is anything wrong with you?"

"Wrong with *me?*" Martin bent over the rocking chair and picked up the tumbler from the floor. "If you could only realize how sick I am—how bad it is for all of us."

Emily spoke in a false, airy voice that had become too familiar to him. Often at such times she affected a slight English accent copying perhaps some actress she admired. "I haven't the vaguest idea what you mean. Unless you are referring to the glass I used for a spot of sherry. I had a finger of sherry—maybe two. But what is the crime in that, pray tell me? I'm quite all right. Quite all right."

"So anyone can see."

As she went into the bedroom Emily walked with careful gravity. She turned on the cold water and dashed some on her face with her cupped hands, then patted herself dry with the corner of a bath towel. Her face was delicately featured and young, unblemished.

"I was just going down to make dinner." She tottered and balanced herself by holding to the door frame.

"I'll take care of dinner. You stay up here. I'll bring it up."

"I'll do nothing of the sort. Why, whoever heard of such a thing?"

"Please," Martin said.

"Leave me alone. I'm quite all right. I was just on the way down——"

"Mind what I say."

"Mind your grandmother."

She lurched toward the door, but Martin caught her by the arm. "I don't want the children to see you in this condition. Be reasonable."

"Condition!" Emily jerked her arm. Her voice rose angrily. "Why, because I drink a couple of sherries in the afternoon you're trying to make me out a drunkard. Condition! Why, I don't even touch whiskey. As well you know. *I* don't swill liquor at bars. And that's more than you can say. I don't even have a cocktail at dinnertime. I only sometimes have a glass of sherry. What, I ask you, is the disgrace of that? Condition!"

Martin sought words to calm his wife. "We'll have a quiet supper by ourselves up here. That's a good girl." Emily sat on the side of the bed and he opened the door for a quick departure.

"I'll be back in a jiffy."

As he busied himself with the dinner downstairs he was lost in the familiar question as to how this problem had come upon his home. He himself had always enjoyed a good drink. When they were still living in Alabama they had served long drinks or cocktails as a matter of course. For years they had drunk one or two—possibly three drinks before dinner, and at bedtime a long nightcap. Evenings before holidays they might get a buzz on, might even become a little tight. But alcohol had never seemed a problem to him, only a bothersome expense that with the increase in the family they could scarcely afford. It was only after his company had transferred him to New York that Martin was aware that certainly his wife was drinking too much. She was tippling, he noticed, during the day.

The problem acknowledged, he tried to analyze the source. The change from Alabama to New York had somehow disturbed her; accustomed to the idle warmth of a small Southern town, the matrix of the family and cousinship and childhood friends, she had failed to accommodate herself to the stricter, lonelier mores of the North. The duties of motherhood and housekeeping were onerous to her. Homesick for Paris City, she had made no friends in the suburban town. She read only magazines and murder books. Her interior life was insufficient without the artifice of alcohol.

The revelations of incontinence insidiously undermined his previous conceptions of his wife. There were times of unexplainable malevolence, times when the alcoholic fuse caused an explosion of unseemly anger. He encountered a latent coarseness in Emily, inconsistent with her natural simplicity. She lied about drinking and deceived him with unsuspected stratagems.

Then there was an accident. Coming home from work one evening about a year ago, he was greeted with screams from the children's room. He found Emily holding the baby, wet and naked from her bath. The baby had been dropped, her frail, frail skull striking the table edge, so that a thread of blood was soaking into the gossamer hair. Emily was sobbing and intoxicated. As Martin cradled the hurt child, so infinitely precious at that moment, he had an affrighted vision of the future.

The next day Marianne was all right. Emily vowed that never again would she touch liquor, and for a few weeks she was sober, cold and down-cast. Then gradually she began—not whiskey or gin—but quantities of beer, or sherry, or outlandish liqueurs; once he had come across a hatbox of empty crème de menthe bottles. Martin found a dependable maid who managed the household competently. Virgie was also from Alabama and Martin had never dared tell Emily the wage scale customary in New York. Emily's drinking was entirely secret now, done before he reached the house. Usually the effects were almost imperceptible—a looseness of movement or the heavy-lidded eyes. The times of irresponsibilities, such as the cayenne-pepper toast were rare, and Martin could dismiss his worries when Virgie was at the house. But, nevertheless, anxiety was always latent, a threat of undefined disaster that underlaid his days.

"Marianne!" Martin called, for even the recollection of that time brought the need for reassurance. The baby girl, no longer hurt, but no less precious to her father, came into the kitchen with her brother. Martin went on with the preparations for the meal. He opened a can of soup and put two chops in the frying pan. Then he sat down by the table and took Marianne on his knees for a pony ride. Andy watched them, his fingers wobbling the tooth that had been loose all that week.

"Andy-the-candyman!" Martin said. "Is that old critter still in your mouth? Come closer, let Daddy have a look."

"I got a string to pull it with." The child brought from his pocket a tangled thread. "Virgie said to tie it to the tooth and tie the other end to the doorknob and shut the door real suddenly."

Martin took out a clean handkerchief and felt the loose tooth carefully. "That tooth is coming out of my Andy's mouth tonight. Otherwise I'm awfully afraid we'll have a tooth tree in the family."

"A what?"

"A tooth tree," Martin said. "You'll bite into something and swallow that tooth. And the tooth will take root in poor Andy's stomach and grow into a tooth tree with sharp little teeth insead of leaves."

"Shoo, Daddy," Andy said. But he held the tooth firmly between his grimy little thumb and forefinger. "There ain't any tree like that. I never seen one."

"There *isn't* any tree like that and I never *saw* one."

Martin tensed suddenly. Emily was coming down the stairs. He listened to her fumbling footsteps, his arm embracing the little boy with dread. When Emily came into the room he saw from her movements and her sullen face that she had again been at the sherry bottle. She began to yank open drawers and set the table.

"Condition!" she said in a furry voice. "You talk to me like that. Don't think I'll forget. I remember every dirty lie you say to me. Don't you think for a minute that I forget."

"Emily!" he begged. "The children——"

"The children—yes! Don't think I don't see through your dirty plots and schemes. Down here trying to turn my own children against me. Don't think I don't see and understand."

"Emily! I beg you—please go upstairs."

"So you can turn my children—my very own children——" Two large tears coursed rapidly down her cheeks. "Trying to turn my little boy, my Andy, against his own mother."

With drunken impulsiveness Emily knelt on the floor before the startled child. Her hands on his shoulders balanced her. "Listen, my Andy—you wouldn't listen to any lies your father tells you? You wouldn't believe what he says? Listen, Andy, what was your father telling you before I came downstairs?" Uncertain, the child sought his father's face. "Tell me. Mama wants to know."

"About the tooth tree."

"What?"

The child repeated the words and she echoed them with unbelieving terror. "The tooth tree!" She swayed and renewed her grasp on the child's shoulder. "I don't know what you're talking about. But listen, Andy, Mama is all right, isn't she?" The tears were spilling down her face and Andy drew back from her, for he was afraid. Grasping the table edge, Emily stood up.

"See! You have turned my child against me."

Marianne began to cry, and Martin took her in his arms.

"That's all right, you can take *your* child. You have always shown partiality from the very first. I don't mind, but at least you can leave me my little boy."

Andy edged close to his father and touched his leg. "Daddy," he wailed.

Martin took the children to the foot of the stairs. "Andy, you take up Marianne and Daddy will follow you in a minute."

"But Mama?" the child asked, whispering.

"Mama will be all right. Don't worry."

Emily was sobbing at the kitchen table, her face buried in the crook of her arm. Martin poured a cup of soup and set it before her. Her rasping sobs unnerved him; the vehemence of her emotion, irrespective of the source, touched in him a strain of tenderness. Unwillingly he laid his hand on her dark hair. "Sit up and drink the soup." Her face as she looked up at him was chastened and imploring. The boy's withdrawal or the touch of Martin's hand had turned the tenor of her mood.

"Ma-Martin," she sobbed. "I'm so ashamed."

"Drink the soup."

Obeying him, she drank between gasping breaths. After a second cup she allowed him to lead her up to their room. She was docile now and more restrained. He laid her nightgown on the bed and was about to leave the room when a fresh round of grief, the alcoholic tumult, came again. "He turned away. My Andy looked at me and turned away."

Impatience and fatigue hardened his voice, but he spoke warily. "You forget that Andy is still a little child—he can't comprehend the meaning of such scenes."

"Did I make a scene? Oh, Martin, did I make a scene before the children?"

Her horrified face touched and amused him against his will. "Forget it. Put on your nightgown and go to sleep."

"My child turned away from me. Andy looked at his mother and turned away. The children——"

She was caught in the rhythmic sorrow of alcohol. Martin withdrew from the room saying: "For God's sake go to sleep. The children will forget by tomorrow."

As he said this he wondered if it was true. Would the scene glide so easily from memory—or would it root in the unconscious to fester in the after-years? Martin did not know, and the last alternative sickened him. He thought of Emily, foresaw the morning-after humiliation: the shards of memory, the lucidities that glared from the obliterating darkness of shame. She would call the New York office twice—possibly three or four times. Martin anticipated his own embarrassment, wondering if the others at the office could possibly suspect. He felt that his secretary had divined the trouble long ago and that she pitied him. He suffered a moment of rebellion against his fate, he hated his wife.

Once in the children's room he closed the door and felt secure for the first time that evening. Marianne fell down on the floor, picked herself up and calling: "Daddy, watch me," fell again, got up, and continued the falling-calling routine. Andy sat in the child's low chair, wobbling the tooth. Martin ran the water in the tub, washed his own hands in the lavatory, and called the boy into the bathroom.

"Let's have another look at that tooth." Martin sat on the toilet, holding Andy between his knees. The child's mouth gaped and Martin grasped the tooth. A wobble, a quick twist and the nacreous milk tooth was free. Andy's face was for the first moment split between terror, astonishment, and delight. He mouthed a swallow of water and spat into the lavatory.

"Look, Daddy! It's blood. Marianne!"

Martin loved to bathe his children, loved inexpressibly the tender, naked bodies as they stood in the water so exposed. It was not fair of Emily to say that he showed partiality. As Martin soaped the delicate boy-body of his son he felt that further love would be impossible. Yet he admitted the difference in the quality of his emotions for the two children. His love for his daughter was graver, touched with a strain of melancholy, a gentleness that was akin to pain. His pet names for the little boy were the absurdities of daily inspiration—he called the little girl always Marianne, and his voice as he spoke it was a caress. Martin patted dry the fat baby stomach and the sweet little genital fold. The washed child faces were radiant as flower petals, equally loved.

"I'm putting the tooth under my pillow. I'm supposed to get a quarter."

"What for?"

"*You* know, Daddy. Johnny got a quarter for his tooth."

"Who puts the quarter there?" asked Martin. "I used to think the fairies left it in the night. It was a dime in my day, though."

"That's what they say in kindergarten."

"Who does put it there?"

"Your parents," Andy said. "You!"

Martin was pinning the cover on Marianne's bed. His daughter was already asleep. Scarcely breathing, Martin bent over and kissed her forehead, kissed again the tiny hand that lay palm-upward, flung in slumber beside her head.

"Good night, Andy-man."

The answer was only a drowsy murmur. After a minute Martin took out his change and slid a quarter underneath the pillow. He left a night light in the room.

As Martin prowled about the kitchen making a late meal, it occurred to him that the children had not once mentioned their mother or the scene that must have seemed to them incomprehensible. Absorbed in the instant—the tooth, the bath, the quarter—the fluid passage of child-time had borne these weightless episodes like leaves in the swift current of a shallow stream while the adult enigma was beached and forgotten on the shore. Martin thanked the Lord for that.

But his own anger, repressed and lurking, rose again. His youth was being frittered by a drunkard's waste, his very manhood subtly undermined. And the children, once the immunity of incomprehension passed—what would it be like in a year or so? With his elbows on the table he ate his food brutishly, untasting. There was no hiding the truth—soon there would be gossip in the office and in the town; his wife was a dissolute woman. Dissolute. And he and his children were bound to a future of degradation and slow ruin.

Martin pushed away from the table and stalked into the living room. He followed the lines of a book with his eyes but his mind conjured miserable images: he saw his children drowned in the river, his wife a disgrace on the public street. By bedtime the dull, hard anger was like a weight upon his chest and his feet dragged as he climbed the stairs.

The room was dark except for the shafting light from the half-opened bathroom door. Martin undressed quietly. Little by little, mysteriously, there came in him a change. His wife was asleep, her peaceful respiration sounding gently in the room. Her high-heeled shoes with the carelessly dropped stockings made to him a mute appeal. Her underclothes were flung in disorder on the chair. Martain picked up the girdle and the soft, silk brassière and stood for a moment with them in his hands. For the first time that evening he looked at his wife. His eyes rested on the sweet forehead, the arch of the fine brow. The brow had descended to Marianne, and the tilt at the end of the delicate nose. In his son he could trace the high cheekbones and pointed chin. Her body was full-bosomed, slender and undulant. As Martin watched the tranquil slumber of his wife the ghost of anger vanished. All thoughts of blame or blemish were distant from him now. Martin put out the bathroom light and raised the window. Careful not to awaken Emily he slid into the bed. By moonlight he watched his wife for the last time. His hand sought the adjacent flesh and sorrow paralleled desire in the immense complexity of love.

INTERPRETATION

This story has to do with a not too eventful evening in Suburbia. An office worker comes home to find his wife a little befuddled with drink, his children neglected, and dinner still to cook. The story recounts his reactions through the rest of the evening from his attending to the children to his final turning in for the night. What happens in this story has to do primarily with his shifting emotions: his exasperation at the disordered house, his anger at his wife, his anxiety for his children, his hurt and despair as he thinks of the future, and his final state of mind as he slips into bed. We shall suggest a little later that the story does more than to describe these feelings. If it did no more than to describe the sequence of them, then it might be a sound psychological account, but we could hardly call it a piece of fiction. The claim that it is fiction requires that we raise the question of its significance—its presenting some kind of theme, however indirectly and concretely it may do so.

In any case, the character of Martin Meadows is of first importance in this story. We are not led to think of Martin as a highly sensitive and imaginative man. Our impression is that he is an ordinary man. Yet though we do not associate Martin with intense introspection or with the cultivated sensitivity of the professional artist, the author probably convinces us of the intensity and even delicacy of his feelings. The special quality of the story inheres in this revelation of the range of feelings to be found in an ordinary man. Martin loves his wife, but love is often a very complex thing.

The character of his wife, Emily, is of course also very important in this story. We see her as she appears on this particular evening. But the author has gone further and sketched in a little account of her background with some specific comments on what has happened to her and what has caused her to take refuge in alcohol. But Emily, important as she is for the story, constituting as she does Martin's problem, is still a subordinate character. The focus is kept steadily on Martin himself.

If the story is successful, we must be made to feel that Martin and Emily are believable and that their actions and thoughts, including Martin's final shift in feeling toward his wife, are true to what this pair of people would do and think and feel. Yet, as has been remarked earlier, if the story involves nothing more than this kind of psychological plausibility, it would not be a piece of fiction. What is the story "about"? Does it have any larger significance than the presentation of these two people? This is a question which the student should ponder and for which he should try to devise an answer. But before attempting this larger question, he might try to answer some of the following questions about the development and technique of the story.

1. How do the first two paragraphs of this story point ahead to what is to come? What details suggest Martin's apprehension? Are there any suggestions as to what kind of man he is?

2. Our first direct view of Emily comes only when Martin, having come into the house and having greeted his children, climbs the stairs to speak to his wife. Since the reader begins with Martin in the city, this is a normal sequence. But what advantages, if any, accrue from this postponement. How are we "prepared" for our first sight of Emily?

3. Can you justify the author's summary account of what ails Emily? Is it adequate? Why did she not work it out dramatically and concretely?

4. Is Martin a weak and indulgent man? A strong and competent man? How would you characterize him?

5. We have already read one story that has to do with the return of a husband to his wife in the evening, "A Piece of News." Does "A Domestic Dilemma" have *anything* in common with "A Piece of News"? Does a comparison of the two stories—admittedly so different—throw any light on either of them?

6. Can you justify the ending of the story? Has Martin's final state of mind been sufficiently prepared for? How does the ending affect the total meaning of the story? What, in your opinion, is the meaning?

SECTION IV

What Theme Reveals

IN discussing the stories we have read thus far we have continually referred to the theme, the idea, the meaning. This is natural and inevitable. We cannot very long consider the action or the characters of a story without coming to some concern with theme, for, as we have already insisted, a story, in so far as it is a good story, is an organic unity in which all the elements have vital interrelations. Each element implies the other elements, and implies them in movement toward a significant end.

Now as we turn to a more systematic treatment of theme in fiction, let us review some of our notions. For one thing, the theme of a piece of fiction is not to be thought of as merely the topic with which the story may be taken to concern itself—though the word is sometimes loosely used in this sense. For instance, we can say that two stories soon to be encountered, "The Killers," by Ernest Hemingway, and "I Want to Know Why," by Sherwood Anderson, have the same topic—the topic of growing up, the initiation into manhood. But in the two stories the meaning of the initiation is very different. Or to take another pair, when we come to "Love," by Maupassant, and "Love," by Jesse Stuart, even though the titles proclaim the same topic, and even though there is considerable similarity in treatment, we shall still find significant differences in meaning and differences indeed in the very "feel" of the stories. The theme is what is made of the topic. It is the comment on the topic that is implied in the process of the story.

The theme, furthermore, is not to be confused with any ideas or pieces

of information, however interesting or important, which we may happen
to take away from our reading of a piece of fiction. For instance, Herman
Melville's novel *Moby Dick* gives a full and fascinating account of whaling,
but that information is not to be confused with either the topic or the
theme. The life of whaling is simply the world in which—the background
against which—the human experience works itself out meaningfully.
Though "The Man Who Would be King" tells us much about life in India
in the late nineteenth century, that information is not to be confused with
the theme.

The theme is what a piece of fiction stacks up to. It is the idea, the
significance, the interpretation of persons and events, the pervasive and
unifying view of life which is embodied in the total narrative. It is, as we
have said in our general remarks on plot (pp. 71–84), what we are to
make of the human experience rendered in the story. And what we make
of such human experience always involves, directly or indirectly, some
comment on values in human nature and human conduct, on good and bad,
on the true and the false, some conception of what the human place is in
the world.

This last remark may provoke two objections. Some may feel that it
makes fiction merely a kind of moralizing, with illustrations. And some
may feel that it gives no accommodation to stories that are gay, light-
hearted, and comic. Both of these objections are well taken, and deserve
discussion.

Let us take a somewhat indirect approach to the first objection. When
we read a good piece of fiction, we may be caught by any of a number of
things, in different degrees. We may simply find a character attractive, and
relish that company much as one would relish the company of a person in
real life, for humor, for kindliness, for wit, for wisdom, for any number of
possible qualities. Or we may find our curiosity stimulated by the strange
world of the story—the kind of curiosity evoked by travel books, or travel.
Or we may be held by the suspense of the plot, our anxiety to know what
will come next and who does what. We may, even, be caught by the writer's
own personality, his charm of style and sprightliness of observation on life
and character, or his poetic perceptions. Or we may enjoy daydreaming
into experiences that we can never have in our own humdrum and conventional lives. We may, in fact, be caught by any number of things or
combination of things.

But in the end there is always the question: What does it add up to?
What does it mean? If we do not feel that things have worked themselves
out to that moment of significant stability which we spoke on in connection with plot (p. 81), we are left feeling defrauded and dissatisfied.

One reason for such a feeling of dissatisfaction is our simple human
craving to have things put in order. We like to observe a story working itself out to a unity. Just as we instinctively demand the logic of cause and

effect, the logic of motivation, in fiction, so we demand that there be a logic of theme—a thematic structure into which the various elements are fitted and in terms of which they achieve unity. It is not, in other words, any moralizing aspect of theme that comes first to mind; it is the structural necessity. If there is no satisfactorily developed theme, all our other interests, no matter how intense they may be, tend to evaporate. If we want a story, we are forced by our very psychological make-up to demand a theme: *No theme, no story.*

That is one approach to the objection that our discussion of theme tends to make fiction seem like mere moralizing, with illustrations, like a Sunday School lesson with colored lantern slides. But there is another approach, related but dissimilar. It is best understood by examining the word *illustration* in the sentence above.

Fiction is not illustration, even though sometimes it pretends to be—as "The Man Who Would Be King" pretends to be an illustration of its motto: "Brother to a Prince and fellow to a beggar if he be found worthy." Fiction is not illustration, because with illustration we are always aware that the idea being illustrated comes first, that the content of the illustration is being dictated by the nature of the thing being illustrated. The illustration is an explanation, not a discovery. The illustration has no independent life.

With fiction, in so far as it is successful, the imagination creates a world, characters and events which exist, as it were, in their own right. They live in our imagination. With great masterpieces, this reality is so compelling that it is often closer to us than things we know to be hard, cold facts. Hamlet, as a person, is more vivid to us than George Washington, Herbert Hoover, or the man next door. But even fiction that is merely good, not great, carries with it some degree of this illusion of independent existence.

How does this impression of an independent existence bear on our question of theme? In a manner as simple as this: In a successful piece of fiction, out of this sense of an independent world, as the characters act and are acted upon, as one event leads to another, we become more and more aware of the significance of the whole. That is, we gradually sense a developing theme. We *seem* * to be caught up in a vital process in which meaning emerges from experience—and that is what, in the end, makes our own lives, in so far as we live above the brute level, interesting to us: the sense of deepening discovery, the satisfaction of learning and achieving, the growth of awareness and appreciation, the fuller understanding of our own experience. Fiction, then, is never the "illustration" of an idea. It is a created image of our very life process by which significance emerges from experience.

Let us turn, at long last, to the second objection, the objection that our

---

* We must say *seem* because we are speaking of the finished story, not of the process of writing it, which may have involved a good deal of cold calculation.

emphasis on the serious place of theme in fiction leaves little play for stories that are gay or comic. A full discussion of this objection would take us into a study of the nature of comedy, but it should be enough here to say that we are aware of the gay only by an implied contrast, however remote, with the serious, that the laughter of comedy always has in it some element of escape from the urgency—even the pain—of life, and that even burlesque and slapstick depend on some acceptance of the thing that is being abused and made sport of.

If we look back at the comic stories we have read thus far—say, "De Mortuis" or "The Drunkard"—we shall readily see that always a slight shift of emphasis would plunge us into a world of an entirely different order from that of the present story. Comedy, including even warm humor as well as savage satire, has to do with disappointment and surprises, confusions and miscarriages, the criticism and defeat of aspirations, contrasts of pretensions and reality, failure of expectations, inability to adjust to the changing demands of life. The man with his head in the clouds and a top hat on his head stepping on the banana peel is the image behind all comedy—but the fall that rebukes his vanity may sometimes also break his neck. The distance between the good laugh and the need to call the ambulance is not very great.

The fact of comedy itself, generally considered, implies a view of life—the notion that an awareness of the rough edges of things may lead to laughter, not tears, that the shrewd observation of human frailty may end in tolerance and enjoyment, not anger and disappointment. The comic story starts with a certain bias of interpretation, but that bias does not deny either the structural importance of theme or its importance as a comment on human values. In its own way, the comic story affirms them.

At this point another question may be asked. Since theme is a comment on human values, how can we appreciate a story that has a theme which we cannot accept? There is no use in trying to evade this question by taking refuge in nice generalities, and no use in minimizing its importance or the difficulty of giving an honest and useful answer.

It may be that a roundabout approach gives us the quickest path to an answer. Let us forget fiction altogether, and think of our relations with other people. We live with a variety of people, and with most of them we have, at some point or other, serious differences of opinion, tastes, and values. With Susie Jones we disagree violently on literary matters, and every time we go to a movie with her we have an argument. With John Jacobs we disagree on politics; with Alfred Kobeck, on how to play a hand of bridge; with Jim Simmons, on religion. And we take a very dim view of Mary Moffett's intelligence. But—and here is the point—we may be good friends with all of them. We may recognize in any one of them some particular qualities which we value and enjoy despite disagreements. More importantly, we may recognize an underlying good will, and an honest attempt to make sense of things and to achieve decency. In recognizing these things, we may discover in ourselves some tolerance and some power of sympathetic imagination that enables us to feel ourselves into another person's skin and to understand how the world looks to him. In this process of recognition through imaginative sympathy, we realize that the world is complicated, and that it is the richer for its very complication. We realize too that opinions, tastes, and values which are opposed to each other may each have a place, that there may be more than one answer to a question, and that our own private convictions and dogmatic beliefs may have to be modified.

This is not to be taken as saying that one thing is as good as another. We each have to work out our own scale of values and try to justify it and live by it. But it does mean that when we encounter differences, we must try to understand their nature and then try to find the underlying common ground that makes human respect possible.

But how does this apply to fiction? In this way: We can think of the authors of stories as we think of our friends and associates. We can try to recognize the values that they offer us even when we disagree with them. We can make the effort of imagination necessary to realize the variety and richness of experience which they offer, and in so doing modify our own dogmatisms. We can try to recognize the logic by which a theme unfolds even in a story that at first glance seems antipathetic to us.

What, then, of the common ground? The common ground is the understanding of the fact that, in so far as a theme is coherently developed through a story, we are witnessing and taking part in the great human effort to achieve meaning through experience. And a story, as we have said, gives us an image of our life process—and in that, an enlightening image of ourselves.

We must here be prepared to make a concession. We must simply recognize that some writers, and some stories, offend us at too deep a level. They embody some attitude toward life, some set of values, which denies our own very basis of life. Sometimes we simply may not be able to find the common ground. In a situation like that we are bound to acknowledge the fact and deal with it. We reject the story, just as we would reject a person in real life. But always we should be very careful that we have made the imaginative effort to understand what values may be there, and what common ground might, with more effort, be found.

Furthermore, in the end, we may find that we have rejected the story not because of its theme as such, but because we have found the story unconvincing. The story failed in its logic of motivation, or in its presentation of character, or in the attempt to make the theme develop from the action. Or perhaps we have found the story guilty of sentimentality; that is, the emotional response demanded by the story is not really justified by the events in the story. In other words, we have rejected the story, not because of the theme, taken as a thing in itself, but because the story is incoherent as a story.

This leads us back to our first section (pp. 26–28) where we discussed the truth of correspondence and the truth of coherence. If we reject a story because the theme offends us, we are appealing to the truth of correspondence: the theme does not correspond to what we take to be the truth about life and human values. If we reject a story because it is, as we ordinarily say, unconvincing, we are appealing to the truth of coherence: the story does not hang together in its own terms, and therefore whatever meaning it may claim to possess does not really come out of the experience of the story. Most of our problems with stories have to do with offences against the truth of coherence.

The mention of coherence leads us to the notion that the meaning of a good story is general and pervasive. If a story possesses an organic unity, then all the parts are significant and have some bearing on the total significance. All contribute to the total meaning. We live, of course, in an imperfect world, and no doubt few stories are free of defects. Even many of the best stories reveal some undigested material. Nevertheless, the principle of organic unity is to be stressed in our reading. We ought to assume that a story is coherent until it is proved otherwise. Assuming this coherence, we then try to find what idea, what feeling, what attitude, is consistently developing throughout the story.

We can look at what kind of characters and what kind of world is presented. That is a starting point, for it tells us something of the interest of the writer and his range of experience. We can ask what problems the characters confront, what is at stake for them—or, if the story is one of developing awareness, what discovery is being made. We can look at the pattern of plot and try to see what significant repetitions appear. We can look at the end and ask, first, if it logically follows from the body of the story; and second, what is the intended significance. We can ask what is the tone of the story? Is it comic, ironical, cold and reportorial, pathetic, or what? We can ask if the author has tried to evoke emotional responses for which there is no justification. We can ask about the speech of the characters and the style of the author—are they in keeping with the rest of the story? All in all, we ask how fully and deeply coherent is the story. As we try to answer these questions, we usually find that we have defined the theme, and have accepted or rejected it.

Our examination of the stories to follow is not to be taken as an exercise in moral-hunting. It is not even to be taken, primarily, as an exercise in giving a general statement to the various themes of the stories—though, of course, the attempt to make such general statements is a necessary part of our study. More important than framing general statements are these two considerations:

First, to see how the theme of a story, if it is a good story, *necessarily* develops from the experience as rendered in the story. To do this means that we must inspect the coherence of the story.

Second, to see how the theme is *uniquely* developed, and to do this means that we must try to see how a theme—even though we suppose we may be able to state it in general terms—is, in fact, qualified and modified by the actual treatment in the story, so that what the story "says" finally becomes something more or less unique.

The stories to follow in this section employ various methods in the presentation of their themes. There may be general statement. There may be allegory and symbolism and parable. There may be a realistic dramatic situation. But always we must remember that the total story, including the general atmosphere, is the embodiment of the theme. As we have said in discussing plot (p. 81), we must think of the whole story as an image, however shadowy, of the meaning of experience.

HONORÉ DE BALZAC

Christ in Flanders

AT a time somewhat indeterminate in Brabantine history, connection between the island of Cadzant and the coast of Flanders was kept up by a boat used for passengers to and fro. The capital of the island, Middleburg, afterward so celebrated in the annals of Protestantism, counted then hardly two or three hundred hearths. Rich Ostend was then an unknown harbor, flanked by a village thinly peopled by a few fisherfolk, and poor dealers, and pirates who plied their trade with impunity. Nevertheless, the borough of Ostend, composed of about twenty houses and three hundred cottages, cabins, and hovels—made with the remains of wrecked ships—rejoiced in a governor, a militia, a gallows, a convent, and a burgomaster, in fact, all the institutions of advanced civilization. Who was reigning at that time in Brabant, Belgium, and Flanders? On this point tradition is mute.

Let us admit that this story is strangely imbued with that vagueness, indefiniteness, and love of the marvelous which the favorite orators of Flemish vigils love to intermingle in their legends, as varied in poetry as they are contradictory in detail. Told from age to age, repeated from hearth to hearth, by grandmothers and by storytellers night and day, this chronicle has received each century a different coloring. Like those buildings planned according to the architectural caprice of each epoch, whose dark, crumbling masses are a pleasure to poets alone, this legend would drive commentators, and wranglers over facts, words, and dates, to desperation. The narrator believes in it, as all superstitious souls in Flanders have believed in it, without being for that reason either more learned or more weak-minded. Admitting the impossibility of harmonizing all the different versions, here is the story, stripped perhaps of its romantic naïveté—for this it is impossible to reproduce—but still, with its daring statements disproved by history, and its morality approved by religion, its fantastic flowers of imagination, and hidden sense which the wise can interpret each to his own liking. Let each one seek his pasture herein and take the trouble to separate the good grain from the tares.

The boat which served to carry over the passengers from the island of Cadzant to Ostend was just about to leave the village. Before undoing the iron chain which held his boat to a stone on the little jetty where people embarked, the skipper blew his horn several times to call the loiterers, for this journey was his last. Night was coming on, the last fires of the setting sun scarcely gave enough light to distinguish the coast of Flanders or the tardy passengers on the island wandering along the earthen walls which surrounded the fields or among the tall reeds of the marshes. The boat was full. "What are you waiting for? Let us be off!" they cried. Just then a man appeared a few steps from the jetty. The pilot, who had neither heard nor seen him approaching, was somewhat surprised. The passenger seemed to have risen from the earth on a sudden. He might have been a peasant sleeping in a field, waiting for the hour for starting, whom the horn had wakened up. Was it a thief, or was it someone from the Customs House or police? When he arrived on the jetty to which the boat was moored, seven persons who were standing in the stern hastened to sit down on the benches, in order to have them to themselves and prevent the stranger from seating himself among them. It was a sudden instinctive feeling, one of those aristocratic instincts which suggest themselves to rich people. Four of these personages belonged to the highest nobility of Flanders.

First of all, there was a young cavalier, with two beautiful greyhounds, wearing over his long hair a cap decked with jewels. He clinked his gilded spurs, and now and again curled his mustache, as he cast disdainful looks at the rest of the freight.

Then there was a proud damosel, who carried a falcon on her wrist and spoke only to her mother or to an ecclesiastic of high rank, a relative, no doubt. These persons made as much noise talking together as if they were the only people on the boat. All the same, next to them sat a man of great importance in the country, a fat merchant from Bruges, enveloped in a large mantle. His servant, armed to the teeth, kept by his side two bags full of money. Beside them was a man of science, a doctor of the University of Louvain, with his clerk. These people, who all despised one another, were separated from the bows by the rower's bench.

When the late passenger put his foot into the boat he gave a swift look at the stern, but when he saw no room there he went to seek a place among the people in the bows. It was the poor who sat there. At the sight of a man bareheaded, whose brown cloth coat and fine linen shirt had no ornament, who held in his hand neither hat nor cap, with neither purse nor rapier at his girdle, all took him for a burgomaster—a good and gentle man, like one of those old Flemings whose nature and simple character have been so well rendered by the painters of their country. The poor passengers welcomed the stranger with a respectful demeanor, which excited mocking whispers among the people in the stern. An old soldier, a man of toil and trouble, gave him his place on the bench, and sat himself at the end of the boat, keeping himself steady by putting his feet against one of the transverse beams which knit the planks together like the backbone of a fish.

A young woman, a mother with her little child, who seemed to belong to the working class of Ostend, moved back to make room for the newcomer. In this movement there was no trace either of servility or disdain. It was merely a mark of that kindliness by which the poor, who know so well how to appreciate a service, show their frank and natural disposition —so simple and obvious in the expression of all their qualities, good or bad.

The stranger thanked them with a gesture full of nobility, and sat down between the young mother and the old soldier. Behind him was a peasant with his son, ten years old. A poor old woman, with a wallet almost empty, old and wrinkled, and in rags—a type of misery and neglect— lay in the prow, crouched upon a coil of ropes. One of the rowers, an old sailor, who had known her when she was rich and beautiful, had let her get in for what the people so beautifully call "the love of God." "Thank you kindly, Thomas," the old woman had said; "I will say two *Paters* and two *Aves* for you in my prayers this evening."

The skipper blew his horn once more, looked at the silent country, cast the chain into his boat, ran along the side to the helm, took the tiller, and stood erect; then, having looked at the sky, called out in a loud voice to the rowers, when they were well in the open sea, "Row hard, make haste; the sea smiles evilly—the witch! I feel the swell at the helm and the storm at my wound." These words, spoken in the language of the sea—a tongue only understood of those accustomed to the sound of the waves—gave to the oars a hastened but ever-cadenced movement, as different from the former manner of rowing as the gallop of a horse from its trot. The fine people sitting at the stern took pleasure in seeing the sinuous arms, the bronzed faces with eyes of fire, the distended muscles, and the different human forms working in unison, just to get *them* the quicker over this narrow strait. So far from being sorry for their labor, they pointed out the rowers to each other, and laughed at the grotesque expressions which their exertion printed on their anxious faces. In the prow the soldier, the peasant, and the old woman regarded the mariners with that kind of compassion natural to people who, living by toil, know its hard anguish and feverish fatigue. Besides, being accustomed to life in the open air, they all divined by the look of the sky the danger which threatened them; so *they* were serious. The young mother was rocking her child to sleep, singing to it some old hymn of the church.

"If we *do* get over," said the old soldier to the peasant, "God will have taken a deal of trouble to keep us alive."

"Ah! He is master," said the old woman; "but I think it is His good pleasure to call us to Himself. Do you see that light, there?" and by a gesture of the head she pointed out the setting sun. Bands of fire streaked vividly the brown-red tinted clouds, which seemed just about to unchain a furious wind. The sea gave forth a suppressed murmur, a sort of internal groan, something like the growling of a dog whose anger will not be appeased.

After all Ostend was not far off. Just now the sky and the sea showed one of those sights to which it is impossible for words or painting to give longer duration than they have in reality. Human creations like powerful contrasts, so artists generally demand from nature its most brilliant aspects, despairing perhaps to be able to render the great and beautiful poetry of her ordinary appearance, although the human soul is often as profoundly moved by calm as by motion, by the silence as much as by the storm.

There was one moment when everyone on the boat was silent and gazed on the sea and sky, whether from presentiment or in obedience to that religious melancholy which comes over nearly all of us at the hour of prayer, at the fall of day, at the moment when nature is silent and the bells speak. The sea cast up a faint, white glimmer, but changing like the color of steel; the sky was mostly gray; in the west, long, narrow spaces looked like waves of blood, whereas in the east, glittering lines, marked as by a fine pencil, were separated from one another by clouds, folded like the wrinkles on an old man's forehead. Thus the sea and the sky formed a neutral background, everything in half tints, which made the fires of the setting sun glare ominously. The face of nature inspired a feeling of terror. If it is allowable to interweave the daring hyperboles of the people into the written language, one might repeat what the soldier said, "Time is rolling away," or what the peasant answered, that the sky had the look of a hangman. All of a sudden the wind rose in the west, and the skipper, who never ceased to watch the sea, seeing it swell toward the horizon, cried, "Ho, ho!" At this cry the sailors stopped immediately, and let their oars float.

"The skipper is right," said Thomas. The boat, borne on the top of a huge wave, seemed to be descending to the bottom of the gaping sea. At this extraordinary movement and this sudden rage of the ocean the people in the stern turned pale, and gave a terrible cry, "We perish!"

"Not yet," answered the skipper quietly. At this moment the clouds were rent in twain by the force of the wind exactly above the boat. The gray masses spread out with ominous quickness from east to west, and the twilight, falling straight down through a rent made by the storm wind, rendered visible every face. The passengers, the rich and the noble, the sailors and the poor, all stopped one moment in astonishment at the aspect of the last comer. His golden hair, parted in the middle on his tranquil, serene forehead, fell in many curls on his shoulders, and outlined against the gray sky a face sublime in its gentleness, radiant with divine love. He did not despise death; he was certain not to perish. But if at first the people at the stern had forgotten for an instant the tempest whose implacable fury menaced them, they soon returned to their selfish sentiments and life-long habits.

"It's lucky for him, that dolt of a burgomaster, that he does not know the danger we are all in. There he stands like a dog, and doesn't seem to mind dying," said the doctor.

Hardly had he completed this judicious remark when the tempest unchained its legions; wind blew from every side, the boat spun round like a top, and the sea swamped it.

"Oh, my poor child! my child! who will save my child?" cried the mother, in a heartrending voice.

"You yourself," replied the stranger. The sound of this voice penetrated the heart of the young woman and put hope therein. She heard this sweet word, in spite of the raging of the storm, in spite of the shrieks of the passengers.

"Holy Virgin of Perpetual Succor, who are at Antwerp, I promise you twenty pounds of wax and a statue if you will only get me out of this," cried the merchant, falling on his knees upon his bags of gold.

"The Virgin is no more at Antwerp than she is here," replied the doctor.

"She is in heaven," said a voice, which seemed to come forth from the sea.

"Who spoke?"

"The devil," said the servant; "he's mocking the Virgin of Antwerp."

"Shut up with your blessed Virgin," said the skipper to the passengers; "take hold of the bowls and help me get the water out of the boat. As to you," he continued, addressing the sailors, "row hard, we have a moment's grace, and in the devil's name, who has left you in this world until now, let us be our own Providence. This little strip of water is horribly dangerous, I know from thirty years' experience. Is this evening the first time I have had a storm to deal with?" Then standing at the helm, the skipper continued to look alternately at the boat, the sea, and the sky.

"The skipper mocks at everything," said Thomas in a low voice.

"Will God let *us* die with these wretched people?" asked the proud damosel of the handsome cavalier.

"No! no! Noble damsel, listen to me." He put his arm round her waist, and spoke in her ear. "I can swim—don't say anything about it; I will take you by your beautiful hair and bring you safely to the shore; but I can save you only."

The damosel looked at her old mother; the dame was on her knees asking absolution from the bishop, who was not listening to her. The cavalier read in the eyes of his beautiful mistress some faint sentiment of filial piety, so he said to her in a low voice, "Submit yourself to the will of God; if He wishes to call your mother to Himself, it will doubtless be for her happiness—in the other world," he added, in a voice still lower, "and for ours in this."

The dame Rupelmonde possessed seven fiefs, besides the barony of Gâvres. The damosel listened to the voice of life, to the interests of love, speaking through the mouth of the handsome adventurer, a young miscreant, who haunted churches, seeking for prey—either a girl to marry or else good ready money.

The bishop blessed the waves and ordered them to be calm, not knowing exactly what to do; he was thinking of his concubine awaiting him with a delicate feast, perhaps at this moment in her bath perfuming herself, or arraying herself in velvet, and fastening on her necklaces and jewels. So far from thinking of the powers of the Church, and consoling these Christians, and exhorting them to trust in God, the perverse bishop mingled worldly regrets and words of lust with the sacred words of the Breviary.

The light, which lit up the pale faces, showed all their varying expressions, when the boat was borne up into the air by a wave, or cast down to the bottom of the abyss; then, shaken like a frail leaf, a plaything of the autumn wind, it cracked its shell, and seemed nigh to break altogether. Then there were horrible cries alternating with awful silence.

The demeanor of the people seated in the prow of the boat contrasted singularly with that of the rich and powerful in the stern. The young mother strained her child to her bosom every time that the waves threatened to engulf the frail bark; but she held to the hope with which the words of the stranger had filled her heart: each time she turned her eyes toward this man she drank in from his face a new faith, the strong faith of a weak woman, the faith of a mother. Living by the divine word, the word of love, which had gone forth from this man, the simple creature awaited trustfully the fulfillment of the sort of promise he had given her, and scarcely feared the tempest any more. Sticking to the side of the boat, the soldier ceased not to contemplate this singular being, on whose impassibility he sought to model his own rough, tanned face, bringing into play all his intelligence and strength of will, whose powerful springs had not been vitiated in the course of a passive mechanical life. He was emulous to show himself tranquil and calm, after the manner of this superior courage; he ended by identifying himself in some measure with the secret principle of its interior power. Then his imagination became an instinctive fanaticism, a love without limit, a faith in this man, like that enthusiasm which soldiers have for their commander when he is a man of power, surrounded with the glory of victories, marching in the midst of the splendid prestige of genius. The poor old woman said in a low voice, "Ah! what a miserable sinner I am! Have I not suffered enough to expiate the pleasures of my youth? Miserable one, why hast thou led the gay life of a Frenchwoman? Why hast thou consumed the goods of God with the people of the Church, the goods of the poor 'twixt the drink shop and the pawn shop? Ah! how wicked I was! Oh! my God! my God! let me finish my hell in this world of misery. Holy Virgin, Mother of God, take pity on me."

"Console yourself, mother, God is not a Lombard; although I have killed here and there good people and wicked, I do not fear for the resurrection."

"Ah! Sir, how happy they are, those beautiful ladies who are near the bishop, holy man!" the old woman went on; "they will have absolution from their sins. Oh! if I could only hear the voice of a priest saying to me, 'Your sins are forgiven you,' I could believe him."

The stranger turned toward her, and his look, full of charity, made her tremble. "Have faith," he said, "and you will be saved."

"May God reward you, good sir," she answered. "If you speak truly, I will go for you and for me on a pilgrimage to Our Lady of Loretto, barefooted."

The two peasants, father and son, remained silent, resigned, and submitting to the will of God, as people accustomed to follow instinctively, like animals, the convulsions of nature.

So on one side there were riches, pride, knowledge, debauchery, crime, all human society such as it is made by arts, thought, and education, the world and its laws; but also on this side, only shrieks, terror, the struggles of a thousand conflicting feelings, with horrible doubt—naught but the anguish of fear. And, towering above these, one powerful man, the skipper of the boat, doubting nothing, the chief, the fatalist king, making his own Providence, crying out for bailing bowls and not on the Virgin to save him, defying the storm, and wrestling with the sea, body to body.

At the other end of the boat, the weak: The mother, holding to her bosom a little child, who smiled at the storm. A wanton once gay, now given over to horrible remorse. A soldier, scarred with wounds, without other reward than his mutilated life, as a price for indefatigable devotion— he had hardly a morsel of bread, steeped in tears; all the same, he laughed at everything, and marched on without care, happy when he could drown his glory at the bottom of a pot of beer, or was telling stories thereof to wondering children; he commended gaily to God the care of his future. Lastly, two peasants, people of toil and weariness, labor incarnate, the work on which the world lives; these simple creatures were guileless of thought and its treasures, but ready to lose themselves utterly in a belief; having a more robust faith, in that they had never discussed or analyzed it; virgin natures, in whom conscience had remained pure and feeling strong. Contrition, misery, love, work had exercised, purified, concentrated, disculpated their will, the only thing which in man resembles that which sages call the soul.

When the boat, piloted by the marvelous dexterity of the skipper, came almost in view of Ostend, fifty paces from the shore, it was driven back by the convulsion of the storm, and suddenly began to sink. The stranger with the light upon his face then said to this little world of sorrow, "Those who have faith shall be saved; let them follow me." This man stood up and walked with a firm step on the waves. At once the young mother took her child in her arms and walked with him on the sea. The soldier suddenly stood at attention, saying in his rough language, "By my pipe! I follow you to the devil." Then, without seeming astonished, he marched on the sea.

The old prostitute, believing in the omnipotence of God, followed the man, and walked on the sea. The two peasants said, "As they are walking on the sea, why should not *we?*" So they got up and hastened after the others, walking on the sea.

Thomas wished to do likewise; but his faith wavered, and he fell several times into the sea, but got out again; and after three failures he too walked upon the sea.

The daring pilot stuck like a leech to the bottom of his boat. The merchant had faith, and had risen, but he wanted to take his gold with him, and his gold took him to the bottom of the sea. Mocking at the charlatan and the imbeciles who listened to him, at the moment when he saw the stranger proposing to the passengers to walk on the sea, the man of science began to laugh, and was swallowed up in the ocean. The damosel was drawn down into the abyss by her lover. The bishop and the old lady went to the bottom, heavy with sin perhaps, heavier still with unbelief and confidence in false images; heavy with devotional practices, light of alms and true religion.

The faithful troop, who trod with firm, dry feet on the plain of the raging waters, heard around them the horrible howling of the storm; great sheets of water broke in their path; irresistible force rent the ocean in twain. Through the mist these faithful ones perceived on the shore a little feeble light, which flickered in the window of a fisherman's cabin. Each one as he marched bravely toward this light seemed to hear his neighbor crying through the roaring sea, "Courage!" Nevertheless, absorbed each in his own danger, no one said a single word. And so they reached the shore. When they were all seated at the hearth of the fisherman, they sought in vain the guide who had a light upon his face. From his seat upon the summit of a rock, at the base of which the hurricane had cast the pilot clinging to his plank with all the strength of a sailor in the throes of death, the MAN descended, picked up the shipwrecked man almost dashed to pieces; then he said, as he held out a helping hand over his head, "It is well this once, but do as thou *hast* done no more; the example would be too bad." He took the mariner on his shoulders, and carried him to the fisherman's cottage. He knocked for the unfortunate man, so that someone would open the door of this humble refuge to him; then the Savior disappeared.

In this place the sailors built the Convent of Mercy, where were long to be seen the prints that the feet of JESUS CHRIST had, it was said, left on the sand.

Afterward, when the French entered Belgium, some monks took away with them this precious relic, the testimony of the last visit JESUS ever paid to the earth.

INTERPRETATION

In previous sections, we have already read stories which illustrate a variety of ways in which fiction may embody its idea, or theme. The present story shows one of the simplest of all methods. It is a method similar to that found in fables and parables. In a parable, for instance, the idea, or truth, is presented by a simple narrative in which the events, persons, and the like, of the narrative are understood as being directly equivalent to elements involved in the statement of the truth. At this point it might be well to turn back to p. 73 and reread the parable of the sower which we quoted there from St. Mark's Gospel. The events in such a parable are, as we saw, summarized as economically as possible. Actually the parable is a kind of metaphor or image, of a basic truth which in reality may assume many forms. For example, the "affliction or persecution" which "ariseth for the word's sake" might assume many forms, and the reaction of the person whose heart, like the stony ground, could give no deep root to the seed, might take many different forms. Ordinarily, fiction is concerned with these specific, individual forms—character, event, experience—and does not content itself with presenting merely the basic image as detached from the details of the particular instance. The story of a man whose heart was like stony ground and whose faith withered under the scorching sun of persecution would be presented as the story of a particular man, living in a particular place and time. The psychological stages in the struggle between faith and persecution would be indicated.

But despite the fact that ordinary fiction, as contrasted with parable or fable, is intensely concerned with specific persons and the circumstantiality of experience, all fiction implies a meaningfulness beyond the particular instances which it presents. The meanings involved in characters and events can be extended to apply to other characters and events. The problems and issues and decisions involved in a particular piece of fiction are not limited to that situation and those persons. For example, in "War," by Pirandello, the conflict between the attitude of the fat woman and that of the old man does not appear, in life, merely in the case of persons whose sons are in an army. It appears in all cases of grief and bereavement. And the pathetic isolation of the cabdriver in "The Lament" can be observed in all sorts and conditions of people.

But the way in which fiction embodies its meaning will vary from story to story. Some stories, like "The Lottery," will approach the method of the parable, in that only the aspect of the characters and events which is directly involved in the meaning will be presented; there will not be, in such cases, much circumstantiality, for the character, or event, tends to "stand for something," for an idea, rather than to be fully developed as an individual person or as a particular event with its own complications. Such a story tends to be *allegorical* (see Glossary). Usually, such stories are relatively simple, because the complexities of individual character and particular event are purged away; once one has grasped the key idea everything falls into its pattern. But in some stories of this general type, such as "The Killing of the Dragon," by Buzzati, which we shall come to later (p. 482), there is great complication and obscurity because the idea behind the allegory is a complicated one and because the "key" is difficult to come by.

At the other extreme we find stories in which the individual and circumstantial aspects are so strongly emphasized that we do not discover any point-to-point equivalents as in fables, parables, and allegories. In such cases the meaning is more generalized. We "get the drift" toward the basic idea, as it were, but many particular events or aspects of character may serve no other purpose than to convince us of the reality of a person or situation. For example, in "Old Red," when the old man goes fishing on the pond, the action is simply in line with the old man's passion for sport, and has no allegorical meaning—though it does carry a general import for the theme. We finally grasp the conflict between old Mister Maury and the world, not through any special individual event, but through a patterning of events which, in themselves, might be ordinary and meaningless enough. The story "Old Red" does conclude with a symbol which points up the theme, the symbol of the fox, but many stories do not depart from the realistic treatment; in such cases we simply follow the pattern of event and of motivation to an understanding of the idea; we simply "get the general drift."

In "Christ in Flanders," however, we have a story which approaches the method of the parable. The persons are presented only in so far as some one aspect of character is involved in the meaning. For instance, the merchant is fat and has two large money bags guarded by an armed servant. The man of science laughs at the stranger's preposterous suggestion that the passengers walk on the sea. The pretty damosel, with the falcon on her wrist, hearkens to the whispered temptation of the cavalier. The old soldier is a little more fully presented, but even in his case we know merely the central fact, the "key" trait, of the character. We are given, in each case, just the aspect of character which means salvation or damnation in the shipwreck, the crucial trait. Thus, the representation of character is simplified to a point where we have little more than a series of equivalents, almost as strict as in allegory: the man of science is pride of intellect; the soldier, fidelity and courage; the damosel and cavalier, pleasure; the merchant, avarice; and so on. Finally, the boatload of people seems to be an image of the world, the high and the low, all confronted by the fact of death.

1. What is the significance of the first two paragraphs of the story? What does the author gain, if anything, by not plunging immediately into the narrative with the third paragraph?

2. What is the basic theme of the story? What are the subsidiary themes associated with this basic theme?

3. Why does Jesus save the skipper, who had not obeyed His command?

GUY DE MAUPASSANT

Love: Three Pages from a Sportsman's Book

I HAVE just read among the general news in one of the papers a drama of passion. He killed her and then he killed himself, so he must have loved her. What matters He or She? Their love alone matters to me, and it does not interest me because it moves me or astonishes me or because it softens me or makes me think, but because it recalls to my mind a remembrance of my youth, a strange recollection of a hunting adventure where Love appeared to me, as the Cross appeared to the early Christians, in the midst of the heavens.

I was born with all the instincts and the senses of primitive man, tempered by the arguments and the restraints of a civilized being. I am passionately fond of shooting, yet the sight of the wounded animal, of the blood on its feathers and on my hands, affects my heart so as almost to make it stop.

That year the cold weather set in suddenly toward the end of autumn, and I was invited by one of my cousins, Karl de Rauville, to go with him and shoot ducks on the marshes at daybreak.

My cousin was a jolly fellow of forty with red hair, very stout and bearded, a country gentleman, an amiable semibrute of a happy disposition and endowed with that Gallic wit which makes even mediocrity agreeable. He lived in a house, half farmhouse, half chateau, situated in a broad valley through which a river ran. The hills right and left were covered with woods, old manorial woods where magnificent trees still remained and where the rarest feathered game in that part of France was to be found. Eagles were shot there occasionally, and birds of passage, such as rarely venture into our overpopulated part of the country, invariably lighted amid these giant oaks as if they knew or recognized some little corner of a primeval forest which had remained there to serve them as a shelter during these short nocturnal halts.

In the valley there were large meadows watered by trenches and separated by hedges; then, further on, the river, which up to that point had been kept between banks, expanded into a vast marsh. That marsh was the best shooting ground I ever saw. It was my cousin's chief care, and he kept it as a preserve. Through the rushes that covered it, and made it rustling and rough, narrow passages had been cut, through which the flat-bottomed boats, impelled and steered by poles, passed along silently over dead water, brushing up against the reeds and making the swift fish take refuge in the weeds and the wild fowl, with their pointed black heads, dive suddenly.

I am passionately fond of the water: of the sea, though it is too vast, too full of movement, impossible to hold; of the rivers which are so beautiful but which pass on and flee away; and above all of the marshes, where the whole unknown existence of aquatic animals palpitates. The marsh is an entire world in itself on the world of earth—a different world which has its own life, its settled inhabitants and its passing travelers, its voices, its noises and above all its mystery. Nothing is more impressive, nothing more disquieting, more terrifying occasionally, than a fen. Why should a vague terror hang over these low plains covered with water? Is it the low rustling of the rushes, the strange will-o'-the-wisp lights, the silence which prevails on calm nights, the still mists which hang over the surface like a shroud; or is it the almost inaudible splashing, so slight and so gentle, yet sometimes more terrifying than the cannons of men or the thunders of the skies,

which make these marshes resemble countries one has dreamed of, terrible
countries holding an unknown and dangerous secret?

No, something else belongs to it—another mystery, perhaps the mystery of the creation itself! For was it not in stagnant and muddy water, amid the heavy humidity of moist land under the heat of the sun, that the first germ of life pulsated and expanded to the day?

I arrived at my cousin's in the evening. It was freezing hard enough to split the stones.

During dinner, in the large room whose sideboards, walls and ceiling were covered with stuffed birds with wings extended or perched on branches to which they were nailed—hawks, herons, owls, nightjars, buzzards, tercels, vultures, falcons—my cousin, who, dressed in a sealskin jacket, himself resembled some strange animal from a cold country, told me what preparations he had made for that same night.

We were to start at half-past three in the morning so as to arrive at the place which he had chosen for our watching place at about half-past four. On that spot a hut had been built of lumps of ice so as to shelter us somewhat from the trying wind which precedes daybreak, a wind so cold as to tear the flesh like a saw, cut it like the blade of a knife, prick it like a poisoned sting, twist it like a pair of pincers, and burn it like fire.

My cousin rubbed his hands. "I have never known such a frost," he said; "it is already twelve degrees below zero at six o'clock in the evening."

I threw myself onto my bed immediately after we had finished our meal and went to sleep by the light of a bright fire burning in the grate.

At three o'clock he woke me. In my turn I put on a sheepskin and found my cousin Karl covered with a bearskin. After having each swallowed two cups of scalding coffee, followed by glasses of liqueur brandy, we started, accompanied by a gamekeeper and our dogs, Plongeon and Pierrot.

From the first moment that I got outside I felt chilled to the very marrow. It was one of those nights on which the earth seems dead with cold. The frozen air becomes resisting and palpable, such pain does it cause; no breath of wind moves it, it is fixed and motionless; it bites you, pierces through you, dries you, kills the trees, the plants, the insects, the small birds themselves, who fall from the branches onto the hard ground and become stiff themselves under the grip of the cold.

The moon, which was in her last quarter and was inclining all to one side, seemed fainting in the midst of space, so weak that she was unable to wane, forced to stay up yonder, seized and paralyzed by the severity of the weather. She shed a cold mournful light over the world, that dying and wan light which she gives us every month at the end of her period.

Karl and I walked side by side, our backs bent, our hands in our pockets and our guns under our arms. Our boots, which were wrapped in wool so that we might be able to walk without slipping on the frozen river, made no sound, and I looked at the white vapor which our dogs' breath made.

We were soon on the edge of the marsh and entered one of the lanes of dry rushes which ran through the low forest.

Our elbows, which touched the long ribbonlike leaves, left a slight noise behind us, and I was seized, as I had never been before, by the powerful and singular emotion which marshes cause in me. This one was dead, dead from cold, since we were walking on it in the middle of its population of dried rushes.

Suddenly, at the turn of one of the lanes, I perceived the ice hut which had been constructed to shelter us. I went in, and as we had nearly an hour to wait before the wandering birds would awake I rolled myself up in my rug in order to try and get warm. Then, lying on my back, I began to look at the misshapen moon, which had four horns through the vaguely transparent walls of this polar house. But the frost of the frozen marshes, the cold of these walls, the cold from the firmament penetrated me so terribly that I began to cough. My cousin Karl became uneasy.

"No matter if we do not kill much today," he said. "I do not want you to catch cold; we will light a fire." And he told the gamekeeper to cut some rushes.

We made a pile in the middle of our hut, which had a hole in the middle of the roof to let out the smoke, and when the red flames rose up to the clear crystal blocks, they began to melt, gently, imperceptibly, as if they were sweating. Karl, who had remained outside, called out to me: "Come and look here!" I went out of the hut and remained struck with astonishment. Our hut, in the shape of a cone, looked like an enormous diamond with a heart of fire which had been suddenly planted there in the midst of the frozen water of the marsh. And inside we saw two fantastic forms, those of our dogs, who were warming themselves at the fire.

But a peculiar cry, a lost, a wandering cry, passed over our heads, and the light from our hearth showed us the wild birds. Nothing moves one so much as the first clamor of a life which one does not see, which passes through the somber air so quickly and so far off, just before the first streak of a winter's day appears on the horizon. It seems to me, at this glacial hour of dawn, as if that passing cry which is carried away by the wings of a bird is the sigh of a soul from the world!

"Put out the fire," said Karl; "it is getting daylight."

The sky was, in fact, beginning to grow pale, and the flights of ducks made long rapid streaks which were soon obliterated on the sky.

A stream of light burst out into the night; Karl had fired, and the two dogs ran forward.

And then nearly every minute now he, now I, aimed rapidly as soon as the shadow of a flying flock appeared above the rushes. And Pierrot and

Plongeon, out of breath but happy, retrieved the bleeding birds whose eyes still, occasionally, looked at us.

The sun had risen, and it was a bright day with a blue sky, and we were thinking of taking our departure, when two birds with extended necks and outstretched wings glided rapidly over our heads. I fired, and one of them fell almost at my feet. It was a teal with a silver breast, and then, in the blue space above me, I heard a voice, the voice of a bird. It was a short, repeated heart-rending lament; and the bird, the little animal that had been spared, began to turn round in the blue sky over our heads, looking at its dead companion which I was holding in my hand.

Karl was on his knees, his gun to his shoulder, watching it eagerly until it should be within shot. "You have killed the duck," he said, "and the drake will not fly away."

He certainly did not fly away; he circled over our heads continually and continued his cries. Never have any groans of suffering pained me so much as that desolate appeal, as that lamentable reproach of this poor bird which was lost in space.

Occasionally he took flight under the menace of the gun which followed his movements and seemed ready to continue his flight alone, but as he could not make up his mind to this he returned to find his mate.

"Leave her on the ground," Karl said to me; "he will come within shot by and by." And he did indeed come near us, careless of danger, infatuated by his animal love, by his affection for his mate which I had just killed.

Karl fired, and it was as if somebody had cut the string which held the bird suspended. I saw something black descend, and I heard the noise of a fall among the rushes. And Pierrot brought it to me.

I put them—they were already cold—into the same gamebag, and I returned to Paris the same evening.

INTERPRETATION

1. State the theme of this story.

2. Now that you have read the story, what do you make of the first paragraph? Why does the story interest the narrator?

3. What is the significance of the second paragraph? What conflict is there in the story?

4. Does the characterization of the cousin serve any purpose in relation to the theme?

5. What is the value, if any, of the long atmospheric description of the marshes?

6. What do you make of the last sentence of the story?

JESSE STUART

Love

YESTERDAY when the bright sun blazed down on the wilted corn my father and I walked around the edge of the new ground to plan a fence. The cows kept coming through the chestnut oaks on the cliff and running over the young corn. They bit off the tips of the corn and trampled down the stubble.

My father walked in the cornbalk. Bob, our Collie, walked in front of my father. We heard a ground squirrel whistle down over the bluff among the dead treetops at the clearing's edge. "Whoop, take him, Bob," said my father. He lifted up a young stalk of corn, with wilted dried roots, where the ground squirrel had dug it up for the sweet grain of corn left on its tender roots. This has been a dry spring and the corn has kept well in the earth where the grain has sprouted. The ground squirrels love this corn. They dig up rows of it and eat the sweet grains. The young corn stalks are killed and we have to replant the corn.

I can see my father keep sicking Bob after the ground squirrel. He jumped over the corn rows. He started to run toward the ground squirrel. I, too, started running toward the clearing's edge where Bob was jumping and barking. The dust flew in tiny swirls behind our feet. There was a cloud of dust behind us.

"It's a big bull blacksnake," said my father. "Kill him, Bob! Kill him, Bob!"

Bob was jumping and snapping at the snake so as to make it strike and throw itself off guard. Bob had killed twenty-eight copperheads this spring. He knows how to kill a snake. He doesn't rush to do it. He takes his time and does the job well.

"Let's don't kill the snake," I said. "A blacksnake is a harmless snake. It kills poison snakes. It kills the copperhead. It catches more mice from the fields than a cat."

I could see the snake didn't want to fight the dog. The snake wanted to get away. Bob wouldn't let it. I wondered why it was crawling toward a heap of black loamy earth at the bench of the hill. I wondered why it had come from the chestnut oak sprouts and the matted greenbriars on the cliff. I looked as the snake lifted its pretty head in response to one of Bob's jumps. "It's not a bull blacksnake," I said. "It's a she-snake. Look at the white on her throat."

293

"A snake is an enemy to me," my father snapped. "I hate a snake. Kill it, Bob. Go in there and get that snake and quit playing with it!"

Bob obeyed my father. I hated to see him take this snake by the throat. She was so beautifully poised in the sunlight. Bob grabbed the white patch on her throat. He cracked her long body like an ox whip in the wind. He cracked it against the wind only. The blood spurted from her fine-curved throat. Something hit against my legs like pellets. Bob threw the snake down. I looked to see what had struck my legs. It was snake eggs. Bob had slung them from her body. She was going to the sand heap to lay her eggs, where the sun is the setting-hen that warms them and hatches them.

Bob grabbed her body there on the earth where the red blood was running down on the gray-piled loam. Her body was still writhing in pain. She acted like a greenweed held over a new-ground fire. Bob slung her viciously many times. He cracked her limp body against the wind. She was now limber as a shoestring in the wind. Bob threw her riddled body back on the sand. She quivered like a leaf in the lazy wind, then her riddled body lay perfectly still. The blood colored the loamy earth around the snake.

"Look at the eggs, won't you?" said my father. We counted thirty-seven eggs. I picked an egg up and held it in my hand. Only a minute ago there was life in it. It was an immature seed. It would not hatch. Mother sun could not incubate it on the warm earth. The egg I held in my hand was almost the size of a quail's egg. The shell on it was thin and tough and the egg appeared under the surface to be a watery egg.

"Well, Bob, I guess you see now why this snake couldn't fight," I said. "It is life. Weaker devour the stronger even among human beings. Dog kills snake. Snake kills birds. Birds kill the butterflies. Man conquers all. Man, too, kills for sport."

Bob was panting. He walked ahead of us back to the house. His tongue was out of his mouth. He was tired. He was hot under his shaggy coat of hair. His tongue nearly touched the dry dirt and white flecks of foam dripped from it. We walked toward the house. Neither my father nor I spoke. I still thought about the dead snake. The sun was going down over the chestnut ridge. A lark was singing. It was late for a lark to sing. The red evening clouds floated above the pine trees on our pasture hill. My father stood beside the path. His black hair was moved by the wind. His face was red in the blue wind of day. His eyes looked toward the sinking sun.

"And my father hates a snake," I thought.

I thought about the agony women know of giving birth. I thought about how they will fight to save their children. Then, I thought of the snake. I thought it was silly for me to think such thoughts.

This morning my father and I got up with the chickens. He says one has to get up with the chickens to do a day's work. We got the posthole digger, ax, spud, measuring pole and the mattock. We started for the clearing's edge. Bob didn't go along.

The dew was on the corn. My father walked behind with the posthole digger across his shoulder. I walked in front. The wind was blowing. It was a good morning wind to breathe and a wind that makes one feel like he can get under the edge of a hill and heave the whole hill upside down.

I walked out the corn row where we had come yesterday afternoon. I looked in front of me. I saw something. I saw it move. It was moving like a huge black rope winds around a windlass. "Steady," I says to my father. "Here is the bull blacksnake." He took one step up beside me and stood. His eyes grew wide apart.

"What do you know about this," he said.

"You have seen the bull blacksnake now," I said. "Take a good look at him! He is lying beside his dead mate. He has come to her. He, perhaps, was on her trail yesterday."

The male snake had trailed her to her doom. He had come in the night, under the roof of stars, as the moon shed rays of light on the quivering clouds of green. He had found his lover dead. He was coiled beside her, and she was dead.

The bull blacksnake lifted his head and followed us as we walked around the dead snake. He would have fought us to his death. He would have fought Bob to his death. "Take a stick," said my father, "and throw him over the hill so Bob won't find him. Did you ever see anything to beat that? I've heard they'd do that. But this is my first time to see it." I took a stick and threw him over the bank into the dewy sprouts on the cliff.

INTERPRETATION

1. This story is clearly very similar to "Love," by Maupassant, but the general "feel" of the treatment is different. What difference do you think this makes in the meaning?

2. Wherein does the conflict lie in this story?

3. What change, if any, comes about in the story?

4. Is there any value in having the narrator? If the story were told in the third person what problems of exposition might arise that do not now appear?

ERNEST HEMINGWAY

The Killers

THE door of Henry's lunchroom opened and two men came in. They sat down at the counter.

"What's yours?" George asked them.

"I don't know," one of the men said. "What do you want to eat, Al?"

"I don't know," said Al. "I don't know what I want to eat."

Outside it was getting dark. The street light came on outside the window. The two men at the counter read the menu. From the other end of the counter Nick Adams watched them. He had been talking to George when they came in.

"I'll have a roast pork tenderloin with apple sauce and mashed potatoes," the first man said.

"It isn't ready yet."

"What the hell do you put it on the card for?"

"That's the dinner," George explained. "You can get that at six o'clock."

George looked at the clock on the wall behind the counter.

"It's five o'clock."

"The clock says twenty minutes past five," the second man said.

"It's twenty minutes fast."

"Oh, to hell with the clock," the first man said. "What have you got to eat?"

"I can give you any kind of sandwiches," George said. "You can have ham and eggs, bacon and eggs, liver and bacon, or a steak."

"Give me chicken croquettes with green peas and cream sauce and mashed potatoes."

"That's the dinner."

"Everything we want's the dinner, eh? That's the way you work it."

"I can give you ham and eggs, bacon and eggs, liver—"

"I'll take ham and eggs," the man called Al said. He wore a derby hat and a black overcoat buttoned across the chest. His face was small and white and he had tight lips. He wore a silk muffler and gloves.

"Give me bacon and eggs," said the other man. He was about the same size as Al. Their faces were different, but they were dressed like twins. Both wore overcoats too tight for them. They sat leaning forward, their elbows on the counter.

"Got anything to drink?" Al asked.

"Silver beer, bevo, ginger ale," George said.

"I mean you got anything to *drink?*"

"Just those I said."

"This is a hot town," said the other. "What do they call it?"

"Summit."

"Ever hear of it?" Al asked his friend.

"No," said the friend.

"What do you do here nights?" Al asked.

"They eat the dinner," his friend said. "They all come here and eat the big dinner."

"That's right," George said.

"So you think that's right?" Al asked George.

"Sure."

"You're a pretty bright boy, aren't you?"

"Sure," said George.

"Well, you're not," said the other little man. "Is he, Al?"

"He's dumb," said Al. He turned to Nick. "What's your name?"

"Adams."

"Another bright boy," Al said. "Ain't he a bright boy, Max?"

"The town's full of bright boys," Max said.

George put the two platters, one of ham and eggs, the other of bacon and eggs, on the counter. He set down two side dishes of fried potatoes and closed the wicket into the kitchen.

"Which is yours?" he asked Al.

"Don't you remember?"

"Ham and eggs."

"Just a bright boy," Max said. He leaned forward and took the ham and eggs. Both men ate with their gloves on. George watched them eat.

"What are *you* looking at?" Max looked at George.

"Nothing."

"The hell you were. You were looking at me."

"Maybe the boy meant it for a joke, Max," Al said.

George laughed.

"*You* don't have to laugh," Max said to him. "*You* don't have to laugh at all, see?"

"All right," said George.

"So he thinks it's all right." Max turned to Al. "He thinks it's all right. That's a good one."

"Oh, he's a thinker," Al said. They went on eating.

"What's the bright boy's name down the counter?" Al asked Max.

"Hey, bright boy," Max said to Nick. "You go around on the other side of the counter with your boy friend."

"What's the idea?" Nick asked.

"There isn't any idea."

"You better go around, bright boy," Al said. Nick went around behind the counter.

"What's the idea?" George asked.

"None of your damn business," Al said. "Who's out in the kitchen?"

"The nigger."

"What do you mean the nigger?"

"The nigger that cooks."

"Tell him to come in."

"What's the idea?"

"Tell him to come in."

"Where do you think you are?"

"We know damn well where we are," the man called Max said, "Do we look silly?"

"You talk silly," Al said to him. "What the hell do you argue with this kid for? Listen," he said to George, "tell the nigger to come out here."

"What are you going to do to him?"

"Nothing. Use your head, bright boy. What would we do to a nigger?"

George opened the slit that opened back into the kitchen. "Sam," he called. "Come in here a minute."

The door to the kitchen opened and the nigger came in. "What was it?" he asked. The two men at the counter took a look at him.

"All right, nigger. You stand right there," Al said.

Sam, the nigger, standing in his apron, looked at the two men sitting at the counter. "Yes, sir," he said. Al got down from his stool.

"I'm going back to the kitchen with the nigger and bright boy," he said. "Go on back to the kitchen, nigger. You go with him, bright boy." The little man walked after Nick and Sam, the cook, back into the kitchen. The door shut after them. The man called Max sat at the counter opposite George. He didn't look at George but looked in the mirror that ran along back of the counter. Henry's had been made over from a saloon into a lunch counter.

"Well, bright boy," Max said, looking into the mirror, "why don't you say something?"

"What's it all about?"

"Hey, Al," Max called, "bright boy wants to know what it's all about."

"Why don't you tell him?" Al's voice came from the kitchen.

"What do you think it's all about?"

"I don't know."

"What do you think?"

Max looked into the mirror all the time he was talking.

"I wouldn't say."

"Hey, Al, bright boy says he wouldn't say what he thinks it's all about."

"I can hear you, all right," Al said from the kitchen. He had propped open the slit that dishes passed through into the kitchen with a catsup bottle. "Listen, bright boy," he said from the kitchen to George. "Stand a little further along the bar. You move a little to the left, Max." He was like a photographer arranging for a group picture.

"Talk to me, bright boy," Max said. "What do you think's going to happen?"

George did not say anything.

"I'll tell you," Max said. "We're going to kill a Swede. Do you know a big Swede named Ole Andreson?"

"Yes."

"He comes here to eat every night, don't he?"

"Sometimes he comes here."

"He comes here at six o'clock, don't he?"

"If he comes."

"We know all that, bright boy," Max said. "Talk about something else. Ever go to the movies?"

"Once in a while."

"You ought to go to the movies more. The movies are fine for a bright boy like you."

"What are you going to kill Ole Andreson for? What did he ever do to you?"

"He never had a chance to do anything to us. He never even seen us."

"And he's only going to see us once," Al said from the kitchen.

"What are you going to kill him for, then?" George asked.

"We're killing him for a friend. Just to oblige a friend, bright boy."

"Shut up," said Al from the kitchen. "You talk too goddamn much."

"Well, I got to keep bright boy amused. Don't I, bright boy?"

"You talk too damn much," Al said. "The nigger and my bright boy are amused by themselves. I got them tied up like a couple of girl friends in a convent."

"I suppose you were in a convent."

"You never know."

"You were in a kosher convent. That's where you were."

George looked up at the clock.

"If anybody comes in you tell them the cook is off, and if they keep after it, you tell them you'll go back and cook yourself. Do you get that, bright boy?"

"All right," George said. "What you going to do with us afterward?"

"That'll depend," Max said. "That's one of those things you never know at the time."

George looked up at the clock. It was a quarter past six. The door from the street opened. A street-car motorman came in.

"Hello, George," he said. "Can I get supper?"

"Sam's gone out," George said. "He'll be back in about half an hour."

"I'd better go up the street," the motorman said. George looked at the clock. It was twenty minutes past six.

"That was nice, bright boy," Max said. "You're a regular little gentleman."

"He knew I'd blow his head off," Al said from the kitchen.

"No," said Max. "It ain't that. Bright boy is nice. He's a nice boy. I like him."

At six-fifty-five George said: "He's not coming."

Two other people had been in the lunchroom. Once George had gone out to the kitchen and made a ham-and-egg sandwich "to go" that a man wanted to take with him. Inside the kitchen he saw Al, his derby hat tipped back, sitting on a stool beside the wicket with the muzzle of a sawed-off shotgun resting on the ledge. Nick and the cook were back to back in the corner, a towel tied in each of their mouths. George had cooked the sandwich, wrapped it up in oiled paper, put it in a bag, brought it in, and the man had paid for it and gone out.

"Bright boy can do everything," Max said. "He can cook and everything. You'd make some girl a nice wife, bright boy."

"Yes?" George said. "Your friend, Ole Andreson, isn't going to come."

"We'll give him ten minutes," Max said.

Max watched the mirror and the clock. The hands of the clock marked seven o'clock, and then five minutes past seven.

"Come on, Al," said Max. "We better go. He's not coming."

"Better give him five minutes," Al said from the kitchen.

In the five minutes a man came in, and George explained that the cook was sick.

"Why the hell don't you get another cook?" the man asked. "Aren't you running a lunch counter?" He went out.

"Come on, Al," Max said.

"What about the two bright boys and the nigger?"

"They're all right."

"You think so?"

"Sure. We're through with it."

"I don't like it," said Al. "It's sloppy. You talk too much."

"Oh, what the hell," said Max. "We got to keep amused, haven't we?"

"You talk too much, all the same," Al said. He came out from the kitchen. The cut-off barrels of the shotgun made a slight bulge under the waist of his too tight-fitting overcoat. He straightened his coat with his gloved hands.

"So long, bright boy," he said to George. "You got a lot of luck."

"That's the truth," Max said. "You ought to play the races, bright boy."

The two of them went out the door. George watched them, through the window, pass under the arc light and cross the street. In their tight overcoats and derby hats they looked like a vaudeville team. George went back through the swinging door into the kitchen and untied Nick and the cook.

"I don't want any more of that," said Sam, the cook. "I don't want any more of that."

Nick stood up. He had never had a towel in his mouth before.

"Say," he said. "What the hell?" He was trying to swagger it off.

"They were going to kill Ole Andreson," George said. "They were going to shoot him when he came in to eat."

"Ole Andreson?"

"Sure."

The cook felt the corners of his mouth with his thumbs.

"They all gone?" he asked.

"Yeah," said George. "They're gone now."

"I don't like it," said the cook. "I don't like any of it at all."

"Listen," George said to Nick. "You better go see Ole Andreson."

"All right."

"You better not have anything to do with it at all," Sam, the cook, said. "You better stay way out of it."

"Don't go if you don't want to," George said.

"Mixing up in this ain't going to get you anywhere," the cook said. "You stay out of it."

"I'll go see him," Nick said to George. "Where does he live?"

The cook turned away.

"Little boys always know what they want to do," he said.

"He lives up at Hirsch's rooming house," George said to Nick.

"I'll go up there."

Outside the arc light shone through the bare branches of a tree. Nick walked up the street beside the car tracks and turned at the next arc light down a side street. Three houses up the street was Hirsch's rooming house. Nick walked up the two steps and pushed the bell. A woman came to the door.

"Is Ole Andreson here?"

"Do you want to see him?"

"Yes, if he's in."

Nick followed the woman up a flight of stairs and back to the end of a corridor. She knocked on the door.

"Who is it?"

"It's somebody to see you, Mr. Andreson," the woman said.

"It's Nick Adams."

"Come in."

Nick opened the door and went into the room. Ole Andreson was lying on the bed with all his clothes on. He had been a heavyweight prize-fighter and he was too long for the bed. He lay with his head on two pillows. He did not look at Nick.

"What was it?" he asked.

"I was up at Henry's," Nick said, "and two fellows came in and tied up me and the cook, and they said they were going to kill you."

It sounded silly when he said it. Ole Andreson said nothing.

"They put us out in the kitchen," Nick went on. "They were going to shoot you when you came in to supper."

Ole Andreson looked at the wall and did not say anything.

"George thought I better come and tell you about it."

"There isn't anything I can do about it," Ole Andreson said.

"I'll tell you what they were like."

"I don't want to know what they were like," Ole Andreson said. He looked at the wall. "Thanks for coming to tell me about it."

"That's all right."

Nick looked at the big man lying on the bed.

"Don't you want me to go and see the police?"

"No," Ole Andreson said. "That wouldn't do any good."

"Isn't there something I could do?"

"No. There ain't anything to do."

"Maybe it was just a bluff."

"No. It ain't just a bluff."

Ole Andreson rolled over toward the wall.

"The only thing is," he said, talking toward the wall, "I just can't make up my mind to go out. I been in here all day."

"Couldn't you get out of town?"

"No," Ole Andreson said. "I'm through with all that running around."

He looked at the wall.

"There ain't anything to do now."

"Couldn't you fix it up some way?"

"No. I got in wrong." He talked in the same flat voice. "There ain't anything to do. After a while I'll make up my mind to go out."

"I better go back and see George," Nick said.

"So long," said Ole Andreson. He did not look toward Nick. "Thanks for coming around."

Nick went out. As he shut the door he saw Ole Andreson with all his clothes on, lying on the bed looking at the wall.

"He's been in his room all day," the landlady said downstairs. "I guess he don't feel well. I said to him: 'Mr. Andreson, you ought to go out and take a walk on a nice fall day like this,' but he didn't feel like it."

"He doesn't want to go out."

"I'm sorry he don't feel well," the woman said. "He's an awfully nice man. He was in the ring, you know."

"I know it."

"You'd never know it except from the way his face is," the woman said. They stood talking just inside the street door. "He's just as gentle."

"Well, good-night, Mrs. Hirsch," Nick said.

"I'm not Mrs. Hirsch," the woman said. "She owns the place. I just look after it for her. I'm Mrs. Bell."

"Well, good-night, Mrs. Bell," Nick said.

"Good-night," the woman said.

Nick walked up the dark street to the corner under the arc light, and then along the car tracks to Henry's eating house. George was inside, back of the counter.

"Did you see Ole?"

"Yes," said Nick. "He's in his room and he won't go out."

The cook opened the door from the kitchen when he heard Nick's voice.

"I don't even listen to it," he said and shut the door.

"Did you tell him about it?" George asked.

"Sure. I told him but he knows what it's all about."

"What's he going to do?"

"Nothing."

"They'll kill him."

"I guess they will."

"He must have got mixed up in something in Chicago."

"I guess so," said Nick.

"It's a hell of a thing."

"It's an awful thing," Nick said.

They did not say anything. George reached down for a towel and wiped the counter.

"I wonder what he did?" Nick said.

"Double-crossed somebody. That's what they kill them for."

"I'm going to get out of this town," Nick said.

"Yes," said George. "That's a good thing to do."

"I can't stand to think about him waiting in the room and knowing he's going to get it. It's too damned awful."

"Well," said George, "you better not think about it."

INTERPRETATION

There are certain fairly obvious points to be made about the technique of this story. It breaks up into one long scene and three short scenes. Indeed, the method is so thoroughly scenic that not over three or four sentences are required to make the transitions. The focus of narration is objective throughout, practically all information being conveyed in simple realistic dialogue. In the first scene the revelation of the mission of the gangsters is accomplished through a few significant details—the fact that the gangsters eat with gloves (to avoid leaving fingerprints), the fact that they keep their eyes on the mirror behind the bar, the fact that, after Nick and the cook have been tied up, the gangster who has the shotgun at the service window stations his friend and George out front "like a photographer arranging for a group picture"—all of this before the specific nature of their mission is made clear.

Other observations concerning the technique of the story could be made—the cleverness of composition, the subtlety with which the suspense is maintained in the first scene by the banter of the gangsters, and then is transferred to another level in the second scene. But such observations, though they are worth making, do not answer the first question which, to the reader, usually presents itself, or should be allowed to present itself. That question is: what is the story about?

The importance of giving an early answer to this question is indicated by the fact that a certain kind of reader, upon first acquaintance with the story, is inclined to feel that the story is exhausted in the first scene, and in fact that the first scene itself does not come to focus—does not have a "point." Another kind of reader sees that the first scene, with its lack of resolution, is really being used to "charge" the second scene. He finds his point in Ole Andreson's decision not to try to escape the gangsters—to stop "all that running around." This reader feels that the story should end here. He sees no relevance in the last several pages of the story, and wonders why the author has flattened out his effect. The first reader we may say, feels that "The Killers" is the gangsters' story—a story of action which does not come off. The second and more sophisticated reader interprets it as Andreson's story, though perhaps with some wonder that Andreson's story has been approached so indirectly and is allowed to trail off so irrelevantly. In other words, the reader is inclined to transpose the question, What is the story? into the question, Whose story is it? When he states the question in this way, he confronts the fact that Hemingway has left the story focused not on the gangsters, nor on Andreson, but on the boys at the lunchroom. Consider the last sentences of the story:

"I'm going to get out of this town," Nick said.

"Yes," said George. "That's a good thing to do."

"I can't stand to think about him waiting in the room and knowing he's going to get it. It's too damned awful."

"Well," said George, "you better not think about it."

So, of the two boys, it is obviously Nick on whom the impression has been made. George has managed to come to terms with the situation. By this line of reasoning, it is Nick's story. And the story is about the discovery of evil. The theme, in a sense, is the Hamlet theme, or the theme of Sherwood Anderson's "I Want to Know Why" (p. 317).

This definition of the theme of the story, even if it appears acceptable, must, of course, be tested against the detailed structure. In evaluating the story, as well as in understanding it, the skill with which the theme has been assimilated must be taken into account. For instance, to put a concrete question: does the last paragraph of the story illuminate for the reader certain details which had, at their first appearance, seemed to be merely casual, realistic items? If we take the theme to be the boy's discovery of evil, several such details do find their fulfillment and meaning. Nick had been bound and gagged by the gangsters, and has been released by George. To quote: "Nick stood up. He had never had a towel in his mouth before. 'Say,' he said. 'What the hell?' He was trying to swagger it off." Being gagged was something you read about in a thriller and not something which happened to you; and the first effect is one of excitement, almost pleasurable, certainly an excuse for a manly pose. (It may be worth noting in this connection that Hemingway uses the specific word *towel* and not the general word *gag*. It is true that the word *towel* has a certain sensory advantage over the word *gag*—because it suggests the coarseness of the fabric and the unpleasant drying effect on the membranes of the mouth. But this advantage in immediacy is probably overshadowed by another: the towel is sanctified in the thriller as the gag, and here that cliché of the thriller has come true.) The way the whole incident is given—"He had *never* had a towel in his mouth *before*"—charges the apparently realistic detail as a pointer to the final discovery.

Another pointer appears in the gangster's wisecrack about the movies: "You ought to go to the movies more. The movies are fine for a bright boy like you." In one sense, of course, the iterated remarks about the movies, coming just after the gangsters have made their arrangements in the lunchroom, serve as a kind of indirect exposition: the reader knows the standard reason and procedure for gang killings. But at another level, these remarks emphasize the discovery that the unreal clichés of horror have a reality.

The boy to whom the gangster speaks understands the allusion to the movies, for he immediately asks: "What are you going to kill Ole Andreson for? What did he ever do to you?"

"He never had a chance to do anything to us. He never even seen us," the gangster replies. The gangster accepts, and even glories a little in, the terms by which he lives—terms which transcend the small-town world. He lives, as it were, by a code, which lifts him above questions of personal likes or personal animosities. This unreal code—unreal because it denies the ordinary personal elements of life—has, like the gag, suddenly been discovered as real. This unreal and theatrical quality is reflected in the description of the gangsters as, after leaving the lunchroom, they go out under the arc light and cross the street: "In their tight overcoats and derby hats they looked like a vaudeville team." It even permeates their dialogue. The dialogue itself has the sleazy quality of mechanized gag and wisecrack, a kind of inflexible and stereotyped banter that is always *a priori* to the situation and overrides the situation. On this level the comparison to the vaudeville team is a kind of explicit summary of details which have been presented more indirectly and dramatically. On another level, the weary and artificial quality of their wit has a grimmer implication. It is an index to the professional casualness with which they accept a situation which to the boys is shocking. They are contemptuous and even bored, with the contempt and boredom of the initiated when confronted by callow lay observers. This code, which has suddenly been transferred from the artificial world of the thriller and movie into reality, is shocking enough, but even more shocking to Nick is the fact that Ole Andreson, the hunted man, accepts the code too. Confronted by the news which Nick brings, he rejects all the responses which the boy would have considered normal: he will not call the police; he will not regard the thing as a mere bluff; he will not leave town. "Couldn't you fix it up some way?" the boy asks. "No. I got in wrong."

As we observed earlier, for a certain type of reader this is the high point of the story, and the story should end here. If one is to convince such a reader that the author is right in proceeding, one is obligated to answer his question: What is the significance of the rather tame, and apparently irrelevant, little incident which follows, the conversation with Mrs. Bell? It is sometimes said that Mrs. Bell serves to give a bit of delayed exposition or even to point the story by gaining sympathy for Andreson, who is, to her, "an awfully nice man," not at all like her idea of a pugilist. But this is not enough to satisfy the keen reader, and he is right in refusing to be satisfied with this. Mrs. Bell is, really, the Porter at Hell Gate in *Macbeth*. She is the world of normality, which is shocking now from the very fact that it continues to flow on in its usual course. To her, Ole Andreson is just a nice man, despite the fact that he has been in the ring; he ought to go out and take his walk on such a nice day. She points to his ordinary individuality, which is in contrast to the demands of the mechanical code. Even if the unreal horror of the movie thriller has become real, even if the hunted man lies upstairs on his bed trying to make up his mind to go out, Mrs Bell is still Mrs. Bell. She is not Mrs. Hirsch. Mrs. Hirsch owns the place, she just looks after it for Mrs. Hirsch. She is Mrs. Bell.

At the door of the rooming house Nick has met Mrs. Bell—normality unconscious of the ironical contrast it presents. Back at the lunchroom, Nick returns to the normal scene, but the normal scene conscious of the impingement of horror. It is the same old lunchroom, with George and the cook going about their business. But they, unlike Mrs. Bell, know what has happened. Yet even they are scarcely deflected from their ordinary routine. George and the cook represent two different levels of response to the situation. The cook, from the first, has wanted no part of it. When he hears Nick's voice, on his return, he says, "I don't even listen to it." And he shuts the door. But George had originally suggested that Nick go see Andreson, telling him, however, "Don't go if you don't want to." After Nick has told his story, George can comment, "It's a hell of a thing," but George, in one sense at least, has accepted the code, too. When Nick says: "I wonder what he did?" George replies, with an echo of the killers' own casualness: "Double-crossed somebody. That's what they kill them for." In other words, the situation is shocking to the cook only in so far as it involves his own safety. George is aware of other implications but can dismiss them. For neither of them, does the situation mean the discovery of evil. But for Nick, it is the discovery, for he has not yet learned to take George's adult advice: "Well, you better not think about it."

To this point the discussion of "The Killers" has been concerned with the structure of the story with regard to the relations among incidents and with regard to the attitudes of the characters. But there remain as important questions such items as the following: What is Hemingway's attitude toward his material? How does this attitude find its expression?

Perhaps the simplest approach to these questions may be through a consideration of the situations and characters which interest Hemingway. These situations are usually violent ones: the hard-drinking and sexually promiscuous world of *The Sun Also Rises;* the chaotic and brutal world of war as in *A Farewell to Arms, For Whom the Bell Tolls,* or "A Way You'll Never Be"; the dangerous and exciting world of the bull ring or the prize ring as in *The Sun Also Rises, Death in the Afternoon,* "The Undefeated," "Fifty Grand"; the world of crime, as in "The Killers," *To Have and to Have Not,* or "The Gambler, the Nun, and the Radio." Hemingway's typical characters are usually tough men, experienced in the hard worlds they inhabit, and apparently insensitive: Lieutenant Henry in *A Farewell to Arms,* the big-game hunter in "The Snows of Kilimanjaro," Robert Jordan in *For Whom the Bell Tolls,* or even Ole Andreson. They are, also, usually defeated men. Out of their practical defeat, however, they have managed to salvage something. And here we come upon Hemingway's basic interest in such situations and such characters. They are not defeated except upon their own terms; some of them have even courted defeat; certainly, they have maintained, even in the practical defeat, an ideal of themselves, formulated or unformulated, by which they have lived. Hemingway's attitude is, in a sense, like that of Robert Louis Stevenson, as Stevenson states it in one of his essays, "Pulvis et Umbra":

"Poor soul, here for so little, cast among so many hardships, filled with desires so incommensurate and so inconsistent, savagely surrounded, savagely descended, irremediably condemned to prey upon his fellow lives: who should have blamed him had he been of a piece with his destiny and a being merely barbarous? And we look and behold him instead filled with imperfect virtues: . . . an ideal of decency, to which he would rise if it were possible; a limit of shame, below which, if it be possible, he will not stoop. . . . Man is indeed marked for failure in his efforts to do right. But where the best consistently miscarry, how tenfold more remarkable that all should continue to strive; and surely we should find it both touching and inspiriting, that in a field from which success is banished, our race should not cease to labor. . . . It matters not where we look, under what climate we observe him, in what stage of society, in what depth of ignorance, burthened with what erroneous morality; by campfires in Assiniboia, the snow powdering his shoulders, the wind plucking his blanket, as he sits, passing the ceremonial calumet and uttering his grave opinions like a Roman senator; in ships at sea, a man inured to hardship and vile pleasures, his brightest hope a fiddle in a tavern and a bedizened trull who sells herself to rob him, and he for all that, simple, innocent, cheerful, kindly like a child, constant to toil, brave to drown, for others; . . . in the brothel, the discard of society, living mainly on strong drink, fed with affronts, a fool, a thief, the comrade of thieves, and even here keeping the point of honor and the touch of pity, often repaying the world's scorn with service, often standing firm upon a scruple, and at a certain cost, rejecting riches;— everywhere some virtue cherished or affected, everywhere some decency of thought and carriage, everywhere the ensign of man's ineffectual goodness! . . . under every circumstance of failure, without hope, without health, without thanks, still obscurely fighting the lost fight of virtue, still clinging, in the brothel or on the scaffold, to some rag of honor, the poor jewel of their souls! They may seek to escape, and yet they cannot; it is not alone their privilege and glory, but their doom, they are condemned to some nobility . . ."

For Stevenson, the world in which this drama is played out is, objectively considered, a violent and meaningless world—"our rotary island loaded with predatory life and more drenched with blood . . . than ever mutinied ship, scuds through space." This is Hemingway's world, too. But its characters, at least those whose story Hemingway cares to tell, make one gallant effort to redeem the incoherence and meaninglessness of this world: they attempt to impose some form upon the disorder of their lives, the technique of the bullfighter or sportsman, the discipline of the soldier, the code of the gangster, which, even though brutal and dehumanizing, has its own ethic. (Ole Andreson is willing to take his medicine without whining. Or the dying Mexican in "The Gambler, the Nun, and the Radio" refuses to squeal, despite the detective's argument: "One can, with honor, denounce one's assailant.") The form is never quite adequate to subdue the world, but the fidelity to it is part of the gallantry of defeat.

It has been said above that the typical Hemingway character is tough and, apparently, insensitive. But only apparently, for the fidelity to a code, to a discipline, may be an index to a sensitivity which allows the characters to see, at moments, their true plight. At times, and usually at times of stress, it is the tough man, for Hemingway, the disciplined man, who actually is aware of pathos or tragedy. The individual toughness (which may be taken to be the private discipline demanded by the world), may find itself in conflict with some more natural and spontaneous human emotion; in contrast with this the discipline may, even, seem to be inhuman; but the Hemingway hero, though he is aware of the claims of this spontaneous human emotion, is afraid to yield to those claims because he has learned that the only way to hold on to "honor," to individuality, to, even, the human order as against the brute chaos of the world, is to live by his code. This is the irony of the situation in which the hero finds himself. Hemingway's heroes are aristocrats in the sense that they are the initiate, and practice a lonely virtue.

Hemingway's heroes utter themselves, not in rant and bombast, but in terms of ironic understatement. This understatement, stemming from the contrast between the toughness and the sensitivity, the violence and the sensitivity, is a constant aspect of Hemingway's method, an aspect which was happily caught in a cartoon in the *New Yorker* some years ago. The cartoonist showed a brawny, hairy forearm and a muscled hand clutching a little rose. The cartoon was entitled "The Soul of Ernest Hemingway." Just as there is a margin of victory in the defeat of the Hemingway characters, so there is a little margin of sensibility in their brutal and violent world. The revelation arises from the most unpromising circumstances and from the most unpromising people—the little streak of poetry or pathos in "The Pursuit Race," "The Undefeated," "My Old Man," and, let us say, "The Killers."

It has already been pointed out that Ole Andreson fits into this pattern. Andreson won't whimper. He takes his medicine quietly. But Ole Andreson's story is buried in the larger story, which is focused on Nick. How does Nick Adams fit into the pattern? Hemingway, as a matter of fact, is accustomed to treat his basic situation at one or the other of two levels. There is the story of the person who is already initiated, who already has adopted his appropriate code, or discipline, in the world which otherwise he cannot cope with. (One finds examples in Jake and Brett in *The Sun Also Rises*, Jordan and Pilar in *For Whom the Bell Tolls*, the bullfighter in "The Undefeated," and many other stories.) There is also the story of the process of the initiation, the discovery of evil and disorder, and the first step toward the mastery of the discipline. This is Nick's story. (But the same basic situation occurs in many other stories by Hemingway, for example, "Up In Michigan," "Indian Camp," and "The Three-Day Blow.")

It has been observed that the typical Hemingway character is tough and apparently insensitive. Usually, too, that character is simple. The impulse which has led Hemingway to the simple character is akin to that which led a Romantic poet like Wordsworth to the same choice. Wordsworth felt that his unsophisticated peasants or children, who are the characters of so many of his poems, were more honest in their responses than the cultivated man, and therefore more poetic. Instead of Wordsworth's typical peasant we find in Hemingway's work the bullfighter, the soldier, the revolutionist, the sportsman, and the gangster; instead of Wordsworth's children, we find the young men like Nick. There are, of course, differences between the approach of Wordsworth and that of Hemingway, but there is little difference on the point of marginal sensibility.

The main difference between the two writers depends on the difference in their two worlds. Hemingway's world is a more disordered world, and more violent, than the simple and innocent world of Wordsworth. Therefore, the sensibility of Hemingway's characters is in sharper contrast to the nature of his world. This creates an irony which is not found in the work of Wordsworth. Hemingway plays down the sensibility as such, and sheathes it in the code of toughness. Gertrude Stein says of Hemingway: "Hemingway is the shyest and proudest and sweetest-smelling storyteller of my reading." When she refers to his "shyness" she is, apparently, thinking of his use of irony and understatement. The typical character is sensitive, but his sensitivity is never insisted upon; he may be worthy of pity, but he never demands it. The underlying attitude in Hemingway's work may be stated like this: pity is only valid when it is wrung from a man who has been seasoned by experience, and is only earned by a man who never demands it, a man who takes his chances. Therefore, a premium is placed upon the fact of violent experience.

A further question suggests itself. How is Hemingway's *style* (see Glossary) related to his basic fictional concerns. In "The Killers," as in many of his other stories, the style is simple even to the point of monotony. The characteristic sentence is simple, or compound; and if compound, there is no implied subtlety in the co-ordination of the clauses. The paragraph structure is, characteristically, based on simple sequence.* First, we can observe that there is an obvious relation between this style and the characters and situations with which the author is concerned: unsophis-

---

* In some of Hemingway's work, especially in the novels, there are examples of a more fluent, lyrical style than is found in "The Killers." But even in such examples, one can observe that the fluency and the lyrical effect is based on the conjunction *and*—that there is no process of subordination but rather a process of sequence in terms of direct perceptions. The lyrical quality of such examples is to be taken as a manifestation of the "marginal sensibility," as can be demonstrated by an analysis of the situations in which the lyrical passages occur.

ticated characters and simple, fundamental situations are rendered in an uncomplicated style. But there is another, and more interesting, aspect of the question which involves, not the sensibility of the characters, but the sensibility of the author himself. The short simple rhythms, the succession of co-ordinate clauses, and the general lack of subordination—all suggest a dislocated and ununified world. Hemingway is apparently trying to suggest in his style the direct experience—things as seen and felt, one after another, and not as the mind arranges and analyzes them. A style which involves subordination and complicated shadings of emphasis—a style which tends toward complex sentences with many qualifying clauses and phrases —implies an exercise of critical discrimination—the sifting of experience through the intellect. But Hemingway, apparently, is primarily concerned with giving the immediate impact of experience rather than with analyzing and evaluating it in detail. (We can notice, in this connection, that in his work he rarely indulges in any psychological analysis, and is rarely concerned with the detailed development of a character.) His very style, then, seems to imply that the use of the intellect, with its careful discriminations, may blur the rendering of experience and may falsify it; and this style, in connection with his basic concern for the character of marginal sensibility, may be taken as implying a distrust of the intellect in solving man's basic problems. It is as though he should say: despite the application of the human intellect to the problems of the world, the world is still a disorderly and brutal mess, in which it is hard to find any sure scale of values; therefore, it is well for one to remember the demands of fundamental situations —those involving sex, love, danger, and death, in which the instinctive life is foremost—which are frequently glossed over or falsified by social conventions or sterile intellectuality, and to remember the simple virtues of courage, honesty, fidelity, discipline.

But is all of this a way of saying that Hemingway is really writing innocently, without calculation, crudely? Now, as a matter of fact, his style is a result of calculation, and is not, strictly speaking, spontaneous and naïve at all. His style is, then, a dramatic device, developed because of its appropriateness to the total effect which he intends to give. A writer who was in point of fact uninstructed and spontaneous would probably not be able to achieve the impression of spontaneity and immediacy which is found in Hemingway's best work, the work in which his basic attitude and subject matter can be truly and functionally co-ordinated.

In our comment on this story we have tried, among other and more obvious concerns, to relate the style of the story to the theme and then to relate the various qualities of this story to the general body of Hemingway's work and his attitude toward his world. Ordinarily we have been studying stories taken individually, but it is time for us to realize that the various (and often quite different) stories done by a good writer always have some fundamental unifying attitudes—for a man can be only himself.

Since this is true, we can nearly aiways enter more deeply into a piece of fiction and understand it more fully when we are prepared to relate it to the writer's other work. A good writer does not offer us, for instance, a glittering variety of themes. He probably treats, over and over, those few themes that seem to him most important in his actual living and observation of life. For we can remember, too, that a good writer is not merely playing a game to amuse his readers or to make a living—though quite properly he may do these things in addition to what else he may do. The good writer is trying in his personal way to find and to say something that he regards as true about life.

1. Either one of the men who are characters in "The Bride Comes to Yellow Sky" (p. 158) is a type that might appear in a story by Hemingway. But is it likely that Hemingway would take the same attitude toward them? How could you state the difference in tone between "The Bride Comes to Yellow Sky" and such stories by Hemingway as you have read?

2. Suppose you had read "A Piece of News" or "The Drunkard" without knowing the author and had been told it was by Hemingway. Would you have believed this? If not, why not?

KATHERINE MANSFIELD

The Fly

"Y'ARE very snug in here," piped old Mr. Woodifield, and he peered out of the great, green leather armchair by his friend, the boss's desk, as a baby peers out of its pram. His talk was over; it was time for him to be off. But he did not want to go. Since he had retired, since his . . . stroke, the wife and the girls kept him boxed up in the house every day of the week except Tuesday. On Tuesday he was dressed up and brushed and allowed to cut back to the City for the day. Though what he did there the wife and girls couldn't imagine. Made a nuisance of himself to his friends, they supposed. . . . Well, perhaps so. All the same, we cling to our last pleasures as the tree clings to its last leaves. So there sat old Woodifield, smoking a cigar and staring almost greedily at the boss, who rolled in his office chair, stout, rosy, five years older than he, and still going strong, still at the helm. It did one good to see him.

Wistfully, admiringly, the old voice added, "It's snug in here, upon my word!"

"Yes, it's comfortable enough," agreed the boss, and he flipped *The Financial Times* with a paper knife. As a matter of fact he was proud of his room; he liked to have it admired, especially by old Woodifield. It gave him a feeling of deep, solid satisfaction to be planted there in the midst of it in full view of that frail old figure in the muffler.

"I've had it done up lately," he explained, as he had explained for the past—how many?—weeks. "New carpet," and he pointed to the bright red carpet with a pattern of large white rings. "New furniture," and he nodded towards the massive bookcase and the table with legs like twisted treacle. "Electric heating!" He waved almost exultantly towards the five transparent, pearly sausages glowing so softly in the tilted copper pan.

But he did not draw old Woodifield's attention to the photograph over the table of a grave-looking boy in uniform standing in one of those spectral photographers' parks with photographers' storm clouds behind him. It was not new. It had been there for over six years.

"There was something I wanted to tell you," said old Woodifield, and his eyes grew dim remembering. "Now what was it? I had it in mind when I started out this morning." His hands began to tremble, and patches of red showed above his beard.

Poor old chap, he's on his last pins, thought the boss. And, feeling kindly, he winked at the old man, and said jokingly, "I tell you what. I've got a little drop of something here that'll do you good before you go out into the cold again. It's beautiful stuff. It wouldn't hurt a child." He took a key off his watch-chain, unlocked a cupboard below his desk, and drew forth a dark, squat bottle. "That's the medicine," said he. "And the man from whom I got it told me on the strict Q.T. it came from the cellars at Windsor Castle."

Old Woodifield's mouth fell open at the sight. He couldn't have looked more surprised if the boss had produced a rabbit.

"It's whisky, ain't it?" he piped, feebly.

The boss turned the bottle and lovingly showed him the label. Whisky it was.

"D'you know," said he, peering up at the boss wonderingly, "they won't let me touch it at home." And he looked as though he was going to cry.

"Ah, that's where we know a bit more than the ladies," cried the boss, swooping across for two tumblers that stood on the table with the water bottle, and pouring a generous finger into each. "Drink it down. It'll do you good. And don't put any water with it. It's sacrilege to tamper with stuff like this. Ah!" He tossed off his, pulled out his handkerchief, hastily wiped his mustaches, and cocked an eye at old Woodifield, who was rolling his in his chaps.

The old man swallowed, was silent a moment, and then said faintly, "It's nutty!"

But it warmed him; it crept into his chill old brain—he remembered.

"That was it," he said, heaving himself out of his chair. "I thought you'd like to know. The girls were in Belgium last week having a look at poor Reggie's grave, and they happened to come across your boy's. They are quite near each other, it seems."

Old Woodifield paused, but the boss made no reply. Only a quiver of his eyelids showed that he heard.

"The girls were delighted with the way the place is kept," piped the old voice. "Beautifully looked after. Couldn't be better if they were at home. You've not been across, have yer?"

"No, no!" For various reasons the boss had not been across.

"There's miles of it," quavered old Woodifield, "and it's all as neat as a garden. Flowers growing on all the graves. Nice broad paths." It was plain from his voice how much he liked a nice broad path.

The pause came again. Then the old man brightened wonderfully.

"D'you know what the hotel made the girls pay for a pot of jam?" he piped. "Ten francs! Robbery, I call it. It was a little pot, so Gertrude says, no bigger than a half-crown. And she hadn't taken more than a spoonful when they charged her ten francs. Gertrude brought the pot away with her to teach 'em a lesson. Quite right, too; it's trading on our feelings. They think because we're over there having a look around we're ready to pay anything. That's what it is." And he turned towards the door.

"Quite right, quite right!" cried the boss, though what was quite right he hadn't the least idea. He came round by his desk, followed the shuffling footsteps to the door, and saw the old fellow out. Woodifield was gone.

For a long moment the boss stayed, staring at nothing, while the gray-haired office messenger, watching him, dodged in and out of his cubbyhole like a dog that expects to be taken for a run: "I'll see nobody for half an hour, Macey," said the boss. "Understand? Nobody at all."

"Very good, sir."

The door shut, the firm, heavy steps recrossed the bright carpet, the fat body plumped down in the spring chair, and leaning forward, the boss covered his face with his hands. He wanted, he intended, he had arranged to weep. . . .

It had been a terrible shock to him when old Woodifield sprang that remark upon him about the boy's grave. It was exactly as though the earth had opened and he had seen the boy lying there with Woodifield's girls staring down at him. For it was strange. Although over six years had passed away, the boss never thought of the boy except as lying unchanged, unblemished in his uniform, asleep for ever. "My son!" groaned the boss. But no tears came yet. In the past, in the first months and even years after the boy's death, he had only to say those words to be overcome by such grief that nothing short of a violent fit of weeping could relieve him. Time, he had declared then, he had told everybody, could make no difference. Other men perhaps might recover, might live their loss down, but not he. How was it possible? His boy was an only son. Ever since his birth the boss had worked at building up this business for him; it had no other meaning if it was not for the boy. Life itself had come to have no other meaning. How on earth could he have slaved, denied himself, kept going all these years without the promise for ever before him of the boy's stepping into his shoes and carrying on where he left off?

And that promise had been so near being fulfilled. The boy had been in the office learning the ropes for a year before the war. Every morning they had started off together; they had come back by the same train. And what congratulations he had received as the boy's father! No wonder; he had taken to it marvelously. As to his popularity with the staff, every man jack of them down to old Macey couldn't make enough of the boy. And he wasn't in the least spoiled. No, he was just his bright, natural self, with the right word for everybody, with that boyish look and his habit of saying, "Simply splendid!"

But all that was over and done with as though it never had been. The day had come when Macey had handed him the telegram that brought the whole place crashing about his head. "Deeply regret to inform you . . ." And he had left the office a broken man, with his life in ruins.

Six years ago, six years . . . . How quickly time passed! It might have happened yesterday. The boss took his hands from his face; he was puzzled. Something seemed to be wrong with him. He wasn't feeling as he wanted to feel. He decided to get up and have a look at the boy's photograph. But it wasn't a favorite photograph of his; the expression was unnatural. It was cold, even stern-looking. The boy had never looked like that.

At that moment the boss noticed that a fly had fallen into his broad inkpot, and was trying feebly but desperately to clamber out again. Help! help! said those struggling legs. But the sides of the inkpot were wet and slippery; it fell back again and began to swim. The boss took up a pen, picked the fly out of the ink, and shook it on to a piece of blotting paper. For a fraction of a second it lay still on the dark patch that oozed round it. Then the front legs waved, took hold, and, pulling its small sodden body up it began the immense task of cleaning the ink from its wings. Over and under, over and under, went a leg along a wing, as the stone goes over and under the scythe. Then there was a pause, while the fly, seeming to stand on the tips of its toes, tried to expand first one wing and then the other. It succeeded at last, and, sitting down, it began, like a minute cat, to clean its face. Now one could imagine that the little front legs rubbed against each other lightly, joyfully. The horrible danger was over; it had escaped; it was ready for life again.

But just then the boss had an idea. He plunged his pen back into the ink, leaned his thick wrist on the blotting paper, and as the fly tried its wings down came a great heavy blot. What would it make of that? What indeed! The little beggar seemed absolutely cowed, stunned, and afraid to move because of what would happen next. But then, as if painfully, it dragged itself forward. The front legs waved, caught hold, and, more slowly this time, the task began from the beginning.

"He's a plucky little devil," thought the boss, and he felt a real admiration for the fly's courage. That was the way to tackle things; that was the right spirit. Never say die; it was only a question of . . . But the fly had again finished its laborious task, and the boss had just time to refill his pen, to shake fair and square on the new-cleaned body yet another dark drop. What about it this time? A painful moment of suspense followed. But behold, the front legs were again waving; the boss felt a rush of relief. He leaned over the fly and said to it tenderly, "You artful little b. . . ." And he actually had the brilliant notion of breathing on it to help the drying process. All the same, there was something timid and weak about its efforts now, and the boss decided that this time should be the last, as he dipped the pen into the inkpot.

It was. The last blot fell on the soaked blotting paper, and the draggled fly lay in it and did not stir. The back legs were stuck to the body; the front legs were not to be seen.

"Come on," said the boss. "Look sharp!" And he stirred it with his pen—in vain. Nothing happened or was likely to happen. The fly was dead.

The boss lifted the corpse on the end of the paper knife and flung it into the wastepaper basket, but such a grinding feeling of wretchedness seized him that he felt positively frightened. He started forward and pressed the bell for Macey.

"Bring me some fresh blotting paper," he said, sternly, "and look sharp about it." And while the old dog padded away he fell to wondering what it was he had been thinking about before. What was it? It was . . . He took out his handkerchief and passed it inside his collar. For the life of him he could not remember.

INTERPRETATION

1. Before attempting to define the theme of this story one should consider several preliminary questions. (*a*) It is obvious that the function of old Woodifield is to provide information—to serve as a device for exposition—and to focus attention on the problem of the boss's relation to the dead son. But other functions are served by the introduction of this character, functions which involve the very meaning of the story. What are they? (*b*) What purpose is served beyond the purpose of mere exposition by the cutback following Woodifield's departure? Is the main conflict of the story presented here? The boss has been accustomed to give way to

his grief, and has expected to give way to it now, but he cannot weep. Why? (*c*) It is obvious that the introduction of the incident of the fly is used to indicate the boss's distraction from his grief, from his intention to weep, but does the incident have a further function? Can the struggling fly be regarded as a symbol? If so, of what?

2. The boss had felt that time would never dull his grief. Relate this fact to the mention of new carpet and new furniture in the office, to the general atmosphere of well-being in the office of the firm, and to the boss's attitude of pity and patronage toward the broken old employee of the firm. The boss's interest in the fly's struggle to maintain its life, to survive somehow, and his final testing of the fly's strength, a test which kills the fly and leaves the boss confused and ashamed, is intended to tell the reader something about the boss's own situation. What is that "something"?

3. What, then, is the theme of the story? Does the end of the story simply mean that the boss has ceased to be sentimental? Has he gained something, or has he lost something at the end? Or has he done both?

4. In the analysis of the story "War," by Pirandello, the question is raised as to when the son of the patriotic father actually "dies"—dies, that is, for the father. Discuss the present story with the same consideration in mind.

SHERWOOD ANDERSON

I Want to Know Why

WE got up at four in the morning, that first day in the east. On the evening before we had climbed off a freight train at the edge of town, and with the true instinct of Kentucky boys had found our way across town and to the racetrack and the stables at once. Then we knew we were all right. Hanley Turner right away found a nigger we knew. It was Bildad Johnson who in the winter works at Ed Becker's livery barn in our home town, Beckersville. Bildad is a good cook as almost all our niggers are and of course he, like everyone in our part of Kentucky who is anyone at all, likes the horses. In the spring Bildad begins to scratch around. A nigger from our country can flatter and wheedle anyone into letting him do most anything he wants. Bildad wheedles the stable men and the trainers from the horse farms in our country around Lexington. The trainers come into town in the evening to stand around and talk and maybe get into a poker game. Bildad gets in with them. He is always doing little favors and telling about things to eat, chicken browned in a pan, and how is the best way to cook sweet potatoes and corn bread. It makes your mouth water to hear him.

When the racing season comes on and the horses go to the races and there is all the talk on the streets in the evenings about the new colts, and everyone says when they are going over to Lexington or to the spring meeting at Churchill Downs or to Latonia, and the horsemen that have been down to New Orleans or maybe at the winter meeting at Havana in Cuba come home to spend a week before they start out again, at such a time when everything talked about in Beckersville is just horses and nothing else and the outfits start out and horse racing is in every breath of air you breathe, Bildad shows up with a job as cook for some outfit. Often when I think about it, his always going all season to the races and working in the livery barn in the winter where horses are and where men like to come and talk about horses, I wish I was a nigger. It's a foolish thing to say, but that's the way I am about being around horses, just crazy. I can't help it.

Well, I must tell you about what we did and let you in on what I'm talking about. Four of us boys from Beckersville, all whites and sons of men who live in Beckersville regular, made up our minds we were going to the races, not just to Lexington or Louisville, I don't mean, but to the big eastern track we were always hearing our Beckersville men talk about, to Saratoga. We were all pretty young then. I was just turned fifteen and I was the oldest of the four. It was my scheme. I admit that and I talked the others into trying it. There was Hanley Turner and Henry Rieback and Tom Tumberton and myself. It had thirty-seven dollars I had earned during the winter working nights and Saturdays in Enoch Myer's grocery. Henry Rieback had eleven dollars and the others, Hanley and Tom, had only a dollar or two each. We fixed it all up and laid low until the Kentucky spring meetings were over and some of our men, the sportiest ones, the ones we envied the most, had cut out—then we cut out too.

I won't tell you the trouble we had beating our way on freights and all. We went through Cleveland and Buffalo and other cities and saw Niagara Falls. We bought things there, souvenirs and spoons and cards and shells with pictures of the Falls on them for our sisters and mothers, but thought we had better not send any of the things home. We didn't want to put the folks on our trail and maybe be nabbed.

We got into Saratoga as I said at night and went to the track. Bildad fed us up. He showed us a place to sleep in hay over a shed and promised to keep still. Niggers are all right about things like that. They won't squeal on you. Often a white man you might meet, when you had run away from home like that, might appear to be all right and give you a quarter or a half dollar or something, and then go right and give you away. White men will do that, but not a nigger. You can trust them. They are squarer with kids. I don't know why.

At the Saratoga meeting that year there were a lot of men from home. Dave Williams and Arthur Mulford and Jerry Myers and others. Then there was a lot from Louisville and Lexington Henry Rieback knew but I didn't. They were professional gamblers and Henry Rieback's father is one too. He is what is called a sheet writer and goes away most of the year to tracks. In the winter when he is home in Beckersville he don't stay there much but goes away to cities and deals faro. He is a nice man and generous, is always sending Henry presents, a bicycle and a gold watch and a boy scout suit of clothes and things like that.

My own father is a lawyer. He's all right, but don't make much money and can't buy me things and anyway I'm getting so old now I don't expect it. He never said nothing to me against Henry, but Hanley Turner and Tom Tumberton's fathers did. They said to their boys that money so come by is no good and they didn't want their boys brought up to hear gamblers' talk and be thinking about such things and maybe embrace them.

That's all right and I guess the men know what they are talking about, but I don't see what it's got to do with Henry or horses either. That's what I'm writing this story about. I'm puzzled. I'm getting to be a man and want to think straight and be O.K., and there's something I saw at the race meeting at the eastern track I can't figure out.

I can't help it, I'm crazy about thoroughbred horses. I've always been that way. When I was ten years old and saw I was growing to be big and couldn't be a rider I was so sorry I nearly died. Harry Hellinfinger in Beckersville, whose father is Postmaster, is grown up and too lazy to work, but likes to stand around in the street and get up jokes on boys like sending them to a hardware store for a gimlet to bore square holes and other jokes like that. He played one on me. He told me that if I would eat a half a cigar I would be stunted and not grow any more and maybe could be a rider. I did it. When father wasn't looking I took a cigar out of his pocket and gagged it down some way. It made me awful sick and the doctor had to be sent for, and then it did no good. I kept right on growing. It was a joke. When I told what I had done and why most fathers would have whipped me but mine didn't.

Well, I didn't get stunted and didn't die. It serves Harry Hellinfinger right. Then I made up my mind I would like to be a stable boy, but had to give that up too. Mostly niggers do that work and I knew father wouldn't let me go into it. No use to ask him.

If you've never been crazy about thoroughbreds it's because you've never been around where they are much and don't know any better. They're beautiful. There isn't anything so lovely and clean and full of spunk and honest and everything as some race horses. On the big horse farms that are all around our town Beckersville there are tracks and the horses run in the early morning. More than a thousand times I've got out of bed before daylight and walked two or three miles to the tracks. Mother wouldn't of let me go but father always says, "Let him alone." So I got some bread out of the bread box and some butter and jam, gobbled it and lit out.

At the tracks you sit on the fence with men, whites and niggers, and they chew tobacco and talk, and then the colts are brought out. It's early and the grass is covered with shiny dew and in another field a man is plowing and they are frying things in a shed where the track niggers sleep, and you know how a nigger can giggle and laugh and say things that make you laugh. A white man can't do it and some niggers can't but a track nigger can every time.

And so the colts are brought out and some are just galloped by stable boys, but almost every morning on a big track owned by a rich man who lives maybe in New York, there are always, nearly every morning, a few colts and some of the old race horses and geldings and mares that are cut loose.

It brings a lump up into my throat when a horse runs. I don't mean all horses but some. I can pick them nearly every time. It's in my blood like in the blood of race-track niggers and trainers. Even when they just go slop-jogging along with a little nigger on their backs I can tell a winner. If my throat hurts and it's hard for me to swallow, that's him. He'll run like Sam Hill when you let him out. If he don't win every time it'll be a wonder and because they've got him in a pocket behind another or he was pulled or got off bad at the post or something. If I wanted to be a gambler like Henry Rieback's father I could get rich. I know I could and Henry says so too. All I would have to do is to wait 'til that hurt comes when I see a horse and then bet every cent. That's what I would do if I wanted to be a gambler, but I don't.

When you're at the tracks in the morning—not the race tracks but the training tracks around Beckersville—you don't see a horse, the kind I've been talking about, very often, but it's nice anyway. Any thoroughbred, that is sired right and out of a good mare and trained by a man that knows how, can run. If he couldn't what would he be there for and not pulling a plow?

Well, out of the stables they come and the boys are on their backs and it's lovely to be there. You hunch down on top of the fence and itch inside you. Over in the sheds the niggers giggle and sing. Bacon is being fried and coffee made. Everything smells lovely. Nothing smells better than coffee and manure and horses and niggers and bacon frying and pipes being smoked out of doors on a morning like that. It just gets you, that's what it does.

But about Saratoga. We was there six days and not a soul from home seen us and everything came off just as we wanted it to, fine weather and horses and races and all. We beat our way home and Bildad gave us a basket with fried chicken and bread and other eatables in, and I had eighteen dollars when we got back to Beckersville. Mother jawed and cried but Pop didn't say much. I told everything we done except one thing. I did and saw that alone. That's what I'm writing about. It got me upset. I think about it at night. Here it is.

At Saratoga we laid up nights in the hay in the shed Bildad had showed us and ate with the niggers early and at night when the race people had all gone away. The men from home stayed mostly in the grandstand and betting field, and didn't come out around the places where the horses are kept except to the paddocks just before a race when the horses are saddled. At Saratoga they don't have paddocks under an open shed as at Lexington and Churchill Downs and other tracks down in our country, but saddle the horses right out in an open place under trees on a lawn as smooth and nice as Banker Bohon's front yard here in Beckersville. It's lovely. The horses are sweaty and nervous and shine and the men come out and smoke cigars and look at them and the trainers are there and the owners, and your heart thumps so you can hardly breathe.

Then the bugle blows for post and the boys that ride come running out with their silk clothes on and you run to get a place by the fence with the niggers.

I always am wanting to be a trainer or owner, and at the risk of being seen and caught and sent home I went to the paddocks before every race. The other boys didn't but I did.

We got to Saratoga on a Friday and on Wednesday the next week the big Mullford Handicap was to be run. Middlestride was in it and Sunstreak. The weather was fine and the track fast. I couldn't sleep the night before.

What had happened was that both these horses are the kind it makes my throat hurt to see. Middlestride is long and looks awkward and is a gelding. He belongs to Joe Thompson, a little owner from home who only has a half-dozen horses. The Mullford Handicap is for a mile and Middlestride can't untrack fast. He goes away slow and is always way back at the half, then he begins to run and if the race is a mile and a quarter he'll just eat up everything and get there.

Sunstreak is different. He is a stallion and nervous and belongs on the biggest farm we've got in our country, the Van Riddle place that belongs to Mr. Van Riddle of New York. Sunstreak is like a girl you think about sometimes but never see. He is hard all over and lovely too. When you look at his head you want to kiss him. He is trained by Jerry Tillford who knows me and has been good to me lots of times, lets me walk into a horse's stall to look at him close and other things. There isn't anything as sweet as that horse. He stands at the post quiet and not letting on, but he is just burning up inside. Then when the barrier goes up he is off like his name, Sunstreak. It makes you ache to see him. It hurts you. He just lays down and runs like a bird dog. There can't anything I ever see run like him except Middlestride when he gets untracked and stretches himself.

Gee! I ached to see that race and those two horses run, ached and dreaded it too. I didn't want to see either of our horses beaten. We had never sent a pair like that to the races before. Old men in Beckersville said so and the niggers said so. It was a fact.

Before the race I went over to the paddocks to see. I looked a last look at Middlestride, who isn't such a much standing in a paddock that way, then I went to see Sunstreak.

It was his day. I knew when I seen him. I forgot all about being seen myself and walked right up. All the men from Beckersville were there and no one noticed me except Jerry Tillford. He saw me and something happened. I'll tell you about that.

I was standing looking at that horse and aching. In some way, I can't tell how, I knew just how Sunstreak felt inside. He was quiet and letting the niggers rub his legs and Mr. Van Riddle himself put the saddle on, but he was just a raging torrent inside. He was like the water in the river at Niagara Falls just before it goes plunk down. That horse wasn't thinking about running. He don't have to think about that. He was just thinking about holding himself back 'til the time for the running came. I knew that. I could just in a way see right inside him. He was going to do some awful running and I knew it. He wasn't bragging or letting on much or prancing or making a fuss, but just waiting. I knew it and Jerry Tillford his trainer knew. I looked up and then that man and I looked into each other's eyes. Something happened to me. I guess I loved the man as much as I did the horse because he knew what I knew. Seemed to me there wasn't anything in the world but that man and the horse and me. I cried and Jerry Tillford had a shine in his eyes. Then I came away to the fence to wait for the race. The horse was better than me, more steadier, and now I know better than Jerry. He was the quietest and he had to do the running.

Sunstreak ran first of course and he busted the world's record for a mile. I've seen that if I never see anything more. Everything came out just as I expected. Middlestride got left at the post and was way back and closed up to be second, just as I knew he would. He'll get a world's record too some day. They can't skin the Beckersville country on horses.

I watched the race calm because I knew what would happen. I was sure. Hanley Turner and Henry Rieback and Tom Tumberton were all more excited than me.

A funny thing had happened to me. I was thinking about Jerry Tillford the trainer and how happy he was all through the race. I liked him that afternoon even more than I ever liked my own father. I almost forgot the horses thinking that way about him. It was because of what I had seen in his eyes as he stood in the paddocks beside Sunstreak before the race started. I knew he had been watching and working with Sunstreak since the horse was a baby colt, had taught him to run and be patient and when to let himself out and not to quit, never. I knew that for him it was like a mother seeing her child do something brave or wonderful. It was the first time I ever felt for a man like that.

After the race that night I cut out from Tom and Hanley and Henry. I wanted to be by myself and I wanted to be near Jerry Tillford if I could work it. Here is what happened.

The track in Saratoga is near the edge of town. It is all polished up and trees around, the evergreen kind, and grass and everything painted and nice. If you go past the track you get to a hard road made of asphalt for automobiles, and if you go along this for a few miles there is a road turns off to a little rummy-looking farmhouse set in a yard.

That night after the race I went along that road because I had seen Jerry and some other men go that way in an automobile. I didn't expect to find them. I walked for a ways and then sat down by a fence to think. It was the direction they went in. I wanted to be as near Jerry as I could. I felt close to him. Pretty soon I went up the side road—I don't know why—and came to the rummy farmhouse. I was just lonesome to see Jerry, like wanting to see your father at night when you are a young kid. Just then an automobile came along and turned in. Jerry was in it and Henry Rieback's father, and Arthur Bedford from home, and Dave Williams and two other men I didn't know. They got out of the car and went into the house, all but Henry Rieback's father who quarreled with them and said he wouldn't go. It was only about nine o'clock, but they were all drunk and the rummy-looking farmhouse was a place for bad women to stay in. That's what it was. I crept up along a fence and looked through a window and saw.

It's what give me the fantods. I can't make it out. The women in the house were all ugly mean-looking women, not nice to look at or be near. They were homely too, except one who was tall and looked a little like the gelding Middlestride, but not clean like him, but with a hard ugly mouth. She had red hair. I saw everything plain. I got up by an old rosebush by an open window and looked. The women had on loose dresses and sat around in chairs. The men came in and some sat on the women's laps. The place smelled rotten and there was rotten talk, the kind a kid hears around a livery stable in a town like Beckersville in the winter but don't ever expect to hear talked when there are women around. It was rotten. A nigger wouldn't go into such a place.

I looked at Jerry Tillford. I've told you how I had been feeling about him on account of his knowing what was going on inside of Sunstreak in the minute before he went to the post for the race in which he made a world's record.

Jerry bragged in that bad-woman house as I know Sunstreak wouldn't never have bragged. He said that he made that horse, that it was him that won the race and made the record. He lied and bragged like a fool. I never heard such silly talk.

And then, what do you suppose he did! He looked at the woman in there, the one that was lean and hard-mouthed and looked a little like the gelding Middlestride, but not clean like him, and his eyes began to shine just as they did when he looked at me and at Sunstreak in the paddocks at the track in the afternoon. I stood there by the window—gee!—but I wished I hadn't gone away from the tracks, but had stayed with the boys and the niggers and the horses. The tall rotten-looking woman was between us just as Sunstreak was in the paddocks in the afternoon.

Then, all of a sudden, I began to hate that man. I wanted to scream and rush in the room and kill him. I never had such a feeling before. I was so mad clean through that I cried and my fists were doubled up so my finger-nails cut my hands.

And Jerry's eyes kept shining and he waved back and forth, and then he went and kissed that woman and I crept away and went back to the tracks and to bed and didn't sleep hardly any, and then next day I got the other kids to start home with me and never told them anything I seen.

I been thinking about it ever since. I can't make it out. Spring has come again and I'm nearly sixteen and go to the tracks mornings same as always, and I see Sunstreak and Middlestride and a new colt named Strident I'll bet will lay them all out, but no one thinks so but me and two or three niggers.

But things are different. At the tracks the air don't taste as good or smell as good. It's because a man like Jerry Tillford, who knows what he does, could see a horse like Sunstreak run, and kiss a woman like that the same day. I can't make it out. Darn him, what did he want to do like that for? I keep thinking about it and it spoils looking at horses and smelling things and hearing niggers laugh and everything. Sometimes I'm so mad about it I want to fight someone. It gives me the fantods. What did he do it for? I want to know why.

INTERPRETATION

This story, like "The Killers," by Hemingway, is a story of the "initiation." That is, the hero—a boy, as in "The Killers"—discovers something about the nature of evil, and tries to find some way of coming to terms with his discovery. Let us try to trace the stages by which the "discovery" is arrived at in the story.

The story is a first-person account of what happens to a boy who runs away to the races at Saratoga. But the boy has a special motive in telling the story. The incident which he narrates raises a problem which he finds difficult to cope with. He does not tell us this in so many words as he begins his account, but as the story develops we get hints as to the nature of the problem, long before it is specified at the climax. These hints are not merely important as a means of providing mechanical preparation for the problem. They do accomplish this, but they also, more importantly, accomplish three other things. First, they suggest the nature of the boy to whom the final incident comes with such impact. To some boys this incident would have been almost meaningless; therefore, the story must provide some dramatic probability for the effect on this particular boy. The boy in his first-person narration can give us the details of his experience, but he cannot tell us in so many words what he himself is like; that, too, must be conveyed by hints which the reader can interpret. Second, the hints, arising from many different circumstances, imply that the final problem is an all-pervasive one and is not to be associated merely with the incident at the climax. Three, the series of hints provides, structurally, the pattern for the telling of the story.

The boy starts off in boy fashion by trying to tell us something about himself, where he lives, how he likes horses, how he wishes he were a Negro so he could be around horses all the time, how Negroes are "squarer" with kids than white men are, how he can't understand how the father of his friend, Henry Rieback, is "a nice man and generous," even though he is a gambler. These details seem merely casual, but we suddenly discover that to the boy they are not casual. They have a bearing on his problem. "That's all right and I guess the men know what they are talking about," he says in commenting on the fact that some families don't want their sons to associate with Henry Rieback because his father is a gambler or don't permit them to hang around the horses because there is gambling at the tracks. But he goes on to say, "I don't see what it's got to do with Henry or with horses either. That's what I'm writing this story about. I'm puzzled. I'm getting to be a man and want to think straight and be O.K."

This pronouncement comes with a little dramatic shock after the apparently casual description of himself and of his home town. How do these details about Negroes and horses and Henry Rieback and gambling have a bearing on thinking straight and being O.K.? We see that the boy has begun to question some of the accepted values and codes of the society in which he lives. (Is the boy's attitude simply one of unthinking rebellion, or are his questions real questions?) He feels that the Negroes, who hold an inferior position in the community in which he lives, have certain points of superiority over the white people; the Negroes love the horses, while many of the white people see the horses only as something associated with the vice of gambling, and the Negroes are, in a sense, more honest, they are "squarer with kids." He feels that the community is unfair in condemning Henry Rieback's father, who, even though he is a gambler, is a "nice man and generous," and is even more unfair in condemning Henry simply because his father is not acceptable. And, furthermore, he feels that something is wrong with people who cannot love horses simply because gambling goes on at race tracks. All of this means that he is beginning to understand that ordinarily accepted standards of inferiority and superiority, of right and wrong, of good and bad, of ugliness and beauty, may really work out unjustly when they are applied by a sort of rule of thumb to particular cases. He is puzzled, because this private discovery is in contradiction to the things he has been taught. So he says: "I guess the men know what they are talking about, but I don't see what it's got to do with Henry or with horses either."

We see, at this point in the story, that the Negroes, the Rieback boy, and the horses are all involved in the problem which puzzles the boy. At first glance, it may seem strange that human beings and horses are bracketed together in his mind. But then the boy begins to develop more fully for us exactly what the horses mean to him. It is not merely the excitement of the race track which attracts him. It is something about the horses themselves. "They're beautiful," he says. And he continues: "There isn't anything so lovely and clean and full of spunk and honest and everything as some race horses." If we examine this sentence, we see that all of the qualities which he admires in the horses, except the first one, are qualities which are specifically human, which have to do with human character—cleanliness, courage, honesty, and "everything." He is reading the human traits into the horses, and he cannot understand why other people cannot see and admire those same traits just as he cannot see why other people cannot give credit to the Negro for being warm-hearted and square with kids or to Henry Rieback's father for being nice and generous.

From this point, which may be said to conclude the preparatory and expository part of the story, the narrative moves rather rapidly to the scene in which the boy finds Sunstreak and the trainer in the paddock. This scene sums up in dramatic form all that the boy has previously said about his feeling for horses. Again, his admiration for the horse is cast in terms which are essentially human. The horse doesn't brag. The horse is "better" than the boy, "steadier." It is implied that the horse is courageous, confident, and ready to do to the utmost what he has to do, but he will do it for nothing, win or lose.

The boy simply "knows" this as a sort of mystical revelation. Here is something which is fine and beautiful and which is beyond perplexing questions. The horse, for him, stands for all that is most valuable and admirable in life. Jerry Tillford, the boy feels, also knows this. In fact, at the moment, because Jerry Tillford does know it, the boy feels that Jerry shares these same qualities with the horse.

After the race has been won by Sunstreak, the boy feels impelled to stay as close to Jerry Tillford as possible. "I liked him that afternoon," the boy says, "even more than I ever liked my own father." In other words, because he has shared the mystical revelation with Jerry Tillford, he finds a tie which is even stronger than the tie of family affection. That evening, he follows Jerry, not even expecting to find him; he is filled with the exaltation which, he is sure, Jerry still shares with him. But in the scene at the "rummy farmhouse," he discovers another Jerry. This Jerry "lied and bragged like a fool," and we see the implied contrast to the horse, which is "honest" and does not "brag." We see another contrast. This scene is filthy and ugly and rotten, whereas the thoroughbreds had attracted the boy because they are "so lovely and clean and full of spunk." But these contrasts, we learn, are merely preliminary contrasts to the key contrast in the scene. Jerry approaches the woman who "looked a little like the gelding Middlestride, but not clean like him." The scene is set as a parallel to the scene in the paddock: "The tall rotten-looking woman was between us just as Sunstreak was in the paddocks in the afternoon." But now, facing the rotten-looking woman, Jerry's eyes have the same gleam which they had had in the afternoon when he had faced Sunstreak. The horror and disgust which the boy feels is emphasized by the very parallelism of the scenes.

The horror does not come from the fact that the boy discovers that evil exists in the world. He knows about bad women, he has heard rotten talk, he understands that there are good and bad people in the world. His discovery is that the good and evil can be so intimately allied—can exist in the same person. Jerry Tillford, who had been capable of sharing the exaltation which the boy felt in the paddock, is also capable of the experience in the rummy farmhouse. Indeed, Jerry enters fully into that world and is at home there.

This discovery, in a sense, is a surprise turn to the story. But we see that it has been prepared for in two ways: first in regard to the boy's psychology, and second, in regard to the structure of the story.

Although the discovery that moral definitions are complicated comes, in the special incident, as a shock to the boy, nevertheless he has been moving toward that discovery through his questioning of the easy, conventional definitions which society had given him. The boy has wanted to "think straight and be O.K." Though in Beckersville Negroes are social outcasts, he sees that they are in many ways superior human beings. Mr. Rieback, though a gambler, is a "nice" man, generous to his son. Though gambling may be an evil, the horses, which are gambled on, are "lovely and clean and full of spunk and honest." To sum up, there has been a logic in the boy's experience, though a logic of which he has been largely unaware. And this logic has provided the logic of the story.

How has the preparation been made in terms of the structure of the story? * We have already said that the series of things the boy wants "to know why" about provides a pattern for the telling of the story. We can now go further. The basic device used by the author to point up the contrast in the rummy farmhouse scene is the symbolism of the horse. Constantly, and for the boy unconsciously, the horse becomes a measure of human values. For the example, Sunstreak "is like a girl you think about sometimes but never see." The woman that Jerry meets in the farmhouse "looks" a little like the gelding Middlestride but not clean like him, and with a hard ugly mouth. (The phrase "hard mouth" works here perhaps in a double sense: a hard mouth, as applied to a human being, tells us something about character, and as applied to a horse, it tells us that the animal is refractory and stubborn, not like the trained thoroughbred. Furthermore, the fact that the woman is compared to a gelding may be significant: a gelding is sterile, and the "love" found in the rummy farmhouse is sterile, too.)

We have seen that the horse symbolism has pointed to the scene in the farmhouse, and has provided certain preparatory items in the course of the story. But what is the full meaning of this symbolism? To answer this question, however, we must take into consideration the last two paragraphs of the story, which follow the actual scene in the farmhouse.

The boy says that he still goes to the track, and enjoys being there, "but things are different." The incident in the farmhouse, now long past, continues to color his attitude and "spoils looking at horses and smelling things and hearing niggers laugh and everything" which he had once enjoyed. It spoils everything, he says, "because a man like Jerry Tillford, who knows what he does, could see a horse like Sunstreak run, and kiss a woman like that the same day." At first glance this seems to be merely a summary of the meaning of the scene in the farmhouse, but on closer inspection we may see that it adds a further interpretation of the scene. For example, the phrase, "who knows what he does," is important. What is the difference in moral terms between a horse and a man? The man is responsible, and the horse is not: the man "knows what he does."

The boy, we have seen, has taken the horse to be the very embodiment of the virtues which he admires most. But virtue is human. The finely bred race horse cannot do other than be "spunky," "honest," and "brave." He is bred that way. With man, however, virtue is a matter of knowledge and choice. A deed is not virtuous in itself; it is only virtuous in terms of a particular man's motivation and awareness. In other words, the horse (nature) is not capable of evil or of goodness, which depend upon human choice. This explains why nature—"looking at horses and smelling things," and the like—has been tainted for the boy. He can no longer lose himself in

---

* Naturally the items involved in the boy's psychological development are also involved in the structure of the story, but in so far as the items operate merely in terms ,of the boy's personal psychology, we may permissibly, as a matter of convenience, distinguish them from the others.

the things which merely seem good to him. The horse is no longer a satisfactory symbol for the things he admires.

But the symbol continues to have an ironical significance. Man, because he is capable of choice—because he "knows" what he does—because he is capable of being better than the brute, becomes, when he fails to exercise his capacity, something worse than the brute. We see this implied in the scene in the farmhouse, when the ugly, hard-mouthed woman is compared to Middlestride. A brute is always innocent, but man, because of his capacity for choice, is always either better or worse than the brute. This ironical use of the beast as a symbol is not a new one. We find it, for example, in Gulliver's adventures among the Houyhnhnms and Yahoos in Swift's *Gulliver's Travels.** The Houyhnhnms, the noble horses, which live clean, orderly, "reasonable" lives, are contrasted with filthy, degenerate "men," the Yahoos, who are far worse than beasts.

In the beginning of this analysis it was said that this story is, like Hemingway's "The Killers," the story of an "initiation." The boy discovers something about the nature of evil. Not that evil exists, for he had known for a long time that there are good and bad people—that is, he was acquainted with the ordinary conventional definitions. But he discovers that good and bad are very intimately wedded in the very nature of a man, and, perhaps more important still, that it is man's capacity for choice which makes good and evil meaningful.

Having said this, having extracted what may seem to be a moral "message," one should remind himself that the "message" is, as such, not the story. The story may be said to be the dramatization of the discovery. Now the message is something of which everyone is aware; it is a platitude. But the platitude ceases to be a platitude, it is revitalized and becomes meaningful again, when it is shown to be operating in terms of experience. It is revitalized if we accept its meaning for the boy.

It is obvious that in this story, which is related by a first-person narrator, Anderson has attempted to use a style which is appropriate to that narrator.

What does Anderson gain by this? To start with, we may ask if this boy could be just any boy? Certainly the kind of questions the boy asks cross the mind of any moderately intelligent and moderately decent boy, but here they appear with more than ordinary clarity and vividness. So the boy is, in that degree, special rather than ordinary. In other words, we have to assume a sensitivity. If the writer, however, should insist upon the special sensitivity, the reader might be inclined to resent the story, or at least to refuse it any very broad human application. To avoid this the writer takes the most subtle way of giving us the exposition of the boy's

---

* Swift's use of the horse symbol is much more complicated than is Anderson's, and it is certainly not to be understood that Anderson derives his symbol from that of Swift.

general personality: he lets the boy speak for himself. What the boy says and the way he says it both continuously define him. The questions he asks, as we have said, set him off, and the kind of observations he makes; but his instinctive description of the thoroughbreds as somehow an image of human virtue, and not merely an excuse for excitement, is even more revealing. Again, the boy's appreciation of natural beauty, the freshness of early morning at the training track or the grace and power of a running horse, help to present him to us. So much for what he says; but in the saying we notice a lyrical fluency of style which, appearing at the moments when he is speaking of what excites him, is very significant.

To sum up, we may say that Anderson's choice of the point of view makes it possible for him to give us a sense of the boy's special sensitivity without ever insisting on it. The point of view used here means that the style itself can work as exposition.

We have said that Anderson uses a style appropriate to his narrator, but at least two instances seem to be violations of this appropriateness. The first of these violations occurs in the first paragraph: ". . . and with the true instinct of Kentucky boys had found our way across town and to the racetrack and the stables at once." The second occurs in the sixth paragraph: ". . . and they didn't want their boys brought up to hear gamblers' talk and be thinking about such things and maybe embrace them." One of these instances seems to be a definite lapse from the dramatic appropriateness of the style; one cannot imagine a boy of this sort putting the matter this way. The other instance may be defended. Consider the two passages. What do you think?

ALBERT CAMUS

The Adulterous Woman

A housefly had been circling for the last few minutes in the bus, though the windows were closed. An odd sight here, it had been silently flying back and forth on tired wings. Janine lost track of it, then saw it light on her husband's motionless hand. The weather was cold. The fly shuddered with each gust of sandy wind that scratched against the windows. In the meager light of the winter morning, with a great fracas of sheet metal and axles, the vehicle was rolling, pitching, and making hardly any progress. Janine looked at her husband. With wisps of graying hair growing low on a narrow forehead, a broad nose, a flabby mouth, Marcel looked like a pouting faun. At each hollow in the pavement she felt him jostle against her. Then his heavy torso would slump back on his widespread legs and he would become inert again and absent, with vacant stare. Nothing about him seemed active but his thick hairless hands, made even shorter by the flannel underwear extending below his cuffs and covering his wrists. His hands were holding so tight to a little canvas suitcase set between his knees that they appeared not to feel the fly's halting progress.

Suddenly the wind was distinctly heard to howl and the gritty fog surrounding the bus became even thicker. The sand now struck the windows in packets as if hurled by invisible hands. The fly shook a chilled wing, flexed its legs, and took flight. The bus slowed and seemed on the point of stopping. But the wind apparently died down, the fog lifted slightly, and the vehicle resumed speed. Gaps of light opened up in the dust-drowned landscape. Two or three frail, whitened palm trees which seemed cut out of metal flashed into sight in the window only to disappear the next moment.

"What a country!" Marcel said.

The bus was full of Arabs pretending to sleep, shrouded in their burnooses. Some had folded their legs on the seat and swayed more than the others in the car's motion. Their silence and impassivity began to weigh upon Janine; it seemed to her as if she had been traveling for days with that mute escort. Yet the bus had left only at dawn from the end of the rail line and for two hours in the cold morning it had been advancing on a stony, desolate plateau which, in the beginning at least, extended its straight lines all the way to reddish horizons. But the wind had risen and gradually swallowed up the vast expanse. From that moment on, the passengers had seen nothing more; one after another, they had ceased talking and were silently progressing in a sort of sleepless night, occasionally wiping their lips and eyes irritated by the sand that filtered into the car.

"Janine!" She gave a start at her husband's call. Once again she thought how ridiculous that name was for someone tall and sturdy like her. Marcel wanted to know where his sample case was. With her foot she explored the empty space under the seat and encountered an object which she decided must be it. She could not stoop over without gasping somewhat. Yet in school she had won the first prize in gymnastics and hadn't known what it was to be winded. Was that so long ago? Twenty-five years. Twenty-five years were nothing, for it seemed to her only yesterday when she was hesitating between an independent life and marriage, just yesterday when she was thinking anxiously of the time she might be growing old alone. She was not alone and that law-student who always wanted to be with her was now at her side. She had eventually accepted him although he was a little shorter than she and she didn't much like his eager, sharp laugh or his black protruding eyes. But she liked his courage in facing up to life, which he shared with all the French of this country. She also liked his crestfallen look when events or men failed to live up to his expectations. Above all, she liked being loved, and he had showered her with attentions. By so often making her aware that she existed for him he made her exist in reality. No, she was not alone. . . .

The bus, with many loud honks, was plowing its way through invisible obstacles. Inside the car, however, no one stirred. Janine suddenly felt someone staring at her and turned toward the seat across the aisle. He was not an Arab, and she was surprised not to have noticed him from the beginning. He was wearing the uniform of the French regiments of the Sahara and an unbleached linen cap above his tanned face, long and pointed like a jackal's. His gray eyes were examining her with a sort of glum disapproval, in a fixed stare. She suddenly blushed and turned back to her husband, who was still looking straight ahead in the fog and wind. She snuggled down in her coat. But she could still see the French soldier, long and thin, so thin in his fitted tunic that he seemed constructed of a dry, friable material, a mixture of sand and bone. Then it was that she saw the thin hands and burned faces of the Arabs in front of her and noticed that they seemed to have plenty of room, despite their ample garments, on the seat where she and her husband felt wedged in. She pulled her coat around her knees. Yet she wasn't so fat—tall and well rounded rather, plump and still desirable, as she was well aware when men looked at her, with her rather childish face, her bright, naïve eyes contrasting with this big body she knew to be warm and inviting.

No, nothing had happened as she had expected. When Marcel had wanted to take her along on his trip she had protested. For some time he had been thinking of this trip—since the end of the war, to be precise, when business had returned to normal. Before the war the small dry-goods business he had taken over from his parents on giving up his study of law had provided a fairly good living. On the coast the years of youth can be happy ones. But he didn't much like physical effort and very soon had given up taking her to the beaches. The little car took them out of town solely for the Sunday afternoon ride. The rest of the time he preferred his shop full of multicolored piece-goods shaded by the arcades of this half-native, half-European quarter. Above the shop they lived in three rooms furnished with Arab hangings and furniture from the Galerie Barbès. They had not had children. The years had passed in the semi-darkness behind the half-closed shutters. Summer, the beaches, excursions, the mere sight of the sky were things of the past. Nothing seemed to interest Marcel but business. She felt she had discovered his true passion to be money, and, without really knowing why, she didn't like that. After all, it was to her advantage. Far from being miserly, he was generous, especially where she was concerned. "If something happened to me," he used to say, "you'd be provided for." And, in fact, it is essential to provide for one's needs. But for all the rest, for what is not the most elementary need, how to provide? This is what she felt vaguely, at infrequent intervals. Meanwhile she helped Marcel keep his books and occasionally substituted for him in the shop. Summer was always the hardest, when the heat stifled even the sweet sensation of boredom.

Suddenly, in summer as it happened, the war, Marcel called up then rejected on grounds of health, the scarcity of piece-goods, business at a standstill, the streets empty and hot. If something happened now, she would no longer be provided for. This is why, as soon as piece-goods came back on the market, Marcel had thought of covering the villages of the Upper Plateaus and of the South himself in order to do without a middleman and sell directly to the Arab merchants. He had wanted to take her along. She knew that travel was difficult, she had trouble breathing, and she would have preferred staying at home. But he was obstinate and she had accepted because it would have taken too much energy to refuse. Here they were and, truly, nothing was like what she had imagined. She had feared the heat, the swarms of flies, the filthy hotels reeking of aniseed. She had not thought of the cold, of the biting wind, of these semi-polar plateaus cluttered with moraines. She had dreamed too of palm trees and soft sand. Now she saw that the desert was not that at all, but merely stone, stone everywhere, in the sky full of nothing but stone-dust, rasping and cold, as on the ground, where nothing grew among the stones except dry grasses.

The bus stopped abruptly. The driver shouted a few words in that language she had heard all her life without ever understanding it. "What's the matter?" Marcel asked. The driver, in French this time, said that the sand must have clogged the carburetor, and again Marcel cursed this country. The driver laughed hilariously and asserted that it was nothing, that he would clean the carburetor and they'd be off again. He opened the door and the cold wind blew into the bus, lashing their faces with a myriad grains of sand. All the Arabs silently plunged their noses into their burnooses and huddled up. "Shut the door," Marcel shouted. The driver laughed as he came back to the door. Without hurrying, he took some tools from under the dashboard, then, tiny in the fog, again disappeared ahead without closing the door. Marcel sighed. "You may be sure he's never seen a motor in his life." "Oh, be quiet!" said Janine. Suddenly she gave a start. On the shoulder of the road close to the bus, draped forms were standing still. Under the burnoose's hood and behind a rampart of veils, only their eyes were visible. Mute, come from nowhere, they were staring at the travelers. "Shepherds," Marcel said.

Inside the car there was total silence. All the passengers, heads lowered, seemed to be listening to the voice of the wind loosed across these endless plateaus. Janine was all of a sudden struck by the almost complete absence of luggage. At the end of the railroad line the driver had hoisted their trunk and a few bundles onto the roof. In the racks inside the bus could be seen nothing but gnarled sticks and shopping-baskets. All these people of the South apparently were traveling empty-handed.

But the driver was coming back, still brisk. His eyes alone were laughing above the veils with which he too had masked his face. He announced that they would soon be under way. He closed the door, the wind became silent, and the rain of sand on the windows could be heard better. The motor coughed and died. After having been urged at great length by the starter, it finally sparked and the driver raced it by pressing on the gas. With a big hiccough the bus started off. From the ragged clump of shepherds, still motionless, a hand rose and then faded into the fog behind them. Almost at once the vehicle began to bounce on the road, which had become worse. Shaken up, the Arabs constantly swayed. Nonetheless, Janine was feeling overcome with sleep when there suddenly appeared in front of her a little yellow box filled with lozenges. The jackal-soldier was smiling at her. She hesitated, took one, and thanked him. The jackal pocketed the box and simultaneously swallowed his smile. Now he was staring at the road, straight in front of him. Janine turned toward Marcel and saw only the solid back of his neck. Through the window he was watching the denser fog rising from the crumbly embankment.

They had been traveling for hours and fatigue had extinguished all life in the car when shouts burst forth outside. Children wearing burnooses, whirling like tops, leaping, clapping their hands, were running around the bus. It was now going down a long street lined with low houses; they were entering the oasis. The wind was still blowing, but the walls intercepted the grains of sand which had previously cut off the light. Yet the sky was still cloudy. Amidst shouts, in a great screeching of brakes, the bus stopped in front of the adobe arcades of a hotel with dirty windows. Janine got out and, once on the pavement, staggered. Above the houses she could see a slim minaret. On her left rose the first palm trees of the oasis, and she would have liked to go toward them. But although it was close to noon, the cold was bitter; the wind made her shiver. She turned toward Marcel and saw the soldier coming toward her. She was expecting him to smile or salute. He passed without looking at her and disappeared. Marcel was busy getting down the trunk of piece-goods, a black foot-locker perched on the bus's roof. It would not be easy. The driver was the only one to take care of the luggage and he had already stopped, standing on the roof, to hold forth to the circle of burnooses gathered around the bus. Janine, surrounded with faces that seemed cut out of bone and leather, besieged by guttural shouts, suddenly became aware of her fatigue. "I'm going in," she said to Marcel, who was shouting impatiently at the driver.

She entered the hotel. The manager, a thin, laconic Frenchman, came to meet her. He led her to a second-floor balcony overlooking the street and into a room which seemed to have but an iron bed, a white-enameled chair, an uncurtained wardrobe, and, behind a rush screen, a washbasin covered with fine sand-dust. When the manager had closed the door, Janine felt the cold coming from the bare, whitewashed walls. She didn't know where to put her bag, where to put herself. She had either to lie down or to remain standing, and to shiver in either case. She remained standing, holding her bag and staring at a sort of window-slit that opened onto the sky near the ceiling. She was waiting, but she didn't know for what. She was aware only of her solitude, and of the penetrating cold, and of a greater weight in the region of her heart. She was in fact dreaming, almost deaf to the sounds rising from the street along with Marcel's vocal outbursts, more aware on the other hand of that sound of a river coming from the window-slit and caused by the wind in the palm trees, so close now, it seemed to her. Then the wind seemed to increase and the gentle ripple of waters became a hissing of waves. She imagined, beyond the walls, a sea of erect, flexible palm trees unfurling in the storm. Nothing was like what she had expected, but those invisible waves refreshed her tired eyes. She was standing, heavy, with dangling arms, slightly stooped, as the cold climbed her thick legs. She was dreaming of the erect and flexible palm trees and of the girl she had once been.

After having washed, they went down to the dining-room. On the bare walls had been painted camels and palm trees drowned in a sticky background of pink and lavender. The arcaded windows let in a meager light. Marcel questioned the hotel manager about the merchants. Then an elderly Arab wearing a military decoration on his tunic served them. Marcel, preoccupied, tore his bread into little pieces. He kept his wife from drinking water. "It hasn't been boiled. Take wine." She didn't like that, for wine made her sleepy. Besides, there was pork on the menu. "They don't eat it because of the Koran. But the Koran didn't know that well-done pork doesn't cause illness. We French know how to cook. What are you thinking about?" Janine was not thinking of anything, or perhaps of that victory of the cooks over the prophets. But she had to hurry. They were to leave the next morning for still farther south; that afternoon they had to see all the important merchants. Marcel urged the elderly Arab to hurry the coffee. He nodded without smiling and pattered out. "Slowly in the morning, not too fast in the afternoon," Marcel said, laughing. Yet eventually the coffee came. They barely took time to swallow it and went out into the dusty, cold street. Marcel called a young Arab to help him carry the trunk, but as a matter of principle quibbled about the payment. His opinion, which he once more expressed to Janine, was in fact based on the vague principle that they always asked for twice as much in the hope of settling for a quarter of the amount. Janine, ill at ease, followed the two trunk-bearers. She had put on a wool dress under her heavy coat and would have liked to take up less space. The pork, although well done, and the small quantity of wine she had drunk also bothered her somewhat.

They walked along a diminutive public garden planted with dusty trees. They encountered Arabs who stepped out of their way without seeming to see them, wrapping themselves in their burnooses. Even when they were wearing rags, she felt they had a look of dignity unknown to the Arabs of her town. Janine followed the trunk, which made a way for her through the crowd. They went through the gate in an earthen rampart and emerged on a little square planted with the same mineral trees and bordered on the far side, where it was widest, with arcades and shops. But they stopped on the square itself in front of a small construction shaped like an artillery shell and painted chalky blue. Inside, in the single room lighted solely by the entrance, an old Arab with white mustaches stood behind a shiny plank. He was serving tea, raising and lowering the teapot over three tiny multicolored glasses. Before they could make out anything else in the darkness, the cool scent of mint tea greeted Marcel and Janine at the door. Marcel had barely crossed the threshold and dodged the garlands of pewter teapots, cups and trays, and the postcard displays when he was up against the counter. Janine stayed at the door. She stepped a little aside so as not to cut off the light. At that moment she perceived in the darkness behind the old merchant two Arabs smiling at them, seated on the bulging sacks that filled the back of the shop. Red-and-black rugs and embroidered scarves hung on the walls; the floor was cluttered with sacks and little boxes filled with aromatic seeds. On the counter, beside a sparkling pair of brass scales and an old yardstick with figures effaced, stood a row of loaves of sugar. One of them had been unwrapped from its coarse blue paper and cut into on top. The smell of wool and spices in the room became apparent behind the scent of tea when the old merchant set down the teapot and said good-day.

Marcel talked rapidly in the low voice he assumed when talking business. Then he opened the trunk, exhibited the wools and silks, pushed back the scale and yardstick to spread out his merchandise in front of the old merchant. He got excited, raised his voice, laughed nervously, like a woman who wants to make an impression and is not sure of herself. Now, with hands spread wide, he was going through the gestures of selling and buying. The old man shook his head, passed the tea tray to the two Arabs behind him, and said just a few words that seemed to discourage Marcel. He picked up his goods, piled them back into the trunk, then wiped an imaginary sweat from his forehead. He called the little porter and they started off toward the arcades. In the first shop, although the merchant began by exhibiting the same Olympian manner, they were a little luckier. "They think they're God almighty," Marcel said, "but they're in business too! Life is hard for everyone."

Janine followed without answering. The wind had almost ceased. The sky was clearing in spots. A cold, harsh light came from the deep holes that opened up in the thickness of the clouds. They had now left the square. They were walking in narrow streets along earthen walls over which hung rotted December roses, or from time to time, a pomegranate, dried and wormy. An odor of dust and coffee, the smoke of a wood fire, the smell of stone and of sheep permeated this quarter. The shops, hollowed out of the walls, were far from one another; Janine felt her feet getting heavier. But her husband was gradually becoming more cheerful. He was beginning to sell and was feeling more kindly; he called Janine "Baby"; the trip would not be wasted. "Of course," Janine said mechanically, "it's better to deal directly with them."

They came back by another street, toward the center. It was late in the afternoon; the sky was now almost completely clear. They stopped in the square. Marcel rubbed his hands and looked affectionately at the trunk in front of them. "Look," said Janine. From the other end of the square was coming a tall Arab, thin, vigorous, wearing a sky-blue burnoose, soft brown boots and gloves, and bearing his bronzed aquiline face loftily. Nothing but the *chèche* that he was wearing swathed as a turban distinguished him from those French officers in charge of native affairs whom Janine had occasionally admired. He was advancing steadily toward them, but seemed to be looking beyond their group as he slowly removed the glove from one hand. "Well," said Marcel as he shrugged his shoulders, "there's one who thinks he's a general." Yes, all of them here had that look of pride; but this one, really, was going too far. Although they were surrounded by the empty space of the square, he was walking straight toward the trunk without seeing it, without seeing them. Then the distance separating them decreased rapidly and the Arab was upon them when Marcel suddenly seized the handle of the foot-locker and pulled it out of the way. The Arab passed without seeming to notice anything and headed with the same regular step toward the ramparts. Janine looked at her husband; he had his crestfallen look. "They think they can get away with anything now," he said. Janine did not reply. She loathed that Arab's stupid arrogance and suddenly felt unhappy. She wanted to leave and thought of her little apartment. The idea of going back to the hotel, to that icy room, discouraged her. It suddenly occurred to her that the manager had advised her to climb up to the terrace around the fort to see the desert. She said this to Marcel and that he could leave the trunk at the hotel. But he was tired and wanted to sleep a little before dinner. "Please," said Janine. He looked at her, suddenly attentive. "Of course, my dear," he said.

She waited for him in the street in front of the hotel. The white-robed crowd was becoming larger and larger. Not a single woman could be seen, and it seemed to Janine that she had never seen so many men. Yet none of them looked at her. Some of them, without appearing to see her, slowly turned toward her that thin, tanned face that made them all look alike to her, the face of the French soldier in the bus and that of the gloved Arab, a face both shrewd and proud. They turned that face toward the foreign woman, they didn't see her, and then, light and silent, they walked around her as she stood there with swelling ankles. And her discomfort, her need of getting away increased. "Why did I come?" But already Marcel was coming back.

When they climbed the stairs to the fort, it was five o'clock. The wind had died down altogether. The sky, completely clear, was now periwinkle blue. The cold, now drier, made their cheeks smart. Halfway up the stairs an old Arab, stretched out against the wall, asked them if they wanted a guide, but didn't budge, as if he had been sure of their refusal in advance. The stairs were long and steep despite several landings of packed earth. As they climbed, the space widened and they rose into an ever broader light, cold and dry, in which every sound from the oasis reached them pure and distinct. The bright air seemed to vibrate around them with a vibration increasing in length as they advanced, as if their progress struck from the crystal of light a sound wave that kept spreading out. And as soon as they reached the terrace and their gaze was lost in the vast horizon beyond the palm grove, it seemed to Janine that the whole sky rang with a single short and piercing note, whose echoes gradually filled the space above her, then suddenly died and left her silently facing the limitless expanse.

From east to west, in fact, her gaze swept slowly, without encountering a single obstacle, along a perfect curve. Beneath her, the blue-and-white terraces of the Arab town overlapped one another, splattered with the dark-red spots of peppers drying in the sun. Not a soul could be seen, but from the inner courts, together with the aroma of roasting coffee, there rose laughing voices or incomprehensible stamping of feet. Farther off, the palm grove, divided into uneven squares by clay walls, rustled its upper foliage in a wind that could not be felt upon the terrace. Still farther off and all the way to the horizon extended the ocher-and-gray realm of stones, in which no life was visible. At some distance from the oasis, however, near the wadi that bordered the palm grove on the west could be seen broad black tents. All around them a flock of motionless dromedaries, tiny at that distance, formed against the gray ground the black signs of a strange handwriting, the meaning of which had to be deciphered. Above the desert, the silence was as vast as the space.

Janine, leaning her whole body against the parapet, was speechless, unable to tear herself away from the void opening before her. Beside her, Marcel was getting restless. He was cold; he wanted to go back down. What was there to see here, after all? But she could not take her gaze from the horizon. Over yonder, still farther south, at that point where sky and earth met in a pure line—over yonder it suddenly seemed there was awaiting her something of which, though it had always been lacking, she had never been aware until now. In the advancing afternoon the light relaxed and softened; it was passing from the crystalline to the liquid. Simultaneously, in the heart of a woman brought there by pure chance a knot tightened by the years, habit, and boredom was slowly loosening. She was looking at the nomads' encampment. She had not even seen the men living in it; nothing was stirring among the black tents, and yet she could think only of them whose existence she had barely known until this day. Homeless, cut off from the world, they were a handful wandering over the vast territory she could see, which however was but a paltry part of an even greater expanse whose dizzying course stopped only thousands of miles farther south, where the first river finally waters the forest. Since the beginning of time, on the dry earth of this limitless land scraped to the bone, a few men had been ceaselessly trudging, possessing nothing but serving no one, poverty-stricken but free lords of a strange kingdom. Janine did not know why this thought filled her with such a sweet, vast melancholy that it closed her eyes. She knew that this kingdom had been eternally promised her and yet that it would never be hers, never again, except in this fleeting moment perhaps when she opened her eyes again on the suddenly motionless sky and on its waves of steady light, while the voices rising from the Arab town suddenly fell silent. It seemed to her that the world's course had just stopped and that, from that moment on, no one would ever age any more or die. Everywhere, henceforth, life was suspended—except in her heart, where, at the same moment, someone was weeping with affliction and wonder.

But the light began to move; the sun, clear and devoid of warmth, went down toward the west, which became slightly pink, while a gray wave took shape in the east ready to roll slowly over the vast expanse. A first dog barked and its distant bark rose in the now even colder air. Janine noticed that her teeth were chattering. "We are catching our death of cold," Marcel said. "You're a fool. Let's go back." But he took her hand awkwardly. Docile now, she turned away from the parapet and followed him. Without moving, the old Arab on the stairs watched them go down toward the town. She walked along without seeing anyone, bent under a tremendous and sudden fatigue, dragging her body, whose weight now seemed to her unbearable. Her exaltation had left her. Now she felt too tall, too thick, too white too, for this world she had just entered. A child, the girl, the dry man, the furtive jackal were the only creatures who could silently walk that earth. What would she do there henceforth except to drag herself toward sleep, toward death?

She dragged herself, in fact, toward the restaurant with a husband suddenly taciturn unless he was telling how tired he was, while she was struggling weakly against a cold, aware of a fever rising within her. Then she dragged herself toward her bed, where Marcel came to join her and put the light out at once without asking anything of her. The room was frigid. Janine felt the cold creeping up while the fever was increasing. She breathed with difficulty, her blood pumped without warming her; a sort of fear grew within her. She turned over and the old iron bedstead groaned under her weight. No, she didn't want to fall ill. Her husband was already asleep; she too had to sleep; it was essential. The muffled sounds of the town reached her through the window-slit. With a nasal twang old phonographs in the Moorish cafés ground out tunes she recognized vaguely; they reached her borne on the sound of a slow-moving crowd. She must sleep. But she was counting black tents; behind her eyelids motionless camels were grazing; immense solitudes were whirling within her. Yes, why had she come? She fell asleep on that question.

She awoke a little later. The silence around her was absolute. But, on the edges of town, hoarse dogs were howling in the soundless night. Janine shivered. She turned over, felt her husband's hard shoulder against hers, and suddenly, half asleep, huddled against him. She was drifting on the surface of sleep without sinking in and she clung to that shoulder with unconscious eagerness as her safest haven. She was talking, but no sound issued from her mouth. She was talking, but she herself hardly heard what she was saying. She could feel only Marcel's warmth. For more than twenty years every night thus, in his warmth, just the two of them, even when ill, even when traveling, as at present . . . Besides, what would she have done alone at home? No child! Wasn't that what she lacked? She didn't know. She simply followed Marcel, pleased to know that someone needed her. The only joy he gave her was the knowledge that she was necessary. Probably he didn't love her. Love, even when filled with hate, doesn't have that sullen face. But what is his face like? They made love in the dark by feel, without seeing each other. Is there another love than that of darkness, a love that would cry aloud in daylight? She didn't know, but she did know that Marcel needed her and that she needed that need, that she lived on it night and day, at night especially—every night, when he didn't want to be alone, or to age or die, with that set expression he assumed which she occasionally recognized on other men's faces, the only common expression of those madmen hiding under an appearance of wisdom until the madness seizes them and hurls them desperately toward a woman's body to bury in it, without desire, everything terrifying that solitude and night reveals to them.

Marcel stirred as if to move away from her. No, he didn't love her; he was merely afraid of what was not she, and she and he should long ago have separated and slept alone until the end. But who can always sleep alone? Some men do, cut off from others by a vocation or misfortune, who go to bed every night in the same bed as death. Marcel never could do so— he above all, a weak and disarmed child always frightened by suffering, her own child indeed who needed her and who, just at that moment, let out a sort of whimper. She cuddled a little closer and put her hand on his chest. And to herself she called him with the little love-name she had once given him, which they still used from time to time without even thinking of what they were saying.

She called him with all her heart. After all, she too needed him, his strength, his little eccentricities, and she too was afraid of death. "If I could overcome that fear, I'd be happy. . . ." Immediately, a nameless anguish seized her. She drew back from Marcel. No, she was overcoming nothing, she was not happy, she was going to die, in truth, without having been liberated. Her heart pained her; she was stifling under a huge weight that she suddenly discovered she had been dragging around for twenty years. Now she was struggling under it with all her strength. She wanted to be liberated even if Marcel, even if the others, never were! Fully awake, she sat up in bed and listened to a call that seemed very close. But from the edges of night the exhausted and yet indefatigable voices of the dogs of the oasis were all that reached her ears. A slight wind had risen and she heard its light waters flow in the palm grove. It came from the south, where desert and night mingled now under the again unchanging sky, where life stopped, where no one would ever age or die any more. Then the waters of the wind dried up and she was not even sure of having heard anything except a mute call that she could, after all, silence or notice. But never again would she know its meaning unless she responded to it at once. At once—yes, that much was certain at least!

She got up gently and stood motionless beside the bed, listening to her husband's breathing. Marcel was asleep. The next moment, the bed's warmth left her and the cold gripped her. She dressed slowly, feeling for her clothes in the faint light coming through the blinds from the street-lamps. Her shoes in her hand, she reached the door. She waited a moment more in the darkness, then gently opened the door. The knob squeaked and she stood still. Her heart was beating madly. She listened with her body tense and, reassured by the silence, turned her hand a little more. The knob's turning seemed to her interminable. At last she opened the door, slipped outside, and closed the door with the same stealth. Then, with her cheek against the wood, she waited. After a moment she made out, in the distance, Marcel's breathing. She faced about, felt the icy night air against her cheek, and ran the length of the balcony. The outer door was closed. While she was slipping the bolt, the night watchman appeared at the top of the stairs, his face blurred with sleep, and spoke to her in Arabic. "I'll be back," said Janine as she stepped out into the night.

Garlands of stars hung down from the black sky over the palm trees and houses. She ran along the short avenue, now empty, that led to the fort. The cold, no longer having to struggle against the sun, had invaded the night; the icy air burned her lungs. But she ran, half blind, in the darkness. At the top of the avenue, however, lights appeared, then descended toward her zigzagging. She stopped, caught the whir of turning sprockets and, behind the enlarging lights, soon saw vast burnooses surmounting fragile bicycle wheels. The burnooses flapped against her; then three red lights sprang out of the black behind her and disappeared at once. She continued running toward the fort. Halfway up the stairs, the air burned her lungs with such cutting effect that she wanted to stop. A final burst of energy hurled her despite herself onto the terrace, against the parapet, which was now pressing her belly. She was panting and everything was hazy before her eyes. Her running had not warmed her and she was still trembling all over. But the cold air she was gulping down soon flowed evenly inside her and a spark of warmth began to glow amidst her shivers. Her eyes opened at last on the expanse of night.

Not a breath, not a sound—except at intervals the muffled crackling of stones that the cold was reducing to sand—disturbed the solitude and silence surrounding Janine. After a moment, however, it seemed to her that the sky above her was moving in a sort of slow gyration. In the vast reaches of the dry, cold night, thousands of stars were constantly appearing, and their sparkling icicles, loosened at once, began to slip gradually toward the horizon. Janine could not tear herself away from contemplating those drifting flares. She was turning with them, and the apparently stationary progress little by little identified her with the core of her being, where cold and desire were now vying with each other. Before her the stars were falling one by one and being snuffed out among the stones of the desert, and each time Janine opened a little more to the night. Breathing deeply, she forgot the cold, the dead weight of others, the craziness or stuffiness of life, the long anguish of living and dying. After so many years of mad, aimless fleeing from fear, she had come to a stop at last. At the same time, she seemed to recover her roots and the sap again rose in her body, which had ceased trembling. Her whole belly pressed against the parapet as she strained toward the moving sky; she was merely waiting for her fluttering heart to calm down and establish silence within her. The last stars of the constellations dropped their clusters a little lower on the desert horizon and became still. Then, with unbearable gentleness, the water of night began to fill Janine, drowned the cold, rose gradually from the hidden core of her being and overflowed in wave after wave, rising up even to her mouth full of moans. The next moment, the whole sky stretched out over her, fallen on her back on the cold earth.

When Janine returned to the room, with the same precautions, Marcel was not awake. But he whimpered as she got back in bed and a few seconds later sat up suddenly. He spoke and she didn't understand what he was saying. He got up, turned on the light, which blinded her. He staggered toward the washbasin and drank a long draught from the bottle of mineral water. He was about to slip between the sheets when, one knee on the bed, he looked at her without understanding. She was weeping copiously, unable to restrain herself. "It's nothing, dear," she said, "it's nothing."

INTERPRETATION

1. When Janine and Marcel go up to the parapet (p. 339) and stare out at the camp of the Arabs, we find this sentence: "She knew that this kingdom had been eternally promised her and yet that it would never be hers, never again, except in this fleeting moment perhaps when she opened her eyes again on the suddenly motionless sky and on its waves of steady light, while the voices rising from the Arab town suddenly fell silent." What is this "kingdom"? In what sense has she now had it? Why will she never have it again?

2. How significant for this story is the fact that Marcel is a rather dull man, absorbed in his business? In other words, is the story merely that of a bored, aging wife, or does it have a more general meaning? If so, how would you state it?

3. This story begins with one attitude toward Marcel, and ends with another. Are there any shifts of attitude in between? In what sense can it be said that Janine's shifts of attitude toward Marcel give us the pattern of the story?

4. This story is a story of contrast between youth and maturity. Compare the author's notion of the contrast with that in "The Killers" and that in "I Want to Know Why."

5. Compare the use of atmosphere in this story with that in "A Piece of News."

WILLIAM FAULKNER

A Rose for Emily

I

WHEN Miss Emily Grierson died, our whole town went to her funeral: the men through a sort of respectful affection for a fallen monument, the women mostly out of curiosity to see the inside of her house, which no one save an old manservant—a combined gardener and cook—had seen in at least ten years.

It was a big, squarish frame house that had once been white, decorated with cupolas and spires and scrolled balconies in the heavily lightsome style of the seventies, set on what had once been our most select street. But garages and cotton gins had encroached and obliterated even the august names of that neighborhood; only Miss Emily's house was left, lifting its stubborn and coquettish decay above the cotton wagons and the gasoline pumps—an eyesore among eyesores. And now Miss Emily had gone to join the representatives of those august names where they lay in the cedar-bemused cemetery among the ranked and anonymous graves of Union and Confederate soldiers who fell at the battle of Jefferson.

Alive, Miss Emily had been a tradition, a duty, and a care; a sort of hereditary obligation upon the town, dating from that day in 1894 when Colonel Sartoris, the mayor—he who fathered the edict that no Negro woman should appear on the streets without an apron—remitted her taxes, the dispensation dating from the death of her father on into perpetuity. Not that Miss Emily would have accepted charity. Colonel Sartoris invented an involved tale to the effect that Miss Emily's father had loaned money to the town, which the town, as a matter of business, preferred this way of repaying. Only a man of Colonel Sartoris' generation and thought could have invented it, and only a woman could have believed it.

When the next generation, with its more modern ideas, became mayors and aldermen, this arrangement created some little dissatisfaction. On the first of the year they mailed her a tax notice. February came, and there was no reply. They wrote her a formal letter, asking her to call at the sheriff's office at her convenience. A week later the mayor wrote her himself, offering to call or to send his car for her, and received in reply a note on paper of an archaic shape, in a thin, flowing calligraphy in faded ink, to the effect that she no longer went out at all. The tax notice was also enclosed, without comment.

They called a special meeting of the Board of Aldermen. A deputation waited upon her, knocked at the door through which no visitor had passed since she ceased giving china-painting lessons eight or ten years earlier. They were admitted by the old Negro into a dim hall from which a stairway mounted into still more shadow. It smelled of dust and disuse—a close, dank smell. The Negro led them into the parlor. It was furnished in heavy, leather-covered furniture. When the Negro opened the blinds of one window, a faint dust rose sluggishly about their thighs, spinning with slow motes in the single sun-ray. On a tarnished gilt easel before the fireplace stood a crayon portrait of Miss Emily's father.

They rose when she entered—a small, fat woman in black, with a thin gold chain descending to her waist and vanishing into her belt, leaning on an ebony cane with a tarnished gold head. Her skeleton was small and spare; perhaps that was why what would have been merely plumpness in another was obesity in her. She looked bloated, like a body long submerged in motionless water, and of that pallid hue. Her eyes, lost in the fatty ridges of her face, looked like two small pieces of coal pressed into a lump of dough as they moved from one face to another while the visitors stated their errand.

She did not ask them to sit. She just stood in the door and listened quietly until the spokesman came to a stumbling halt. Then they could hear the invisible watch ticking at the end of the gold chain.

Her voice was dry and cold. "I have no taxes in Jefferson. Colonel Sartoris explained it to me. Perhaps one of you can gain access to the city records and satisfy yourselves."

"But we have. We are the city authorities, Miss Emily. Didn't you get a notice from the sheriff, signed by him?"

"I received a paper, yes," Miss Emily said. "Perhaps he considers himself the sheriff. . . . I have no taxes in Jefferson."

"But there is nothing on the books to show that, you see. We must go by the—"

"See Colonel Sartoris. I have no taxes in Jefferson."

"But, Miss Emily—"

"See Colonel Sartoris." (Colonel Sartoris had been dead almost ten years.) "I have no taxes in Jefferson. Tobe!" The Negro appeared. "Show these gentlemen out."

II

So she vanquished them, horse and foot, just as she had vanquished their fathers thirty years before about the smell. That was two years after her father's death and a short time after her sweetheart—the one we believed would marry her—had deserted her. After her father's death she went out very little; after her sweetheart went away, people hardly saw her at all. A few of the ladies had the temerity to call, but were not received, and the only sign of life about the place was the Negro man—a young man then—going in and out with a market basket.

"Just as if a man—any man—could keep a kitchen properly," the ladies said; so they were not surprised when the smell developed. It was another link between the gross, teeming world and the high and mighty Griersons.

A neighbor, a woman, complained to the mayor, Judge Stevens, eighty years old.

"But what will you have me do about it, madam?" he said.

"Why, send her word to stop it," the woman said. "Isn't there a law?"

"I'm sure that won't be necessary," Judge Stevens said. "It's probably just a snake or a rat that nigger of hers killed in the yard. I'll speak to him about it."

The next day he received two more complaints, one from a man who came in diffident deprecation. "We really must do something about it, Judge. I'd be the last one in the world to bother Miss Emily, but we've got to do something." That night the Board of Aldermen met—three graybeards and one younger man, a member of the rising generation.

"It's simple enough," he said. "Send her word to have her place cleaned up. Give her a certain time to do it in, and if she don't . . ."

"Dammit, sir," Judge Stevens said, "will you accuse a lady to her face of smelling bad?"

So the next night, after midnight, four men crossed Miss Emily's lawn and slunk about the house like burglars, sniffing along the base of the brickwork and at the cellar openings while one of them performed a regular sowing motion with his hand out of a sack slung from his shoulder. They broke open the cellar door and sprinkled lime there, and in all the outbuildings. As they recrossed the lawn, a window that had been dark was lighted and Miss Emily sat in it, the light behind her, and her upright torso motionless as that of an idol. They crept quietly across the lawn and into the shadow of the locusts that lined the street. After a week or two the smell went away.

That was when people had begun to feel really sorry for her. People in our town, remembering how old lady Wyatt, her great-aunt, had gone completely crazy at last, believed that the Griersons held themselves a little too high for what they really were. None of the young men were quite good enough for Miss Emily and such. We had long thought of them as a tableau; Miss Emily a slender figure in white in the background, her father a spraddled silhouette in the foreground, his back to her and clutching a horsewhip, the two of them framed by the back-flung front door. So when she got to be thirty and was still single, we were not pleased exactly, but vindicated; even with insanity in the family she wouldn't have turned down all of her chances if they had really materialized.

When her father died, it got about that the house was all that was left to her; and in a way, people were glad. At last they could pity Miss Emily. Being left alone, and a pauper, she had become humanized. Now she too would know the old thrill and the old despair of a penny more or less.

The day after his death all the ladies prepared to call at the house and offer condolence and aid, as is our custom. Miss Emily met them at the door, dressed as usual and with no trace of grief on her face. She told them that her father was not dead. She did that for three days, with the ministers calling on her, and the doctors, trying to persuade her to let them dispose of the body. Just as they were about to resort to law and force, she broke down, and they buried her father quickly.

We did not say she was crazy then. We believed she had to do that. We remembered all the young men her father had driven away, and we knew that with nothing left, she would have to cling to that which had robbed her, as people will.

III

She was sick for a long time. When we saw here again, her hair was cut short, making her look like a girl, with a vague resemblance to those angels in colored church windows—sort of tragic and serene.

The town had just let the contracts for paving the sidewalks, and in the summer after her father's death they began to work. The construction company came with niggers and mules and machinery, and a foreman named Homer Barron, a Yankee—a big, dark, ready man, with a big voice and eyes lighter than his face. The little boys would follow in groups to hear him cuss the niggers, and the niggers singing in time to the rise and fall of picks. Pretty soon he knew everybody in town. Whenever you heard a lot of laughing anywhere about the square, Homer Barron would be in the center of the group. Presently we began to see him and Miss Emily on Sunday afternoons driving in the yellow-wheeled buggy and the matched team of bays from the livery stable.

At first we were glad that Miss Emily would have an interest, because the ladies all said, "Of course a Grierson would not think seriously of a Northerner, a day laborer." But there were still others, older people, who said that even grief could not cause a real lady to forget *noblesse oblige*—without calling it *noblesse oblige*. They just said, "Poor Emily. Her kins-folk should come to her." She had some kin in Alabama; but years ago her father had fallen out with them over the estate of old lady Wyatt, the crazy woman, and there was no communication between the two families. They had not even been represented at the funeral.

And as soon as the old people said, "Poor Emily," the whispering began. "Do you suppose it's really so?" they said to one another. "Of course it is. What else could . . ." This behind their hands; rustling of craned silk and satin behind jalousies closed upon the sun of Sunday afternoon as the thin, swift clop-clop-clop of the matched team passed: "Poor Emily."

She carried her head high enough—even when we believed that she was fallen. It was as if she demanded more than ever the recognition of her dignity as the last Grierson; as if it had wanted that touch of earthiness to reaffirm her imperviousness. Like when she bought the rat poison, the arsenic. That was over a year after they had begun to say "Poor Emily," and while the two female cousins were visiting her.

"I want some poison," she said to the druggist. She was over thirty then, still a slight woman, though thinner than usual, with cold, haughty black eyes in a face the flesh of which was strained across the temples and about the eyesockets as you imagine a lighthouse-keeper's face ought to look. "I want some poison," she said.

"Yes, Miss Emily. What kind? For rats and such? I'd recom—"

"I want the best you have. I don't care what kind."

The druggist named several. "They'll kill anything up to an elephant. But what you want is—"

"Arsenic," Miss Emily said. "Is that a good one?"

"Is . . . arsenic? Yes ma'am. But what you want—"

"I want arsenic."

The druggist looked down at her. She looked back at him, erect, her face like a strained flag. "Why, of course," the druggist said. "If that's what you want. But the law requires you to tell what you are going to use it for."

Miss Emily just stared at him, her head tilted back in order to look him eye for eye, until he looked away and went and got the arsenic and wrapped it up. The Negro delivery boy brought her the package; the druggist didn't come back. When she opened the package at home there was written on the box, under the skull and bones: "For rats."

IV

So the next day we all said, "She will kill herself"; and we said it would be the best thing. When she had first begun to be seen with Homer Barron, we had said, "She will marry him." Then we said, "She will persuade him yet," because Homer himself had remarked—he liked men, and it was known that he drank with the younger men in the Elk's Club—that he was not a marrying man. Later we said, "Poor Emily," behind the jalousies as they passed on Sunday afternoon in the glittering buggy, Miss Emily with her head high and Homer Barron with his hat cocked and a cigar in his teeth, reins and whip in a yellow glove.

Then some of the ladies began to say that it was a disgrace to the town and a bad example to the young people. The men did not want to interfere, but at last the ladies forced the Baptist minister—Miss Emily's people were Episcopal—to call upon her. He would never divulge what happened during that interview, but he refused to go back again. The next Sunday they again drove about the streets, and the following day the minister's wife wrote to Miss Emily's relations in Alabama.

So she had blood-kin under her roof again and we sat back to watch developments. At first nothing happened. Then we were sure that they were to be married. We learned that Miss Emily had been to the jeweler's and ordered a man's toilet set in silver, with the letters H.B. on each piece. Two days later we learned that she had bought a complete outfit of men's clothing, including a nightshirt, and we said, "They are married." We were really glad. We were glad because the two female cousins were even more Grierson than Miss Emily had ever been.

So we were not surprised when Homer Barron—the streets had been finished some time since—was gone. We were a little disappointed that there was not a public blowing-off, but we believed that he had gone on to prepare for Miss Emily's coming, or to give her a chance to get rid of the cousins. (By that time it was a cabal, and we were all Miss Emily's allies to help circumvent the cousins.) Sure enough, after another week they departed. And, as we had expected all along, within three days Homer Barron was back in town. A neighbor saw the Negro man admit him at the kitchen door at dusk one evening.

And that was the last we saw of Homer Barron. And of Miss Emily for some time. The Negro man went in and out with the market basket, but the front door remained closed. Now and then we would see her at a window for a moment, as the men did that night when they sprinkled the lime, but for almost six months she did not appear on the streets. Then we knew that this was to be expected too; as if that quality of her father which had thwarted her woman's life so many times had been too virulent and too furious to die.

When we next saw Miss Emily, she had grown fat and her hair was turning gray. During the next few years it grew grayer and grayer until it attained an even pepper-and-salt iron-gray, when it ceased turning. Up to the day of her death at seventy-four it was still that vigorous iron-gray, like the hair of an active man.

From that time on her front door remained closed, save for a period of six or seven years, when she was about forty, during which she gave lessons in china-painting. She fitted up a studio in one of the downstairs rooms, where the daughters and granddaughters of Colonel Sartoris' contemporaries were sent to her with the same regularity and in the same spirit that they were sent on Sundays with a twenty-five cent piece for the collection plate. Meanwhile her taxes had been remitted.

Then the newer generation became the backbone and the spirit of the town, and the painting pupils grew up and fell away and did not send their children to her with boxes of color and tedious brushes and pictures cut from the ladies' magazines. The front door closed upon the last one and remained closed for good. When the town got free postal delivery Miss Emily alone refused to let them fasten the metal numbers above her door and attach a mailbox to it. She would not listen to them.

Daily, monthly, yearly we watched the Negro grow grayer and more stooped, going in and out with the market basket. Each December we sent her a tax notice, which would be returned by the post office a week later, unclaimed. Now and then we would see her in one of the downstairs windows—she had evidently shut up the top floor of the house—like the carven torso of an idol in a niche, looking or not looking at us, we could never tell which. Thus she passed from generation to generation—dear, inescapable, impervious, tranquil, and perverse.

And so she died. Fell ill in the house filled with dust and shadows, with only a doddering Negro man to wait on her. We did not even know she was sick; we had long since given up trying to get any information from the Negro. He talked to no one, probably not even to her, for his voice had grown harsh and rusty, as if from disuse.

She died in one of the downstairs rooms, in a heavy walnut bed with a curtain, her gray head propped on a pillow yellow and moldy with age and lack of sunlight.

V

The Negro met the first of the ladies at the front door and let them in, with their hushed, sibilant voices and their quick, curious glances, and then he disappeared. He walked right through the house and out the back and was not seen again.

The two female cousins came at once. They held the funeral on the second day, with the town coming to look at Miss Emily beneath a mass of bought flowers, with the crayon face of her father musing profoundly above the bier and the ladies sibilant and macabre; and the very old men—some in their brushed Confederate uniforms—on the porch and the lawn, talking of Miss Emily as if she had been a contemporary of theirs, believing that they had danced with her and courted her perhaps, confusing time with its mathematical progression, as the old do, to whom all the past is not a diminishing road, but, instead, a huge meadow which no winter ever quite touches, divided from them now by the narrow bottleneck of the most recent decade of years.

Already we knew that there was one room in that region above stairs which no one had seen in forty years, and which would have to be forced. They waited until Miss Emily was decently in the ground before they opened it.

The violence of breaking down the door seemed to fill this room with pervading dust. A thin, acrid pall as of the tomb seemed to lie everywhere upon this room decked and furnished as for a bridal: upon the valance curtains of faded rose color, upon the rose-shaded lights, upon the dressing table, upon the delicate array of crystal and the man's toilet things backed with tarnished silver, silver so tarnished that the monogram was obscured. Among them lay a collar and tie, as if they had just been removed, which, lifted, left upon the surface a pale crescent in the dust. Upon a chair hung the suit, carefully folded; beneath it the two mute shoes and the discarded socks.

The man himself lay in the bed.

For a long while we just stood there, looking down at the profound and fleshless grin. The body had apparently once lain in the attitude of an embrace, but now the long sleep that outlasts love, that conquers even the grimace of love, had cuckolded him. What was left of him, rotted beneath what was left of the nightshirt, had become inextricable from the bed in which he lay; and upon him and upon the pillow beside him lay that even coating of the patient and biding dust.

Then we noticed that in the second pillow was the indentation of a head. One of us lifted something from it, and leaning forward, that faint and invisible dust dry and acrid in the nostrils, we saw a long strand of iron-gray hair.

INTERPRETATION

This is a story of horror. We have a decaying mansion in which the protagonist, shut away from the world, grows into something monstrous, and becomes as divorced from the human as some fungus growing in the dark on a damp wall. Miss Emily Grierson remains in voluntary isolation (or perhaps fettered by some inner compulsion) away from the bustle and dust and sunshine of the human world of normal affairs, and what in the end is found in the upstairs room gives perhaps a sense of penetrating and gruesome horror.

Has this sense of horror been conjured up for its own sake? If not, then why has the author contrived to insert so much of the monstrous into the story? In other words, does the horror contribute to the theme of Faulkner's story? Is the horror meaningful?

In order to answer this question, we shall have to examine rather carefully some of the items earlier in the story. In the first place, why does Miss Emily commit her monstrous act? Is she supplied with a proper motivation? Faulkner has, we can see, been rather careful to prepare for his dénouement. Miss Emily, it becomes obvious fairly early in the story, is one of those persons for whom the distinction between reality and illusion has blurred out. For example, she refuses to admit that she owes any taxes. When the mayor protests, she does not recognize him as mayor. Instead, she refers the committee to Colonel Sartoris, who, as the reader is told, has been dead for nearly ten years. For Miss Emily, apparently, Colonel Sartoris is still alive. Most specific preparation of all, when her father dies, she denies to the townspeople for three days that he is dead· "Just as they were about to resort to law and force, she broke down, and they buried her father quickly."

Miss Emily is obviously a pathological case. The narrator indicates plainly enough that people felt that she was crazy. All of this explanation prepares us for what Miss Emily does in order to hold her lover—the dead lover is in one sense still alive for her—the realms of reality and appearance merge. But having said this, we have got no nearer to justifying the story: for, if Faulkner is merely interested in relating a case history of abnormal psychology, the story lacks meaning and justification as a story and we are back to fiction as "clinical report" which we spoke of in connection with "The Occurrence at Owl Creek Bridge" (p. 123). If the story is to be justified, there must be what may be called a moral significance, a meaning in moral terms—not merely psychological terms.

Incidentally, it is very easy to misread the story as merely a horrible case history, presented in order to titillate the reader. Faulkner has been frequently judged to be doing nothing more than this in his work.

The lapse of the distinction between illusion and reality, between life and death, is important, therefore, in helping to account for Miss Emily's motivation, but merely to note this lapse is not fully to account for the theme of the story.

Suppose we approach the motivation again in these terms: what is

Miss Emily like? What are the mainsprings of her character? What causes the distinction between illusion and reality to blur out for her? She is obviously a woman of tremendous firmness of will. In the matter of the taxes, crazed though she is, she is never at a loss. She is utterly composed. She dominates the rather frightened committee of officers who see her. In the matter of her purchase of the poison, she completely overawes the clerk. She makes no pretense. She refuses to tell him what she wants the poison for. And yet this firmness of will and this iron pride have not kept her from being thwarted and hurt. Her father has run off the young men who came to call upon her, and for the man who tells the story, Miss Emily and her father form a tableau: "Miss Emily a slender figure in white in the background, her father a spraddled silhouette in the foreground, his back to her and clutching a horsewhip, the two of them framed by the back-flung front door." Whether the picture is a remembered scene, or merely a symbolical construct, this is the picture which remains in the storyteller's mind.

We have indicated that her pride is connected with her contempt for public opinion. This comes to the fore, of course, when she rides around about the town with the foreman whom everybody believes is beneath her. And it is her proud refusal to admit an external set of codes, or conventions, or other wills which contradict her own will, which makes her capable at the end of keeping her lover from going away. Confronted with his jilting her, she tries to override not only his will and the opinion of other people, but the laws of death and decay themselves.

But this, still, hardly gives the meaning of the story. For in all that has been said thus far, we are still merely accounting for a psychological aberration—we are still merely dealing with a case history in abnormal psychology. In order to make a case for the story as "meaningful," we shall have to tie Miss Emily's thoughts and actions back into the normal life of the community, and establish some sort of relationship between them. And just here one pervasive element in the narration suggests a clue. The story is told by one of the townspeople. And in it, as a constant factor, is the reference to what the community thought of Miss Emily. Continually through the story is it what "we" said, and then what "we" did, and what seemed true to "us," and so on. The narrator puts the matter even more sharply still. He says, in the course of the story, that to the community Miss Emily seemed "dear, inescapable, impervious, tranquil, and perverse." Each of the adjectives is important and meaningful. In a sense, Miss Emily because of her very fact of isolation and perversity belongs to the whole community. She is even something treasured by it. Ironically, because of Emily's perversion of an aristocratic independence of mores and because of her contempt for "what people say," her life is public, even communal. And various phrases used by the narrator underline this view of her position. For example, her face looks "as you imagine a lighthouse-keeper's face ought to look," like the face of a person who lives in the kind of isolation imposed on a lighthouse-keeper, who looks out into the blackness and whose light serves a public function. Or, again, after her father's death, she becomes very ill, and when she appears after the illness, she has "a vague resemblance to those angels in colored church windows—sort of tragic and serene." Whatever we make of these descriptions, certainly the author is trying to suggest a kind of calm and dignity which is super-mundane, unearthly, or "over-earthly," such as an angel might possess.

Miss Emily, then, is a combination of idol and scapegoat for the community. On the one hand, the community feels admiration for Miss Emily —she represents something in the past of the community which the community is proud of. They feel a sort of awe of her, as is illustrated by the behavior of the mayor and the committee in her presence. On the other hand, her queerness, the fact that she cannot compete with them in their ordinary life, the fact that she is hopelessly out of touch with the modern world—all of these things make them feel superior to her, and also to that past which she represents. It is, then, Miss Emily's complete detachment which gives her actions their special meaning for the community.

Miss Emily, since she is the conscious aristocrat, since she is consciously "better" than other people, since she is above and outside their canons of behavior, can, at the same time, be worse than other people; and she *is* worse, horribly so. She is worse than other people, but at the same time, as the narrator implies, she remains somehow admirable. This raises a fundamental question: why is this true?

Perhaps the horrible and the admirable aspects of Miss Emily's final deed arise from the same basic fact of her character: she insists on meeting the world on her own terms. She never cringes, she never begs for sympathy, she refuses to shrink into an amiable old maid, she never accepts the community's ordinary judgments or values. This independence of spirit and pride can, and does in her case, twist the individual into a sort of monster, but, at the same time, this refusal to accept the herd values carries with it a dignity and courage. The community senses this, as we gather from the fact that the community carries out the decencies of the funeral before breaking in the door of the upper room. There is, as it were, a kind of secret understanding that she has won her right of privacy, until she herself has entered history. Furthermore, despite the fact that, as the narrator says, "already we knew that there was one room in that region above stairs which no one had seen in forty years, and which would have to be forced," her funeral is something of a state occasion, with "the very old men—some in their brushed Confederate uniforms—on the porch and the lawn, talking of Miss Emily as if she had been a contemporary of theirs, believing that they had danced with her and courted her perhaps . . ." In other words, the community accepts her into its honored history. All of this works as a kind of tacit recognition of Miss Emily's triumph of will.

The community, we are told earlier, had wanted to pity Miss Emily when she had lost her money, just as they had wanted to commiserate over her when they believed that she had actually become a fallen woman, but she had triumphed over their pity and commiseration and condemnation, just as she had triumphed over all their other attitudes.

But, as we have indicated earlier, it may be said that Miss Emily is mad. This may be true, but there are two things to consider in this connection. First, one must consider the special terms which her "madness" takes. Her madness is simply a development of her pride and her refusal to submit to ordinary standards of behavior. So, because of this fact, her "madness" is meaningful after all. It involves issues which in themselves are really important and have to do with the world of conscious moral choice. Second, the community interprets her "madness" as meaningful. They admire her, even if they are disappointed by her refusals to let herself be pitied, and the narrator, who is a spokesman for the community, recognizes the last grim revelation as an instance of her having carried her own values to their ultimate conclusion. She would marry the common laborer, Homer Barron, let the community think what it would. She would not be jilted. And she would hold him as a lover. But it would all be on her own terms. She remains completely dominant, and contemptuous of the day-to-day world.

It has been suggested by many critics that tragedy implies a hero who is completely himself, who insists on meeting the world on his own terms, who wants something so intensely, or lives so intensely, that he cannot accept any compromise. It cannot be maintained that this story is comparable to any of the great tragedies, such as *Hamlet* or *King Lear,* but it can be pointed out that this story, in its own way, involves some of the same basic elements. Certainly, Miss Emily's pride, isolation, and independence remind one of factors in the character of the typical tragic hero. And it can be pointed out that, just as the horror of her deed lies outside the ordinary life of the community, so the magnificence of her independence lies outside its ordinary virtues.

1. What difficulties would be raised if one should try to tell this story from the point of view of the third person?

2. Why is it significant that Miss Emily chooses for her lover a man who is scornfully regarded by the community as a "Northerner, a day laborer"?

3. Look back at "R.M.S. *Titanic,*" "Old Red," "The Lottery," and "The Killers," in the light of their general symbolic significance. Can it be argued that the present story, like them, has a more general significance —that it is a symbolic commentary on our society?

FLANNERY O'CONNOR

A Good Man Is Hard to Find

THE grandmother didn't want to go to Florida. She wanted to visit some of her connections in east Tennessee and she was seizing at every chance to change Bailey's mind. Bailey was the son she lived with, her only boy. He was sitting on the edge of his chair at the table, bent over the orange sports section of the *Journal.* "Now look here, Bailey," she said, "see here, read this," and she stood with one hand on her thin hip and the other rattling the newspaper at his bald head. "Here this fellow that calls himself The Misfit is aloose from the Federal Pen and headed toward Florida and you read what it says he did to these people. Just you read it. I wouldn't take my children in any direction with a criminal like that aloose in it. I couldn't answer to my conscience if I did."

Bailey didn't look up from his reading so she wheeled around then and faced the children's mother, a young woman in slacks, whose face was as broad and innocent as a cabbage and was tied around with a green head-kerchief that had two points on the top like rabbit's ears. She was sitting on the sofa, feeding the baby his apricots out of a jar. "The children have been to Florida before," the old lady said. "You all ought to take them somewhere else for a change so they would see different parts of the world and be broad. They never have been to east Tennessee."

The children's mother didn't seem to hear her but the eight-year-old boy, John Wesley, a stocky child with glasses, said, "If you don't want to go to Florida, why dontcha stay at home?" He and the little girl, June Star, were reading the funny papers on the floor.

"She wouldn't stay at home to be queen for a day," June Star said without raising her yellow head.

"Yes, and what would you do if this fellow, The Misfit, caught you?" the grandmother asked.

"I'd smack his face," John Wesley said.

"She wouldn't stay at home for a million bucks," June Star said. "Afraid she'd miss something. She has to go everywhere we go."

"All right, Miss," the grandmother said. "Just remember that the next time you want me to curl your hair."

June Star said her hair was naturally curly.

The next morning the grandmother was the first one in the car, ready to go. She had her big black valise that looked like the head of a hippopotamus in one corner, and underneath it she was hiding a basket with Pitty Sing, the cat, in it. She didn't intend for the cat to be left alone in the house for three days because he would miss her too much and she was afraid he might brush against one of the gas burners and accidentally asphyxiate himself. Her son, Bailey, didn't like to arrive at a motel with a cat.

She sat in the middle of the back seat with John Wesley and June Star on either side of her. Bailey and the children's mother and the baby sat in front and they left Atlanta at eight forty-five with the mileage on the car at 55890. The grandmother wrote this down because she thought it would be interesting to say how many miles they had been when they got back. It took them twenty minutes to reach the outskirts of the city.

The old lady settled herself comfortably, removing her white cotton gloves and putting them up with her purse on the shelf in front of the back window. The children's mother still had on slacks and still had her head tied up in a green kerchief, but the grandmother had on a navy blue straw sailor hat with a bunch of white violets on the brim and a navy blue dress with a small white dot in the print. Her collars and cuffs were white organdy trimmed with lace and at her neckline she had pinned a purple spray of cloth violets containing a sachet. In case of an accident, anyone seeing her dead on the highway would know at once that she was a lady.

She said she thought it was going to be a good day for driving, neither too hot nor too cold, and she cautioned Bailey that the speed limit was fifty-five miles an hour and that the patrolmen hid themselves behind billboards and small clumps of trees and sped out after you before you had a chance to slow down. She pointed out interesting details of the scenery: Stone Mountain; the blue granite that in some places came up to both sides of the highway; the brilliant red clay banks slightly streaked with purple; and the various crops that made rows of green lace-work on the ground. The trees were full of silver-white sunlight and the meanest of them sparkled. The children were reading comic magazines and their mother had gone back to sleep.

"Let's go through Georgia fast so we won't have to look at it much," John Wesley said.

"If I were a little boy," said the grandmother, "I wouldn't talk about my native state that way. Tennessee has the mountains and Georgia has the hills."

"Tennessee is just a hillbilly dumping ground," John Wesley said, "and Georgia is a lousy state too."

"You said it," June Star said.

"In my time," said the grandmother, folding her thin veined fingers, "children were more respectful of their native states and their parents and everything else. People did right then. Oh look at the cute little pickaninny!" she said and pointed to a Negro child standing in the door of a shack. "Wouldn't that make a picture, now?" she asked and they all turned and looked at the little Negro out of the back window. He waved.

"He didn't have any britches on," June Star said.

"He probably didn't have any," the grandmother explained. "Little niggers in the country don't have things like we do. If I could paint, I'd paint that picture," she said.

The children exchanged comic books.

The grandmother offered to hold the baby and the children's mother passed him over the front seat to her. She set him on her knee and bounced him and told him about the things they were passing. She rolled her eyes and screwed up her mouth and stuck her leathery thin face into his smooth bland one. Occasionally he gave her a faraway smile. They passed a large cotton field with five or six graves fenced in the middle of it, like a small island. "Look at the graveyard!" the grandmother said, pointing it out. "That was the old family burying ground. That belonged to the planta-tion."

"Where's the plantation?" John Wesley asked.

"Gone With the Wind," said the grandmother. "Ha. Ha."

When the children finished all the comic books they had brought, they opened the lunch and ate it. The grandmother ate a peanut butter sandwich and an olive and would not let the children throw the box and the paper napkins out the window. When there was nothing else to do they played a game by choosing a cloud and making the other two guess what shape it suggested. John Wesley took one the shape of a cow and June Star guessed a cow and John Wesley said, no, an automobile, and June Star said he didn't play fair, and they began to slap each other over the grandmother.

The grandmother said she would tell them a story if they would keep quiet. When she told a story, she rolled her eyes and waved her head and was very dramatic. She said once when she was a maiden lady she had been courted by a Mr. Edgar Atkins Teagarden from Jasper, Georgia. She said he was a very good-looking man and a gentleman and that he brought her a watermelon every Saturday afternoon with his initials cut in it, E. A. T. Well, one Saturday, she said, Mr. Teagarden brought the watermelon and there was nobody at home and he left it on the front porch and returned in his buggy to Jasper, but she never got the watermelon, she said, because a nigger boy ate it when he saw the initials, E. A. T.! This story tickled John Wesley's funny bone and he giggled and giggled but June Star didn't think it was any good. She said she wouldn't marry a man that just brought her a watermelon on Saturday. The grandmother said she would have done well to marry Mr. Teagarden because he was a gentleman and had bought Coca-Cola stock when it first came out and that he had died only a few years ago, a very wealthy man.

They stopped at The Tower for barbecued sandwiches. The Tower was a part stucco and part wood filling station and dance hall set in a clearing outside of Timothy. A fat man named Red Sammy Butts ran it and there were signs stuck here and there on the building and for miles up and down the highway saying, TRY RED SAMMY'S FAMOUS BARBECUE. NONE LIKE FAMOUS RED SAMMY'S! RED SAM! THE FAT BOY WITH THE HAPPY LAUGH. A VETERAN! RED SAMMY'S YOUR MAN!

Red Sammy was lying on the bare ground outside The Tower with his head under a truck while a gray monkey about a foot high, chained to a small chinaberry tree, chattered nearby. The monkey sprang back into the tree and got on the highest limb as soon as he saw the children jump out of the car and run toward him.

Inside, The Tower was a long dark room with a counter at one end and tables at the other and dancing space in the middle. They all sat down at a board table next to the nickelodeon and Red Sam's wife, a tall burntbrown woman with hair and eyes lighter than her skin, came and took their order. The children's mother put a dime in the machine and played "The Tennessee Waltz," and the grandmother said that tune always made her want to dance. She asked Bailey if he would like to dance but he only glared at her. He didn't have a naturally sunny disposition like she did and trips made him nervous. The grandmother's brown eyes were very bright. She swayed her head from side to side and pretended she was dancing in her chair. June Star said play something she could tap to so the children's mother put in another dime and played a fast number and June Star stepped out onto the dance floor and did her tap routine.

"Ain't she cute?" Red Sam's wife said, leaning over the counter. "Would you like to come be my little girl?"

"No I certainly wouldn't," June Star said. "I wouldn't live in a broken-down place like this for a million bucks!" and she ran back to the table.

"Ain't she cute?" the woman repeated, stretching her mouth politely.

"Aren't you ashamed?" hissed the grandmother.

Red Sam came in and told his wife to quit lounging on the counter and hurry up with these people's order. His khaki trousers reached just to his hip bones and his stomach hung over them like a sack of meal swaying under his shirt. He came over and sat down at a table nearby and let out a combination sigh and yodel. "You can't win," he said. "You can't win," and he wiped his sweating red face off with a gray handkerchief. "These days you don't know who to trust," he said. "Ain't that the truth?"

"People are certainly not nice like they used to be," said the grandmother.

"Two fellers come in here last week," Red Sammy said, "driving a Chrysler. It was a old beat-up car but it was a good one and these boys looked all right to me. Said they worked at the mill and you know I let them fellers charge the gas they bought? Now why did I do that?"

"Because you're a good man!" the grandmother said at once.

"Yes'm, I suppose so," Red Sam said as if he were struck with this answer.

His wife brought the orders, carrying the five plates all at once without a tray, two in each hand and one balanced on her arm. "It isn't a soul in this green world of God's that you can trust," she said. "And I don't count nobody out of that, not nobody," she repeated, looking at Red Sammy.

"Did you read about that criminal, The Misfit, that's escaped?" asked the grandmother.

"I wouldn't be a bit surprised if he didn't attack this place right here," said the woman. "If he hears about it being here, I wouldn't be none surprised to see him. If he hears it's two cent in the cash register, I wouldn't be at all surprised if he . . ."

"That'll do," Red Sam said. "Go bring these people their Co'-Colas," and the woman went off to get the rest of the order.

"A good man is hard to find," Red Sammy said. "Everything is getting terrible. I remember the day you could go off and leave your screen door unlatched. Not no more."

He and the grandmother discussed better times. The old lady said that in her opinion Europe was entirely to blame for the way things were now. She said the way Europe acted you would think we were made of money and Red Sam said it was no use talking about it, she was exactly right. The children ran outside into the white sunlight and looked at the monkey in the lacy chinaberry tree. He was busy catching fleas on himself and biting each one carefully between his teeth as if it were a delicacy.

They drove off again into the hot afternoon. The grandmother took cat naps and woke up every few minutes with her own snoring. Outside of Toombsboro she woke up and recalled an old plantation that she had visited in this neighborhood once when she was a young lady. She said the house had six white columns across the front and that there was an avenue of oaks leading up to it and two little wooden trellis arbors on either side in front where you sat down with your suitor after a stroll in the garden. She recalled exactly which road to turn off to get to it. She knew that Bailey would not be willing to lose any time looking at an old house, but the more she talked about it, the more she wanted to see it once again and find out if the little twin arbors were still standing. "There was a secret panel in this house," she said craftily, not telling the truth but wishing that she were, "and the story went that all the family silver was hidden in it when Sherman came through but it was never found . . ."

"Hey!" John Wesley said. "Let's go see it! We'll find it! We'll poke all the woodwork and find it! Who lives there? Where do you turn off at? Hey Pop, can't we turn off there?"

"We never have seen a house with a secret panel!" June Star shrieked. "Let's go to the house with the secret panel! Hey Pop, can't we go see the house with the secret panel!"

"It's not far from here, I know," the grandmother said. "It wouldn't take over twenty minutes."

Bailey was looking straight ahead. His jaw was as rigid as a horseshoe. "No," he said.

The children began to yell and scream that they wanted to see the house with the secret panel. John Wesley kicked the back of the front seat and June Star hung over her mother's shoulder and whined desperately into her ear that they never had any fun even on their vacation, that they could never do what THEY wanted to do. The baby began to scream and John Wesley kicked the back of the seat so hard that his father could feel the blows in his kidney.

"All right!" he shouted and drew the car to a stop at the side of the road. "Will you all shut up? Will you all just shut up for one second? If you don't shut up, we won't go anywhere."

"It would be very educational for them," the grandmother murmured.

"All right," Bailey said, "but get this: this is the only time we're going to stop for anything like this. This is the one and only time."

"The dirt road that you have to turn down is about a mile back," the grandmother directed. "I marked it when we passed."

"A dirt road," Bailey groaned.

After they had turned around and were headed toward the dirt road, the grandmother recalled other points about the house, the beautiful glass over the front doorway and the candle-lamp in the hall. John Wesley said that the secret panel was probably in the fireplace.

"You can't go inside this house," Bailey said. "You don't know who lives there."

"While you all talk to the people in front, I'll run around behind and get in a window," John Wesley suggested.

"We'll all stay in the car," his mother said.

They turned onto the dirt road and the car raced roughly along in a swirl of pink dust. The grandmother recalled the times when there were no paved roads and thirty miles was a day's journey. The dirt road was hilly and there were sudden washes in it and sharp curves on dangerous embankments. All at once they would be on a hill, looking down over the blue tops of trees for miles around, then the next minute, they would be in a red depression with the dust-coated trees looking down on them.

"This place had better turn up in a minute," Bailey said, "or I'm going to turn around."

The road looked as if no one had traveled on it in months.

"It's not much farther," the grandmother said and just as she said it, a horrible thought came to her. The thought was so embarrassing that she turned red in the face and her eyes dilated and her feet jumped up, upsetting her valise in the corner. The instant the valise moved, the newspaper top she had over the basket under it rose with a snarl and Pitty Sing, the cat, sprang onto Bailey's shoulder.

The children were thrown to the floor and their mother, clutching the baby, was thrown out the door onto the ground; the old lady was thrown into the front seat. The car turned over once and landed right-side-up in a gulch off the side of the road. Bailey remained in the driver's seat with the cat—gray-striped with a broad white face and an orange nose —clinging to his neck like a caterpillar.

As soon as the children saw they could move their arms and legs, they scrambled out of the car, shouting, "We've had an ACCIDENT!" The grandmother was curled up under the dashboard, hoping she was injured so that Bailey's wrath would not come down on her all at once. The horrible thought she had had before the accident was that the house she had remembered so vividly was not in Georgia but in Tennessee.

Bailey removed the cat from his neck with both hands and flung it out the window against the side of a pine tree. Then he got out of the car and started looking for the children's mother. She was sitting against the side of the red gutted ditch, holding the screaming baby, but she only had a cut down her face and a broken shoulder. "We've had an ACCIDENT!" the children screamed in a frenzy of delight.

"But nobody's killed," June Star said with disappointment as the grandmother limped out of the car, her hat still pinned to her head but the broken front brim standing up at a jaunty angle and the violet spray hanging off the side. They all sat down in the ditch, except the children, to recover from the shock. They were all shaking.

"Maybe a car will come along," said the children's mother hoarsely.

"I believe I have an injured organ," said the grandmother, pressing her side, but no one answered her. Bailey's teeth were clattering. He had on a yellow sport shirt with bright blue parrots designed on it and his face was as yellow as the shirt. The grandmother decided that she would not mention that the house was in Tennessee.

The road was about ten feet above and they could see only the tops of the trees on the other side of it. Behind the ditch they were sitting in there were more woods, tall and dark and deep. In a few minutes they saw a car some distance away on top of a hill, coming slowly as if the occupants were watching them. The grandmother stood up and waved both arms dramatically to attract their attention. The car continued to come on slowly, disappeared around a bend and appeared again, moving even slower, on top of the hill they had gone over. It was a big black battered hearse-like automobile. There were three men in it.

It came to a stop just over them and for some minutes, the driver looked down with a steady expressionless gaze to where they were sitting, and didn't speak. Then he turned his head and muttered something to the other two and they got out. One was a fat boy in black trousers and a red sweat shirt with a silver stallion embossed on the front of it. He moved around on the right side of them and stood staring, his mouth partly open in a kind of loose grin. The other had on khaki pants and a blue striped coat and a gray hat pulled down very low, hiding most of his face. He came around slowly on the left side. Neither spoke.

The driver got out of the car and stood by the side of it, looking down at them. He was an older man than the other two. His hair was just beginning to gray and he wore silver-rimmed spectacles that give him a scholarly look. He had a long creased face and didn't have on any shirt or undershirt. He had on blue jeans that were too tight for him and was holding a black hat and a gun. The two boys also had guns.

"We've had an ACCIDENT!" the children screamed.

The grandmother had the peculiar feeling that the bespectacled man was someone she knew. His face was as familiar to her as if she had known him all her life but she could not recall who he was. He moved away from the car and began to come down the embankment, placing his feet carefully so that he wouldn't slip. He had on tan and white shoes and no socks, and his ankles were red and thin. "Good afternoon," he said. "I see you all had you a little spill."

"We turned over twice!" said the grandmother.

"Oncet," he corrected. "We seen it happen. Try their car and see will it run, Hiram," he said quietly to the boy with the gray hat.

"What you got that gun for?" John Wesley asked. "Whatcha gonna do with that gun?"

"Lady," the man said to the children's mother, "would you mind calling them children to sit down by you? Children make me nervous. I want all you to sit down right together there where you're at."

"What are you telling US what to do for?" June Star asked.

Behind them the line of woods gaped like a dark open mouth. "Come here," said their mother.

"Look here now," Bailey began suddenly, "we're in a predicament! We're in . . ."

The grandmother shrieked. She scrambled to her feet and stood staring. "You're The Misfit!" she said. "I recognized you at once!"

"Yes'm," the man said, smiling slightly as if he were pleased in spite of himself to be known, "but it would have been better for all of you, lady, if you hadn't of reckernized me."

Bailey turned his head sharply and said something to his mother that shocked even the children. The old lady began to cry and The Misfit reddened.

"Lady," he said, "don't you get upset. Sometimes a man says things he don't mean. I don't reckon he meant to talk to you thataway."

"You wouldn't shoot a lady, would you?" the grandmother said and removed the clean handkerchief from her cuff and began to slap at her eyes with it.

The Misfit pointed the toe of his shoe into the ground and made a little hole and then covered it up again. "I would hate to have to," he said.

"Listen," the grandmother almost screamed, "I know you're a good man. You don't look a bit like you have common blood. I know you must come from nice people!"

"Yes mam," he said, "finest people in the world." When he smiled he showed a row of strong white teeth. "God never made a finer woman than my mother and my daddy's heart was pure gold," he said. The boy with the red sweat shirt had come around behind them and was standing with his gun at his hip. The Misfit squatted down on the ground. "Watch them children, Bobby Lee," he said. "You know they make me nervous." He looked at the six of them huddled together in front of him and he seemed to be embarrassed as if he couldn't think of anything to say. "Ain't a cloud in the sky," he remarked, looking up at it. "Don't see no sun but don't see no cloud neither."

"Yes, it's a beautiful day," said the grandmother. "Listen," she said, "you shouldn't call yourself The Misfit because I know you're a good man at heart. I can just look at you and tell."

"Hush!" Bailey yelled. "Hush! Everybody shut up and let me handle this!" He was squatting in the position of a runner about to sprint forward but he didn't move.

"I pre-chate that, lady," The Misfit said and drew a little circle in the ground with the butt of his gun.

"It'll take a half a hour to fix this here car," Hiram called, looking over the raised hood of it.

"Well, first you and Bobby Lee get him and that little boy to step over yonder with you," The Misfit said, pointing to Bailey and John Wesley. "The boys want to ask you something," he said to Bailey. "Would you mind stepping back in them woods there with them?"

"Listen," Bailey began, "we're in a terrible predicament! Nobody realizes what this is," and his voice cracked. His eyes were as blue and intense as the parrots on his shirt and he remained perfectly still.

The grandmother reached up to adjust her hat brim as if she were going to the woods with him but it came off in her hand. She stood staring at it and after a second she let it fall on the ground. Hiram pulled Bailey up by the arm as if he were assisting an old man. John Wesley caught hold of his father's hand and Bobby Lee followed. They went off toward the woods and just as they reached the dark edge, Bailey turned and supported himself against a gray naked pine trunk, he shouted, "I'll be back in a minute, Mamma, wait on me!"

"Come back this instant!" his mother shrilled but they all disappeared into the woods.

"Bailey Boy!" the grandmother called in a tragic voice but she found she was looking at The Misfit squatting on the ground in front of her. "I just know you're a good man," she said desperately. "You're not a bit common!"

"Nome, I ain't a good man," The Misfit said after a second as if he had considered her statement carefully, "but I ain't the worst in the world neither. My daddy said I was a different breed of dog from my brothers and sisters. 'You know,' Daddy said, 'it's some that can live their whole life out without asking about it and it's others has to know why it is, and this boy is one of the latters. He's going to be into everything!' " He put on his black hat and looked up suddenly and then away deep into the woods as if he were embarrassed again. "I'm sorry I don't have on a shirt before you ladies," he said, hunching his shoulders slightly. "We buried our clothes that we had on when we escaped and we're just making do until we can get better. We borrowed these from some folks we met," he explained.

"That's perfectly all right," the grandmother said. "Maybe Bailey has an extra shirt in his suitcase."

"I'll look and see terrectly," The Misfit said.

"Where are they taking him?" the children's mother screamed.

"Daddy was a card himself," The Misfit said. "You couldn't put anything over on him. He never got in trouble with the Authorities though. Just had the knack of handling them."

"You could be honest too if you'd only try," said the grandmother. "Think how wonderful it would be to settle down and live a comfortable life and not have to think about somebody chasing you all the time."

The Misfit kept scratching in the ground with the butt of his gun as if he were thinking about it. "Yes'm, somebody is always after you," he murmured.

The grandmother noticed how thin his shoulder blades were just behind his hat because she was standing up looking down on him. "Do you ever pray?" she asked.

He shook his head. All she saw was the black hat wiggle between his shoulder blades. "Nome," he said.

There was a pistol shot from the woods, followed closely by another. Then silence. The old lady's head jerked around. She could hear the wind move through the tree tops like a long satisfied insuck of breath. "Bailey Boy!" she called.

"I was a gospel singer for a while," The Misfit said. "I been most everything. Been in the arm service, both land and sea, at home and abroad, been twict married, been an undertaker, been with the railroads, plowed Mother Earth, been in a tornado, seen a man burnt alive oncet," and he looked up at the children's mother and the little girl who were sitting close together, their faces white and their eyes glassy; "I even seen a woman flogged," he said.

"Pray, pray," the grandmother began, "pray, pray . . ."

"I never was a bad boy that I remember of," The Misfit said in an almost dreamy voice, "but somewheres along the line I done something wrong and got sent to the penitentiary. I was buried alive," and he looked up and held her attention to him by a steady stare.

"That's when you should have started to pray," she said. "What did you do to get sent to the penitentiary that first time?"

"Turn to the right, it was a wall," The Misfit said, looking up again at the cloudless sky. "Turn to the left, it was a wall. Look up it was a ceiling, look down it was a floor. I forget what I done, lady. I set there and set there, trying to remember what it was I done and I ain't recalled it to this day. Oncet in a while, I would think it was coming to me, but it never come."

"Maybe they put you in by mistake," the old lady said vaguely.

"Nome," he said. "It wasn't no mistake. They had the papers on me."

"You must have stolen something," she said.

The Misfit sneered slightly. "Nobody had nothing I wanted," he said. "It was a head-doctor at the penitentiary said what I had done was kill my daddy but I known that for a lie. My daddy died in nineteen ought nineteen of the epidemic flu and I never had a thing to do with it. He was buried in the Mount Hopewell Baptist churchyard and you can go there and see for yourself."

"If you would pray," the old lady said, "Jesus would help you."

"That's right," The Misfit said.

"Well then, why don't you pray?" she asked trembling with delight suddenly.

"I don't want no hep," he said. "I'm doing all right by myself."

Bobby Lee and Hiram came ambling back from the woods. Bobby Lee was dragging a yellow shirt with bright blue parrots in it.

"Throw me that shirt, Bobby Lee," The Misfit said. The shirt came flying at him and landed on his shoulder and he put it on. The grandmother couldn't name what the shirt reminded her of. "No, lady," The Misfit said while he was buttoning it up, "I found out the crime don't matter. You can do one thing or you can do another, kill a man or take a tire off his car, because sooner or later you're going to forget what it was you done and just be punished for it."

The children's mother had begun to make heaving noises as if she couldn't get her breath. "Lady," he asked, "would you and that little girl like to step off yonder with Bobby Lee and Hiram and join your husband?"

"Yes, thank you," the mother said faintly. Her left arm dangled helplessly and she was holding the baby, who had gone to sleep, in the other. "Hep that lady up, Hiram," The Misfit said as she struggled to climb out of the ditch, "and Bobby Lee, you hold onto that little girl's hand."

"I don't want to hold hands with him," June Star said. "He reminds me of a pig."

The fat boy blushed and laughed and caught her by the arm and pulled her off into the woods after Hiram and her mother.

Alone with The Misfit, the grandmother found that she had lost her voice. There was not a cloud in the sky nor any sun. There was nothing around her but woods. She wanted to tell him that he must pray. She opened and closed her mouth several times before anything came out. Finally she found herself saying, "Jesus, Jesus," meaning, Jesus will help you, but the way she was saying it, it sounded as if she might be cursing.

"Yes'm," The Misfit said as if he agreed. "Jesus thown everything off balance. It was the same case with Him as with me except He hadn't committed any crime and they could prove I had committed one because they had the papers on me. Of course," he said, "they never shown me my papers. That's why I sign myself now. I said long ago, you get you a signature and sign everything you do and keep a copy of it. Then you'll know what you done and you can hold up the crime to the punishment and see do they match and in the end you'll have something to prove you ain't been treated right. I call myself The Misfit," he said, "because I can't make what all I done wrong fit what all I gone through in punishment."

There was a piercing scream from the woods, followed closely by a pistol report. "Does it seem right to you, lady, that one is punished a heap and another ain't punished at all?"

"Jesus!" the old lady cried. "You've got good blood! I know you wouldn't shoot a lady! I know you come from nice people! Pray! Jesus, you ought not to shoot a lady. I'll give you all the money I've got!"

"Lady," The Misfit said, looking beyond her far into the woods, "there never was a body that give the undertaker a tip."

There were two more pistol reports and the grandmother raised her head like a parched old turkey hen crying for water and called, "Bailey Boy, Bailey Boy!" as if her heart would break.

"Jesus was the only One that ever raised the dead," The Misfit continued, "and He shouldn't have done it. He thown everything off balance. If He did what He said, then it's nothing for you to do but throw away everything and follow Him, and if He didn't, then it's nothing for you to do but enjoy the few minutes you got left the best way you can—by killing somebody or burning down his house or doing some other meanness to him. No pleasure but meanness," he said and his voice had become almost a snarl.

"Maybe He didn't raise the dead," the old lady mumbled, not knowing what she was saying and feeling so dizzy that she sank down in the ditch with her legs twisted under her.

"I wasn't there so I can't say He didn't," The Misfit said. "I wisht I had of been there," he said, hitting the ground with his fist. "It ain't right I wasn't there because if I had of been there I would of known. Listen lady," he said in a high voice, "if I had of been there I would of known and I wouldn't be like I am now." His voice seemed about to crack and the grandmother's head cleared for an instant. She saw the man's face twisted close to her own as if he were going to cry and she murmured, "Why you're one of my babies. You're one of my own children!" She reached out and touched him on the shoulder. The Misfit sprang back as if a snake had bitten him and shot her three times through the chest. Then he put his gun down on the ground and took off his glasses and began to clean them.

Hiram and Bobby Lee returned from the woods and stood over the ditch, looking down at the grandmother who half sat and half lay in a puddle of blood with her legs crossed under her like a child's and her face smiling up at the cloudless sky.

Without his glasses, The Misfit's eyes were red-rimmed and pale and defenseless-looking. "Take her off and thow her where you thown the others," he said, picking up the cat that was rubbing itself against his leg.

"She was a talker, wasn't she?" Bobby Lee said, sliding down the ditch with a yodel.

"She would of been a good woman," The Misfit said, "if it had been somebody there to shoot her every minute of her life."

"Some fun!" Bobby Lee said.

"Shut up, Bobby Lee," The Misfit said. "It's no real pleasure in life."

INTERPRETATION

1. This story, like "A Rose For Emily," presents us with a shocking piece of pathology. Viewed objectively, the story is an account of how a homicidal maniac slaughters a family of ordinary, innocent people whom he happens to encounter on the road. How does the author interpret this special situation as a comment on general human values? (Of course, in so far as the story is coherent, everything in it will bear on the answer to this question, but especially important for an answer is the dialogue between the old lady and The Misfit. Study very carefully this dialogue and then try to make a statement about the theme of the story.)

2. What is the character of the old lady? Pleasant or unpleasant? Admirable or unadmirable? Selfish or unselfish? How does her character bear on the interpretation of the story?

3. The story can be said to be in two parts—the long first part dealing with the trip, and the second part after the encounter with The Misfit.

What, if anything, holds these two parts together? How does this connection between the parts relate to the theme of the story? In connection with this we may say that the encounter is pure coincidence—The Misfit just happens to come along at the moment when the family has the accident. We have said that, in general, dependence on coincidence is a fault in fiction. What about this instance? Does the fact of the coincidence bear on the theme?

4. What is the significance, if any, of the scene at the highway restaurant?

5. What responsibility does the old lady have for the family's disaster? Can we detect a pattern here? If so, what does it mean?

6. Let us suppose that the old lady were of unusual intelligence and were a completely devout Christian. What effect would this change have on the irony of the conclusion? In thinking of this question go back to the dialogue between the old lady and The Misfit. Which of the two, the sane woman or the maniac, is the more deeply involved in the religious question?

7. What significance for the story lies in the fact that the old lady feels that she has come down socially?

8. What impression do you have of the family in general? How do you relate this impression to the theme of the story?

9. What is the significance of the old lady's last words to The Misfit? For plot? For theme?

FRANZ KAFKA

In the Penal Colony

Translated by Eugene Jolas

"IT'S a curious machine," said the officer to the explorer, and despite the fact that he was well acquainted with the apparatus, he nevertheless looked at it with a certain admiration, as it were. It was apparently merely out of courtesy that the explorer had accepted the invitation of the commanding officer to attend the execution of a private soldier condemned for disobedience and insulting a superior officer. Nor did there appear to be great interest in this execution in the penal colony. At any rate, here in the deep, sandy little valley shut in on every side by naked slopes, there were present, beside the officer and the explorer, only the condemned man—an obtuse, wide-mouthed fellow, with neglected face and hair—and a soldier acting as guard. The latter held the heavy chain to which were attached the little chains that fettered the offender's ankles and wrists as well as his neck, and which were themselves linked together by connecting chains. As a matter of fact, however, the condemned man looked so doglike and submissive, one had the impression that he might be allowed to run freely about the slopes, and that, when the execution was about to begin, one would have only to whistle for him to come right back.

The explorer had little thought for the apparatus and started walking up and down behind the condemned man with almost visible indifference. Meanwhile, the officer began the final preparations, now crawling beneath the machine, which was built deep in the ground, now climbing a ladder in order to inspect the upper parts. These were tasks which could easily have been left to a mechanic, but the officer performed them with great zeal, either because he was a special advocate of this apparatus, or because for other reasons the work could not be entrusted to anyone else. "Now everything's ready," he finally called out and climbed down the ladder. He was exceedingly fatigued, breathing with his mouth wide open, and had stuck two dainty lady's handkerchiefs under the collar of his uniform. "These uniforms are much too heavy for the tropics," commented the explorer instead of making inquiries about the machine, as the officer had expected him to do. "Certainly," said the officer, washing his hands, stained with oil and grease, in a pail of water that stood ready near-by, "but they are the symbols of home, and we don't want to lose our homeland. But take a look at this machine," he added immediately, as he dried his hands with a towel, pointing at the same time to the apparatus. "Up till now, it still had to be worked by hand; now it works entirely alone." The explorer nodded and followed the officer. The latter, wanting to safeguard himself against all eventualities, said: "Of course disturbances do occur; I hope there will be none today, yet we must always reckon with one. For the apparatus has to run for twelve consecutive hours. But if there should be any disturbances, they will only be insignificant ones, and they will be repaired at once."

"Don't you want to sit down?" he finally asked, and choosing a wicker chair from a heap of others, he offered it to the explorer, who could not refuse. He was now sitting on the edge of a pit, into which he cast a fugitive glance. It was not very deep. On one side of the pit the turned-up earth had been heaped into a wall: on the other side stood the machine. "I don't know," said the officer, "if the commanding officer has already explained the apparatus to you." The explorer made a vague gesture of the hand; the officer asked nothing better, for now he could explain the apparatus himself. "This machine," he said, grasping the crankshaft, on which he was leaning, "is an invention of our former commanding officer. I coilaborated with him in the early experiments and took part in all the stages of the work up till the end. But credit for the invention belongs to him alone. Have you ever heard of our former commander? No? Well, I'm not exaggerating when I say that the organizing of the entire penal colony is his work. We who were his friends knew already, at the time of his death, that the organization of the colony was so complete in itself, that his successor, even though he were to have a thousand new ideas in his head, would not be able to change anything for many years to come, at least. What we foresaw has come about: the new commander has had to recognize this. It's too bad you did not know the former commander. But"—here the officer interrupted himself, "here I am gabbling away, and his apparatus is standing right here before us. It consists, as you see, of three parts. In the course of time, each of these parts has come to be designated by certain folk names, as it were. The lower one is called the 'bed,' the upper one the 'draughtsman,' and the middle one hanging up there is called the 'harrow.' " "The harrow?" asked the explorer. He had not been listening with undivided attention; the sun was much too tightly ensnared in the shadowless valley; it was hard to concentrate one's thoughts. The officer seemed to him all the more admirable, therefore, as he explained his cause so zealously, in his tight dress uniform, heavy with epaulets and hung with gold braid. Moreover, as he spoke he was busying himself with a screwdriver, tightening a screw here and there. The soldier seemed to be in a state of mind similar to that of the explorer. He had tied the condemned man's chain around both his wrists and was now leaning with one hand on his gun, his head drooping from the nape of his neck, indifferent to everything. The explorer was not surprised by this, for the officer was speaking French and certainly neither the soldier nor the condemned man understood French. It was, therefore, all the more striking that the condemned man should nevertheless have made an effort to follow the explanations of the officer. With a kind of sleepy perseverance he continued to direct his glance where the officer happened to be pointing. When the latter was now interrupted by a question from the explorer, he, too, looked, as did the officer, at the explorer.

"Yes, harrow," said the officer. "It's a suitable name. The needles are arranged as in a harrow and the whole thing is worked like a harrow, although always on the same spot, and much more artistically. You'll understand it right away, anyhow. The condemned man is laid here on the bed.— But I shall first of all describe the apparatus, and after that, I'll get the operation itself under way. You will then be able to follow it more easily. Also, there is a cog-wheel in the draughtsman which has gotten too worn down; it makes a creaking noise when it runs so that a person can hardly understand what is being said. Spare parts are hard to get here, too, unfortunately.—Well, then, as I said, here's the bed. It is entirely covered with a layer of cotton, the purpose of which you will learn later on. The condemned man is laid on this cotton, belly down and naked, of course; these straps for the hands, these for the feet, these for the throat, so as to fasten him tight. Here, at the head of the bed where, as I said, the man first lies on his face, there is this little ball of felt, which can be easily adjusted so that it goes right into the man's mouth. Its purpose is to prevent his screaming and biting his tongue. Of course, the man must take hold of the ball of felt since, otherwise, his neck would be broken by the throat-straps." "Is this cotton?" asked the explorer, bending forward. "Why certainly," said the officer smiling, "just feel it yourself." He seized the explorer's hand and guided it across the bed. "It's a specially prepared cotton, that's why it looks so unfamiliar; I'll have something to say about its purpose later on." The explorer was already won over a little in favor of the apparatus; he put his hands over his eyes as a protection against the sun and looked up at it. It was a large structure. The bed and the draughtsman were of equal dimensions and looked like two dark chests. The draughtsman was placed about two meters above the bed; both were connected at the corners by four brass poles which almost gave forth rays in the sunlight. The harrow was hanging between the chests, on a steel band.

The officer had hardly noticed the explorer's earlier indifference; he became aware, however, that his interest was now awakening; he therefore interrupted his explanations to give the explorer time for undisturbed contemplation. The condemned man imitated the explorer; since he could not place his hand over his eyes, he blinked directly upward.

"So the man lies down," said the explorer, and he leaned back in his armchair, crossing his legs.

"Yes," said the officer, pushing his cap back a little and passing his hand over his hot face, "now listen! Both the bed and the draughtsman have their own electric batteries; the bed needs one for itself, the draughtsman one for the harrow. As soon as the man has been strapped down, the bed is put in motion. It quivers simultaneously from side to side, as well as up and down, in tiny, very rapid vibrations. You will probably have seen similar machines in hospitals; only, in the case of our bed, all the motions are very precisely calculated; for they have to be painstakingly accorded to the motions of the harrow. But the execution proper of the sentence is left to this harrow."

"What is the sentence, anyway?" asked the explorer. "So you don't know that, either?" said the officer with astonishment, biting his lips. "Please excuse me; if my explanations are perhaps a bit disjointed, I sincerely beg your pardon. For these explanations were formerly given by the commanding officer; the new commander, however, has shunned this duty of rank; but that he should have failed to enlighten such an important visitor"—the explorer sought to wave away the mark of honor with both hands, but the officer insisted on the expression—"such an important visitor, about the form of our sentence, is another innovation which—," he had a curse on his lips, but restrained himself and said: "I was not informed, it is not my fault. As a matter of fact, I am the best qualified to explain our ways of judging, for I carry here"—he tapped his breast pocket—"the original drawings on the subject, made by the former commander."

"Drawings made by the commander himself?" asked the explorer. "Did he combine everything in his own person? Was he a soldier, a judge, a builder, a chemist, a draughtsman, all in one?"

"Surely," said the officer, nodding his head with a fixed, meditative expression. Then he examined his hands: they did not seem to him to be clean enough to touch the drawings; so he went to the pail and washed them once more. Then he took out a small leather brief case. "Our sentence does not sound severe," he said. "The law which the condemned man broke is written on his body with the harrow. For instance, this offender"—the officer pointed to the condemned man—"will have inscribed on his body: 'HONOR YOUR SUPERIOR.'"

The explorer gave a fleeting glance at the man; when the officer pointed towards him, he hung his head and seemed to be concentrating all his powers of hearing, on finding out something. But the motions of his tightly pressed, puffy lips showed clearly that he could understand nothing. The explorer had wanted to ask various questions but at the sight of the man he only asked: "Does he know his sentence?" "No," the officer said, and wanted to go right ahead with his explanations. But the explorer interrupted him: "So he does not know his sentence?" "No," said the officer again, and he hesitated a moment, as if demanding further justification of his question from the explorer. "It would be useless to announce it to him," he said, "he'll learn it anyway, on his own body." The explorer was inclined to remain silent, when he felt the condemned man's gaze upon him; it seemed to be asking if he could approve of the procedure described. So the explorer, who had already leaned back, bent forward once more and asked: "But he certainly must know that he has been condemned, doesn't he?" "He doesn't know that either," said the officer, smiling at the explorer, as if expecting further strange disclosures. "Well, then," said the explorer, passing his hand over his forehead, "so this man still does not know how his defense was undertaken?" "He had no opportunity of defending himself," said the officer, and looked to one side, as if he were talking to himself and did not want to embarrass the explorer by telling these things which seemed to him self-evident. "But he must surely have had a chance to defend himself?" said the explorer, rising from the armchair.

The officer realized that he was in danger of being held up for some time in his explanation of the apparatus. So he walked over to the explorer, took his arm, pointed towards the condemned man who, seeing that interest was so obviously directed his way, now stood at attention, while the guard drew the chain tighter. "The situation is as follows," said the officer. "I was appointed judge in the penal colony, despite my youth. For I was assistant to the former commander in all punitive matters and I am the one who knows the machine best. The principle on which I base my decisions is this: There is never any doubt about the guilt! Other courts cannot follow this principle, for they consist of many heads and also have still higher courts over them. Such is not the case here, or at least it was not the case with our former commander. To be sure, the new commander has already shown an inclination to meddle with my decisions, but I have always succeeded so far in warding him off, and I shall continue to do so.—You wanted an explanation of this case: it is as simple as all of them. The captain notified us this morning that this man, who had been assigned to his personal service and who slept in front of his door, had fallen asleep while on duty. For it is his duty to get up each time the hour strikes and salute before the captain's door. This is certainly not a difficult duty, but it is a necessary one, for he must be alert while on guard as well as while serving his superior. Last night the captain wanted to see if the servant was doing his duty. He opened the door at two o'clock sharp and found him asleep in a crouching position. He took his riding whip and lashed the man across the face. Now, instead of getting up and asking forgiveness, the man seized his superior by the legs, shook him, and shouted: 'Throw that whip away, or I'll eat you up.' These are the facts. The captain came to me an hour ago. I wrote down his statement and added the sentence immediately. Then I ordered the man to be put in chains. That was all very simple. If I had called the man first and questioned him, it would have only resulted in confusion. He would have lied; then, if I had succeeded in contradicting the first lies, he would have replaced these with new ones, and so forth. But now I've got hold of him, and I'll not let him go.—Is everything clear now? But time passes, the execution should have begun, and I am not yet through with the explanation of the apparatus." He forced the explorer back into his armchair, went back over to the machine and began: "As you see, this harrow corresponds to the form of a human being; here is the harrow for the upper part of the body, here are the harrows for the legs. For the head, this little burin alone is designated. Have I made myself clear?" He bent amiably towards the explorer, prepared to give the most exhaustive explanations.

The explorer looked at the harrow with wrinkled forehead. The information about the court proceedings had not satisfied him. After all, he was forced to tell himself, this was a penal colony; special measures were necessary here, and they were obliged to proceed according to military regulations up to the very last detail. Besides, he placed some hope in the new commander, who obviously intended to introduce—slowly, to be sure—a new procedure which could not penetrate the limited mind of this officer. This train of thought led the explorer to ask: "Is the commander going to attend the execution?" "That's not certain," said the officer, painfully affected by the unmotivated question, and his friendly expression became distorted. "That's exactly why we have to hurry," he continued. "I shall even have to cut my explanations short, as much as I regret to do so. But then I might add further explanations tomorrow, when the apparatus will have been cleaned again—the fact that it gets so dirty is its only defect. So now I'll give you only the most essential facts.—When the man lies on the bed and it has been made to vibrate, the harrow is lowered onto the body. Of itself it assumes a position that permits the sharp points just barely to touch the body; once it is in place, this steel cord tautens at once into a rod. And then the play begins. The uninitiated notice no external difference in the penalties. The harrow appears to be working uniformly. Tremblingly it sticks its points into the body, which has begun to tremble too, because of the bed. To make it possible for everyone to verify the execution of the sentence, the harrow was made of glass. A few technical difficulties had to be surmounted in order to fasten the needles into it, but we finally succeeded after many attempts. We simply spared no pains. And now everyone can watch the progress of the writing on the body through the glass. Would you mind coming nearer to look at the needles?"

Slowly the explorer arose, walked over and bent over the harrow. "You can see," said the officer, "two kinds of needles in different arrangements. Each long one has a short one next to it. For the long one writes and the short one sprays water in order to wash off the blood, and so keep the writing always clear. The bloody water is then conducted into little drains and finally flows into this principal drain which has an overflow pipe leading into the ditch." The officer pointed out the exact direction which the blood-water had to take. As he held both hands to the mouth of the overflow pipe in order to best illustrate his point, the explorer lifted his head and, groping behind him, was about to return to his seat. At that moment he saw to his horror that the condemned man, like himself, had acted on the invitation of the officer to inspect closely the construction of the harrow. He had dragged the drowsy guard a little way forward with his chain, and was also bending over the glass. He could be seen looking with uncertain eyes for the thing the two gentlemen had just been examining but, because he lacked the explanation, he was not successful. He bent first to one side, then to the other. Again and again his eye roved over the glass. The explorer wanted to push him back, for what he was doing was probably punishable. But the officer held the explorer back with one hand, took a clod of earth from the ditch with the other and threw it at the guard. The latter lifted his eyes suddenly, saw what the condemned man had dared do, let his gun drop and, digging his heels into the ground, he wrenched the condemned man back so that he fell right over. The guard looked down at the man as he writhed and clanked his chains. "Stand him up straight!" the officer shouted, for he noticed that the explorer's attention was far too diverted by the offender. What's more, the explorer was bending across the harrow, without bothering about it, intent only on finding out what was going to happen to the condemned man. "Handle him carefully," the officer shouted again. He ran around the apparatus, seized the condemned man, whose feet kept slipping from under him, by the shoulders and stood him upright, with the help of the guard.

"Now I know everything," said the explorer when the officer came back to him again. "Except the most important part," said the latter and grasping the explorer by the arm, he pointed upward; "There, in the draughtsman is the clockwork that determines the motions of the harrow, and this clockwork is regulated according to the drawing called for by the sentence. I still use the sketches made by the former commanding officer. Here they are,"—he pulled a few sheets out of his leather brief case—"but unfortunately I cannot let you take them in your hand, for they are my most precious possession. Please sit down, I'll show them to you from this distance, so that you may see everything well." He showed him the first page. The explorer would have liked to say a word of approval, but he only saw labyrinthine lines that frequently crossed and recrossed each other and covered the paper so densely that one could recognize only with difficulty the white spaces in between. "Please read this," said the officer. "I can't," said the explorer. "Why, it's perfectly clear," said the officer. "It's undoubtedly very artistic," said the explorer evasively, "but I cannot decipher it." "Of course," said the officer laughing, as he put the brief case away, "it's not fine penmanship for schoolchildren. You have to pore over it for a long while. In the end, you too would certainly make it out. Naturally it can't be ordinary handwriting, for it is not supposed to kill at once, but within an average space of twelve hours; the turning point being calculated for the sixth hour. The writing proper has to be surrounded by many, many embellishments; the real writing only encircles the body in a narrow girdle; the rest of the body is intended for decorative effects. Can you now understand the value of the work of the harrow, and of the entire machine? Just look at this!" He jumped onto the ladder, turned a wheel and called down: "Look out! step aside!" Everything began to move. If the wheel had not creaked, it would have been wonderful. As if surprised by this disturbing wheel, the officer threatened it with his fist; then, excusing himself, stretched his arms out towards the explorer and hurriedly climbed down in order to observe the action of the apparatus from below. Something was still out of order which he alone noticed. He climbed up again, grasped the inner part of the draughtsman with both hands and then, in order to get down quickly, instead of using the ladder, slid down one of the rods. To make himself understood above the noise, he shouted as loudly as possible into the ear of the explorer: "Do you understand what's happening now? The harrow is beginning to write: when it has finished the first inscription on the man's back, the layer of cotton begins to furl up and rolls the body slowly over on its side so as to present a fresh surface to the harrow. In the meantime, the wound-written parts take their place on the cotton, which stops the bleeding at once, by means of a special preparation, and makes further deepening of the writing possible. Just here, the spikes on the edge of the harrow tear the cotton from the wounds, as the body is turned over again, hurl it into the ditch, and the harrow starts working again. Thus it writes more and more deeply during the whole twelve hours. The first six hours the condemned man lives about as before, he only suffers pain. After two hours the piece of felt is removed, for the man hasn't the strength to scream any more. Here, at the head end, we put warm rice porridge into this electrically heated tray, from which the man, if he cares to, can eat whatever he can lap up with his tongue. None of them ever misses this opportunity. I know really of none, and my experience is great. Only around the sixth hour does he lose his pleasure in eating. Then I usually kneel down here and observe the following phenomenon. Rarely does the man swallow the last morsel. All he does is to turn it about in his mouth and spit it out into the ditch. I have to stoop over then; otherwise I would catch it in the face. But around the sixth hour how quiet the man becomes! Even the dullest begins to understand. It starts around the eyes. From here it spreads out. It's a sight which could tempt you to lie down under the harrow with him. But nothing further happens, the man is just beginning to decipher the writing, and he purses his lips as if listening. You have seen that it is not easy to decipher the writing with the eye; but our man deciphers it with his wounds. Of course, that means a lot of work; he needs six hours to accomplish it. Then the harrow spears him clean through and hurls him into the ditch, where he plumps down into the bloody water and cotton. The tribunal is ended and we, the soldier and I, shovel him under."

The explorer had bent his ear to the officer and, with his hands in his coat pockets, observed the work of the machine. The condemned man was also observing it but without comprehension. He leaned over a little to follow the oscillating needles, when the guard, at a sign from the officer, slashed his shirt and trousers from behind with a knife so that they fell down off him. The man tried to seize the falling garments in order to cover his nakedness, but the soldier lifted him into the air and shook the last shreds from him. The officer brought the machine to a standstill and in the silence that now reigned the condemned man was placed under the harrow. The chains were undone and straps fastened in their place. Just at first it seemed almost to spell relief for the condemned man. Then the harrow settled down a bit lower, for he was a thin man. When the points touched him, a shudder ran over his skin; while the guard was busy with his right hand, he reached out blindly with his left; but it was towards where the explorer was standing. Uninterruptedly the officer kept looking at the explorer from the side, as if trying to read on his face the impression that the execution, which he had explained to him at least superficially, was making on him.

The strap intended for the wrist broke; the guard had probably pulled on it too hard. The guard showed him the broken bit of strap and the officer was obliged to help. Turning his face toward the explorer, he walked over to the guard and said: "This machine is quite complicated; here and there something is bound to tear or break; but one should not for this reason allow oneself to be misled as to one's general judgment. As a matter of fact, a substitute for the strap may be had promptly; I am going to use a chain, only the delicacy of the vibration of the right arm will in that case of course be reduced." And as he attached the chain, he added: "The means at my disposal for the upkeep of the machine are very limited now. Under the former commander there existed a fund intended only for this purpose, to which I had free access. There was also a warehouse here in which all kinds of spare parts were kept. I confess I was almost wasteful with them, I mean formerly, not now, as the new commander—to whom everything is only a pretext for combating old institutions—asserts. Now he administers the Machine Fund himself, and whenever I send for a new strap the broken one is required as proof, the new one takes ten days to arrive, then it's of poor quality and not worth much. But in the meantime how am I to make the machine go without straps? Nobody bothers about that!"

The explorer reflected: It is always a delicate matter to intervene effectively in other people's affairs. He was neither a citizen of the penal colony nor a citizen of the state to which it belonged. If he wanted to condemn the execution, or even to prevent it, they could say to him: You are a foreigner, be silent. To this he would not be able to reply other than to add that as far as this matter was concerned, he didn't understand it himself, for he was traveling with the sole intention of observing and certainly not with that of changing foreign court procedures. But here, however, the situation appeared to be very tempting. There was no doubt about the injustice of the proceedings and the inhumanity of the execution. Nobody would assume that the explorer had any personal interest in the matter, for the condemned man was a stranger to him. They were not compatriots, nor was he at all a man who invited pity. The explorer himself had recommendations from high officials, he had been received with great courtesy, and the fact that he had been asked to the execution seemed even to indicate that they might desire his opinion concerning this procedure. This was all the more likely in fact since the commanding officer, as he had just heard distinctly, was not a partisan of this procedure and maintained an almost hostile attitude towards the officer.

At that moment, the explorer heard a cry of rage from the officer. Not without difficulty, he had just succeeded in shoving the felt gag into the mouth of the offender, when the latter closed his eyes in an irresistible nausea and vomited. Hurriedly the officer wrenched him away from the gag and tried to turn his head towards the ditch; but it was too late, the slop was already running all over the machine. "All this is the commander's fault!" the officer cried and shook the brass rods in front without rhyme or reason. "They're getting my machine as filthy as a stable." His hands shaking, he showed the explorer what had happened. "Haven't I tried for hours to make the commander understand that no meals should be given for a day before the execution? But the new, lenient tendency disagrees. The ladies of the commander's family stuff the man's mouth with sweets before he is led away. All his life he has fed on stinking fish, and now he has to eat candy! But it certainly would be possible, I wouldn't object—why on earth don't they get a new felt gag, as I have urged for the last three months? How can anyone take into his mouth, without loathing, a gag on which more than a hundred dying men have sucked and bitten?"

The condemned man had laid his head back and looked very peaceful, the guard was busy cleaning the machine with the condemned man's shirt. The officer walked towards the explorer, who took a step backwards in some sort of premonition, but the officer took his hand and drew him to one side. "I want to say a few words to you in confidence," he said, "may I?" "Certainly," said the explorer, and listened, his eyes lowered.

"This procedure and this execution, which you now have the opportunity to admire, no longer have any open adherents in our colony at present. I am their only advocate, as well as the only advocate of the old commander's legacy. I am no longer able to consider further improvements of the procedure; I exhaust all my strength trying to preserve what already exists. During the old commander's lifetime, the colony was filled with his adherents; I possess some of his strength of conviction, but I entirely lack his power; in consequence, the adherents have slipped away. There are still a good many, but nobody admits it. If you go to the tea house today, that is, on an execution day, and listen around a bit, you will perhaps hear only ambiguous utterances. These people are all adherents, but they are quite useless to me under the present commander with his present views. And now I ask you: Shall such a lifework as this"—here he pointed to the machine—"be allowed to perish just because of this commander and the women in his family who influence him? Can we allow this? Even though one is only on our island for a few days, as a stranger? But there is no time to lose, there is something afoot to undermine my jurisdiction; discussions are already taking place in the commander's office to which I am not summoned. Even your visit today seems to me to be characteristic of the entire situation; they are cowards, so they send you, a stranger, ahead of them.—How different the executions were in the old days! Already, a day before the execution, the entire valley was overcrowded with people; they all came just to watch; early in the morning the commander appeared with his ladies; a flourish of trumpets awakened the entire encampment; I made the announcement that everything was ready; the society people—no high official was allowed to be absent—took their places around the machine;

this heap of wicker chairs is a miserable relic of those times. The machine was freshly painted and shone brightly, I used new spare parts for almost every execution. Before hundreds of eyes—all the spectators stood on tiptoe as far back as those slopes over there—the condemned man was laid under the harrow by the commander himself. What a common soldier is allowed to do today, was then my task, as presiding judge, and I felt honored by it. And now the execution began! Not a single discord disturbed the work of the machine. Many stopped looking, even, and just lay there in the sand with their eyes closed. Everybody realized: Justice is now being done. In the stillness only the sighing of the condemned man, muffled by the felt, could be heard. Today the machine no longer succeeds in wringing from the condemned man a sigh that is sufficiently loud for the felt not to stifle it. In those days, however, the writing needles dripped a corrosive liquid which we are not allowed to use today. Well, then came the sixth hour! It was impossible to grant all the petitions to be allowed to witness the spectacle from close by. The commander in his wisdom gave orders that the children should be considered first; of course I was always allowed to stand close by on account of my position; many's the time I used to crouch there with a small child in each arm. How we all absorbed the expression of transfiguration from the man's tortured face, how we lifted our cheeks into the glow of this justice, finally achieved and already fading! What times those were, comrade!" The officer had evidently forgotten who it was standing before him; he had embraced the explorer and laid his head on his shoulder. The latter was greatly embarrassed and looked impatiently beyond the officer. The guard had finished the cleaning job and was now pouring rice porridge from a can into the tray. The condemned man, who seemed to have almost completely recovered, no sooner noticed this than he began to clack with his tongue for the porridge. The guard kept shoving him away, for the porridge was undoubtedly intended for a later moment, but it was nevertheless unseemly for him to put his dirty hands in the tray and eat out of it in front of the ravenous offender.

The officer quickly pulled himself together. "I was not really trying to touch your emotions," he said. "I know it is impossible to make those times comprehensible today. Besides, the machine still works and can speak for itself. It speaks for itself, even when it is standing all alone in this valley. And in the end, the corpse still falls with an unbelievably gentle flying motion into the ditch, even though there are no longer hundreds to gather around the ditch like flies, as there used to be. At that time we had to put up a strong railing around the ditch, but that has been torn down long ago."

The explorer looked aimlessly about him, wanting to keep his face from the officer. The latter, thinking he was looking at the barrenness of the valley, seized his hands and walked around him in order to catch his glance: "Do you see the shame of it?" he said.

But the explorer remained silent. For a little while the officer left him alone; with outspread legs and his hands on his hips, he stood still, looking at the ground. Then he smiled encouragingly at the explorer and said: "I was standing near-by yesterday, when the commander gave you the invitation. I heard it. I know the commander. I understood at once what he had in mind with that invitation. Although his power would be sufficient to take measures against me, he does not yet dare do so; but he wants to expose me to your judgment, as being that of a distinguished foreigner. He has made a careful calculation; this is your second day on the island, you did not know the old commander and his thought processes, you are prejudiced by the European point of view, you are perhaps, on principle, an opponent of capital punishment in general, and of such a machinelike type of execution in particular; furthermore you see how the execution takes place, without public sympathy, sadly, on a machine that is already somewhat damaged; now would it not be easily possible—this is what the commander thinks—that you should not approve of my procedure? And if you did not approve of it, would you not keep silent about it—I am still speaking from the commander's point of view—for you certainly have complete confidence in your own much tried convictions? You have surely seen and learned to appreciate the different peculiarities of many peoples; therefore you will in all probability not speak out with all your might against the procedure as you would, perhaps, do in your own country. But that isn't at all necessary for the commander. A haphazard, merely an incautious, word suffices. It need not in any way correspond to your convictions, if only it appears to meet with his wishes. I am sure he will question you with all the cunning he possesses. And the ladies will sit around in a circle, all ears. You'll probably say: 'In our country the court proceedings are different,' or, 'In our country the accused is examined before judgment is pronounced,' or, 'In our country there are other penalties than the death penalty,' or, 'In our country there have been no tortures since the Middle Ages.' These are all observations that are as right as they appear self-evident to you; innocent observations that do not touch my procedure. But how will the commander take them? I can see him now, our friend the commander, as he pushes his chair aside and hurries to the balcony, I can see his ladies flocking after him, I can hear his voice—the ladies call it a thunder voice—as he says: 'A great occidental researcher designated to examine court proceedings in many countries, has just announced that our procedure in accordance with old customs is an inhuman one. After this judgment, pronounced by such a distinguished man, it is of course no longer possible for me to tolerate this method. Beginning today, I therefore issue the following order—and so forth.' You want to protest, you did not really say what he announces you did, you did not call my method inhuman; on the contrary, in your innermost thoughts you regard it as the most human and most worthy of humanity; you also admire this mechanism—but it is too late; you can't even reach the balcony, which is already crowded with ladies; you try to attract attention, you try to shout, but a lady's hand holds your mouth shut—and I, and the old commander's work, are lost."

The explorer had to suppress a smile; so the task he had regarded as being so difficult was really as easy as that. He said evasively, "You overestimate my influence; the commander has read my letter of introduction; he knows that I am no connoisseur of court proceedings. If I were to express an opinion, it would be the opinion of a private individual, of no more importance than that of anyone else, and certainly much less important than that of the commander who, unless I am mistaken, has very extensive powers in this penal colony. If his opinion concerning this procedure is such a positive one as you believe, then, I am afraid that its end is indeed here, without there being any need of my modest co-operation."

Did the officer understand this? No, he did not yet understand. He shook his head vigorously and threw a brief glance back at the condemned man and the soldier, who was startled and let go of the rice. The officer came quite near the explorer, and without looking at him directly but at something or other on his coat, said more softly than before: "You don't know the commander; you are, as it were, under no obligations—if you'll pardon my expression—to him, or to us all. Believe me, your influence cannot be too highly estimated. I was indeed delighted when I heard that you were to attend the execution alone. This order of the commander was aimed at me, but now I am going to turn it to my own advantage. Uninfluenced by false insinuations and contemptuous looks—which would have been inevitable with a larger attendance at the execution—you have listened to my explanations, you have seen the machine and are now about to witness the execution. Surely your judgment is already formed; should there still be a few uncertainties in your mind, the sight of the execution will do away with them. And now I make this plea to you: help me with the commander!"

The explorer did not allow him to continue. "But how could I do that?" he cried. "That's quite impossible. I am as powerless to help you as to hinder you."

"You certainly can," said the officer. The explorer noticed somewhat anxiously that the officer's fists were clenched. "You certainly can," he repeated, still more insistently. "I have a plan that must succeed. You believe your influence is insufficient. I know it is sufficient. But allowing that you're right, isn't it necessary then to try everything, even what may possibly fail, in order to maintain this procedure? So listen to my plan. In order to carry it out, it is above all necessary for you to be as reticent as possible concerning your judgment of this procedure in the colony today. Unless someone questions you directly, you must by no means say anything; your utterances should be brief and vague; people should notice that it becomes increasingly difficult for you to talk about it, that you are acrimonious, that you practically have to burst into invective, were you to talk openly. I don't ask you to lie, in any sense; you should give only the briefest answers, such as: 'Yes, I've seen the execution,' or, 'Yes, I've heard all the explanations.' Only that, no more. Of course there is sufficient cause for the acrimony people should notice in you, even though it does not correspond to the commander's viewpoint. Of course he will misunderstand completely and give it his own interpretation. That is the basis of my plan. Tomorrow an important meeting of all the higher administrative officers will take place under the chairmanship of the commander at headquarters. The commander naturally knows how to make a spectacle out of these sessions. A gallery has been built which is always occupied by spectators. I am obliged to attend these consultations, but I am loath to do so. In any case, you will certainly be invited to this meeting; if you will follow my plan today, the invitation will become an urgent request. Should you not be invited, however, for some undiscoverable reason, you must ask for an invitation; you will get it then without any doubt. So tomorrow you're seated with the ladies in the commander's box. He reassures himself frequently, by looking upward, that you are there. After disposing of diverse indifferent and ludicrous subjects, calculated solely to interest the spectators,—mostly about port constructions, eternally about port constructions— the court procedure also comes up for discussion. If this point should not occur to the commander, or rather not early enough, I'll see to it that it does. I'll stand up and make a report of today's execution. Quite brief, only a report. Such a report is not customary, but I make it nevertheless. The commander thanks me, as always, with a friendly smile; and then he cannot restrain himself, he sees his chance: "A report of today's execution has just been made,' he will say, or something similar to this. 'I'd only like to add to this report that this particular execution was attended by the great scholar, whose visit—an exceptional honor for our colony—you all know about. Our session today also takes on an added significance as a result of his presence. Let us now question this great scholar as to his opinion of this execution, carried out in accordance with early customs, as well as of the procedure that led up to it.' Naturally, applause throughout the house, and general approval; I am the loudest. The commander makes a bow before you and says: 'Then I put the question in the name of everyone present.' And now you step up to the balustrade. Lay your hands on it, so that they are visible to everybody, otherwise the ladies will take hold of them and dally with your fingers.—And now, finally, comes a word from you. I don't know how I shall stand the tension of the hours until that moment. You must place no limit on your speech, blare forth the truth; lean over the balustrade, bellow your opinion, yes, bellow it, at the commander, your unshakable opinion! But maybe you don't want to do this, maybe it does not correspond to your character; in your country people

act differently in such situations; this too is all right; this too is quite sufficient; don't get up at all, say only a few words, whisper them so that they
may be heard by the officials below you, that'll do. You needn't even mention the small attendance at the execution, the creaking wheel, the broken
strap, the repulsive felt gag; no, I'll take care of everything else. And believe me, if my speech doesn't chase him from the hall, it'll force him to his
knees, so that he will have to acknowledge: I bow down before you, old
commander!—That's my plan; won't you help me to carry it out? But of
course you will; what's more, you must." And the officer seized the explorer by both arms and looked into his face, breathing heavily. He had
shouted the last sentences so loudly that even the guard and the condemned
man became attentive; although they understood nothing, they stopped
eating and looked towards the explorer, chewing the while.

The explorer had no doubt from the very beginning as to the answer
he would have to give. He had experienced too much in his life to vacillate
now; at bottom he was an honest man, and he was not afraid. Nevertheless,
he hesitated, just the time of a breath, at the sight of the soldier and the
condemned man. But finally he said what he had to say: "No." The officer
blinked several times and did not take his eyes off him. "Do you want an
explanation?" asked the explorer. The officer nodded silently. "I am opposed to this procedure," the explorer then said. "Before you even took me
into your confidence—I'll not abuse this confidence, of course, under any
circumstances—I had already considered whether I would be justified in
taking steps against this procedure, and whether there would be the slightest prospect of success in case I did so. It was clear to me to whom I should
have to turn first: to the commander, of course. You have made it still
clearer, but without having strengthened my resolution; on the contrary,
your honest conviction moves me, even though it could never influence
me."

The officer remained silent, turned to the machine and, seizing one
of the brass rods, leaned slightly backwards to look up at the draughtsman,
as if to check whether or not everything was in order. The guard and the
condemned man seemed to have become friends; the condemned man was
making signs to the guard, despite the fact that the tight straps which
bound him made this difficult: the soldier bent over towards him; the
condemned man whispered something to him and the soldier nodded.

The explorer followed the officer: "You don't know yet what I am
going to do," he said. "Of course, I shall give my opinion about the procedure to the commander, not at the meeting, however, but *tête-à-tête*;
nor shall I stay here long enough to be drawn into any meeting: I am going
away early tomorrow morning, or at least I'll board ship then."

It seemed as though the officer had been listening. "So the procedure
did not convince you," he said to himself, and smiled as an old man smiles
at a child's nonsense, withholding his own real musings behind the smile.

"Then the time has come," he said finally, and looked suddenly at the explorer, his eyes shining with a certain challenge, a certain appeal for co-operation. "Time for what?" the explorer asked anxiously, but received no answer.

"You're free," said the officer to the condemned man in the latter's own language. At first the condemned man did not believe it. "You're free now," the officer said. The face of the condemned man showed signs of life for the first time. Was this the truth? Or was it only a passing whim on the part of the officer? Had the foreign explorer obtained pardon for him? Which was it? His face semed to ask these questions. But not for long. Whatever it might be, if he could, he really wanted to be free, and he began to shake himself as much as the harrow permitted.

"You're breaking my straps," the officer shouted. "Keep quiet, we'll unfasten them for you." And with the help of the guard, to whom he had made a sign, he got to work. The condemned man chuckled gently to himself, saying nothing; he turned his face first to the left towards the officer, then to the right towards the guard; not forgetting the explorer.

"Pull him out," the officer ordered the guard. To do this, they were obliged to move with a certain caution, on account of the harrow. The condemned man, due to his impatience, already had a few slight lacerations on his back.

From this moment on, however, the officer hardly bothered about him any more. He walked over to the explorer, took out again his small leather brief case, rummaged through it, finally found the paper he was looking for and showed it to the explorer. "Read this," he said. "I can't," said the explorer. "I told you before I can't read those pages." "But take a good look at the page anyway," said the officer, stepping to the explorer's side to read with him. When this did not help, either, in order to facilitate the explorer's reading, he ran his little finger across the page, well above it, as if the paper must not be touched under any condition. The explorer made an effort, in order to be agreeable to the officer at least in this, but it was impossible. Now the officer began to spell out the writing, then he read it once more connectedly. "It says: 'BE JUST!'—Now you can read it," he said. The explorer bent so low over the paper that the officer drew it back, fearing he might touch it; actually the explorer said nothing more, but it was clear that he still had not been able to read it. "It says: 'BE JUST!'" the officer repeated. "That may be so," said the explorer, "I believe that's what it says." "All right then," said the officer, at least partially satisfied, and he climbed the ladder still holding the page; with great caution he laid it on the draughtsman, and then began apparently to rearrange the entire mechanism; it was a very tedious job, for the wheels in question must have been very tiny; sometimes his head disappeared completely in the draughtsman, he was obliged to examine the wheelwork so closely.

The explorer continued to follow the work from below, his neck grew stiff, his eyes began to smart from the sunlight-flooded sky. The guard and the condemned man were now occupied only with each other. With the point of his bayonet, the guard lifted up the condemned man's shirt and trousers which were lying in the ditch. The shirt was frightfully dirty, and the condemned man washed it in the water-pail. Both had to laugh aloud when the condemned man put the shirt and trousers on, for both garments had been slashed in two behind. Perhaps the offender thought it his duty to entertain the guard; in his slit clothes he made circles around the guard, who was crouching on the ground, laughing and beating his knees. Nevertheless they restrained themselves somewhat, out of respect for the presence of the two gentlemen.

When the officer had finally finished up above, he smilingly surveyed the whole in all its parts once more, banged shut the cover of the draughtsman, which until now had been open, climbed down and looked first into the ditch, then at the condemned man; noticed with satisfaction that the latter had recovered his garments, walked towards the pail to wash his hands, recognized too late the repulsive filth in it, became saddened at the fact that now he could not wash his hands, at last dipped his fingers in the sand—this substitute did not suffice but he had to accommodate himself—then rose and began to unbutton the coat of his uniform. At this, the two lady's handkerchiefs which he had stuck in his collar fell into his hands. "Here, take your handkerchiefs," he said, and threw them towards the condemned man. In explanation he said to the explorer: "Gifts from the ladies."

In spite of the evident hurry with which he took off his coat and then undressed completely, he nevertheless handled each garment very carefully. He even let his fingers run over the silver cord on his tunic and shook one of the tassels straight. Yet it was little in keeping with this carefulness that, as soon as he had finished handling a garment, he immediately threw it into the ditch, with an angry gesture. The last thing that remained was his smallsword and belt. He drew the sword from its scabbard, broke it, then gathered everything together—the pieces of the sword, the scabbard and the belt—and threw them away so violently that they clinked together in the ditch.

Now he stood there naked. The explorer bit his lips and said nothing. To be sure, he knew what was going to happen, yet he had no right to prevent the officer from doing anything. If the court procedure to which the officer was so attached really was about to be abolished—possibly as a consequence of the action which the explorer had felt obliged to take—then the officer was acting entirely rightly; the explorer would not have acted differently in his place.

The guard and the condemned man understood nothing at first; in the beginning, they did not even look on. The condemned man was overjoyed at having got back his pocket handkerchiefs, but he was not allowed to enjoy them very long, for the soldier snatched them away from him with a quick, unpredictable gesture. The condemned man now tried once more to pull the handkerchiefs from the soldier's belt, into which the latter had carefully put them, but the soldier was on his guard. So they struggled, half in jest. Only when the officer was completely naked did they pay any attention to him. The condemned man especially seemed to be seized with a foreboding of some great change. What had happened to him, was now happening to the officer. It might even go on to the very end. Most likely, the foreign explorer had given the order for it. So this was revenge. Without himself having suffered to the end, he was nevertheless avenged to the end. A broad, noiseless laughter appeared now in his face, and remained there.

The officer turned towards the machine. If it had already been clear before that he understood the machine well, it was now almost horrifying to see the way he took charge of it, and the way it obeyed him. He had hardly brought his hand near the harrow when it rose and sank several times until it had reached the right position to receive him; he took hold of the bed by the edge only, and it started to vibrate right away; the ball of felt came toward his mouth. One saw that the officer did not really want to take it, but his hesitancy lasted just a moment, he submitted at once and took it in his mouth. Everything was ready, only the straps were still hanging down at the sides, but they were obviously unnecessary, as the officer did not need to be strapped in. Then the condemned man noticed the hanging straps; in his opinion the execution would not be complete unless the straps were tightly fastened; he waved excitedly to the guard and both of them ran to buckle the officer in. The latter had already stretched out one foot in order to push the crank that was to start the draughtsman going; then he saw that the two men had come near him. He drew his foot back and let himself be strapped in. Now, however, he was no longer able to reach the crank; neither the guard nor the condemned man would be able to find it, and the explorer was determined not to make a move. This was not necessary; hardly had the straps been fastened, when the machine began to work; the bed trembled, the needles danced on the skin, the harrow swung up and down. The explorer had been staring at it quite a while before he remembered that a wheel in the draughtsman should have made a creaking noise; yet all was silent, not the slightest hum was to be heard.

Because of this silent action the machine ceased to be the focus of attention. The explorer looked over towards the soldier and the condemned man. The latter was the more lively of the two, everything about the machine interested him; first he would bend down, then he would stretch himself, holding his index finger constantly extended to point out something to the guard. The explorer felt uncomfortable. He was determined to remain there till the end, but he could not have borne the sight of the two men very long. "Go home," he said. The soldier would, perhaps, have been ready to go, but the condemned man considered the order as a sort of punishment. He begged and implored with clasped hands to be allowed to stay, and when the explorer, shaking his head, refused to give in, he even went on his knees. The explorer saw that orders were of no avail here and he was about to go over and drive the two of them away. At that moment he heard a noise up in the draughtsman. He looked up. Could that one cogwheel be giving trouble? But it was something else. Slowly the cover of the draughtsman rose and then fell wide open. The teeth of a cogwheel began to show, then rose up; soon the whole wheel appeared; it was as if some great force were pressing the draughtsman together so that there was no room left for this wheel; it kept rotating till it reached the edge of the draughtsman, fell down, reeled upright a bit in the sand, then lay there. But already another one rose up above, followed by many more, big ones, little ones, and others that could hardly be told apart; the same thing happened to them all, one kept thinking that the draughtsman must surely be emptied by now, when a new, particularly numerous lot appeared, rose up, fell down, reeled in the sand and lay there. At the sight of this occurrence the condemned man forgot all about the explorer's orders; the cogwheels completely fascinated him; he kept trying to seize one of them, at the same time urging the soldier to help him; but he withdrew his hand in fright, for another cogwheel always followed at once, and this, at least at first when it would come rolling towards him, frightened him.

The explorer, however, was very disturbed; the machine was evidently going to pieces; its quiet action was a delusion; he had the feeling that he would have to care for the officer now, since the latter was no longer able to care for himself. But while the dropping of the cogwheels had claimed his entire attention, he had neglected to watch the rest of the machine; now, however, when the last cogwheel had left the draughtsman, he bent over the harrow, only to have a fresh, more annoying surprise. The harrow was not writing, it was just sticking the body, nor was the bed rolling it but just lifting it, trembling, up to the needles. The explorer wanted to interfere and, if possible, bring the whole thing to a stop, for this was not the torture the officer had wanted to arrive at, this was outright murder. He stretched out his hands. But at that moment the harrow was already beginning to rise sideways with the impaled body, the way it usually did only at the twelfth hour. Blood was flowing in a hundred streams, unmixed with water, for the little water pipes had also failed this time. And now the last thing failed too, the body did not release itself from the long needles, but, bleeding profusely, hung over the ditch without falling into it. The harrow was ready to fall back into its usual position, but, as if it had noticed itself that it was not yet freed of its burden, it remained suspended above the ditch. "Why don't you help?" the explorer shouted over to the guard and the condemned man, as he, himself, seized the officer's feet. He tried to hold the feet down on his side and the other two were to take hold of the officer's head from the other side, so that he might be slowly lifted off the needles. But the two could not make up their minds to join him; the condemned man practically turned away; the explorer had to go over to them and force them to come over near the officer's head. Just here he saw the face of the corpse, almost against his will. It was as it had been in life; no sign of the promised redemption was to be detected; that which all the others had found in the machine, the officer had not found; his lips were tightly pressed together, his eyes were open, and had an expression of life; their look was calm and convinced; the point of the big iron prong pierced his forehead.

When the explorer reached the first houses of the colony, with the soldier and the condemned man behind him, the soldier pointed at one house and said, "That's the tea house."

On the ground floor of one house there was a deep, low, cavernous room with smoke-stained walls and ceiling. On the street side it was wide open. Although the tea house differed little from the other houses in the colony, which were all very run-down, with the exception of the palatial structures that housed headquarters, it nevertheless gave the impression to the explorer of an historic memory, and he felt the power of other days. He walked nearer and, followed by his companions, he passed between the unoccupied tables standing on the street before the tea house, and inhaled the cool, musty air which came from the inside. "The old man's buried here," said the soldier. "The priest refused him a place in the cemetery. At first they were undecided as to where to bury him, but they finally buried him here. I'm sure the officer did not tell you anything about it, for that was the thing he was most ashamed of. He even tried a few times to disinter the old man at night, but he was always chased away." "Where is the grave?" asked the explorer, who found it hard to believe the guard. Both the guard and the condemned man immediately dashed ahead of him and with outstretched hands pointed to the spot where the grave was to be found. They led the explorer straight to the back wall where customers were sitting at a few of the tables. They were probably longshoremen, sturdy-looking men with short, glossy, full black beards. All of them were coatless, their shirts torn; they were poor humble folk. As the explorer approached, several of them rose, flattened themselves up against the wall and looked in his direction. "He's a foreigner," was the whisper that went about the explorer; "he wants to see the grave." They shoved one of the tables aside, underneath which there really was a tombstone. It was a simple slab, low enough to be hidden under the table. On it was an inscription in quite small letters, to read which the explorer was obliged to kneel down. It read: "HERE LIES THE OLD COMMANDER. HIS ADHERENTS, WHO MAY NO LONGER BEAR A NAME, HAVE DUG THIS GRAVE FOR HIM AND ERECTED

THIS STONE. THERE EXISTS A PROPHECY TO THE EFFECT THAT, AFTER A CERTAIN NUMBER OF YEARS, THE COMMANDER WILL RISE FROM THE DEAD AND LEAD THEM OUT OF THIS HOUSE TO THE RECONQUEST OF THE COLONY. BELIEVE AND WAIT!" When he had finished reading, the explorer rose and saw the men standing about him and smiling as if they had read the inscription with him, had found it ridiculous and were calling upon him to join in their viewpoint. The explorer acted as though he had noticed nothing, distributed a few coins among them, waited until the table had been shoved back over the grave, then left the tea house and walked towards the port.

The guard and the condemned man had come across acquaintances in the tea house who detained them. But they must have torn themselves away soon after, for the explorer was no further than the middle of the long stairway leading to the boats, when they came running after him. They probably wanted to force the explorer at the last moment to take them along. While the explorer was negotiating with a sailor down below for his crossing to the liner, the two men rushed down the steps, silently, for they did not dare cry out. But when they arrived below, the explorer was already in the boat and the sailor was just about to shove off. They might still have been able to jump into the boat, but the explorer picked up a heavy, knotted towrope from the floor, threatened them with it, and thus prevented them from jumping.

INTERPRETATION

One realizes that this story is not intended to be a realistic account of events which are to be judged by ordinary notions of probability. It is a fantasy. The strangeness of the situation, the unusual behavior of the condemned man and the soldier, the mysterious nature of the machine, all indicate that we are dealing with fantasy, just as we are in "The Lottery."

But are we to take the story to be merely fantastic? Do we not, rather, expect that the unrealistic and fantastic elements in such a piece of fiction as "In the Penal Colony" shall have some bearing, finally, on real human experience? The violation of our ordinary notions of probability, which is characteristic of fantasy, seems to promise an imaginative escape from ordinary experience, but in the end we discover that the intention of the creator of the fantasy is not to provide us with an escape from our ordinary experience but to provide us with an interpretation of our experience. In other words, fantasy as a type of fiction differs from other types of fiction merely in method and not in its basic intention.

The specific method employed by "In the Penal Colony" is allegorical. In an allegory, one finds a surface narrative the items of which—characters, objects, and events—stand for ideas and relations among ideas. That is, in so far as the allegory is strictly maintained, there is a point-to-point equating of the surface narrative with the background meaning. This method of communicating meaning is essentially different from that of ordinary realistic fiction. For instance, in "The Lament" the persons do not stand for ideas, and events do not indicate relationships among ideas. The old man does not stand for grief, for example, but is simply himself, an old man who is suffering from grief and loneliness. The meaning of the story, then, does not come from our grasp of particular concepts and relations as exemplified, item by item, in the narrative, but as a result of the total story: in so far as the character and situation of the old man work on our imagination, we become aware of the unthinking callousness of the world, and our comprehension of, and our sympathy for, the lonely and outcast are awakened. That is, we arrive at the meaning of a realistic story much as we arrive at the meaning of an event in real life.

This leads to a second distinction between allegory and realistic fiction. In realistic fiction, we are convinced by the logic of character and event, by our notion of probability. But in allegory the principle of organization does not finally depend upon the logic in the surface narrative, but upon the logic of the relationships among the ideas represented. Though the surface narrative may be more or less realistic, and in so far as it is realistic possess an independent logic, the emphasis is always upon the logic of the background.

"In the Penal Colony," as interpreted by one critic, Austin Warren,* is an allegory concerning the state of religion in the modern world. We know that the characteristic beliefs of the modern world are primarily founded on science. Science is concerned with the realm of the natural and not with the realm of the supernatural. Its assumption is that the events of the world are in accord with natural laws, and that by the use of his reason man may become acquainted with natural law and can, in so far as his knowledge of that law is perfect, predict the course of nature. It pictures a completely rational world, in which there is no place for the irrational, the miraculous, the supernatural. It assumes that miraculous and supernatural manifestations would, if man's scientific knowledge were adequate, be seen to be merely natural phenomena. Associated with this belief in science is the belief in progress: as man learns more his control of nature increases and he can improve his world. That is, perfect knowledge, in the scientific sense, would bring perfect control of nature, including human nature. And associated with this purely natural or secular view of the world we find the belief in humanitarianism. Pain is the great evil, according to such a belief, and the conquest of pain becomes the greatest good. Furthermore, the idea of natural law as applied in human affairs leads to an emphasis on the idea of determinism—people are good or bad as a result of heredity and environment and not as a matter of responsible moral choice. Over against these beliefs which are characteristic of modernism as

* "An Exegetical Note on 'In the Penal Colony,'" *The Southern Review*, vii, 2, pp. 363–365.

it is popularly understood are the traditional religious beliefs: that there is a supernatural realm, that God's will is finally inscrutable and that man must have faith, that the salvation of the soul is the greatest good, and that men are free moral agents. According to Austin Warren's interpretation, "In the Penal Colony" is an allegory of the conflict between these two sets of beliefs:

"The earth is a penal colony, and we are all under sentence of judgment for sin. There was once a very elaborate machine, of scholastic theology, for the pronouncement of sentence, and an elaborate ecclesiastic system for its administration. Now it is in the process of disappearance: the Old Commander (God) has died, though there is a legend, which you can believe or not, that He will come again. Meanwhile the 'machine' seems antiquated and inhuman to ladies, who are sentimental about criminals, and to the new governor, who is a humanitarian.

"The two interlocutors are an old official, still faithful to the inventor of the machine, and an explorer: the former a survivor from the old theology, a member of the saving remnant of believers in God and sin; the latter is a naturalist, a scientist who shares the humanitarian views of his secularist generation but who, as a social scientist, is capable of intellectual curiosity and a suspension of judgment. When he sees that the old officer is willing to testify to his faith by martyrdom, by taking his own place in the machine (which only a moral-professional law requires), he respects him for his loyalty to his code, and 'would not have acted differently in his place': Scientist and theologian have in common a respect for law, an adherence to professional duty over personal comfort, and a willingness to see life as it painfully is.

"Important is the setting of the machine's draughtsman. The first victim suffers under 'Honor your Superior,' the moral law which he has broken: this is a law appropriate to his caste of servant. For his own use, the old officer adjusts the legend to 'Be just.' Has he violated this injunction? Not consciously; but a judge of his fellowmen should be 'just' and no mortal man can be: 'none is Good save God': the old officer can be sure that, whatever his intentions, he has been unjust in the sight of Justice.

"At the end of the story, the explorer has become converted to the doctrine of the machine: he excludes from his boat those who wish to escape from the penal island. 'Converted' is too strong: if really converted, he would stay on the island—at least if the machine still operated. But at least he makes no report to the new commander; and he takes the Prophecy of Return seriously: when the men about him ridicule the inscription, he does not join in their laughter: the Prophecy may be true. Like Pilate, he refuses to judge; he finds no fault in the just manipulators of the machine.

"In its tone, the story is a matter-of-fact description of an elaborate method of punishment, no longer believed in by the 'enlightened.' kept going a little longer by the devotion of an old man who doesn't understand it very well and can't repair it. Narration is from the point of view of, through the eyes of, the explorer, who is shocked by what he sees and yet who, unlike the present management of the penal colony, can understand the possible use of the machine in what is, after all, a penal colony; and who becomes increasingly sympathetic as he sees that the operator of the machine believes in it for himself as well as for others. But it is essential to Kafka's purpose that there shall be no suppression of the difficulties in accepting the gospel of the machine: it is cruel; it makes errors; it is costly to keep up; people have ceased to believe in it; its inventor has died, and it is generally thought ridiculous to credit the pious legend that he will come again. 'My ways are not your ways, neither my thoughts as your thoughts,' saith the Lord. . . . Kafka, fearful of softening religion, wants to present it in all its rigor, its repellence to the flesh—in its irrationality and inscrutability and uncertainty, too. We must put up with the professional pride and the pedantry of the old officer: religionists are always forgetting ends in absorption with means, taking human (and impious) pride in the details of their theological and ecclesiastical systems. Nothing is simple, nothing unmixed. We never get reality straight, but always . . . through a veil of illusion. If we are determined to be scrupulously positivistic and 'accept no illusion,' then we shall have to content ourselves with no more than statistics: we shan't find reality."

If Mr. Warren's interpretation of "In the Penal Colony" is acceptable, then one sees that the allegory of the story is strict rather than loose—that most of the details of the surface narrative have specific parallels at the level of ideas. One sees also that here we have a contrast between the fantastic surface—which cannot be judged in terms of the logic of actual experience —and the represented argument—which can be judged in terms of actual experience. That is, the argument in the background is a possible view of the subject under discussion, and is held by many intelligent people. There is an ironical contrast between the fantastic way of representing the ideas and the ideas themselves, which are not fantastic, which are one way of interpreting an actual situation; in other words, the fantasy may, ironically, be logical after all.

A similar irony is indicated in the contrast between the fantastic events and the style in which they are narrated. The style is a rather bare, factual style—the style of a person who is trying to be scrupulously accurate and does not wish to color the truth by indulging in any literary and rhetorical devices. It implies that the narrator is willing to let the case rest on the facts alone. It does not try, we might say, to provoke the reader to horror or sympathy.

This contrast between the fantastic events and setting and the particular style* is commented on by Mr. Warren: "Its [the story's] powerful effect is indeed produced by its complete absence of fantasy in detail: The story offers, by its method, the sense of a fact which you can interpret as you like, of which you can make what you will: I'm telling you, as a sober scientist, what I saw." The style, then, has a dramatic function, in connection with the total story, just as it does in "The Killers" or "I Want to Know Why" or any other successful piece of fiction. It here indicates a fusion, an interpenetration, of the fantastic and realistic elements of experience, an idea which is to be associated with the basic meaning of the story.

1. In the light of Mr. Warren's general interpretation, what is one to make of such a passage as the following: " 'These uniforms are much too heavy for the tropics,' commented the explorer. . . . 'Certainly,' said the officer, washing his hands, stained with oil and grease, in a pail of water that stood near-by, 'but they are the symbols of home, and we don't want to lose our homeland.' " One might approach the problem in this way: If the penal colony is the world, then what is the "homeland"? Is this a contrast between time and eternity, the natural and the supernatural realms, with the implication that man's true "home" is not in the natural world of time? In that case, what about the "uniforms" which are not comfortable by the standards of the penal colony? Is there any significance in the pail of water?

2. What is represented by the original drawings of the machine made by the Old Commander?

3. What interpretation could you make of the strange expression which, according to the old officer, always comes over the victim's face toward the end? Why does it not appear on the face of the officer himself when he is in the machine?

4. What distinction is made between the attitude of the explorer, whom we may take to be a figure representing the "true" scientist, and the attitude of the new commander and the ordinary inhabitants of the penal colony? Develop the hints on this point which are given in Mr. Warren's analysis.

* A similar contrast between the fantasy of the surface narrative and the style in which it is rendered may be observed in Jonathan Swift's *Gulliver's Travels* and John Bunyan's *Pilgrim's Progress*.

▨ SECTION V

Stories for Study

▨ THE stories that follow have been selected for a variety of reasons. For one thing, they all have a great deal of interest, by reason either of absolute merit or of the problems which they raise. For another thing they help to fill out the picture of the development of the short story in our time. Some are by older acknowledged masters, like Joseph Conrad, and others are by newer talents, like Saul Bellow; but all, the recognized masterpieces as well as the less well known or less impressive stories, should be approached in a spirit both appreciative and inquiring.

Aside from the pleasure which these stories may give, the principal value of this section will lie in the opportunity afforded the student to test and refine some of the principles with which he has been concerned earlier in this book. The student will undoubtedly find parallels and certain natural affiliations in subject matter, theme, tone, or method, between stories here and some previously studied. For example, some of these stories have surprise endings, some raise the question of sentimentality, some use the method of parable. Or, to suggest more specific kinds of comparative treatment, the satire in "Realpolitik," by Angus Wilson, may well be compared and contrasted with the satire of such a story as "Cruel and Barbarous Treatment," by Mary McCarthy. Or, the allegorical method used in "The Lottery," by Shirley Jackson, may be compared with that used in "The Killing of the Dragon," by Dino Buzzati.

As he reads these stories, the student will find that such parallelisms present themselves quite naturally. But he may want to make them more consciously and systematically, especially when he comes upon a story about the meaning of which he has trouble, or a story about the value of which he finds it difficult to decide. In any case, he may often deepen his understanding of a story (and thus deepen his pleasure in it) if he will bring to his reading what he has learned from the stories that he has come to understand. He may even find it useful to prepare for himself some "Exercises" for these stories, thereby putting himself in the position of the instructor, and trying to suggest the basic issues of the story, comparisons with other stories, problems of technique involved in the story, and even "ways into" the story.

WILLIAM SANSOM

Through the Quinquina Glass

ALTHOUGH we shared the same table, Jean sat in the shade whereas I was able to enjoy the sunlight. Between us the crenelated shadow of the café awning drew a sharp division across the table. Cigarette tips burned like white gold in the light and in the shade siphons made from blue glass glinted evilly.

Over on the quay a sailor in a striped sweater trundled a barrel of oil through the hot sunlight. Three curiously tall boys played a game of bowls with some small wooden balls. In the very middle of the road a lean honey-colored dog with degenerate pale blue eyes stretched itself lazily for the flies. An old woman sat knitting beneath a dusty plane tree. This was the only life on an empty stage. From the campanile back in the town came the slow tolling of a funeral bell. It was three o'clock, the hour for siesta, and no time for men to be abroad. And yet . . . here was a man in a severe black coat just arrived and taking his place in the long row of empty café tables. The man was a stranger to us. We watched him lazily. He looked like an office worker from the town, an advocate perhaps.

Jean was saying, "Damn that waiter! Why must he bring me quinquina instead of pastis? Why must he be insolent in the bargain?"

"Because he's a man," I said. "Because he has a private life beneath his dicky. Because his wife may be delivering and he just can't stand being a waiter this afternoon. How can you know the facts?"

Jean mumbled, "Nevertheless he's a waiter—and on duty."

"But I can't agree. You are influenced in advance by the dicky. You deny the man. If you had seen the man first, you would deny the waiter.

We see a man cleaning a car—and we say to ourselves 'There is a man cleaning a car.' But perhaps that man is really wondering whether he should propose marriage to his girl. That, of course, is of more moment than cleaning a car. So what we are seeing is in truth a man wondering about a proposal—not a man cleaning a car. We should be more humble in our judgments: we should say, at the most, 'There is a man.' "

I raised my glass and drank the quinquina. Then, holding the glass to the light, I looked through it. In that café, they serve quinquina in green glasses. Framed in the green glass I found the stranger who had recently arrived.

"Take our new arrival," I said. "There he sits, a man. By some accident of taste, he chooses to wear a black coat. Let us reconstruct his story. He is not only a man in a black coat. His name, let us say, is . . . Aristide Fougeres. He is forty years old, he is an advocate in this small Corsican town, he discovered six months ago that his wife had deceived him. Let us see what might be the story of Aristide."

Through the quinquina glass the scene was sunless. The life had left it. It had taken the quality of a picture in oils when the pigments have faded with age. Or it seemed that a mysterious storm had drifted from nowhere, that sudden clouds shrouded our world with gloom. I lowered the glass. I was just beginning to speak when I realized that something was wrong. Something unearthly had happened. I had lowered the glass—yet the scene retained its lurid quality. There was no sun—yet the green gloom persisted. The air was leaden. I could not believe it. I knew there was no real storm. The fact was simply that the quinquina glass had left its imprint on the world. I refused to admit this. I imagined it to be a momentary hallucination. So that I went on talking—consciously avoiding my fearful impression.

"Well, this M. Fougeres discovered that his wife had spent the night with a commercial traveler from Auxerres. Let us return through six months to that occasion. The circumstances of the discovery are unimportant. Perhaps it was a letter, a word from an unkind neighbor, or a sock found at the bottom of his bed. However it went, the evidence was confirmed. What is more important is the action taken by M. Fougeres on his discovery. For he neither sought the man out, nor accused his wife. M. Fougeres remained silent upon the matter. He contained his misery within himself, never breathing a word to a living soul.

"The shock of the discovery affected M. Fougeres in two ways. First his vanity was wounded. Secondly, he found himself in possession of a secret which he soon discovered he was using as a weapon. Mme. Fougeres was a woman whose forceful character dominated husband and household. Now M. Fougeres found that he held a trump card with which he could annihilate his wife's ascendancy at any moment of his choosing. On the production of such an accusation her composure would crumble, a sense of guilt would sweep the certainty from her eyes, her voice would tremble with a refreshing note of appeal. Thus he felt a sudden secret sensation of power. Yet this was not the only effect the discovery had on M. Fougeres."

(This story was coming to my lips with a peculiar fluency. Ordinarily I would have hesitated. I would have paused before the choice of alternatives to the story. Now, it was as if I repeated a story already known to me. I would not say that I felt actually *impelled* to speak. But I was curiously *sure* of my words. The dull light of the quinquina glass alone illumined the scene. The air was breathless.)

"They lived in a narrow house just off the market square. M. Fougeres occupied the ground floor with his offices, while the two upper floors served as dwelling quarters. M. Fougeres had managed to maintain the privacy of his own personal office. This was his holy of holies, upon the door of which even Mme. must knock and wait his leisured 'Entrez.' In this room stood the big desk. It was a heavy mahogany piece with a sturdy roll-top that could drop a reassuring curtain over his private affairs. One day, two weeks after the discovery, Mr. Fougeres cleared out one half of this desk. All the old papers he crammed away into a strong-box—and there lay eight empty pigeon-holes and three clean drawers! This clearance was to be part of a new system. Its purpose was to house evidence of the guilt of Mme. and the collection of evidence relating to any future misdemeanor. For M. Fougeres had decided to employ a detective.

"M. Fougeres wanted more information for a variety of reasons. I have said that his vanity had suffered. In addition to this, the memory of his courting days had been sullied. He had not treasured his wife's body for some years now. She was still a handsome woman, but the perfection he himself had once known was fading. Yet he still treasured the memory of her young loveliness. And for this he felt a fierce jealousy. This memory lived somewhere within the frame of his wife in her present form. That another man should know intimately even the ghost of his young love brought a thrill of horror to the stomach. At night in bed, in the privacy of darkness, with his wife asleep and unseeing beside him, he would torment himself with deliberate images of the commercial traveler's caresses. The torture was voluntary, and it was he who exerted every imaginative effort to devise new and ingenious refinements. His first, and understandable, sense of injury changed to a deliberate masochistic delight. And that was why M. Fougeres had commissioned a detective. He told himself that he must be sure that her infidelity had been no more than a passing 'one night affair. He deprecated that this was 'wishful thinking'; yet excused himself on these same grounds. Actually, it was 'wishful thinking'—of another sort. Perversely, he really wished to discover a new infidelity. He did not yet admit this to himself. But soon he realized that he was disappointed when the detective brought him no news of an incriminating nature.

"As the weeks went by, he developed new and exciting methods of detection. First, he took great trouble to obtain a duplicate key to his wife's bureau. There he found and read her private letters. From these he gleaned nothing—except for one short note from the commercial traveler himself, alongside a photograph of that gentleman. With these trophies M. Fougeres would amuse himself for hours on end. He would choose an hour when there could be no fear of disturbance. Nevertheless he would lock the door behind him with precise care. As he walked from the door to the desk, he would experience a delightful sense of anticipation. He was like a child who stores up a secret moment for the inspection of some very special treasure—a bird's nest, a hidden cupboard in a doll's house, the hour when the candle is snuffed and the nursery fire flickers strangely on the ceiling, the hour reserved for delicious speculation on fine times to come.

"M. Fougeres would unroll his desk and spend some time selecting his first subject. Then he would sit for perhaps two hours, sometimes reading a detective's report, sometimes studying the photograph, sometimes the letter. He would invent new interconnections, new possibilities. At times his temples would throb with the hot blood of indignation, at times he would sink into an apathy of self-pity. There were occasions when he granted himself the luxury of striding the length of his office—right on the point of a stern decision to go and 'have it out' with the commercial traveler. Again, he would engineer periods of 'clear thinking,' when his was the generous, logical mind that could honestly admit a sympathy with the commercial traveler; after all, they were surely men of similar taste? And then he would dream of the day when he would reveal his knowledge to his wife. But most of all he would sit and wonder at the absolute irrevocability of what had been done. Nothing could undo this terrible wrong. And the tears would well in his eyes as he exaggerated the importance of the injury done to him. Each one of these different sensations was a lasting pleasure. And to refine his torment still further, M. Fougeres would constantly accuse himself for his whole attitude over the matter. Normally he was a balanced man. Up to this point he realized that he, too, was committing an underhand action. Two wrongs do not make a right. In deceiving the deceiver, he was acting in a mean and ungenerous manner. M. Fougeres accused himself.

"Added to these pleasures was a more elementary thrill. It was the thrill of adventure. He took risks, he gambled at 'not being found out.' When, for instance, he would quickly run through his wife's bag while she was in the very next room, while he could actually hear the rustle of her skirts! How quickly his fingers worked on such occasions! How alert was his brain!

"But as the weeks passed into months, such little perverted pleasures developed into a dangerous mania. This happened because no new evidence of infidelity presented itself. M. Fougeres sensed that the importance of the matter was fading. Perhaps the moment for taking some dramatic advantage of his secret had slipped by. Time dulls the finer edges of resentment. Gradually he could only think of the episode in minuscule—much as though he were regarding some grand object through the wrong end of a telescope. As its importance eluded him, so he redoubled his efforts to discover something new.

"On returning from any period of absence—even an afternoon's business in some neighboring town—he would examine immediately and in detail every ash-tray in the house. Perhaps one day he would find a cigar stub, the end of an unfamiliar brand of cigarette! He took great care to smell the cushions and the curtains for the aroma of a strange pomade or the stale breath of tobacco. He interrupted for a period his usual custom of shaving in the wash basin: he endured the discomfort of shaving over the bath, some yards from his mirror, because he wished to leave the wash basin plughole free from the trace of his own shaved whiskers. Thus, returning from some overnight absence, he would make his way immediately to the bathroom, lock the door, and scrape out the film of soap and dirt that clung to the dark sides of the hole. He would spread this film over a shaving paper and inspect it thoroughly. One day he might discover a bristle shaved off by his own razor! His own razor callously lent by his wife to her visitor of the night!

"The mania developed and M. Fougeres endured greater discomforts, went to greater lengths to achieve his object. He would arrange fake visits to fictitious friends in the country. During these periods he would watch for hours outside the house, sitting in the darkness of a workman's cafe or pressed self-consciously into the shade of a small alley. Then he would have to sleep at an hotel in the town. The money he spent! And the valuable hours of business wasted! For sometimes, having previously arranged to be absent for the night, he would interrupt negotiations in a distant town to catch the last bus home so that he might appear unexpectedly. On these occasions, his excitement rose to great heights. For on his entrance he would imagine that the man might still be secreted somewhere in the house. He delighted to scrutinize his wife's face for a revealing embarrassment. He loved to search every room and every closet, watching her in between operations and at the same time making subtle excuses that he was looking for this thing or that thing. Sometimes he would make some casual reference to a fictitious acquaintance bearing the same name as the commercial traveler. Once, even, he hinted that he had run into the fellow on a fictitious visit to Auxerres. On this occasion his wife's eyes had brightened and she had looked away. So she still remembered! In addition he would engineer long conversations with his wife on the subject of infidelity.

"Some two months ago M. Fougeres tried another tack. In a moment of delirious misery he visited a brothel. He parted the bead curtains of a brothel and accompanied a girl up the stairs. Every night for a week he continued to visit this place. His pleasure was vicarious. He bathed in the squalor of this medical experience. He delighted in the clinical efficiency of the beds and the bathrooms. He prolonged the money bargain, enjoying its indignity. He always chose the ugliest and oldest woman in the house.

"But these visits were soon to cease. In the first place, they had been a gesture and became tedious on reiteration. In the second place, Fougeres became terrified that his wife would by chance find him out—and in her turn remain silent. Thus she would again be in the ascendant. So M. Fougeres cast around for some other plan. And he found one. It was the finest plan of all. He hit upon it only last week. It was so ingenious that he shuddered to imagine that perhaps it might never have entered his mind. Perhaps he would have died without thinking of it! It was so simple a plan as to be elusive: it was so far-reaching a plan that it might never have occurred to him. It was this. It was that he should go to Auxerres, meet the commercial traveler, and make of him a bosom friend. In this way he would always have the man near him—a far more satisfactory instrument of torture than a photograph. And in a certain sense, the situation would make up a deficiency in his wife's guilt. For his wife's liaison of one night might have been but a passionate lapse, duly regretted, which a generous husband might even forgive. But now, in a roundabout way, she would have deceived him with his best friend. Oh, the injustice of it! And, to make matters worse, she might even be tempted to offer herself to this man again.

"Well . . . M. Fougeres has just returned from Auxerres. After four days of inquiries at the hotels—and later at the Town Hall—he has discovered that the commercial traveler has died from a tubercular kidney five months before. So that all this time he has been jealous of a dead man! Death can turn the tables completely on life. Dead men tell no tales, dead men feel no pride in the past possession of women. In a sense, his wife is a widow—and in some artificial manner suddenly rendered blameless. M. Fougeres has just left the station. He is sitting down to a glass of coffee. Dressed in his fusty black coat, he sits there bereft in a moment of his exclusive interest in life—his secret. Now just what is M. Fougeres to do?"

I paused. I did not quite know how to finish the story.

Just then the sunlight snapped on. The green of the quinquina glass vanished as queerly as it had arrived. Suddenly the air was fresh.

At that identical moment, the man in the black coat rose from his chair. He stood for a few seconds staring at the ground just in front of his table. Then he raised his hand quickly to his ear. A shot rang out. I saw the black revolver fall from his hand before he himself toppled stupidly over the table, off the table, and down onto the ground.

COLETTE

The Bitch

WHEN the sergeant arrived in Paris on leave, he found his mistress not at home. He was nevertheless greeted with tremulous cries of surprise and joy, embraced and covered with wet kisses. His bitch, Vorace, the sheep-dog whom he had left with his young sweetheart, enveloped him like a flame and licked him with a tongue pale with emotion. Meanwhile, the charwoman was making as much noise as the dog and kept exclaiming:

"Of all the bad luck! Madame's just gone to Marlotte for a couple of days to shut up her house there. Madame's tenants have just left and she's going through the inventory of the furniture. Fortunately, it isn't all that far away! Will Monsieur write out a telegram for Madame? If it goes immediately, Madame will be here tomorrow morning before lunch. Monsieur must sleep here. Shall I turn on the geyser?"

"My good Lucie, I had a bath at home. Soldiers on leave are pretty good at washing!"

He eyed his reflection in the glass; he was both bluish and ruddy, like the granite rocks of Brittany. The Briard sheep-dog, standing close to him in a reverent silence, was trembling in every hair. He laughed because she looked so like him, gray and blue and shaggy.

"Vorace!"

She raised her head and looked lovingly at her master, and the sergeant's heart turned over as he suddenly thought of his mistress Jeannine, so young and so gay—a little too young and often too gay.

During dinner the dog faithfully observed all the ritual of their former life, catching the pieces of bread he tossed for her and barking at certain words. So ardent was the worship in which she was rooted that the moment of return abolished for her the months of absence.

"I've missed you a lot," he told her in a low voice. "Yes, you too!"

He was smoking now, half lying on the divan. Crouching like a greyhound on a tombstone, the dog was pretending to be asleep, her ears quite still. Only her eyebrows, twitching at the slightest noise, revealed that she was on the alert.

Worn out as he was, the silence gradually lulled the man, until his hand which held the cigarette slid down the cushion, scorching the silk. He roused himself, opened a book, fingered a few new knick-knacks and a

401

photograph, which he had not seen before, of Jeannine in a short skirt, with bare arms, in the country.

"An amateur snapshot . . . How charming she looks!"

On the back of the unmounted print he read:

" 'June the fifth 1916.' Where was I on June the fifth? . . . Oh, I know, over in the direction of Arras. June the fifth. I don't know the writing."

He sat down again and was overcome by a sleep which drove all thought away. Ten o'clock struck; he was still just sufficiently awake to smile at the rich and solemn sound of the little clock whose voice, Jeannine used to say, was bigger than its stomach. But as it struck ten the dog got up.

"Quiet!" said the sleepy sergeant. "Lie down!"

But Vorace did not lie down. She snorted and stretched her paws which, for a dog, is the same as putting on a hat to go out. She went up to her master and her yellow eyes asked plainly:

"Well?"

"Well," he answered, "What's the matter with you?"

Out of respect she dropped her ears while he was speaking, raising them again immediately.

"Oh, what a bore you are!" sighed the sergeant. "You're thirsty. D'you want to go out?"

At the words "go out," Vorace grinned and began to pant gently, showing her beautiful teeth and the fleshy petal of her tongue.

"All right, then, we'll go out. But not for long, because I'm absolutely dropping with sleep."

In the road Vorace was so excited that she barked like a wolf, jumped right up to her master's neck, charged a cat and spun round playing "inner circle" with her tail. Her master scolded her tenderly and she did all her tricks for him. Finally, she sobered down again and walked along sedately. The sergeant suited his pace to hers, enjoying the warm night and making a little song out of two or three idle thoughts:

"I'll see Jeannine tomorrow morning . . . I'm going to sleep in a comfy bed . . . I've got seven more days to spend here . . ."

He became aware that his dog, who had trotted ahead, was waiting for him under a gas lamp with the same look of impatience. Her eyes, her wagging tail and her whole body asked:

"Well? Are you coming?"

As soon as he caught up with her, she turned the corner at a determined trot. It was then that he realized she was going somewhere.

"Perhaps," he thought to himself, "the charwoman usually . . . Or Jeannine . . ."

He stood still for a moment, then went on again, following the dog, without even noticing that he had, all at once, stopped feeling tired, and sleepy, and happy. He quickened his pace and the delighted dog went before, like a good guide.

"Go on, go on!" ordered the sergeant from time to time.

He looked at the name of a road, then went on again. They passed gardens with lodges at the gates; the road was dimly lit and they met no one. On her excitement, the dog pretended to bite the hand that hung at his side, and he had to restrain a brutal impulse, which he could not explain, in order not to beat her.

At last she stopped, as though saying: "Well, here we are!" before an old, broken-down railing protecting the garden of a little low house smothered in vines and bignonia, a timid shrouded little house.

"Well, why don't you open it?" said the dog, who had taken up a position before the wooden wicket-gate.

The sergeant lifted his hand to the latch and let it fall again. He bent down to the dog, pointed with his finger to a thread of light along the closed shutters, and asked her in a low voice:

"Who's there? . . . Jeannine?"

The dog gave a shrill "Hi!" and barked.

"Shhh!" breathed the sergeant, clapping his hands over her cool wet mouth.

Once more he stretched out a hesitant arm towards the door and the dog bounded forward. But he held her back by her collar and led her to the opposite pavement, whence he gazed at the unknown house and the thread of rosy light. He sat down on the pavement beside the dog. He had not yet gathered together all those images and thoughts which spring up round a possible betrayal, but he felt singularly alone, and weak.

"Do you love me?" he murmured in the dog's ear.

She licked his cheek.

"Come on; let's go away."

They set off, he in front this time. And when they were once more in the little sitting-room, she saw that he was putting his linen and slippers in a sack that she knew well. Desperate but respectful, she followed all his movements, while tears, the color of gold, trembled in her yellow eyes. He laid his hand on her neck to reassure her:

"You're coming too. You're not going to leave me any more. Next time you won't be able to tell me what happened 'after.' Perhaps I'm mistaken. Perhaps I haven't understood you properly. But you mustn't stay here. Your soul wasn't meant to guard any secrets but mine."

And while the dog shivered, still uncertain, he held her head in his hands, saying to her in a low voice:

"Your soul . . . Your doggy soul . . . Your beautiful soul . . ."

SAUL BELLOW

A Father-to-Be

THE strangest notions had a way of forcing themselves into Rogin's mind. Just thirty-one and passable-looking, with short black hair, small eyes, but a high, open forehead, he was a research chemist, and his mind was generally serious and dependable. But on a snowy Sunday evening while this stocky man, buttoned to the chin in a Burberry coat and walking in his preposterous gait—feet turned outward— was going toward the subway, he fell into a peculiar state.

He was on his way to have supper with his fiancée. She had phoned him a short while ago and said, "You'd better pick up a few things on the way."

"What do we need?"

"Some roast beef, for one thing. I bought a quarter of a pound coming home from my aunt's."

"Why a quarter of a pound, Joan?" said Rogin, deeply annoyed. "That's just about enough for one good sandwich."

"So you have to stop at a delicatessen. I had no more money."

He was about to ask, "What happened to the thirty dollars I gave you on Wednesday?" but he knew that would not be right.

"I had to give Phyllis money for the cleaning woman," said Joan.

Phyllis, Joan's cousin, was a young divorcée, extremely wealthy. The two women shared an apartment.

"Roast beef," he said, "and what else?"

"Some shampoo, sweetheart. We've used up all the shampoo. And hurry, darling, I've missed you all day."

"And I've missed you," said Rogin, but to tell the truth he had been worrying most of the time. He had a younger brother whom he was putting through college. And his mother, whose annuity wasn't quite enough in these days of inflation and high taxes, needed money, too. Joan had debts he was helping her to pay, for she wasn't working. She was looking for something suitable to do. Beautiful, well educated, aristocratic in her attitude, she couldn't clerk in a dime store; she couldn't model clothes (Rogin thought this made girls vain and stiff, and he didn't want her to); she couldn't be a waitress or a cashier. What could she be? Well, something would turn up, and meantime Rogin hesitated to complain. He paid her bills—the dentist, the department store, the osteopath, the doctor, the psychiatrist. At Christmas, Rogin almost went mad. Joan bought him a velvet smoking jacket with frog fasteners, a beautiful pipe, and a pouch. She bought Phyllis a garnet brooch, an Italian silk umbrella, and a gold cigarette holder. For other friends, she bought Dutch pewter and Swedish glassware. Before she was through, she had spent five hundred dollars of Rogin's money. He loved her too much to show his suffering. He believed she had a far better nature than his. She didn't worry about money. She had a marvelous character, always cheerful, and she really didn't need a psychiatrist at all. She went to one because Phyllis did and it made her curious. She tried too much to keep up with her cousin, whose father had made millions in the rug business.

While the woman in the drugstore was wrapping the shampoo bottle, a clear idea suddenly arose in Rogin's thoughts: Money surrounds you in life as the earth does in death. Superimposition is the universal law. Who is free? No one is free. Who has no burdens? Everyone is under pressure. The very rocks, the waters of the earth, beasts, men, children—everyone has some weight to carry. This idea was extremely clear to him at first. Soon it became rather vague, but it had a great effect nevertheless, as if someone had given him a valuable gift. (Not like the velvet smoking jacket he couldn't bring himself to wear, or the pipe it choked him to smoke.) The notion that all were under pressure and affliction, instead of saddening him, had the opposite influence. It put him in a wonderful mood. It was extraordinary how happy he became and, in addition, clear-sighted. His eyes all at once were opened to what was around him. He saw with delight how the druggist and the woman who wrapped the shampoo bottle were smiling and flirting, how the lines of worry in her face went over into lines of cheer and the druggist's receding gums did not hinder his kidding and friendliness. And in the delicatessen, also, it was amazing how much Rogin noted and what happiness it gave him simply to be there.

Delicatessens on Sunday night, when all other stores are shut, will overcharge you ferociously, and Rogin would normally have been on guard, but he was not tonight, or scarcely so. Smells of pickle, sausage, mustard, and smoked fish overjoyed him. He pitied the people who would buy the chicken salad and chopped herring; they could do it only because their sight was too dim to see what they were getting—the fat flakes of pepper on the chicken, the soppy herring, mostly vinegar-soaked stale bread. Who would buy them? Late risers, people living alone, waking up in the darkness of the afternoon, finding their refrigerators empty, or people whose gaze was turned inward. The roast beef looked not bad, and Rogin ordered a pound.

While the storekeeper was slicing the meat, he yelled at a Puerto Rican kid who was reaching for a bag of chocolate cookies, "Hey, you want to pull me down the whole display on yourself? You, *chico*, wait a half a minute." This storekeeper, though he looked like one of Pancho Villa's bandits, the kind that smeared their enemies with syrup and staked them down on anthills, a man with toadlike eyes and stout hands made to clasp pistols hung around his belly, was not so bad. He was a New York man, thought Rogin—who was from Albany himself—a New York man toughened by every abuse of the city, trained to suspect everyone. But in his own realm, on the board behind the counter, there was justice. Even clemency.

The Puerto Rican kid wore a complete cowboy outfit—a green hat with white braid, guns, chaps, spurs, boots, and gauntlets—but he couldn't speak any English. Rogin unhooked the cellophane bag of hard circular cookies and gave it to him. The boy tore the cellophane with his teeth and began to chew one of those dry chocolate discs. Rogin recognized his state—the energetic dream of childhood. Once, he too, had found these dry biscuits delicious. It would have bored him now to eat one.

What else would Joan like? Rogin thought fondly. Some strawberries? "Give me some frozen strawberries. No, raspberries, she likes those better. And heavy cream. And some rolls, cream cheese, and some of those rubber-looking gherkins."

"What rubber?"

"Those, deep green, with eyes. Some ice cream might be in order, too."

He tried to think of a compliment, a good comparison, an endearment, for Joan when she'd open the door. What about her complexion? There was really nothing to compare her sweet, small, daring, shapely, timid, defiant, loving face to. How difficult she was, and how beautiful!

As Rogin went down into the stony, odorous, metallic, captive air of the subway, he was diverted by an unusual confession made by a man to his friend. These were two very tall men, shapeless in their winter clothes, as if their coats concealed suits of chain mail.

"So, how long have you known me?" said one.

"Twelve years."

"Well, I have an admission to make," he said. "I've decided that I might as well. For years I've been a heavy drinker. You didn't know. Practically an alcoholic."

But his friend was not surprised, and he answered immediately, "Yes, I did know."

"You knew? Impossible! How could you?"

Why, thought Rogin, as if it could be a secret! Look at that long, austere, alcohol-washed face, that drink-ruined nose, the skin by his ears like turkey wattles, and those whiskey-saddened eyes.

"Well, I did know, though."

"You couldn't have. I can't believe it." He was upset, and his friend didn't seem to want to soothe him. "But it's all right now," he said. "I've been going to a doctor and taking pills, a new revolutionary Danish discovery. It's a miracle. I'm beginning to believe they can cure you of anything and everything. You can't beat the Danes in science. They do everything. They turned a man into a woman."

"That isn't how they stop you from drinking, is it?"

"No. I hope not. This is only like asprin. It's super-aspirin. They call it the aspirin of the future. But if you use it, you have to stop drinking."

Rogin's illuminated mind asked of itself while the human tides of the subway swayed back and forth, and cars linked and transparent like fish bladders raced under the streets: How come he thought nobody would know what everybody couldn't help knowing? And, as a chemist, he asked himself what kind of compound this new Danish drug might be, and started thinking about various inventions of his own, synthetic albumen, a cigarette that lit itself, a cheaper motor fuel. Ye gods, but he needed money! As never before. What was to be done? His mother was growing more and more difficult. On Friday night, she had neglected to cut up his meat for him, and he was hurt. She had sat at the table motionless, with her long-suffering face, severe, and let him cut his own meat, a thing she almost never did. She had always spoiled him and made his brother envy him. But what she expected now! Oh, Lord, how he had to pay, and it had never even occurred to him formerly that these things might have a price.

Seated, one of the passengers, Rogin recovered his calm, happy, even clairvoyant state of mind. To think of money was to think as the world wanted you to think; then you'd never be your own master. When people said they wouldn't do something for love or money, they meant that love and money were opposite passions and one the enemy of the other. He went on to reflect how little people knew about this, how they slept through life, how small a light the light of consciousness was. Rogin's clean, snub-nosed face shone while his heart was torn with joy at these deeper thoughts of our ignorance. You might take this drunkard as an example, who for long years thought his closest friends never suspected he drank. Rogin looked up and down the aisle for this remarkable knightly symbol, but he was gone.

However, there was no lack of things to see. There was a small girl with a new white muff; into the muff a doll's head was sewn, and the child was happy and affectionately vain of it, while her old man, stout and grim, with a huge scowling nose, kept picking her up and resetting her in the seat, as if he were trying to change her into something else. Then another child, led by her mother, boarded the car, and this other child carried the very same doll-faced muff, and this greatly annoyed both parents. The woman, who looked like a difficult, contentious woman, took her daughter away. It seemed to Rogin that each child was in love with its own muff and didn't even see the other, but it was one of his foibles to think he understood the hearts of little children.

A foreign family next engaged his attention. They looked like Central

Americans to him. On one side the mother, quite old, dark-faced, white-haired, and worn out; on the other a son with the whitened, porous hands of a dishwasher. But what was the dwarf who sat between them—a son or a daughter? The hair was long and wary and the cheeks smooth, but the shirt and tie were masculine. The overcoat was feminine, but the shoes—the shoes were a puzzle. A pair of brown oxfords with an outer seam like a man's, but Baby Louis heels like a woman's—a plain toe like a man's, but a strap across the instep like a woman's. No stockings. That didn't help much. The dwarf's fingers were beringed, but without a wedding band. There were small grim dents in the cheeks. The eyes were puffy and concealed, but Rogin did not doubt that they could reveal strange things if they chose and that this was a creature of remarkable understanding. He had for many years owned De la Mare's *Memoirs of a Midget*. Now he took a resolve; he would read it. As soon as he had decided, he was free from his consuming curiosity as to the dwarf's sex and was able to look at the person who sat beside him.

Thoughts very often grow fertile in the subway, because of the motion, the great company, the subtlety of the rider's state as he rattles under streets and rivers, under the foundations of great buildings, and Rogin's mind had already been strangely stimulated. Clasping the bag of groceries from which there rose odors of bread and pickle spice, he was following a train of reflections, first about the chemistry of sex determination, the X and Y chromosomes, hereditary linkages, the uterus, afterward about his brother as a tax exemption. He recalled two dreams of the night before. In one, an undertaker had offered to cut his hair, and he had refused. In another, he had been carrying a woman on his head. Sad dreams, both! Very sad! Which was the woman—Joan or Mother? And the undertaker—his lawyer? He gave a deep sigh, and by force of habit began to put together his synthetic albumen that was to revolutionize the entire egg industry.

Meanwhile, he had not interrupted his examination of the passengers and had fallen into a study of the man next to him. This was a man whom he had never in his life seen before but with whom he now suddenly felt linked through all existence. He was middle-aged, sturdy, with clear skin and blue eyes. His hands were clean, well formed, but Rogin did not approve of them. The coat he wore was a fairly expensive blue check such as Rogin would never have chosen for himself. He would not have worn blue suede shoes, either, or such a faultless hat, a cumbersome felt animal of a hat encircled by a high, fat ribbon. There are all kinds of dandies, not all of them are of the flaunting kind; some are dandies of respectability, and Rogin's fellow passenger was one of these. His straight-nosed profile was handsome, yet he had betrayed his gift, for he was flat-looking. But in his flat way he seemed to warn people that he wanted no difficulties with them, he wanted nothing to do with them. Wearing such blue suède shoes, he could not afford to have people treading on his feet, and he seemed to draw about himself a circle of privilege, notifying all others to mind their own business and let him read his paper. He was holding a *Tribune*, and perhaps it would be overstatement to say that he was reading. He was holding it.

His clear skin and blue eyes, his straight and purely Roman nose—even the way he sat—all strongly suggested one person to Rogin: Joan. He tried to escape the comparison, but it couldn't be helped. This man not only looked like Joan's father, whom Rogin detested; he looked like Joan herself. Forty years hence, a son of hers, provided she had one, might be like this. A son of hers? Of such a son, he himself, Rogin, would be the father. Lacking in dominant traits as compared with Joan his heritage would not appear. Probably the children would resemble her. Yes, think forty years ahead, and a man like this, who sat by him knee to knee in the hurtling car among their fellow creatures, unconscious participants in a sort of great carnival of transit—such a man would carry forward what had been Rogin.

This was why he felt bound to him through all existence. What were forty years reckoned against eternity! Forty years were gone, and he was gazing at his own son. Here he was. Rogin was frightened and moved. "My son! My son!" he said to himself, and the pity of it almost made him burst into tears. The holy and frightful work of the masters of life and death brought this about. We were their instruments. We worked toward ends we thought were our own. But no! The whole thing was so unjust. To suffer, to labor, to toil and force your way through the spikes of life, to crawl through its darkest caverns, to push through the worst, to struggle under the weight of economy, to make money—only to become the father of a fourth-rate man of the world like this, so flat-looking, with his ordinary, clean, rosy, uninteresting, self-satisfied, fundamentally bourgeois face. What a curse to have a dull son! A son like this, who could never understand his father. They had absolutely nothing, but nothing, in common, he and this neat, chubby, blue-eyed man. He was so pleased, thought Rogin, with all he owned and all he did and all he was that he could hardly unfasten his lip. Look at that lip, sticking up at the tip like a little thorn or egg tooth. He wouldn't give anyone the time of day. Would this perhaps be general forty years from now? Would personalities be chillier as the world aged and grew colder? The inhumanity of the next generation incensed Rogin. Father and son had no sign to make to each other. Terrible! Inhuman! What a vision of existence it gave him. Man's personal aims were nothing, illusion. The life force occupied each of us in turn in its progress toward its own fulfillment, trampling on our individual humanity, using us for its own ends like mere dinosaurs or bees, exploiting love heartlessly, making us engage in the social process, labor, struggle for money, and submit to the law of pressure, the universal law of layers, superimposition!

What the blazes am I getting into? Rogin thought. To be the father of a throwback to *her* father. The image of this white-haired, gross, peevish old man with his ugly selfish blue eyes revolted Rogin. This was how his grandson would look. Joan, with whom Rogin was now more and more displeased, could not help that. For her, it was inevitable. But did it have to be inevitable for him? Well, then, Rogin, you fool, don't be a damned instrument. Get out of the way!

But it was too late for this, because he had already experienced the sensation of sitting next to his own son, his son and Joan's. He kept staring at him, waiting for him to say something, but the presumptive son remained coldly silent though he must have been aware of Rogin's scrutiny. They even got out at the same stop—Sheridan Square. When they stepped to the platform, the man, without even looking at Rogin, went away in a different direction in his detestable blue-checked coat, with his rosy, nasty face.

The whole thing upset Rogin very badly. When he approached Joan's door and heard Phyllis's little dog Henri barking even before he could knock, his face was very tense. "I won't be used," he declared to himself. "I have my own right to exist." Joan had better watch out. She had a light way of bypassing grave questions he had given earnest thought to. She always assumed no really disturbing thing would happen. He could not afford the luxury of such a carefree, debonair attitude himself, because he had to work hard and earn money so that disturbing things would *not* happen. Well, at the moment this situation could not be helped, and he really did not mind the money if he could feel that she was not necessarily the mother of such a son as his subway son or entirely the daughter of that awful, obscene father of hers. After all, Rogin was not himself so much like either of his parents, and quite different from his brother.

Joan came to the door, wearing one of Phyllis's expensive housecoats. It suited her very well. At first sight of her happy face, Rogin was brushed by the shadow of resemblance; the touch of it was extremely light, almost figmentary, but it made his flesh tremble.

She began to kiss him, saying, "Oh, my baby. You're covered with snow. Why didn't you wear your hat? It's all over its little head"—her favorite third-person endearment.

"Well, let me put down this bag of stuff. Let me take off my coat," grumbled Rogin, and escaped from her embrace. Why couldn't she wait making up to him? "It's so hot in here. My face is burning. Why do you keep the place at this temperature? And that damned dog keeps barking. If you didn't keep it cooped up, it wouldn't be so spoiled and noisy. Why doesn't anybody ever walk him?"

"Oh, it's not really so hot here! You've just come in from the cold. Don't you think this housecoat fits me better than Phyllis? Especially across the hips. She thinks so, too. She may sell it to me."

"I hope not," Rogin almost exclaimed.

She brought a towel to dry the melting snow from his short black hair. The flurry of rubbing excited Henri intolerably, and Joan locked him up in the bedroom, where he jumped persistently against the door with a rhythmic sound of claws on the wood.

Joan said, "Did you bring the shampoo?"

"Here it is."

"Then I'll wash your hair before dinner. Come."

"I don't want it washed."

"Oh, come on," she said, laughing.

Her lack of consciousness of guilt amazed him. He did not see how it could be. And the carpeted, furnished, lamplit, curtained room seemed to stand against his vision. So that he felt accusing and angry, his spirit sore and bitter, but it did not seem fitting to say why. Indeed, he began to worry lest the reason for it all slip away from him.

They took off his coat and his shirt in the bathroom, and she filled the sink. Rogin was full of his troubled emotions; now that his chest was bare he could feel them even more distinctly inside, and he said to himself, I'll have a thing or two to tell her pretty soon. I'm not letting them get away with it. "Do you think," he was going to tell her, "that I alone was made to carry the burden of the whole world on me? Do you think I was born just to be taken advantage of and sacrificed? Do you think I'm just a natural resource, like a coal mine, or oil well, or fishery, or the like? Remember, that I'm a man is not reason why I should be loaded down. I have a soul in me no bigger or stronger than yours.

"Take away the externals, like the muscles, deeper voice, and so forth, and what remains? A pair of spirits, practically alike. So why shouldn't there also be equality? I can't always be the strong one."

"Sit here," said Joan, bringing up a kitchen stool to the sink. "Your hair's gotten all matted."

He sat with his breast against the cool enamel, his chin on the edge of the basin, the green, hot, radiant water reflecting the glass and the tile, and the sweet, cool, fragrant juice of the shampoo poured on his head. She began to wash him.

"You have the healthiest-looking scalp," she said. "It's all pink."

He answered, "Well, it should be white. There must be something wrong with me."

"But there's absolutely nothing wrong with you," she said, and pressed against him from behind, surrounding him, pouring the water gently over him until it seemed to him that the water came from within him, it was the warm fluid of his own secret loving spirit overflowing into the sink, green and foaming, and the words he had rehearsed he forgot, and his anger at his son-to-be disappeared altogether, and he sighed, and said to her from the water-filled hollow of the sink, "You always have such wonderful ideas, Joan. You know? You have a kind of instinct, a regular gift."

DYLAN THOMAS

The Fight

I WAS standing at the end of the lower playground and annoying Mr. Samuels, who lived in the house just below the high railings. Mr. Samuels complained once a week that boys from the school threw apples and stones and balls through his bedroom window. He sat in a deck chair in a small square of trim garden and tried to read the newspaper. I was only a few yards from him. I was staring him out. He pretended not to notice me, but I knew he knew I was standing there rudely and quietly. Every now and then he peeped at me from behind his newspaper, saw me still and serious and alone, with my eyes on his. As soon as he lost his temper I was going to go home. Already I was late for dinner. I had almost beaten him, the newspaper was trembling, he was breathing heavily, when a strange boy, whom I had not heard approach, pushed me down the bank.

I threw a stone at his face. He took off his spectacles, put them in his coat pocket, took off his coat, hung it neatly on the railings, and attacked. Turning round as we wrestled on the top of the bank, I saw that Mr. Samuels had folded his newspaper on the deck chair and was standing up to watch us. It was a mistake to turn round. The strange boy rabbit-punched me twice. Mr. Samuels hopped with excitement as I fell against the railings. I was down in the dust, hot and scratched and biting, then up and dancing, and I butted the boy in the belly and we tumbled in a heap. I saw through a closing eye that his nose was bleeding. I hit his nose. He tore at my collar and spun me round by the hair.

"Come on! come on!" I heard Mr. Samuels cry.

We both turned towards him. He was shaking his fists and dodging about in the garden. He stopped then, and coughed, and set his panama straight, and avoided our eyes, and turned his back and walked slowly to the deck chair.

We both threw gravel at him.

"I'll give him 'Come on!'" the boy said, as we ran along the playground away from the shouts of Mr. Samuels and down the steps on to the hill.

We walked home together. I admired his bloody nose. He said that my eye was like a poached egg, only black.

"I've never seen such a lot of blood," I said.

He said I had the best black eye in Wales, perhaps it was the best black eye in Europe; he bet Tunney never had a black eye like that.

"And there's blood all over your shirt."

"Sometimes I bleed in dollops," he said.

On Walter's Road we passed a group of high school girls, and I cocked my cap and hoped my eye was as big as a blue-bag, and he walked with his coat flung open to show the bloodstains.

I was a hooligan all during dinner, and a bully, and as bad as a boy from the Sandbanks, and I should have more respect, and I sat silently, like Tunney, over the sago pudding. That afternoon I went to school with an eye-shade on. If I had had a black silk sling I would have been as gay and desperate as the wounded captain in the book that my sister used to read, and that I read under the bed-clothes at night, secretly with a flash-lamp.

On the road, a boy from an inferior school, where the parents did not have to pay anything, called me "One eye!" in a harsh, adult voice. I took no notice, but walked along whistling, my good eye on the summer clouds sailing, beyond insult, above Terrace Road.

The mathematics master said: "I see that Mr. Thomas at the back of the class has been straining his eyesight. But it isn't over his homework, is it, gentlemen?"

Gilbert Rees, next to me, laughed loudest.

"I'll break your leg after school!" I said.

He'd hobble, howling, up to the head master's study. A deep hush in the school. A message on a plate brought by the porter. "The head master's compliments, sir, and will you come at once?" "How did you happen to break this boy's leg?" "Oh! damn and bottom, the agony!" cried Gilbert Rees. "Just a little twist," I would say. "I don't know my own strength. I apologize. But there's nothing to worry about. Let me set the leg, sir." A rapid manipulation, the click of a bone. "Doctor Thomas, sir, at your service." Mrs. Rees was on her knees. "How can I thank you?" "It's nothing at all, dear lady. Wash his ears every morning. Throw away his rulers. Pour his red and green inks down the sink."

In Mr. Trotter's drawing class we drew naked girls inaccurately on sheets of paper under our drawings of a vase and passed them along under the desks. Some of the drawings were detailed strangely, others were tailed off like mermaids. Gilbert Rees drew the vase only.

"Sleep with your wife, sir?"

"What did you say?"

"Lend me a knife, sir?"

"What would you do if you had a million pounds?"

"I'd buy a Bugatti and a Rolls and a Bentley and I'd go two hundred miles an hour on Pendine sands."

"I'd buy a harem and keep the girls in the gym."

"I'd buy a house like Mrs. Cotmore-Richard's, twice as big as hers, and a cricket field and a football field and a proper garage with mechanics and a lift."

"And a lavatory as big as, as big as the Melba pavilion, with plush seats and golden chains and . . ."

"And I'd smoke cigarettes with real gold tips, better than Morris's Blue Book."

"I'd buy all the railway trains, and only 4A could travel in them."

"And not Gilbert Rees either."

"What's the longest you've been?"

"I went to Edinburgh."

"My father went to Salonika in the War."

"Where's that, Cyril?"

"Cyril, tell us about Mrs. Pussie Edwards in Hanover Street."

"Well, my brother says he can do anything."

I drew a wild guess below the waist, and wrote Pussie Edwards in small letters at the foot of the page.

"*Cave!*"

"Hide your drawings."

"I bet you a greyhound can go faster than a horse."

Everybody liked the drawing-class, except Mr. Trotter.

In the evening, before calling on my new friend, I sat in my bedroom by the boiler and read through my exercise-books full of poems. There were Danger Don'ts on the backs. On my bedroom walls were pictures of Shakespeare, Walter de la Mare torn from my father's Christmas *Bookman*, Robert Browning, Stacy Aumonier, Rupert Brooke, a bearded man who I had discovered was Whittier, "Watts's Hope," and a Sunday school certificate I was ashamed to want to pull down. A poem I had had printed in the "Wales Day by Day" column of the *Western Mail* was pasted on the mirror to make me blush, but the shame of the poem had died. Across the poem I had written, with a stolen quill and in flourishes: "Homer Nods." I was always waiting for the opportunity to bring someone into my bedroom—"Come into my den; excuse the untidiness; take a chair. No! not that one, it's broken!"—and force him to see the poem accidentially. "I put it there to make me blush." But nobody ever came in except my mother.

Walking to his house in the early dusk through solid, deserted professional avenues lined with trees, I recited pieces of my poems and heard my voice, like a stranger's voice in Park Drive accompanied by the tap-tapping of nailed boots, rise very thinly up through the respectable autumn evening.

"My mind is fashioned
In the ways of intertissue;
Veiled and passioned
Are the thoughts that issue
From its well of furtive lust
Raptured by the devil's dust."

If I looked through a window on to the road, I would see a scarlet-capped boy with big boots striding down the middle, and would wonder who it could be. If I were a young girl watching, my face like Mona Lisa's, my coal-black hair coiled in earphones, I'd see bnneath the "Boys'-Department" suit a manly body with hair and sun tan, and call him and ask, "Will you have tea or cocktails?" and hear his voice reciting the *Grass Blade's Psalm* in the half-dark of the heavily curtained and coloured drawing-room hung about with famous reproductions and glowing with books and wine bottles:

"The frost has lain,
Frost that is dark with flowered slain,
   Fragilely strewn
   With patches of illuminated moon,
About my lonely head in flagged unlovely red.

"The frost has spake,
Frost secretive and thrilled in silent flake,
   With unseen lips of blue
   Glass in the glaze stars threw,
Only to my ears, has spake in visionary tears.

"The frost has known,
From scattered conclave by the few winds blown,
   That the lone genius in my roots,
   Bare down there in a jungle of fruits,
Has planted a green year, for praise,
      in the heart of my upgrowing days.

"The frost has filled,
My heart with longing that the night's sleeve spilled,
   Frost of celestial vapour fraught,
   Frost that the columns of unfallen snow have sought,
With desire for the fields of space
      hovering about my single place."

"Look! there's a strange boy, walking alone like a prince."

"No, no, like a wolf! Look at his long stride!" Sketty church was shaking its bells for me.

> "When I am strewn low
> And all my ashes are
> Dust in a dumb provoking show
> Of minatory star . . ."

I recited. A young man and woman, arm in arm, suddenly appeared from a back lane between houses. I changed my recitation into a tune and hummed past them. They would be tittering together now, with their horrid bodies close. Cissy, moony, long hair. I whistled hard and loud, kicked a tradesmen's entrance, and glanced back over my shoulder. The couple were gone. Here's a kick at "The Elms." "Where are the bleedy elms, mister?" "Here's a handful of gravel, Mrs." "The Croft," right at your window. One night I would paint "Bum" all over the front gate of "Kia-Ora."

A woman stood on "Lyndhurst" steps with a hissing pom, and, stuffing my cap in my pocket, I was off down the road; and there was Dan's house, "Warmley," with music coming loudly out of it.

He was a composer and a poet too; he had written seven historical novels before he was twelve, and he played the piano and the violin; his mother made wool pictures, his brother was a clerk at the docks and syncopated, his aunt kept a preparatory school on the first floor, and his father wrote music for the organ. All this he had told me as we walked home bleeding, strutting by the gym-frocks, waving to boys in the trams.

My new friend's mother answered the door with a ball of wool in her hand. Dan, in the upstairs drawing-room, heard my arrival and played the piano faster.

"I didn't hear you come in," he said when he found him. He finished on a grand chord, stretching all his fingers.

The room was splendidly untidy, full of wool and paper and open cupboards stacked with things you could never find; all the expensive furniture had been kicked; a waistcoat hung on the chandelier. I thought I could live for ever in that room, writing and fighting and spilling ink, having my friends for picnics there after midnight with Waller's rum-and-butter and charlotte russes from Eynon's, and Cydrax and Vino.

He showed me his books and his seven novels. All the novels were about battles, sieges, and kings. "Just early stuff," he said.

He let me take out his violin and make a cat noise.

We sat on a sofa in the window and talked as though we had always known each other. Would the "Swans" beat the "Spurs"? When could girls have babies? Was Arnott's average last year better than Clay's?

"That's my father outside there on the road," he said, "the tall one waving his arms."

Two men were talking on the tram-lines. Mr. Jenkyn looked as if he were trying to swim down Eversley Road, he breast-stroked the air and beat on the ground with his feet, and then he limped and raised one shoulder higher than the other.

"Perhaps he's describing a fight," I said.

"Or telling Mr. Morris a story about cripples," said Dan. "Can you play the piano?"

"I can do chords, but not tunes," I said.

We played a duet with crossed hands.

"Now who's that sonata by?"

We made a Dr. Percy, who was the greatest composer for four hands in the world, and I was Paul America, the pianist, and Dan was Winter Vaux.

I read him an exercise-book full of poems. He listened wisely, like a boy aged a hundred, his head on one side and his spectacles shaking on his swollen nose. "This is called *Warp*," I said:

> "Like suns red from running tears
> Five suns in the glass,
> Together, separate yet, yet separately round,
> Red perhaps, but the glass is as pale as grass,
> Glide, without sound.
> In unity, five tears lid-awake, suns yet, but salt,
> Five inscrutable spears in the head,
> Each sun but an agony,
> Twist perhaps, pain bled of hate,
> Five into one, the one made of five into one, early
> Suns distorted to late.
> All of them now, madly and desolate,
> Spun with the cloth of the five, run
> Widely and foaming, wildly and desolate,
> Shoot through and dive. One of the five is the sun."

The noise of the trams past the house clattered away as far as the sea or farther, into the dredgered bay. Nobody had ever listened like that before. The school had vanished, leaving on Mount Pleasant hill a deep hole that smelt of cloak-rooms and locker mice, and "Warmley" shone in the dark of a town I did not know. In the still room, that had never been strange to me, sitting in heaps of coloured wool, swollen-nosed and one-eyed, we acknowledged our gifts. The future spread out beyond the window, over Singleton Park, crowded with lovers messing about, and into smoky London paved with poems.

Mrs. Jenkyn peered round the door and switched the light on. "There, that's more homely," she said. "You aren't cats."

The future went out with the light, and we played a thumping piece by Dr. Percy—"Have you ever heard anything so beautiful? Louder, louder, America!" said Dan. "Leave a bit of bass for me," I said—until the next-door wall was rapped.

"That's the Careys. Mr. Carey's a Cape Horner," Dan said.

We played him one harsh, whaling piece before Mrs. Jenkyn, with wool and needles, ran upstairs.

When she had gone, Dan said: "Why is a man always ashamed of his mother?"

"Perhaps he isn't when he's older," I said, but I doubted it. The week before I was walking down High Street with three boys after school, and I saw my mother with a Mrs. Partridge outside the Kardomah. I knew she would stop me in front of the others and say, "Now you be home early for tea," and I wanted High Street to open and suck me down. I loved her and disowned her. "Let's cross over," I said, "there's some sailors' boots in Griffith's window." But there was only a dummy with a golf-suit on, and a roll of tweed.

"Supper isn't for half an hour yet. What shall we do?"

"Let's see who can hold that chair up the longest," I said.

"No, let's edit a paper; you do the literature, I'll do the music."

"What shall we call it, then?"

He wrote, "*The ——*, edited by D. Jenkyn and D. Thomas," on the back of a hat-box from under the sofa. The rhythm was better with D. Thomas and D. Jenkyn, but it was his house.

"What about *The Maestersingers?*"

"No, that's too musical," I said.

"*The Warmley Magazine?*"

"No," I said, "I live in 'Glanrhyd.'"

After the hat-box was covered, we wrote "*The Thunderer,* edited by

D. JENKYN
THOMAS

in chalk on a piece of cardboard and pinned it on the wall.

"Would you like to see our maid's bedroom?" asked Dan. We whispered up to the attic.

"What's her name?"

"Hilda."

"Is she young?"

"No, she's twenty or thirty."

Her bed was untidy. "My mother says you can always smell a maid." We smelled the sheets. "I can't smell anything."

In her brass-bound box was a framed photograph of a young man wearing plus-fours.

"That's her boy."

"Let's give him a moustache."

Somebody moved downstairs, a voice called, "Supper now!" and we hurried out, leaving the box open. "One night we'll hide under her bed," Dan said as we opened the dining-room door.

Mr. Jenkyn, Mrs. Jenkyn, Dan's aunt, and a Reverend Bevan and Mrs. Bevan were seated at the table.

Mr. Bevan said grace. When he stood up, it was just as though he were still sitting down, he was so short. "Bless our repast this evening," he said, as though he didn't like the food at all. But once "Amen" was over, he went at the cold meat like a dog.

Mrs. Bevan didn't look all there. She stared at the tablecloth and made hesitant movements with her knife and fork. She appeared to be wondering which to cut up first, the meat or the cloth.

Dan and I stared at her with delight; he kicked me under the table and I spilt the salt. In the commotion I managed to put some vinegar on his bread.

Mrs. Jenkyn said, while every one except Mr. Bevan was watching Mrs. Bevan moving her knife slowly along the edge of her plate: "I do hope you like cold lamb."

Mrs. Bevan smiled at her, assured, and began to eat. She was grey-haired and grey-faced. Perhaps she was grey all over. I tried to undress her, but my mind grew frightened when it came to her short flannel petticoat and navy bloomers to the knees. I couldn't even dare unbutton her tall boots to see how grey her legs were. She looked up from her plate and gave me a wicked smile.

Blushing, I turned to answer Mr. Jenkyn, who was asking me how old I was. I told him, but added one year. Why did I lie then? I wondered. If I lost my cap and found it in my bedroom, and my mother asked me where I had found it, I would say, "In the attic," or, "Under the hall-stand." It was exciting to have to keep wary all the time in case I contradicted myself, to make up the story of a film I pretended to have seen and put Jack Holt in Richard Dix's place.

"Fifteen and three-quarters," said Mr. Jenkyns, "that's a very exact age. I see we have a mathematician with us. Now see if he can do this little sum."

He finished his supper and laid out matches on the plate.

"That's an old one, dad," Dan said.

"Oh, I'd like to see it very much," I said in my best voice. I wanted to come to the house again. This was better than home, and there was a woman off her head, too.

When I failed to place the matches rightly, Mr. Jenkyn showed me how it was done, and, still not understanding, I thanked him and asked him for another one. It was almost as good being a hypocrite as being a liar, it made you warm and shameful.

"What were you talking to Mr. Morris about in the street, dad?" asked Dan. "We saw you from upstairs."

"I was telling him how the Swansea and District Male Voice did the *Messiah*, that's all. Why do you ask?"

Mr. Bevan couldn't eat any more, he was full. For the first time since supper began, he looked round the table. He didn't seem to like what he saw. "How are studies progressing, Daniel?"

"Listen to Mr. Bevan, Dan, he's asking you a question."

"Oh, so so."

"So so?"

"I mean they're going very well, thank you, Mr. Bevan."

"Young people should attempt to say what they mean."

Mrs. Bevan giggled, and asked for more meat. "More meat," she said.

"And you, young man, have you a mathematical bent?"

"No, sir," I said, "I like English."

"He's a poet," said Dan, and looked uncomfortable.

"A brother poet," Mr. Bevan corrected, showing his teeth.

"Mr. Bevan has published books," said Mr. Jenkyn. "*Proserpine, Psyche——*"

"*Orpheus*," said Mr. Bevan sharply.

"And *Orpheus*. You must show Mr. Bevan some of your verses."

"I haven't got anything with me, Mr. Jenkyn."

"A poet," said Mr. Bevan, "should carry his verses in his head."

"I remember them alright," I said.

"Recite me your latest one; I'm always very interested."

"What a gathering," Mrs. Jenkyn said, "poets, musicians, preachers. We only want a painter now, don't we?"

"I don't think you'll like the very latest one," I said.

"Perhaps," said Mr. Bevan, smiling, "I am the best judge of that."

"Frivolous is my hate," I said, wanting to die, watching Mr. Bevan's teeth,

> "Singed with bestial remorse
> Of unfulfilment of desired force,
> And lust of tearing late;
>
> "Now could I raise
> Her dead, dark body to my own
> And hear the joyous rustle of her bone
> And in her eyes see deathly blaze;
>
> "Now could I wake
> To passion after death, and taste

The rapture of her hating, tear the waste
Of body. Break, her dead, dark body, break."

Dan kicked my shins in the silence before Mr. Bevan said: "The influence is obvious, of course 'Break, break, break, on the cold, grey stones, O sea.' "

"Hubert knows Tennyson backwards," said Mrs. Bevan, "backwards."

"Can we go upstairs now?" Dan asked.

"No annoying Mr. Carey then."

And we shut the door softly behind us and ran upstairs with our hands over our mouths.

"Damn! damn! damn!" said Dan. "Did you see the reverend's face?"

We imitated him up and down the room, and had a short fight on the carpet. Dan's nose began to bleed again. "That's nothing, it'll stop in a minute. I can bleed when I like."

"Tell me about Mrs. Bevan. Is she mad?"

"She's terribly mad, she doesn't know who she is. She tried to throw herself out of the window but he didn't take any notice, so she came up to our house and told mother all about it."

Mrs. Bevan knocked and walked in. "I hope I'm not interrupting you."

"No, of course not, Mrs. Bevan."

"I wanted a little change of air," she said. She sat down in the wool on the sofa by the window.

"Isn't it a close night?" said Dan. "Would you like the window open?" She looked at the window.

"I can easily open it for you," Dan said, and winked at me.

"Let me open it for you, Mrs. Bevan," I said.

"It's good to have the window open."

"And this is a nice high window too."

"Plenty of air from the sea."

"Let it be, dear," she said, "I'll just sit here and wait for my husband." She played with the balls of wool, picked up a needle and tapped it gently on the palm of her hand.

"Is Mr. Bevan going to be long?"

"I'll just sit and wait for my husband," she said.

We talked to her some more about windows, but she only smiled and undid the wool, and once she put the blunt end of the long needle in her ear. Soon we grew tired of watching her, and Dan played the piano—"My twentieth sonata," he said, "this one is *Homage to Beethoven*"—and at half-past nine I had to go home.

I said good night to Mrs. Bevan, who waved the needle and bowed sitting down, and Mr. Bevan downstairs gave me his cold hand to shake, and Mr. and Mrs. Jenkyn told me to come again, and the quiet aunt gave me a Mars bar.

"I'll send you a bit of the way," said Dan.

Outside, on the pavement, in the warm night, we looked up at the lighted drawing-room window. It was the only light in the road.

"Look! there she is!"

Mrs. Bevan's face was pressed against the glass, her hook nose flattened, her lips pressed tight, and we ran all the way down Eversley Road in case she jumped.

At the corner, Dan said: "I must leave you now, I've got to finish a string trio tonight."

"I'm working on a long poem," I said, "about the princes of Wales and the wizards and everybody."

We both went home to bed.

THOMAS WOLFE

The Far and the Near

ON the outskirts of a little town upon a rise of land that swept back from the railway there was a tidy little cottage of white boards, trimmed vividly with green blinds. To one side of the house there was a garden neatly patterned with plots of growing vegetables, and an arbor for the grapes which ripened late in August. Before the house there were three mighty oaks which sheltered it in their clean and massive shade in summer, and to the other side there was a border of gay flowers. The whole place had an air of tidiness, thrift, and modest comfort.

Every day, a few minutes after two o'clock in the afternoon, the limited express between two cities passed this spot. At that moment the great train, having halted for a breathing-space at the town near by, was beginning to lengthen evenly into its stroke, but it had not yet reached the full drive of its terrific speed. It swung into view deliberately, swept past with a powerful swaying motion of the engine, a low smooth rumble of its heavy cars upon pressed steel, and then it vanished in the cut. For a moment the progress of the engine could be marked by heavy bellowing puffs of smoke that burst at spaced intervals above the edges of the meadow grass, and finally nothing could be heard but the solid clacking tempo of the wheels receding into the drowsy stillness of the afternoon.

Every day for more than twenty years, as the train had approached this house, the engineer had blown on the whistle, and every day, as soon as she heard this signal, a woman had appeared on the back porch of the little house and waved to him. At first she had a small child clinging to her skirts, and now this child had grown to full womanhood, and every day she, too, came with her mother to the porch and waved.

The engineer had grown old and gray in service. He had driven his great train, loaded with its weight of lives, across the land ten thousand times. His own children had grown up and married, and four times he had seen before him on the tracks the ghastly dot of tragedy converging like a cannon ball to its eclipse of horror at the boiler head—a light spring wagon filled with children, with its clustered row of small stunned faces; a cheap automobile stalled upon the tracks, set with the wooden figures of people paralyzed with fear; a battered hobo walking by the rail, too deaf and old to hear the whistle's warning; and a form flung past his window with a scream—all this the man had seen and known. He had known all the grief, the joy, the peril and the labor such a man could know; he had grown seamed and weathered in his loyal service, and now, schooled by the qualities of faith and courage and humbleness that attended his labor, he had grown old, and had the grandeur and the wisdom these men have.

But no matter what peril or tragedy he had known, the vision of the little house and the women waving to him with a brave free motion of the arm had become fixed in the mind of the engineer as something beautiful and enduring, something beyond all change and ruin, and something that would always be the same, no matter what mishap, grief or error might break the iron schedule of his days.

The sight of the little house and of these two women gave him the most extraordinary happiness he had ever known. He had seen them in a thousand lights, a hundred weathers. He had seen them through the harsh bare light of wintry gray across the brown and frosted stubble of the earth, and he had seen them again in the green luring sorcery of April.

He felt for them and for the little house in which they lived such tenderness as a man might feel for his own children, and at length the picture of their lives was carved so sharply in his heart that he felt that he knew their lives completely, to every hour and moment of the day, and he resolved that one day, when his years of service should be ended, he would go and find these people and speak at last with them whose lives had been so wrought into his own.

That day came. At last the engineer stepped from a train onto the station platform of the town where these two women lived. His years upon the rail had ended. He was a pensioned servant of his company, with no more work to do. The engineer walked slowly through the station and out into the streets of the town. Everything was as strange to him as if he had never seen this town before. As he walked on, his sense of bewilderment and confusion grew. Could this be the town he had passed ten thousand times? Were these the same houses he had seen so often from the high windows of his cab? It was all as unfamiliar, as disquieting as a city in a dream, and the perplexity of his spirit increased as he went on.

Presently the houses thinned into the straggling outposts of the town, and the street faded into a country road—the one on which the women lived. And the man plodded on slowly in the heat and dust. At length he stood before the house he sought. He knew at once that he had found the proper place. He saw the lordly oaks before the house, the flower beds, the garden and the arbor, and farther off, the glint of rails.

Yes, this was the house he sought, the place he had passed so many times, the destination he had longed for with such happiness. But now that he had found it, now that he was here, why did his hand falter on the gate; why had the town, the road, the earth, the very entrance to this place he loved turned unfamiliar as the landscape of some ugly dreams? Why did he now feel this sense of confusion, doubt, and hopelessness?

At length he entered by the gate, walked slowly up the path and in a moment more had mounted three short steps that led up to the porch, and was knocking at the door. Presently he heard steps in the hall, the door was opened, and a woman stood facing him.

And instantly, with a sense of bitter loss and grief, he was sorry he had come. He knew at once that the woman who stood there looking at him with a mistrustful eye was the same woman who had waved to him so many thousand times. But her face was harsh and pinched and meager; the flesh sagged wearily in sallow folds, and the small eyes peered at him with timid suspicion and uneasy doubt. All the brave freedom, the warmth and the affection that he had read into her gesture, vanished in the moment that he saw her and heard her unfriendly tongue.

And now his own voice sounded unreal and ghastly to him as he tried to explain his presence, to tell her who he was and the reason he had come. But he faltered on, fighting stubbornly against the horror of regret, confusion, disbelief that surged up in his spirit, drowning all his former joy and making his act of hope and tenderness seem shameful to him.

At length the woman invited him almost unwillingly into the house, and called her daughter in a harsh shrill voice. Then, for a brief agony of time, the man sat in an ugly little parlor, and he tried to talk while the two women stared at him with a dull, bewildered hostility, a sullen, timorous restraint.

And finally, stammering a crude farewell, he departed. He walked away down the path and then along the road toward town, and suddenly he knew that he was an old man. His heart, which had been brave and confident when it looked along the familiar vista of the rails, was now sick with doubt and horror as it saw the strange and unsuspected visage of an earth which had always been within a stone's throw of him, and which he had never seen or known. And he knew that all the magic of that bright lost way, the vista of that shining line, the imagined corner of that small good universe of hope's desire, was gone forever, could never be got back again.

F. SCOTT FITZGERALD

The Sensible Thing

AT the Great American Lunch Hour young George O'Kelly straightened his desk deliberately and with an assumed air of interest. No one in the office must know that he was in a hurry, for success is a matter of atmosphere, and it is not well to advertise the fact that your mind is separated from your work by a distance of seven hundred miles.

But once out of the building he set his teeth and began to run, glancing now and then at the gay noon of early spring which filled Times Square and loitered less than twenty feet over the heads of the crowd. The crowd all looked slightly upward and took deep March breaths, and the sun dazzled their eyes so that scarcely any one saw any one else but only their own reflection on the sky.

George O'Kelly, whose mind was over seven hundred miles away, thought that all outdoors was horrible. He rushed into the subway, and for ninety-five blocks bent a frenzied glance on a car-card which showed vividly how he had only one chance in five of keeping his teeth for ten years. At 137th Street he broke off his study of commercial art, left the subway, and began to run again, a tireless, anxious run that brought him this time to his home—one room in a high, horrible apartment-house in the middle of nowhere.

There it was on the bureau, the letter—in sacred ink, on blessed paper —all over the city, people, if they listened, could hear the beating of George O'Kelly's heart. He read the commas, the blots, and the thumb-smudge on the margin—then he threw himself hopelessly upon his bed.

He was in a mess, one of those terrific messes which are ordinary incidents in the life of the poor, which follow poverty like birds of prey. The poor go under or go up or go wrong or even go on, somehow, in a way the poor have—but George O'Kelly was so new to poverty that had any one denied the uniqueness of his case he would have been astounded.

Less than two years ago he had been graduated with honors from the Massachusetts Institute of Technology and had taken a position with a firm of construction engineers in southern Tennessee. All his life he had thought in terms of tunnels and skyscrapers and great squat dams and tall, three-towered bridges, that were like dancers holding hands in a row, with heads as tall as cities and skirts of cable strand. It had seemed romantic to George O'Kelly to change the sweep of rivers and the shape of mountains so that life could flourish in the old bad lands of the world where it had never taken root before. He loved steel, and there was always steel near him in his dreams, liquid steel, steel in bars, and blocks and beams and formless plastic masses, waiting for him, as paint and canvas to his hand. Steel inexhaustible, to be made lovely and austere in his imaginative fire . . .

At present he was an insurance clerk at forty dollars a week with his dream slipping fast behind him. The dark little girl who had made this mess, this terrible and intolerable mess, was waiting to be sent for in a town in Tennessee.

In fifteen minutes the woman from whom he sublet his room knocked and asked him with maddening kindness if, since he was home, he would have some lunch. He shook his head, but the interruption aroused him, and getting up from the bed he wrote a telegram.

"Letter depressed me have you lost your nerve you are foolish and just upset to think of breaking off why not marry me immediately sure we can make it all right——"

He hesitated for a wild minute, and then added in a hand that could scarcely be recognized as his own: "In any case I will arrive to-morrow at six o'clock."

When he finished he ran out of the apartment and down to the telegraph office near the subway stop. He possessed in this world not quite one hundred dollars, but the letter showed that she was "nervous" and this left him no choice. He knew what "nervous" meant—that she was emotionally depressed, that the prospect of marrying into a life of poverty and struggle was putting too much strain upon her love.

George O'Kelly reached the insurance company at his usual run, the run that had become almost second nature to him, that seemed best to express the tension under which he lived. He went straight to the manager's office.

"I want to see you, Mr. Chambers," he announced breathlessly.

"Well?" Two eyes, eyes like winter windows, glared at him with ruthless impersonality.

"I want to get four days' vacation."

"Why, you had a vacation just two weeks ago!" said Mr. Chambers in surprise.

"That's true," admitted the distraught young man, "but now I've got to have another."

"Where'd you go last time? To your home?"

"No, I went to—a place in Tennessee."

"Well, where do you want to go this time?"

"Well, this time I want to go to—a place in Tennessee."

"You're consistent, anyhow," said the manager dryly. "But I didn't realize you were employed here as a travelling salesman."

"I'm not," cried George desperately, "but I've got to go."

"All right," agreed Mr. Chambers, "but you don't have to come back. So don't!"

"I won't." And to his own astonishment as well as Mr. Chambers' George's face grew pink with pleasure. He felt happy, exultant—for the first time in six months he was absolutely free. Tears of gratitude stood in his eyes, and he seized Mr. Chambers warmly by the hand.

"I want to thank you," he said with a rush of emotion, "I don't want to come back. I think I'd have gone crazy if you'd said that I could come back. Only I couldn't quit myself, you see, and I want to thank you for—for quitting for me."

He waved his hand magnanimously, shouted aloud, "You owe me three days' salary but you can keep it!" and rushed from the office. Mr. Chambers rang for his stenographer to ask if O'Kelly had seemed queer lately. He had fired many men in the course of his career, and they had taken it in many different ways, but none of them had thanked him—ever before.

II

Jonquil Cary was her name, and to George O'Kelly nothing had ever looked so fresh and pale as her face when she saw him and fled to him eagerly along the station platform. Her arms were raised to him, her mouth was half parted for his kiss, when she held him off suddenly and lightly and, with a touch of embarrassment, looked around. Two boys, somewhat younger than George, were standing in the background.

"This is Mr. Craddock and Mr. Holt," she announced cheerfully. "You met them when you were here before."

Disturbed by the transition of a kiss into an introduction and suspecting some hidden significance, George was more confused when he found that the automobile which was to carry them to Jonquil's house belonged to one of the two young men. It seemed to put him at a disadvantage. On the way Jonquil chattered between the front and back seats, and when he tried to slip his arm around her under cover of the twilight she compelled him with a quick movement to take her hand instead.

"Is this street on the way to your house?" he whispered. "I don't recognize it."

"It's the new boulevard. Jerry just got this car today, and he wants to show it to me before he takes us home."

When, after twenty minutes, they were deposited at Jonquil's house, George felt that the first happiness of the meeting, the joy he had recognized so surely in her eyes back in the station, had been dissipated by the intrusion of the ride. Something that he had looked forward to had been rather casually lost, and he was brooding on this as he said good night stiffly to the two young men. Then his ill-humor faded as Jonquil drew him into a familiar embrace under the dim light of the front hall and told him in a dozen ways, of which the best was without words, how she had missed him. Her emotion reassured him, promised his anxious heart that everything would be all right.

They sat together on the sofa, overcome by each other's presence, beyond all except fragmentary endearments. At the supper hour Jonquil's father and mother appeared and were glad to see George. They liked him, and had been interested in his engineering career when he had first come to Tennessee over a year before. They had been sorry when he had given it up and gone to New York to look for something more immediately profitable, but while they deplored the curtailment of his career they sympathized with him and were ready to recognize the engagement. During dinner they asked about his progress in New York.

"Everything's going fine," he told them with enthusiasm. "I've been promoted—better salary."

He was miserable as he said this—but they were all *so* glad.

"They must like you," said Mrs. Cary, "that's certain—or they wouldn't let you off twice in three weeks to come down here."

"I told them they had to," explained George hastily; "I told them if they didn't I wouldn't work for them any more."

"But you ought to save your money," Mrs. Cary reproached him gently. "Not spend it all on this expensive trip."

Dinner was over—he and Jonquil were alone and she came back into his arms.

"So glad you're here," she sighed. "Wish you never were going away again, darling."

"Do you miss me?"

"Oh, so much, so much."

"Do you—do other men come to see you often? Like those two kids?"

The question surprised her. The dark velvet eyes stared at him.

"Why, of course they do. All the time. Why—I've told you in letters that they did, dearest."

This was true—when he had first come to the city there had been already a dozen boys around her, responding to her picturesque fragility with adolescent worship, and a few of them perceiving that her beautiful eyes were also sane and kind.

"Do you expect me never to go anywhere"—Jonquil demanded, leaning back against the sofa-pillows until she seemed to look at him from many miles away—"and just fold my hands and sit still—forever?"

"What do you mean?" he blurted out in a panic. "Do you mean you think I'll never have enough money to marry you?"

"Oh, don't jump at conclusions so, George."

"I'm not jumping at conclusions. That's what you said."

George decided suddenly that he was on dangerous grounds. He had not intended to let anything spoil this night. He tried to take her again in his arms, but she resisted unexpectedly, saying:

"It's hot. I'm going to get the electric fan."

When the fan was adjusted they sat down again, but he was in a super-sensitive mood and involuntarily he plunged into the specific world he had intended to avoid.

"When will you marry me?"

"Are you ready for me to marry you?"

All at once his nerves gave way, and he sprang to his feet.

"Let's shut off that damned fan," he cried, "it drives me wild. It's like a clock ticking away all the time I'll be with you. I came here to be happy and forget everything about New York and time——"

He sank down on the sofa as suddenly as he had risen. Jonquil turned off the fan, and drawing his head down into her lap began stroking his hair.

"Let's sit like this," she said softly, "just sit quiet like this, and I'll put you to sleep. You're all tired and nervous and your sweetheart'll take care of you."

"But I don't want to sit like this," he complained, jerking up suddenly, "I don't want to sit like this at all. I want you to kiss me. That's the only thing that makes me rest. And anyways I'm not nervous—it's you that's nervous. I'm not nervous at all."

To prove that he wasn't nervous he left the couch and plumped himself into a rocking-chair across the room.

"Just when I'm ready to marry you you write me the most nervous letters, as if you're going to back out, and I have to come rushing down here——"

"You don't have to come if you don't want to."

"But I *do* want to!" insisted George.

It seemed to him that he was being very cool and logical and that she was putting him deliberately in the wrong. With every word they were drawing farther and farther apart—and he was unable to stop himself or to keep worry and pain out of his voice.

But in a minute Jonquil began to cry sorrowfully and he came back to the sofa and put his arm around her. He was the comforter now, drawing her head close to his shoulder, murmuring old familiar things until she grew calmer and only trembled a little, spasmodically, in his arms. For over an hour they sat there, while the evening pianos thumped their last cadences into the street outside. George did not move, or think, or hope, lulled into numbness by the premonition of disaster. The clock would tick on, past eleven, past twelve, and then Mrs. Cary would call down gently over the banister—beyond that he saw only tomorrow and despair.

III

In the heat of the next day the breaking-point came. They had each guessed the truth about the other, but of the two she was the more ready to admit the situation.

"There's no use going on," she said miserably, "you know you hate the insurance business, and you'll never do well in it."

"That's not it," he insisted stubbornly; "I hate going on alone. If you'll marry me and come with me and take a chance with me, I can make good at anything, but not while I'm worrying about you down here."

She was silent a long time before she answered, not thinking—for she had seen the end—but only waiting, because she knew that every word would seem more cruel than the last. Finally she spoke:

"George, I love you with all my heart, and I don't see how I can ever love any one else but you. If you'd been ready for me two months ago I'd have married you—now I can't because it doesn't seem to be the sensible thing."

He made wild accusations—there was some one else—she was keeping something from him!

"No, there's no one else."

This was true. But reacting from the strain of this affair she had found relief in the company of young boys like Jerry Holt, who had the merit of meaning absolutely nothing in her life.

George didn't take the situation well, at all. He seized her in his arms and tried literally to kiss her into marrying him at once. When this failed, he broke into a long monologue of self-pity, and ceased only when he saw that he was making himself despicable in her sight. He threatened to leave when he had no intention of leaving, and refused to go when she told him that, after all, it was best that he should.

For a while she was sorry, then for another while she was merely kind.

"You'd better go now," she cried at last, so loud that Mrs. Cary came down-stairs in alarm.

"Is something the matter?"

"I'm going away, Mrs. Cary," said George brokenly. Jonquil had left the room.

"Don't feel so badly, George." Mrs. Cary blinked at him in helpless sympathy—sorry and, in the same breath, glad that the little tragedy was almost done. "If I were you I'd go home to your mother for a week or so. Perhaps after all this is the sensible thing——"

"Please don't talk," he cried. "Please don't say anything to me now!"

Jonquil came into the room again, her sorrow and her nervousness alike tucked under powder and rouge and hat.

"I've ordered a taxicab," she said impersonally. "We can drive around until your train leaves."

She walked out on the front porch. George put on his coat and hat and stood for a minute exhausted in the hall—he had eaten scarcely a bite since he had left New York. Mrs. Cary came over, drew his head down and kissed him on the cheek, and he felt very ridiculous and weak in his knowledge that the scene had been ridiculous and weak at the end. If he had only gone the night before—left her for the last time with a decent pride.

The taxi had come, and for an hour these two that had been lovers rode along the less-frequented streets. He held her hand and grew calmer in the sunshine, seeing too late that there had been nothing all along to do or say.

"I'll come back," he told her.

"I know you will," she answered, trying to put a cheery faith into her voice. "And we'll write each other—sometimes."

"No," he said, "we won't write. I couldn't stand that. Some day I'll come back."

"I'll never forget you, George."

They reached the station, and she went with him while he bought his ticket. . . .

"Why, George O'Kelly and Jonquil Cary!"

It was a man and a girl whom George had known when he had worked in town, and Jonquil seemed to greet their presence with relief. For an interminable five minutes they all stood there talking; then the train roared into the station, and with ill-concealed agony in his face George held out his arms toward Jonquil. She took an uncertain step toward him, faltered, and then pressed his hand quickly as if she were taking leave of a chance friend.

"Good-by, George," she was saying, "I hope you have a pleasant trip."

"Good-by, George. Come back and see us all again."

Dumb, almost blind with pain, he seized his suitcase, and in some dazed way got himself aboard the train.

Past clanging street-crossings, gathering speed through wide suburban spaces toward the sunset. Perhaps she too would see the sunset and pause for a moment, turning, remembering, before he faded with her sleep into the past. This night's dusk would cover up forever the sun and the trees and the flowers and laughter of his young world.

IV

On a damp afternoon in September of the following year a young man with his face burned to a deep copper glow got off a train at a city in Tennessee. He looked around anxiously, and seemed relieved when he found that there was no one in the station to meet him. He taxied to the best hotel in the city where he registered with some satisfaction as George O'Kelly, Cuzco, Peru.

Up in his room he sat for a few minutes at the window looking down into the familiar street below. Then with his hand trembling faintly he took off the telephone receiver and called a number.

"Is Miss Jonquil in?"

"This is she."

"Oh—" His voice after overcoming a faint tendency to waver went on with friendly formality.

"This is George O'Kelly. Did you get my letter?"

"Yes. I thought you'd be in today."

Her voice, cool and unmoved, disturbed him, but not as he had expected. This was the voice of a stranger, unexcited, pleasantly glad to see him—that was all. He wanted to put down the telephone and catch his breath.

"I haven't seen you for—a long time." He succeeded in making this sound offhand. "Over a year."

He knew how long it had been—to the day.

"It'll be awfully nice to talk to you again."

"I'll be there in about an hour."

He hung up. For four long seasons every minute of his leisure had been crowded with anticipation of this hour, and now this hour was here. He had thought of finding her married, engaged, in love—he had not thought she would be unstirred at his return.

There would never again in his life, he felt, be another ten months like these he had just gone through. He had made an admittedly remarkable showing for a young engineer—stumbled into two unusual opportunities, one in Peru, whence he had just returned, and another, consequent upon it, in New York, whither he was bound. In this short time he had risen from poverty into a position of unlimited opportunity.

He looked at himself in the dressing-table mirror. He was almost black with tan, but it was a romantic black, and in the last week, since he had had time to think about it, it had given him considerable pleasure. The hardiness of his frame, too, he appraised with a sort of fascination. He had lost part of an eyebrow somewhere, and he still wore an elastic bandage on his knee, but he was too young not to realize that on the steamer many women had looked at him with unusual tributary interest.

His clothes, of course, were frightful. They had been made for him by a Greek tailor in Lima—in two days. He was young enough, too, to have explained this sartorial deficiency to Jonquil in his otherwise laconic note. The only further detail it contained was a request that he should *not* be met at the station.

George O'Kelly, of Cuzco, Peru, waited an hour and a half in the hotel, until, to be exact, the sun had reached a midway position in the sky. Then, freshly shaven and talcum-powdered toward a somewhat more Caucasian hue, for vanity at the last minute had overcome romance, he engaged a taxicab and set out for the house he knew so well.

He was breathing hard—he noticed this but he told himself that it was excitement, not emotion. He was here; she was not married—that was enough. He was not even sure what he had to say to her. But this was the moment of his life that he felt he could least easily have dispensed with. There was no triumph, after all, without a girl concerned, and if he did not lay his spoils at her feet he could at least hold them for a passing moment before her eyes.

The house loomed up suddenly beside him, and his first thought was that it had assumed a strange unreality. There was nothing changed—only everything was changed. It was smaller and it seemed shabbier than before —there was no cloud of magic hovering over its roof and issuing from the windows of the upper floor. He rang the door-bell and an unfamiliar colored maid appeared. Miss Jonquil would be down in a moment. He wet his lips nervously and walked into the sitting-room—and the feeling of unreality increased. After all, he saw, this was only a room, and not the enchanted chamber where he had passed those poignant hours. He sat in a chair, amazed to find it a chair, realizing that his imagination had distorted and colored all these simple familiar things.

Then the door opened and Jonquil came into the room—and it was as though everything in it suddenly blurred before his eyes. He had not re- membered how beautiful she was, and he felt his face grow pale and his voice diminish to a poor sigh in his throat.

She was dressed in pale green, and a gold ribbon bound back her dark, straight hair like a crown. The familiar velvet eyes caught his as she came through the door, and a spasm of fright went through him at her beauty's power of inflicting pain.

He said "Hello," and they each took a few steps forward and shook hands. Then they sat in chairs quite far apart and gazed at each other across the room.

"You've come back," she said, and he answered just as tritely: "I wanted to stop in and see you as I came through."

He tried to neutralize the tremor in his voice by looking anywhere but at her face. The obligation to speak was on him, but, unless he im- mediately began to boast, it seemed that there was nothing to say. There had never been anything casual in their previous relations—it didn't seem possible that people in this position would talk about the weather.

"This is ridiculous," he broke out in sudden embarrassment. "I don't know exactly what to do. Does my being here bother you?"

"No." The answer was both reticent and impersonally sad. It depressed him.

"Are you engaged?" he demanded.

"No."

"Are you in love with some one?"

She shook her head.

"Oh." He leaned back in his chair. Another subject seemed exhausted —the interview was not taking the course he had intended.

"Jonquil," he began, this time on a softer key, "after all that's happened between us, I wanted to come back and see you. Whatever I do in the future I'll never love another girl as I've loved you."

This was one of the speeches he had rehearsed. On the steamer it had seemed to have just the right note—a reference to the tenderness he would always feel for her combined with a non-committal attitude toward his present state of mind. Here with the past around him, beside him, growing minute by minute more heavy on the air, it seemed theatrical and stale.

She made no comment, sat without moving, her eyes fixed on him with an expression that might have meant everything or nothing.

"You don't love me any more, do you?" he asked her in a level voice. "No."

When Mrs. Cary came in a minute later, and spoke to him about his success—there had been a half-column about him in the local paper—he was a mixture of emotions. He knew now that he still wanted this girl, and he knew that the past sometimes comes back—that was all. For the rest he must be strong and watchful and he would see.

"And now," Mrs. Cary was saying, "I want you two to go and see the lady who has the chrysanthemums. She particularly told me she wanted to see you because she'd read about you in the paper."

They went to see the lady with the chrysanthemums. They walked along the street, and he recognized with a sort of excitement just how her shorter footsteps always fell in between his own. The lady turned out to be nice, and the chrysanthemums were enormous and extraordinarily beautiful. The lady's gardens were full of them, white and pink and yellow, so that to be among them was a trip back into the heart of summer. There were two gardens full, and a gate between them; when they strolled toward the second garden the lady went first through the gate.

And then a curious thing happened. George stepped aside to let Jonquil pass, but instead of going through she stood still and stared at him for a minute. It was not so much the look, which was not a smile, as it was the moment of silence. They saw each other's eyes, and both took a short, faintly accelerated breath, and then they went on into the second garden. That was all.

The afternoon waned. They thanked the lady and walked home slowly, thoughtfully, side by side. Through dinner, too, they were silent. George told Mr. Cary something of what had happened in South America, and managed to let it be known that everything would be plain sailing for him in the future.

Then dinner was over, and he and Jonquil were alone in the room which had seen the beginning of their love affair and the end. It seemed to him long ago and inexpressibly sad. On that sofa he had felt agony and grief such as he would never feel again. He would never be so weak or so tired and miserable and poor. Yet he knew that that boy of fifteen months before had had something, a trust, a warmth that was gone forever. The sensible thing—they had done the sensible thing. He had traded his first youth for strength and carved success out of despair. But with his youth, life had carried away the freshness of his love.

"You won't marry me, will you?" he said quietly.

Jonquil shook her dark head.

"I'm never going to marry," she answered.

He nodded.

"I'm going on to Washington in the morning," he said.

"Oh——"

"I have to go. I've got to be in New York by the first, and meanwhile I want to stop off in Washington."

"Business!"

"No-o," he said as if reluctantly. "There's some one there I must see who was very kind to me when I was so—down and out."

This was invented. There was no one in Washington for him to see—but he was watching Jonquil narrowly, and he was sure that she winced a little, that her eyes closed and then opened wide again.

"But before I go I want to tell you the things that happened to me since I saw you, and, as maybe we won't meet again, I wonder if—if just this once you'd sit in my lap like you used to. I wouldn't ask except since there's no one else—yet—perhaps it doesn't matter."

She nodded, and in a moment was sitting in his lap as she had sat so often in that vanished spring. The feel of her head against his shoulder, of her familiar body, sent a shock of emotion over him. His arms holding her had a tendency to tighten around her, so he leaned back and began to talk thoughtfully into the air.

He told her of a despairing two weeks in New York which had terminated with an attractive if not very profitable job in a construction plant in Jersey City. When the Peru business had first presented itself it had not seemed an extraordinary opportunity. He was to be third assistant engineer on the expedition, but only ten of the American party, including eight rodmen and surveyors, had ever reached Cuzco. Ten days later the chief of the expedition was dead of yellow fever. That had been his chance, a chance for anybody but a fool, a marvellous chance——

"A chance for anybody but a fool?" she interrupted innocently.

"Even for a fool," he continued. "It was wonderful. Well, I wired New York——"

"And so," she interrupted again, "they wired that you ought to take a chance?"

"Ought to!" he exclaimed, still leaning back. "That I *had* to. There was no time to lose——"

"Not a minute?"

"Not a minute."

"Not even time for—" she paused.

"For what?"

"Look."

He bent his head forward suddenly, and she drew herself to him in the same moment, her lips half open like a flower.

"Yes," he whispered into her lips. "There's all the time in the world. . . ."

All the time in the world—his life and hers. But for an instant as he kissed her he knew that though he search through eternity he could never recapture those lost April hours. He might press her close now till the muscles knotted on his arms—she was something desirable and rare that he had fought for and made his own—but never again an intangible whisper in the dusk, or on the breeze of night. . . .

Well, let it pass, he thought; April is over, April is over. There are all kinds of love in the world, but never the same love twice.

TRUMAN CAPOTE

A Christmas Memory

IMAGINE a morning in late November. A coming of winter morning more than twenty years ago. Consider the kitchen of a spreading old house in a country town. A great black stove is its main feature; but there is also a big round table and a fireplace with two rocking chairs placed in front of it. Just today the fireplace commenced its seasonal roar.

A woman with shorn white hair is standing at the kitchen window.

She is wearing tennis shoes and a shapeless gray sweater over a summery calico dress. She is small and sprightly, like a bantam hen; but, due to a long youthful illness, her shoulders are pitifully hunched. Her face is remarkable—not unlike Lincoln's, craggy like that, and tinted by sun and wind; but it is delicate too, finely boned, and her eyes are sherry-colored and timid. "Oh my," she exclaims, her breath smoking the windowpane, "it's fruitcake weather!"

The person to whom she is speaking is myself. I am seven; she is sixty-something. We are cousins, very distant ones, and we have lived together —well, as long as I can remember. Other people inhabit the house, relatives; and though they have power over us, and frequently make us cry, we are not, on the whole, too much aware of them. We are each other's best friend. She calls me Buddy, in memory of a boy who was formerly her best friend. The other Buddy died in the 1880's, when she was still a child. She is still a child.

"I knew it before I got out of bed," she says, turning away from the window with a purposeful excitement in her eyes. "The courthouse bell sounded so cold and clear. And there were no birds singing; they've gone to warmer country, yes indeed. Oh, Buddy, stop stuffing biscuit and fetch our buggy. Help me find my hat. We've thirty cakes to bake."

It's always the same: a morning arrives in November, and my friend, as though officially inaugurating the Christmas time of year that exhilarates her imagination and fuels the blaze of her heart, announces: "It's fruitcake weather! Fetch our buggy. Help me find my hat."

The hat is found, a straw cartwheel corsaged with velvet roses out-of-doors has faded: it once belonged to a more fashionable relative. Together, we guide our buggy, a dilapidated baby carriage, out to the garden and into a grove of pecan trees. The buggy is mine; that is, it was bought for me when I was born. It is made of wicker, rather unraveled, and the wheels wobble like a drunkard's legs. But it is a faithful object; spring-times, we take it to the woods and fill it with flowers, herbs, wild fern for our porch pots; in the summer, we pile it with picnic paraphernalia and sugar-cane fishing poles and roll it down to the edge of a creek; it has its winter uses, too: as a truck for hauling firewood from the yard to the kitchen, as a warm bed for Queenie, our tough little orange and white rat terrier, who has survived distemper and two rattlesnake bites. Queenie is trotting beside it now.

Three hours later we are back in the kitchen hulling a heaping buggy-load of windfall pecans. Our backs hurt from gathering them: how hard they were to find (the main crop having been shaken off the trees and sold by the orchard's owners, who are not us) among the concealing leaves, the frosted, deceiving grass. Caarackle! A cheery crunch, scraps of miniature thunder sound as the shells collapse and the golden mound of sweet oily ivory meat mounts in the milk-glass bowl. Queenie begs to taste, and now and again my friend sneaks her a mite, though insisting we deprive ourselves. "We mustn't, Buddy. If we start, we won't stop. And there's scarcely enough as there is. For thirty cakes." The kitchen is growing dark. Dusk turns the window into a mirror: our reflections mingle with the rising moon as we work by the fireside in the firelight. At last, when the moon is quite high, we toss the final hull into the fire and with joined sighs, watch it catch flame. The buggy is empty, the bowl is brimful.

We eat our supper (cold biscuits, bacon, blackberry jam) and discuss tomorrow. Tomorrow the kind of work I like best begins: buying. Cherries and citron, ginger and vanilla and canned Hawaiian pineapple, rinds and raisins and walnuts and whiskey and oh, so much flour, butter, so many eggs, spices, flavorings: why, we'll need a pony to pull the buggy home.

But before these purchases can be made, there is the question of money. Neither of us has any. Except for skinflint sums persons in the house occasionally provide (a dime is considered very big money); or what we earn ourselves from various activities: holding rummage sales, selling buckets of hand-picked blackberries, jars of homemade jam and apple jelly and peach preserves, rounding up flowers for funerals and weddings. Once we won seventy-ninth prize, five dollars, in a national football contest. Not that we know a fool thing about football. It's just that we enter any contest we hear about: at the moment our hopes are centered on the fifty-thousand-dollar Grand Prize being offered to name a new brand of coffee (we suggested "A.M."; and, after some hesitation, for my friend thought it perhaps sacrilegious, the slogan "A.M.! Amen!"). To tell the truth, our only *really* profitable enterprise was the Fun and Freak museum we conducted in a back-yard woodshed two summers ago. The Fun was a stereopticon with slide views of Washington and New York lent us by a relative who had been to those places (she was furious when she discovered why we'd borrowed it); the Freak was a three-legged biddy chicken hatched by one of our own hens. Everybody hereabouts wanted to see that biddy: we charged grownups a nickel, kids two cents. And took in a good twenty dollars before the museum shut down due to the decease of the main attraction.

But one way and another we do each year accumulate Christmas savings, a Fruitcake Fund. These moneys we keep hidden in an ancient bead purse under a loose board under the floor under a chamber pot under my friend's bed. The purse is seldom removed from this safe location except to make a deposit, or, as happens every Saturday, a withdrawal; for on Saturdays I am allowed ten cents to go to the picture show. My friend has never been to a picture show, nor does she intend to: "I'd rather hear you tell the story, Buddy. That way I can imagine it more. Besides, a person my age shouldn't squander their eyes. When the Lord comes, let me see him clear." In addition to never having seen a movie, she has never: eaten in a restaurant, traveled more than five miles from home, received or sent a telegram, read anything except funny papers and the Bible, worn cosmetics, cursed, wished someone harm, told a lie on purpose, let a hungry dog go hungry. Here are a few things she has done, does do: killed with a hoe the biggest rattlesnake ever seen in this county (sixteen rattles), dip snuff (secretly), tame hummingbirds (just try it) till they balance on her finger, tell ghost stories (we both believe in ghosts) so tingling they chill you in July, talk to herself, take walks in the rain, grow the prettiest japonicas in town, know the recipe for every sort of old-time Indian cure, including a magical wart-remover.

Now, with supper finished, we retire to the room in a faraway part of the house where my friend sleeps in a scrap-quilt-covered iron bed painted rose pink, her favorite color. Silently, wallowing in the pleasures of conspiracy, we take the bead purse from its secret place and spill its contents on the scrap quilt. Dollar bills, tightly rolled and green as May buds. Somber fifty-cent pieces, heavy enough to weight a dead man's eyes. Lovely dimes, the liveliest coin, the one that really jingles. Nickels and quarters, worn smooth as creek pebbles. But mostly a hateful heap of bitter-odored pennies. Last summer others in the house contracted to pay us a penny for every twenty-five flies we killed. Oh, the carnage of August: the flies that flew to heaven! Yet it was not work in which we took pride. And, as we sit counting pennies, it is as though we were back tabulating dead flies. Neither of us has a head for figures; we count slowly, lose track, start again. According to her calculations, we have $12.73. According to mine, exactly $13. "I do hope you're wrong, Buddy. We can't mess around with thirteen. The cakes will fall. Or put somebody in the cemetery. Why, I wouldn't dream of getting out of bed on the thirteenth." This is true: she always spends thirteenths in bed. So, to be on the safe side, we subtract a penny and toss it out the window.

Of the ingredients that go into our fruitcakes, whiskey is the most expensive, as well as the hardest to obtain: State laws forbid its sale. But everybody knows you can buy a bottle from Mr. Haha Jones. And the next day, having completed our more prosaic shopping, we set out for Mr. Haha's business address, a "sinful" (to quote public opinion) fish-fry and dancing café down by the river. We've been there before, and on the same errand; but in previous years our dealings have been with Haha's wife, an iodine-dark Indian woman with brassy peroxided hair and a dead-tired disposition. Actually, we've never laid eyes on her husband, though we've heard that he's an Indian too. A giant with razor scars across his cheeks. They call him Haha because he's so gloomy, a man who never laughs. As we approach his café (a large log cabin festooned inside and out with chains of garish-gay naked light bulbs and standing by the river's muddy edge under the shade of river trees where moss drifts through the branches like gray mist) our steps slow down. Even Queenie stops prancing and sticks close by. People have been murdered in Haha's café. Cut to pieces.

Hit on the head. There's a case coming up in court next month. Naturally these goings-on happen at night when the colored lights cast crazy patterns and the victrola wails. In the daytime Haha's is shabby and deserted. I knock at the door, Queenie barks, my friend calls: "Mrs. Haha, ma'am? Anyone to home?"

Footsteps. The door opens. Our hearts overturn. It's Mr. Haha Jones himself! And he *is* a giant; he *does* have scars; he *doesn't* smile. No, he glowers at us through Satan-tilted eyes and demands to know: "What you want with Haha?"

For a moment we are too paralyzed to tell. Presently my friend half-finds her voice, a whispery voice at best: "If you please, Mr. Haha, we'd like a quart of your finest whiskey."

His eyes tilt more. Would you believe it? Haha is smiling! Laughing, too. "Which one of you is a drinkin' man?"

"It's for making fruitcakes, Mr. Haha. Cooking."

This sobers him. He frowns. "That's no way to waste good whiskey." Nevertheless, he retreats into the shadowed café and seconds later appears carrying a bottle of daisy yellow unlabeled liquor. He demonstrates its sparkle in the sunlight and says: "Two dollars."

We pay him with nickels and dimes and pennies. Suddenly, jangling the coins in his hands like a fistful of dice, his face softens. "Tell you what," he proposes, pouring the money back into our bead purse, "just send me one of them fruitcakes instead."

"Well," my friend remarks on our way home, "there's a lovely man. We'll put an extra cup of raisins in *his* cake."

The black stove, stoked with coal and firewood, glows like a lighted pumpkin. Eggbeaters whirl, spoons spin round in bowls of butter and sugar, vanilla sweetens the air, ginger spices it; melting, nose-tingling odors saturate the kitchen, suffuse the house, drift out to the world on puffs of chimney smoke. In four days our work is done. Thirty-one cakes, dampened with whiskey, bask on window sills and shelves.

Who are they for?

Friends. Not necessarily neighbor friends: indeed, the larger share are intended for persons we've met maybe once, perhaps not at all. People who've struck our fancy. Like President Roosevelt. Like the Reverend and Mrs. J. C. Lucey, Baptist missionaries to Borneo who lectured here last winter. Or the little knife grinder who comes through town twice a year. Or Abner Packer, the driver of the six o'clock bus from Mobile, who exchanges waves with us every day as he passes in a dust-cloud whoosh. Or the young Wistons, a California couple whose car one afternoon broke down outside the house and who spent a pleasant hour chatting with us on the porch (young Mr. Wiston snapped our picture, the only one we've ever had taken). Is it because my friend is shy with everyone *except* strangers that these strangers, or merest acquaintances, seem to us our truest friends? I think yes. Also, the scrapbooks we keep of thank-you's on White House stationery, time-to-time communications from California and Borneo, the knife grinder's penny post cards, make us feel connected to eventual worlds beyond the kitchen with its view of a sky that stops.

Now a nude December fig branch grates against the window. The kitchen is empty, the cakes are gone; yesterday we carted the last of them to the post office, where the cost of stamps turned our purse inside out. We're broke. That rather depresses me, but my friend insists on celebrating —with two inches of whiskey left in Haha's bottle. Queenie has a spoonful in a bowl of coffee (she likes her coffee chicory-flavored and strong). The rest we divide between a pair of jelly glasses. We're both quite awed at the prospect of drinking straight whiskey; the taste of it brings screwed-up expressions and sour shudders. But by and by we begin to sing, the two of us singing different songs simultaneously. I don't know the words to mine, just: *Come on along, come on along, to the dark-town strutters' ball*. But I can dance: that's what I mean to be, a tap dancer in the movies. My dancing shadow rollicks on the walls; our voices rock the chinaware; we giggle: as if unseen hands were tickling us. Queenie rolls on her back, her paws plow the air, something like a grin stretches her black lips. Inside myself, I feel warm and sparky as those crumbling logs, carefree as the wind in the chimney. My friend waltzes round the stove, the hem of her poor calico skirt pinched between her fingers as though it were a party dress: *Show me the way to go home*, she sings, her tennis shoes squeaking on the floor. *Show me the way to go home*.

Enter: two relatives. Very angry. Potent with eyes that scold, tongues that scald. Listen to what they have to say, the words tumbling together into a wrathful tune: "A child of seven! whiskey on his breath! are you out of your mind? feeding a child of seven! must be loony! road to ruination! remember Cousin Kate? Uncle Charlie? Uncle Charlie's brother-in-law? shame! scandal! humiliation! kneel, pray, beg the Lord!"

Queenie sneaks under the stove. My friend gazes at her shoes, her chin quivers, she lifts her skirt and blows her nose and runs to her room. Long after the town has gone to sleep and the house is silent except for the chimings of clocks and the sputter of fading fires, she is weeping into a pillow already as wet as a widow's handkerchief.

"Don't cry," I say, sitting at the bottom of her bed and shivering despite my flannel nightgown that smells of last winter's cough syrup, "don't cry," I beg, teasing her toes, tickling her feet, "you're too old for that."

"It's because," she hiccups, "I *am* too old. Old and funny."

"Not funny. Fun. More fun than anybody. Listen. If you don't stop crying you'll be so tired tomorrow we can't go cut a tree."

She straightens up. Queenie jumps on the bed (where Queenie is not allowed) to lick her cheeks. "I know where we'll find real pretty trees,

Buddy. And holly, too. With berries big as your eyes. It's way off in the woods. Farther than we've ever been. Papa used to bring us Christmas trees from there: carry them on his shoulder. That's fifty years ago. Well, now: I can't wait for morning."

Morning. Frozen rime lusters the grass; the sun, round as an orange and orange as hot-weather moons, balances on the horizon, burnishes the silvered winter woods. A wild turkey calls. A renegade hog grunts in the undergrowth. Soon, by the edge of knee-deep, rapid-running water, we have to abandon the buggy. Queenie wades the stream first, paddles across barking complaints at the swiftness of the current, the pneumonia-making coldness of it. We follow, holding our shoes and equipment (a hatchet, a burlap sack) above our heads. A mile more: of chastising thorns, burs and briers that catch at our clothes; of rusty pine needles brilliant with gaudy fungus and molted feathers. Here, there, a flash, a flutter, an ecstasy of shrillings remind us that not all the birds have flown south. Always, the path unwinds through lemony sun pools and pitch vine tunnels. Another creek to cross: a disturbed armada of speckled trout froths the water round us, and frogs the size of plates practice belly flops; beaver workmen are building a dam. On the farther shore, Queenie shakes herself and trembles. My friend shivers, too: not with cold but enthusiasm. One of her hat's ragged roses sheds a petal as she lifts her head and inhales the pine-heavy air. "We're almost there; can you smell it, Buddy?" she says, as though we were approaching an ocean.

And, indeed, it is a kind of ocean. Scented acres of holiday trees, prickly-leafed holly. Red berries shiny as Chinese bells: black crows swoop upon them screaming. Having stuffed our burlap sacks with enough greenery and crimson to garland a dozen windows, we set about choosing a tree. "It should be," muses my friend, "twice as tall as a boy. So a boy can't steal the star." The one we pick is twice as tall as me. A brave handsome brute that survives thirty hatchet strokes before it keels with a creaking rending cry. Lugging it like a kill, we commence the long trek out. Every few yards we abandon the struggle, sit down and pant. But we have the strength of triumphant huntsmen; that and the tree's virile, icy perfume revive us, goad us on. Many compliments accompany our sunset return along the red clay road to town; but my friend is sly and noncommittal when passers-by praise the treasure perched in our buggy: what a fine tree and where did it come from? "Yonderways," she murmurs vaguely. Once a car stops and the rich mill owner's lazy wife leans out and whines: "Giveya two-bits cash for that ol tree." Ordinarily my friend is afraid of saying no; but on this occasion she promptly shakes her head: "We wouldn't take a dollar." The mill owner's wife persists. "A dollar, my foot! Fifty cents. That's my last offer. Goodness, woman, you can get another one." In answer, my friend gently reflects: "I doubt it. There's never two of anything."

Home: Queenie slumps by the fire and sleeps till tomorrow, snoring loud as a human.

A trunk in the attic contains: a shoebox of ermine tails (off the opera cape of a curious lady who once rented a room in the house), coils of frazzled tinsel gone gold with age, one silver star, a brief rope of dilapidated, undoubtedly dangerous candy-like light bulbs. Excellent decorations, as far as they go, which isn't far enough: my friend wants our tree to blaze "like a Baptist window," droop with weighty snows of ornament. But we can't afford the made-in-Japan splendors at the five-and-dime. So we do what we've always done: sit for days at the kitchen table with scissors and crayons and stacks of colored paper. I make sketches and my friend cuts them out: lots of cats, fish too (because they're easy to draw), some apples, some watermelons, a few winged angels devised from saved-up sheets of Hershey-bar tin foil. We use safety pins to attach these creations to the tree; as a final touch, we sprinkle the branches with shredded cotton (picked in August for this purpose). My friend, surveying the effect, clasps her hands together. "Now honest, Buddy. Doesn't it look good enough to eat?" Queenie tries to eat an angel.

After weaving and ribboning holly wreaths for all the front windows, our next project is the fashioning of family gifts. Tie-dye scarves for the ladies, for the men a home-brewed lemon and licorice and aspirin syrup to be taken "at the first Symptoms of a Cold and after Hunting." But when it comes time for making each other's gift, my friend and I separate to work secretly. I would like to buy her a pearl-handled knife, a radio, a whole pound of chocolate-covered cherries (we tasted some once, and she always swears: "I could live on them, Buddy, Lord yes I could—and that's not taking His name in vain"). Instead, I am building her a kite. She would like to give me a bicycle (she's said so on several million occasions: "If only I could, Buddy. It's bad enough in life to do without something *you* want; but confound it, what gets my goat is not being able to give somebody something you want *them* to have. Only one of these days I will, Buddy. Locate you a bike. Don't ask how. Steal it, maybe"). Instead, I'm fairly certain that she is building me a kite—the same as last year, and the year before: the year before that we exchanged slingshots. All of which is fine by me. For we are champion kite-fliers who study the wind like sailors; my friend, more accomplished than I, can get a kite aloft when there isn't enough breeze to carry clouds.

Christmas Eve afternoon we scrape together a nickel and go to the butcher's to buy Queenie's traditional gift, a good gnawable beef bone. The bone, wrapped in funny paper, is placed high in the tree near the silver star. Queenie knows it's there. She squats at the foot of the tree staring up in a trance of greed: when bedtime arrives she refuses to budge. Her excitement is equaled by my own. I kick the covers and turn my pillow as though it were a scorching summer's night. Somewhere a rooster crows: falsely, for the sun is still on the other side of the world.

"Buddy, are you awake?" It is my friend, calling from her room, which is next to mine; and an instant later she is sitting on my bed holding a candle. "Well, I can't sleep a hoot," she declares. "My mind's jumping like a jack rabbit. Buddy, do you think Mrs. Roosevelt will serve our cake at dinner?" We huddle in the bed, and she squeezes my hand I-love-you. "Seems like your hand used to be so much smaller. I guess I hate to see you grow up. When you're grown up, will we still be friends?" I say always. "But I feel so bad, Buddy. I wanted so bad to give you a bike. I tried to sell my cameo Papa gave me. Buddy—" she hesitates, as though embarrassed —"I made you another kite." Then I confess that I made her one, too; and we laugh. The candle burns too short to hold. Out it goes, exposing the starlight, the stars spinning at the window like a visible caroling that slowly, slowly daybreak silences. Possibly we doze; but the beginnings of dawn splash us like cold water: we're up, wide-eyed and wandering while we wait for others to waken. Quite deliberately my friend drops a kettle on the kitchen floor. I tap-dance in front of closed doors. One by one the household emerges, looking as though they'd like to kill us both; but it's Christmas, so they can't. First, a gorgeous breakfast: just everything you can imagine—from flapjacks and fried squirrel to hominy grits and honey-in-the-comb. Which puts everyone in a good humor except my friend and I. Frankly, we're so impatient to get at the presents we can't eat a mouthful.

Well, I'm disappointed. Who wouldn't be? With socks, a Sunday school shirt, some handkerchiefs, a hand-me-down sweater and a year's subscription to a religious magazine for children. *The Little Shepherd*. It makes me boil. It really does.

My friend has a better haul. A sack of Satsumas, that's her best present. She is proudest, however, of a white wool shawl knitted by her married sister. But she *says* her favorite gift is the kite I built her. And it *is* very beautiful; though not as beautiful as the one she made me, which is blue and scattered with gold and green Good Conduct stars; moreover, my name is painted on it, "Buddy."

"Buddy, the wind is blowing."

The wind is blowing, and nothing will do till we've run to a pasture below the house where Queenie has scooted to bury her bone (and where, a winter hence, Queenie will be buried, too.) There, plunging through the healthy waist-high grass, we unreel our kites, feel them twitching at the string like sky fish as they swim into the wind. Satisfied, sun-warmed, we sprawl in the grass and peel Satsumas and watch our kites cavort. Soon I forget the socks and hand-me-down sweater. I'm as happy as if we'd already won the fifty-thousand-dollar Grand Prize in that coffee-naming contest.

"My, how foolish I am!" my friend cries, suddenly alert, like a woman remembering too late she has biscuits in the oven. "You know what I've always thought?" she asks in a tone of discovery, and not smiling at me but a point beyond. "I've always thought a body would have to be sick and dying before they saw the Lord. And I imagined that when He came it would be like looking at the Baptist window: pretty as colored glass with the sun pouring through, such a shine you don't know it's getting dark. And it's been a comfort: to think of that shine taking away all the spooky feeling. But I'll wager it never happens. I'll wager at the very end a body realizes the Lord has already shown Himself. That things as they are"—her hand circles in a gesture that gathers clouds and kites and grass and Queenie pawing earth over her bone—"just what they've always seen, was seeing Him. As for me, I could leave the world with today in my eyes."

This is our last Christmas together.

Life separates us. Those who Know Best decide that I belong in a military school. And so follows a miserable succession of bugle-blowing prisons, grim reveille-ridden summer camps. I have a new home too. But it doesn't count. Home is where my friend is, and there I never go.

And there she remains, puttering around the kitchen. Alone with Queenie. Then alone. ("Buddy dear," she writes in her wild hard-to-read script, "yesterday Jim Macy's horse kicked Queenie bad. Be thankful she didn't feel much. I wrapped her in a Fine Linen sheet and rode her in the buggy down to Simpson's pasture where she can be with all her Bones . . ."). For a few Novembers she continues to bake her fruitcakes single-handed; not as many, but some: and, of course, she always sends me "the best of the batch." Also, in every letter she encloses a dime wadded in toilet paper: "See a picture show and write me the story." But gradually in her letters she tends to confuse me with her other friend, the Buddy who died in the 1880's; more and more thirteenths are not the only days she stays in bed: a morning arrives in November, a leafless birdless coming of winter morning, when she cannot rouse herself to exclaim: "Oh my, it's fruitcake weather!"

And when that happens, I know it. A message saying so merely confirms a piece of news some secret vein had already received, severing from me an irreplaceable part of myself, letting it loose like a kite on a broken string. That is why, walking across a school campus on this particular December morning, I keep searching the sky. As if I expected to see, rather like hearts, a lost pair of kites hurrying toward heaven.

ANGUS WILSON

Realpolitik

JOHN Hobday sat on the edge of his desk and swung his left leg with characteristic boyishness. He waited for the staff to get settled in their seats and then spoke with careful informality.

"I know how frightfully busy you are. As a matter of fact I am myself," he said with the half-humorous urchin smile that he used for such jokes. Only his secretary, Veronica, gave the helpful laugh he expected. It was not going to be an easy meeting, he decided. "So I'm not going to waste your time with a lot of talk," he went on. "I just thought . . ." He paused and beat with his pencil against the desk whilst Mrs. Scrutton moved her chair fussily out of the sunlight. "Ready?" he asked with an over-elaborate smile. "Right. Then we'll start again. As I was saying, we're all very busy, but all the same I thought it was time we had a little meeting. I've been here a week now and although I've had some very helpful chats with each of you in turn, we've never had a chance to get together and outline our plans." None of the three who formed his audience made any response. Veronica, who remembered him taking over new departments at the Ministry during the war, thought he hasn't got the right tone, he doesn't realize that he's coming up against deeper loyalties with these people, loyalties to scholarship and ideas. She almost felt like letting him fend for himself, but old habits were too strong.

"I'm sure it's what everybody's been wanting," she said in her deep voice. She had gauged rightly, his moment of uncertainty had gone, her faithful bark had guided him at the crucial moment. Mrs. Scrutton tried to discomfort him. She rustled the papers on her lap and whispered audibly to Major Sarson, "Our plans. *His* plans for us would be more honest." But it was too late; she had missed her chance. John merely frowned at the interruption and it was Mrs. Scrutton who was left with burning cheeks, hiding her embarrassment by lighting a fresh cigarette.

"As you know," John went on, and Veronica could tell by the loud, trumpeting, rhetorical note of his voice that he was once more the confident salesman lost in the dream world of the grandiose schemes he was putting before them, "I've got some very big ideas for the Gallery. I'm not an expert in any way, as you people are, but I think that's possibly why Sir Harold's executors chose me for the job. They felt the Gallery had already got its full weight of scholars and experts, what it needed was a

446

man with administrative experience, whose training had led him to take an over-all view of things, to think, shall I say, widely rather than deeply. That's why they got me in. But I'm going to be absolutely frank with you" —tossing a lock of brown, wavy hair from his forehead, he stared at his audience with a wide-eyed appeal—"I need *your* help; without my staff I can get nowhere."

Major Sarson winced slightly. All this theatricality and the loud pitch of John's voice got on his nerves, besides he could feel a draught round his legs. It's like some damned Methodist preacher fellow, he thought.

"You've been grand in this first week," John went on, "absolutely grand. I don't mind telling you now that when I arrived I was dead scared. You'd all been here for years, you knew the collections backwards, you had your own ways of running the place, and above all you'd had the inestimable advantage of knowing Sir Harold, of hearing exactly what was in his mind when he bought this picture or that object, of knowing what his ideals were in giving the public the benefit of his taste and experience. I felt sure you were bound to resent me as an outsider, and I knew I'd have done the same in your place."

The faces in front of him were quite unresponsive. He isn't going to get anywhere with sentimental appeals, thought Veronica, these people are idealists, there's nothing more hardboiled. The damned fools, thought John, they have the chance of turning this tin pot, cranky provincial gallery into a national institution and they won't play ball. Well, if they can't see which way their own chances lie, they're not getting in the way of mine. They'll have to come to heel or go. His voice became a little sharper, a shade less ingenuous and friendly.

"You've all told me your views ' . . ur various little chats. Sometimes we've agreed, sometimes we haven'. You've inclin⁻ .o the feeling that all is for the best in the best of all possible wo⁻ ₃, I've felt that some changes were needed, that the scope of the work here wanted broadening, that the organization wanted, let's face it, bringing up to date a bit, and in all this the Board has agreed with me."

Tony Parnell's baby face had grown steadily more pouting and scowling as John had been speaking. To think of this mountebank in charge of the Gallery, a professional careerist, who understood nothing of Sir Harold's ideas and aims, who had even laughed when he'd spoken to him of the metaphysical aspects of technique in painting. He had banked so much on becoming Curator. Sir Harold had spoken so often of him as "my torchbearer, the youngest member of our staff," and now these awful businessmen who had got control of the estate had put this creature in. Major Sarson and Mrs. Scrutton were too old to fight these changes, he had promised before the meeting that *he* would make the challenge. Now was his opportunity. Red in the face, he opened his mouth, but in his nervousness his voice emerged a high falsetto. John smiled across at Veronica.

"The Board haven't had much opportunity of agreeing with us since they haven't heard our views," Tony squeaked.

"My dear Parnell," said John, and his tone was purposely patronizing and offensive. The old ones he regarded without rancour as dead wood to be cleared away, but Tony he disliked personally for his assumptions of scholarly disinterestedness and moral superiority. "Don't let that worry you. As soon as you've got your ideas clear come along and push them at the Board as much as you like. I shouldn't use too much of your favourite art jargon if I was you; the Board are anxious to help but they're only ordinary businessmen and they might not understand. If you follow my advice you'll come down to earth a bit, but of course that's entirely your affair."

Mrs. Scrutton fingered the buttons on her checked tweed coat nervously. "There's no need to bully Mr. Parnell," she said.

"Oh, come," said John jocosely, "if Parnell's going to have the ladies on his side I shall have to surrender." To his delight he saw that Tony was frowning with annoyance.

"Do let me deal with this in my own way," Parnell said to Mrs. Scrutton, whose lip began to tremble.

So that severe grey bobbed hair and man's collar and tie could dissolve early into tears, thought John, so much the better.

"Mrs. Scrutton was only trying to help you, Parnell," said Major Sarson. "Don't let us forget our manners, please."

John yawned slightly. "When the little civil war's over," he said, "I'd just like to outline our main functions. As I see them they're these: Relations with the Public, that's you, Parnell; Display, Mrs. Scrutton; Research, Major Sarson. Miss Clay," he indicated Veronica, "is maid of all work. And I, well, I'm the Aunt Sally, ready to stop the bricks and pass on the bouquets."

Major Sarson looked at his watch impatiently. "I quite agree with you, Major," said John; "the sooner we get finished, the better. No true gentlemen continue to hold meetings after opening time." The old man's face twitched violently, no one before had referred overtly to his notorious weakness.

"I'd like to take the public first," said John. "You've done a first-rate job, Parnell—within its limits. But you haven't gone far enough. You've got real enthusiasm and that's half the battle—but only half. You give the public first-rate value in lectures and catalogues when they get here, but you don't try to get them to come. I know what you're going to say: 'They'll come if they're interested.' But aren't you being a bit hard on the poor, tired, pushed-around public of today? They've got to be told about the place. You've got to compete with the cinema the football team *and* the fireside radio. In short you've got to advertise and you can't do that unless you have figures." Here John paused and picked up a file of papers.

"You have all the figures there," said Tony sulkily.

"I know," said John, "but don't you think they're just a bit too general? 'So many people visited the Gallery on August 5th, so many on November 3rd.' But what sort of people? Who are we catering for? Were they Chinamen, shopgirls, farmers, or just plain deaf-mutes? To tell us anything these figures want breaking down into groups—so many foreigners, so many over-forties, so many under-twenties. That's the way to build up a picture. Now supposing you run over these figures in the way that I suggest and we'll talk again."

Tony was about to protest that this task was impossible, but John held up his hand. "No, no, time's very short and there's one more point I want to raise before we pass on to display." Mrs. Scrutton drew her coat tightly round her. "It's about the lecture room. Sir Louis Crippen was saying something at the last Board meeting about its not being free for his archaeological society when he needed it. Do you know anything about that?"

Tony Parnell hesitated. "Well, actually," he said, "Mrs. Scrutton makes all the lecture hall arrangements."

"But isn't it the P.R.O.'s pigeon?" asked John.

"Yes," said Tony, "but . . . well . . . Mrs. Scrutton . . ."

"I see," said John coldly "Perhaps you'd enlighten me, then, Mrs. Scrutton."

The grey bob shook as she answered, an involuntary shake that was to prove the prelude to age's palsy. "Sir Louis asked for Tuesday and Tuesdays are always booked by Miss Copley," she said.

"Miss Copley?"

Mrs. Scrutton guessed that he knew the answer and her reply attempted a rebuke. "Miss Copley is an old and true friend to the Gallery," she said. "She's been giving her lectures to Schools on Tuesdays for many years."

"No doubt," said John, "but I still think Sir Louis should have preference."

"I don't agree at all," said Major Sarson; "it would be most unfair."

"Yes, why should Sir Louis receive special treatment?" asked Mrs. Scrutton.

"Well, frankly," replied John, "because although Miss Copley may be a very old friend, Sir Louis is a very influential one and the Gallery needs influential friends."

Before Mrs. Scrutton there floated Sir Harold's features, like Erasmus she had thought him, the last of the humanists. Major Sarson too remembered his old friend's handshake and his firm clear voice. "Sarson," he had said, "this money came to me through false standards, false distinctions. There shall be no distinctions in its use but those of scholarship." The eyes of both these old people filled with tears.

John turned to Veronica. "You've nothing to do, Miss Clay." he said. "In future you will take on the lecture hall arrangements. Anything important you'll refer to me." Mrs. Scrutton made a gesture of protest. "No, no," said John. "I'm not going to let you wear yourself out on these minor details, you're far too valuable to the Gallery. Besides, you've got more than a full-time job with Display if it's properly carried out."

Tony Parnell half rose from his chair. "I thought the lecture hall arrangements came under Public Relations?"

"So did I," said John, "until you disillusioned me."

"Next we come to Display. I suppose no side of our work has been more revolutionized in recent years. The Philadelphia report, you know, and the Canadian Association series," he went on, smiling at Mrs. Scrutton. She suddenly felt very tired, she had seen these documents but had never been able to bring herself to read them. "But there's no need for me to mention these things to you," John continued. "Your arrangement of the miniature collection," and he sighed in wonder. "Well, I'm going to pay you a great compliment there. Your arrangement of the miniatures not only makes one want to look at them, it makes it impossible for one not to look at them. I'm sure, Mrs. Scrutton, you'll agree with my wish that some other sides of the collection had the same advantages as the miniatures—the jewellery, for instance, and the armour. But that's not your fault. There's just too much for one person, that's all there is to it. The same applies to the research. I'm not going to embarrass Major Sarson by talking about his position as a scholar"—he waved his hand towards the old man who went red round the ears—"suffice it to say what we all know, that the Gallery is honoured by the presence of the world's greatest authority on the Dutch school, and a great scholar of painting generally. Though I doubt, by the way, whether the Major's exactly fond of the moderns. I sometimes wish that the Gallery possessed only paintings, I'm sure Major Sarson does. Unfortunately that isn't the case. I fully sympathized with him when he spoke to me as he did of 'those wretched pots and pans' "—here John laughed patronizingly—"but I doubt if a ceramics man would. Frankly," he said, turning to Major Sarson, "I consider it disgraceful that a scholar of your caliber should be taken off your real work in this way. Now how, you may ask, do I suppose to remedy the stiuation? Well, the answer is that I propose to treble the staff. From next month new staff will begin to arrive—some students from the Universities, some more experienced men from other galleries and museums."

There was silence for a minute, then Mrs. Scrutton spoke. "Does the Board know of this?"

"Yes," said John, "they fully approve the scheme."

"Do they realize the expense involved?" asked Tony, the practical man.

"The Board are businessmen," said John; "they know that outlay must precede returns." He looked round at their faces. "Well, I think that's all," he said. "I know you will give the new members of the staff the same co-operation you have given me, whether it is a question of instructing and training them, or in some cases of working under them." His tone was openly sarcastic.

"Do I understand that people will be put over us?" asked Mrs. Scrutton.

"In cases where experts are brought in, it may be necessary to make revisions in seniority," said John.

"You realize, of course, that in such an eventuality we should resign," said Major Sarson.

"That would be a great loss to the Gallery, but we could not, of course, control your decisions," replied John, and opening the door, he bowed them out.

"Golly," said Veronica, "you do tell some lies, don't you? Or have the Board ratified your staff changes?"

"How many more times must I tell you, Veronica, that truth is relative," said John.

Veronica looked down for a minute. "I'll make you some coffee," she said.

"Yes," said John. "Victory always makes me thirsty. I cannot help being satisfied when I think of the well-merited unpleasant few weeks those three are going to have. The punishment of incompetence is always satisfactory."

"Mm," said Veronica doubtfully.

"What's that mean? You've not fallen for this sentimental stuff about Sir Harold, have you?"

"Good Lord, no," said Veronica. "It's not those misfits I'm worrying about, it's you."

"Me?" said John. "Why?"

"You're getting too fond of bullying," said Veronica; "it interferes with your charm, and charm's essential for your success." She went out to make the coffee.

What Veronica said was very true, thought John, and he made a note to be more detached in his attitude. All the same these criticisms were bad for his self-esteem. For all her loyalty Veronica knew him too well, got too near home. Charm was important to success, but self-esteem was more so. His imagination began to envisage further staff changes, perhaps a graduate secretary would really be more suitable now.

ISAK DINESEN

The Sailor-Boy's Tale

THE barque *Charlotte* was on her way from Marseille to Athens, in grey weather, on a high sea, after three days' heavy gale. A small sailor-boy, named Simon, stood on the wet, swinging deck, held on to a shroud, and looked up towards the drifting clouds, and to the upper top-gallant yard of the main-mast.

A bird, that had sought refuge upon the mast, had got her feet entangled in some loose tackle-yarn of the halliard, and, high up there, struggled to get free. The boy on the deck could see her wings flapping and her head turning from side to side.

Through his own experience of life he had come to the conviction that in this world everyone must look after himself, and expect no help from others. But the mute, deadly fight kept him fascinated for more than an hour. He wondered what kind of bird it would be. These last days a number of birds had come to settle in the barque's rigging: swallows, quails, and a pair of peregrine falcons; he believed that this bird was a peregrine falcon. He remembered how, many years ago, in his own country and near his home, he had once seen a peregrine falcon quite close, sitting on a stone and flying straight up from it. Perhaps this was the same bird. He thought: "That bird is like me. Then she was there, and now she is here."

At that a fellow-feeling rose in him, a sense of common tragedy; he stood looking at the bird with his heart in his mouth. There were none of the sailors about to make fun of him; he began to think out how he might go up by the shrouds to help the falcon out. He brushed his hair back and pulled up his sleeves, gave the deck round him a great glance, and climbed up. He had to stop a couple of times in the swaying rigging.

It was indeed, he found when he got to the top of the mast, a peregrine falcon. As his head was on a level with hers, she gave up her struggle, and looked at him with a pair of angry, desperate yellow eyes. He had to take hold of her with one hand while he got his knife out, and cut off the tackle-yarn. He was scared as he looked down, but at the same time he felt that he had been ordered up by nobody, but that this was his own venture, and this gave him a proud, steadying sensation, as if the sea and the sky, the ship, the bird and himself were all one. Just as he had freed the falcon, she hacked him in the thumb, so that the blood ran, and he nearly let her

452

go. He grew angry with her, and gave her a clout on the head, then he put her inside his jacket, and climbed down again.

When he reached the deck the mate and the cook were standing there, looking up; they roared to him to ask what he had had to do in the mast. He was so tired that the tears were in his eyes. He took the falcon out and showed her to them, and she kept still within his hands. They laughed and walked off. Simon set the falcon down, stood back and watched her. After a while he reflected that she might not be able to get up from the slippery deck, so he caught her once more, walked away with her and placed her upon a bolt of canvas. A little after she began to trim her feathers, made two or three sharp jerks forward, and then suddenly flew off. The boy could follow her flight above the troughs of the grey sea. He thought: "There flies my falcon."

When the *Charlotte* came home, Simon signed aboard another ship, and two years later he was a light hand on the schooner *Hebe* lying at Bodø, high up on the coast of Norway, to buy herrings.

To the great herring-markets of Bodø ships came together from all corners of the world; here were Swedish, Finnish and Russian boats, a forest of masts, and on shore a turbulent, irregular display of life, with many languages spoken, and mighty fists. On the shore booths had been set up, and the Lapps, small yellow people, noiseless in their movements, with watchful eyes, whom Simon had never seen before, came down to sell bead-embroidered leather-goods. It was April, the sky and the sea were so clear that it was difficult to hold one's eyes up against them—salt, infinitely wide and filled with bird-shrieks—as if someone were incessantly whetting invisible knives, on all sides, high up in Heaven.

Simon was amazed at the lightness of these April evenings. He knew no geography, and did not assign it to the latitude, but he took it as a sign of an unwonted good-will in the Universe, a favor. Simon had been small for his age all his life, but this last winter he had grown, and had become strong of limb. That good luck, he felt, must spring from the very same source as the sweetness of the weather, from a new benevolence in the world. He had been in need of such encouragement, for he was timid by nature; now he asked for no more. The rest he felt to be his own affair. He went about slowly, and proudly.

One evening he was ashore with land-leave, and walked up to the booth of a small Russian trader, a Jew who sold gold watches. All the sailors knew that his watches were made from bad metal, and would not go, still they bought them, and paraded them about. Simon looked at these watches for a long time, but did not buy. The old Jew had divers goods in his shop, and amongst others a case of oranges. Simon had tasted oranges on his journeys; he bought one and took it with him. He meant to go up on a hill, from where he could see the sea, and suck it there.

As he walked on, and had got to the outskirts of the place, he saw a little girl in a blue frock, standing at the other side of a fence and looking at him. She was thirteen or fourteen years old, as slim as an eel, but with a round, clear, freckled face, and a pair of long plaits. The two looked at one another.

"Who are you looking out for?" Simon asked, to say something. The girl's face broke into an ecstatic, presumptuous smile. "For the man I am going to marry, of course," she said. Something in her countenance made the boy confident and happy; he grinned a little at her. "That will perhaps be me," he said. "Ha, ha," said the girl, "he is a few years older than you, I can tell you." "Why," said Simon, "you are not grown up yourself." The little girl shook her head solemnly. "Nay," she said, "but when I grow up I will be exceedingly beautiful, and wear brown shoes with heels, and a hat." "Will you have an orange?" asked Simon, who could give her none of the things she had named. She looked at the orange and at him. "They are very good to eat," said he. "Why do you not eat it yourself then?" she asked. "I have eaten so many already," said he, "when I was in Athens. Here I had to pay a mark for it." "What is your name?" asked she. "My name is Simon," said he. "What is yours?" "Nora," said the girl. "What do you want for your orange now, Simon?"

When he heard his name in her mouth Simon grew bold. "Will you give me a kiss for the orange?" he asked. Nora looked at him gravely for a moment. "Yes," she said, "I should not mind giving you a kiss." He grew as warm as if he had been running quickly. When she stretched out her hand for the orange he took hold of it. At that moment somebody in the house called out for her. "That is my father," said she, and tried to give him back the orange, but he would not take it. "Then come again tomorrow," she said quickly, "then I will give you a kiss." At that she slipped off. He stood and looked after her, and a little later went back to his ship.

Simon was not in the habit of making plans for the future, and now he did not know whether he would be going back to her or not.

The following evening he had to stay aboard, as the other sailors were going ashore, and he did not mind that either. He meant to sit on the deck with the ship's dog, Balthasar, and to practise upon a concertina that he had purchased some time ago. The pale evening was all round him, the sky was faintly roseate, the sea was quite calm, like milk-and-water, only in the wake of the boats going inshore it broke into streaks of vivid indigo. Simon sat and played; after a while his own music began to speak to him so strongly that he stopped, got up and looked upwards. Then he saw that the full moon was sitting high on the sky.

The sky was so light that she hardly seemed needed there; it was as if she had turned up by a caprice of her own. She was round, demure and presumptuous. At that he knew that he must go ashore, whatever it was to cost him. But he did not know how to get away, since the others had taken the yawl with them. He stood on the deck for a long time, a small lonely figure of a sailor-boy on a boat, when he caught sight of a yawl coming in from a ship farther out, and hailed her. He found that it was the Russian crew from a boat named *Anna,* going ashore. When he could make himself understood to them, they took him with them; they first asked him for money for his fare, then, laughing, gave it back to him. He thought: "These people will be believing that I am going to town, wenching." And then he felt, with some pride, that they were right, although at the same time they were infinitely wrong, and knew nothing about any-thing.

When they came ashore they invited him to come in and drink in their company, and he would not refuse, because they had helped him. One of the Russians was a giant, as big as a bear; he told Simon that his name was Ivan. He got drunk at once, and then fell upon the boy with a bear-like affection, pawed him, smiled and laughed into his face, made him a present of a gold watch-chain, and kissed him on both cheeks. At that Simon reflected that he also ought to give Nora a present when they met again, and as soon as he could get away from the Russians he walked up to a booth that he knew of, and bought a small blue silk handkerchief, the same colour as her eyes.

It was Saturday evening, and there were many people amongst the houses; they came in long rows, some of them singing, all keen to have some fun that night. Simon, in the midst of this rich, bawling life under the clear moon, felt his head light with the flight from the ship and the strong drinks. He crammed the handkerchief in his pocket; it was silk, which he had never touched before, a present for his girl.

He could not remember the path up to Nora's house, lost his way, and came back to where he had started. Then he grew deadly afraid that he should be too late, and began to run. In a small passage between two wooden huts he ran straight into a big man, and found that it was Ivan once more. The Russian folded his arms round him and held him. "Good! Good!" he cried in high glee, "I have found you, my little chicken. I have looked for you everywhere, and poor Ivan has wept because he lost his friend." "Let me go, Ivan," cried Simon. "Oho," said Ivan, "I shall go with you and get you what you want. My heart and my money are all yours, all yours; I have been seventeen years old myself, a little lamb of God, and I want to be so again tonight." "Let me go," cried Simon, "I am in a hurry." Ivan held him so that it hurt, and patted him with his other hand. "I feel it, I feel it," he said. "Now trust to me, my little friend. Nothing shall part you and me. I hear the others coming; we will have such a night together as you will remember when you are an old grandpapa."

Suddenly he crushed the boy to him, like a bear that carries off a sheep. The odious sensation of male bodily warmth and the bulk of a man close to him made the lean boy mad. He thought of Nora waiting, like a slender ship in the dim air, and of himself, here, in the hot embrace of a hairy animal. He struck Ivan with all his might. "I shall kill you, Ivan," he cried out, "if you do not let me go." "Oh, you will be thankful to me later on," said Ivan, and began to sing. Simon fumbled in his pocket for his knife, got it open. He could not lift his hand, but he drove the knife, furiously in under the big man's arm. Almost immediately he felt the blood spouting out, and running down in his sleeve. Ivan stopped short in the song, let go his hold of the boy and gave two long deep grunts. The next second he tumbled down on his knees. "Poor Ivan, poor Ivan," he groaned. He fell straight on his face. At that moment Simon heard the other sailors coming along, singing, in the by-street.

He stood still for a minute, wiped his knife, and watched the blood spread into a dark pool underneath the big body. Then he ran. As he stopped for a second to choose his way, he heard the sailors behind him scream out over their dead comrade. He thought: "I must get down to the sea, where I can wash my hand." But at the same time he ran the other way. After a little while he found himself on the path that he had walked on the day before, and it seemed as familiar to him, as if he had walked it many hundred times in his life.

He slackened his pace to look round, and suddenly saw Nora standing on the other side of the fence; she was quite close to him when he caught sight of her in the moonlight. Wavering and out of breath he sank down on his knees. For a moment he could not speak. The little girl looked down at him. "Good evening, Simon," she said in her small coy voice. "I have waited for you a long time," and after a moment she added: "I have eaten your orange."

"Oh, Nora," cried the boy. "I have killed a man." She stared at him, but did not move. "Why did you kill a man?" she asked after a moment. "To get here," said Simon. "Because he tried to stop me. But he was my friend." Slowly he got on to his feet. "He loved me!" the boy cried out, and at that burst into tears. "Yes," said she slowly and thoughtfully. "Yes, because you must be here in time." "Can you hide me?" he asked. "For they are after me." "Nay," said Nora, "I cannot hide you. For my father is the parson here at Bodø, and he would be sure to hand you over to them, if he knew that you had killed a man." "Then," said Simon, "give me something to wipe my hands on." "What is the matter with your hands?" she asked, and took a little step forward. He stretched out his hands to her. "Is that your own blood?" she asked. "No," said he, "it is his." She took the step back again. "Do you hate me now?" he asked. "No, I do not hate you," said she. "But do put your hands at your back."

As he did so she came up close to him, at the other side of the fence, and clasped her arms round his neck. She pressed her young body to his, and kissed him tenderly. He felt her face, cool as the moonlight, upon his own, and when she released him, his head swam, and he did not know if the kiss had lasted a second or an hour. Nora stood up straight, her eyes wide open. "Now," she said slowly and proudly, "I promise you that I will never marry anybody, as long as I live." The boy kept standing with his hands on his back, as if she had tied them there. "And now," she said, "you must run, for they are coming." They looked at one another. "Do not forget Nora," said she. He turned and ran.

He leapt over a fence, and when he was down amongst the houses he walked. He did not know at all where to go. As he came to a house, from where music and noise streamed out, he slowly went through the door. The room was full of people; they were dancing in here. A lamp hung from the ceiling, and shone down on them, the air was thick and brown with the dust rising from the floor. There were some women in the room, but many of the men danced with each other, and gravely or laughingly stamped the floor. A moment after Simon had come in the crowd withdrew to the walls to clear the floor for two sailors, who were showing a dance from their own country.

Simon thought: "Now, very soon, the men from the boat will come round to look for their comrade's murderer, and from my hands they will know that I have done it." These five minutes during which he stood by the wall of the dancing-room, in the midst of the gay, sweating dancers, were of great significance to the boy. He himself felt it, as if during this time he grew up, and became like other people. He did not entreat his destiny, nor complain. Here he was, he had killed a man, and had kissed a girl. He did not demand any more from life, nor did life now demand more from him. He was Simon, a man like the men round him, and going to die, as all men are going to die.

He only became aware of what was going on outside him, when he saw a woman had come in, and was standing in the midst of the cleared floor, looking round her. She was a short, broad old woman, in the clothes of the Lapps, and she took her stand with such majesty and fierceness as if she owned the whole place. It was obvious that most of the people knew her, and were a little afraid of her, although a few laughed; the din of the dancing-room stopped when she spoke.

"Where is my son?" she asked in a high shrill voice, like a bird's. The next moment her eyes fell on Simon himself, and she steered through the crowd, which opened up before her, stretched out her old skinny, dark hand, and took him by the elbow. "Come home with me now," she said. "You need not dance here tonight. You may be dancing a high enough dance soon."

Simon drew back, for he thought that she was drunk. But as she looked him straight in the face with her yellow eyes, it seemed to him that he had met her before, and that he might do well in listening to her. The old woman pulled him with her across the floor, and he followed her without a word. "Do not birch your boy too badly, Sunniva," one of the men in the room cried to her. "He has done no harm, he only wanted to look at the dance."

At the same moment as they came out through the door, there was an alarm in the street, a flock of people came running down it, and one of them, as he turned into the house, knocked against Simon, looked at him and the old woman, and ran on.

While the two walked along the street, the old woman lifted up her skirt, and put the hem of it into the boy's hand. "Wipe your hand on my skirt," she said. They had not gone far before they came to a small wooden house, and stopped; the door to it was so low that they must bend to get through it. As the Lapp-woman went in before Simon, still holding on to his arm, the boy looked up for a moment. The night had grown misty; there was a wide ring round the moon.

The old woman's room was narrow and dark, with but one small window to it; a lantern stood on the floor and lighted it up dimly. It was all filled with reindeer skins and wolf skins, and with reindeer horn, such as the Lapps use to make their carved buttons and knife-handles, and the air in here was rank and stifling. As soon as they were in, the woman turned to Simon, took hold of his head, and with her crooked fingers parted his hair and combed it down in Lapp fashion. She clapped a Lapp cap on him and stood back to glance at him. "Sit down on my stool, now," she said. "But first take out your knife." She was so commanding in voice and manner that the boy could not but choose to do as she told him; he sat down on the stool, and he could not take his eyes off her face, which was flat and brown, and as if smeared with dirt in its net of fine wrinkles. As he sat there he heard many people come along outside, and stop by the house; then someone knocked at the door, waited a moment and knocked again. The old woman stood and listened, as still as a mouse.

"Nay," said the boy and got up. "This is no good, for it is me that they are after. It will be better for you to let me go out to them." "Give me your knife," said she. When he handed it to her, she stuck it straight into her thumb, so that the blood spouted out, and she let it drip all over her skirt. "Come in, then," she cried.

The door opened, and two of the Russian sailors came and stood in the opening; there were more people outside. "Has anybody come in here?" they asked. "We are after a man who has killed our mate, but he has run away from us. Have you seen or heard anybody this way?" The old Lapp-woman turned upon them, and her eyes shone like gold in the lamplight. "Have I seen or heard anyone?" she cried. "I have heard you shriek murder all over the town. You frightened me, and my poor silly boy there, so that I cut my thumb as I was ripping the skin-rug that I sew. The boy is too scared to help me, and the rug is all ruined. I shall make you pay me for that. If you are looking for a murderer, come in and search my house for me, and I shall know you when we meet again." She was so furious that she danced where she stood, and jerked her head like an angry bird of prey.

The Russian came in, looked round the room, and at her and her blood-stained hand and skirt. "Do not put a curse on us now, Sunniva," he said timidly. "We know that you can do many things when you like. Here is a mark to pay you for the blood you have spilled." She stretched out her hand, and he placed a piece of money in it. She spat on it. "Then go, and there shall be no bad blood between us," said Sunniva, and shut the door after them. She stuck her thumb in her mouth, and chuckled a little.

The boy got up from his stool, stood straight up before her and stared into her face. He felt as if he were swaying high up in the air, with but a small hold. "Why have you helped me?" he asked her. "Do you not know?" she answered. "Have you not recognized me yet? But you will remember the peregrine falcon which was caught in the tackle-yarn of your boat, the *Charlotte*, as she sailed in the Mediterranean. That day you climbed up by the shrouds of the top-gallantmast to help her out, in a stiff wind, and with a high sea. That falcon was me. We Lapps often fly in such a manner, to see the world. When I first met you I was on my way to Africa, to see my younger sister and her children. She is a falcon too, when she chooses. By that time she was living at Takaunga, within an old ruined tower, which down there they call a minaret." She swathed a corner of her skirt round her thumb, and bit at it. "We do not forget," she said. "I hacked your thumb, when you took hold of me; it is only fair that I should cut my thumb for you tonight."

She came close to him, and gently rubbed her two brown, clawlike fingers against his forehead. "So you are a boy," she said, "who will kill a man rather than be late to meet your sweetheart? We hold together, the females of this earth. I shall mark your forehead now, so that the girls will know of that, when they look at you, and they will like you for it." She played with the boy's hair, and twisted it round her finger.

"Listen now, my little bird," said she. "My great grand-son's brother-in-law is lying with his boat by the landing-place at this moment; he is to take a consignment of skins out to a Danish boat. He will bring you back to your boat, in time, before your mate comes. The *Hebe* is sailing to-morrow morning, is it not so? But when you are aboard, give him back my cap for me." She took up his knife, wiped it in her skirt and handed it to him. "Here is your knife," she said. "You will stick it into no more men; you will not need to, for from now you will sail the seas like a faithful seaman. We have enough trouble with our sons as it is."

The bewildered boy began to stammer his thanks to her. "Wait," said she, "I shall make you a cup of coffee, to bring back your wits, while I wash your jacket." She went and rattled an old copper kettle upon the fireplace. After a while she handed him a hot, strong, black drink in a cup without a handle to it. "You have drunk with Sunniva now," she said; "you have drunk down a little wisdom, so that in the future all your thoughts shall not fall like raindrops into the salt sea."

When he had finished and set down the cup, she led him to the door and opened it for him. He was so surprised to see that it was almost clear morning. The house was so high up that the boy could see the sea from it, and a milky mist about it. He gave her his hand to say good-bye.

She stared into his face. "We do not forget," she said. "And you, you knocked me on the head there, high up in the mast. I shall give you that blow back." With that she smacked him on the ear as hard as she could, so that his head swam. "Now we are quits," she said, gave him a great, mischievous, shining glance, and a little push down the doorstep, and nodded to him.

In this way the sailor-boy got back to his ship, which was to sail the next morning, and lived to tell the story.

JOSEPH CONRAD

Amy Foster

KENNEDY is a country doctor, and lives in Colebrook, on the shores of Eastbay. The high ground rising abruptly behind the red roofs of the little town crowds the quaint High Street against the wall which defends it from the sea. Beyond the sea wall there curves for miles in a vast and regular sweep the barren beach of shingle, with the village of Brenzett standing out darkly across the water, a spire in a clump of trees; and still farther out the perpendicular column of a lighthouse, looking in the distance no bigger than a lead pencil, marks the vanishing point of the land. The country at the back of Brenzett is low and flat; but the bay is fairly well sheltered from the seas, and occasionally a big ship, windbound or through stress of weather, makes use of the anchoring ground a mile and a half due north from you as you stand at the back door of the "Ship Inn" in Brenzett. A dilapidated windmill near by, lifting its shattered arms from a mount no loftier than a rubbish heap, and a Martello tower squatting at the water's edge half a mile to the south of the Coastguard cottages, are familiar to the skippers of small craft. These are the official seamarks for the patch of trustworthy bottom represented on the Admiralty charts by an irregular oval of dots enclosing several figure sixes, with a tiny anchor engraved among them, and the legend "mud and shells" over all.

The brow of the upland overtops the square tower of the Colebrook Church. The slope is green and looped by a white road. Ascending along this road, you open a valley broad and shallow, a wide green trough of pastures and hedges merging inland into a vista of purple tints and flowing lines closing the view.

In this valley down to Brenzett and Colebrook and up to Darnford, the market town fourteen miles away, lies the practice of my friend Kennedy. He had begun life as surgeon in the Navy, and afterwards had been the companion of a famous traveler, in the days when there were continents with unexplored interiors. His papers on the fauna and flora made him known to scientific societies. And now he had come to a country practice—from choice. The penetrating power of his mind, acting like a corrosive fluid, had destroyed his ambition, I fancy. His intelligence is of a scientific order, of an investigating habit, and of that unappeasable curiosity which believes that there is a particle of a general truth in every mystery.

A good many years ago now, on my return from abroad, he invited me to stay with him. I came readily enough, and as he could not neglect his patients to keep me company, he took me on his rounds—thirty miles or so of an afternoon, sometimes. I waited for him on the roads; the horse reached after the leafy twigs, and, sitting high in the dogcart, I could hear Kennedy's laugh through the half-open door of some cottage. He had a big, hearty laugh that would have fitted a man twice his size, a brisk manner, a bronzed face, and a pair of gray, profoundly attentive eyes. He had the talent of making people talk to him freely, and an inexhaustible patience in listening to their tales.

One day, as we trotted out of a large village into a shady bit of road, I saw on our left hand a low, black cottage, with diamond panes in the windows, a creeper on the end wall, a roof of shingle, and some roses climbing on the rickety trelliswork of the tiny porch. Kennedy pulled up to a walk. A woman, in full sunlight, was throwing a dripping blanket over a line stretched between two old apple trees. And as the bobtailed, long-necked chestnut, trying to get his head, jerked the left hand, covered by a thick dogskin glove, the doctor raised his voice over the hedge: "How's your child, Amy?"

I had time to see her dull face, red, not with a mantling blush, but as if her flat cheeks had been vigorously slapped, and to take in the squat figure, the scanty, dusty brown hair drawn into a tight knot at the back of the head. She looked quite young. With a distinct catch in her breath, her voice sounded low and timid.

"He's well, thank you."

We trotted again. "A young patient of yours," I said; and the doctor, flicking the chestnut absently, muttered, "Her husband used to be."

"She seems a dull creature," I remarked, listlessly.

"Precisely," said Kennedy. "She is very passive. It's enough to look at the red hands hanging at the end of those short arms, at those slow, prominent brown eyes, to know the inertness of her mind—an inertness that one would think made it everlastingly safe from all the surprises of imagination. And yet which of us is safe? At any rate, such as you see her, she had enough imagination to fall in love. She's the daughter of one Isaac Foster, who from a small farmer has sunk into a shepherd; the beginning of his misfortunes dating from his runaway marriage with the cook of his widowed father—a well-to-do, apoplectic grazier, who passionately struck his name off his will, and had been heard to utter threats against his life. But this old affair, scandalous enough to serve as a motive for a Greek tragedy, arose from the similarity of their characters. There are other tragedies, less scandalous and of a subtler poignancy, arising from irreconcilable differences and from that fear of the Incomprehensible that hangs over all our heads—over all our heads. . . ."

The tired chestnut dropped into a walk; and the rim of the sun, all red in a speckless sky, touched familiarly the smooth top of a plowed rise near the road as I had seen it times innumerable touch the distant horizon of the sea. The uniform brownness of the harrowed field glowed with a rose tinge, as though the powdered clods had sweated out in minute pearls of blood the toil of uncounted plowmen. From the edge of a copse a wagon with two horses was rolling gently along the ridge. Raised above our heads upon the skyline, it loomed up against the red sun, triumphantly big, enormous, like a chariot of giants drawn by two slow-stepping steeds of legendary proportions. And the clumsy figure of the man plodding at the head of the leading horse projected itself on the background of the ınfinite with a heroic uncouthness. The end of his carter's whip quivered high up in the blue. Kennedy discoursed.

"She's the eldest of a large family. At the age of fifteen they put her out to service at the New Barns Farm. I attended Mrs. Smith, the tenant's wife, and saw that girl there for the first time. Mrs. Smith, a genteel person with a sharp nose, made her put on a black dress every afternoon. I don't know what induced me to notice her at all. There are faces that call your attention by a curious want of definiteness in their whole aspect, as, walking in a mist, you peer attentively at a vague shape which, after all, may be nothing more curious or strange than a signpost. The only peculiarity I perceived in her was a slight hesitation in her utterance, a sort of preliminary stammer which passes away with the first word. When sharply spoken to, she was apt to lose her head at once; but her heart was of the kindest. She had never been heard to express a dislike for a single human being, and she was tender to every living creature. She was devoted to Mrs. Smith, to Mr. Smith, to their dogs, cats, canaries; and as to Mrs. Smith's gray parrot, its peculiarities exercised upon her a positive fascination. Nevertheless, when that outlandish bird, attacked by the cat, shrieked for help in human accents, she ran out into the yard stopping her ears, and did not prevent the crime. For Mrs. Smith this was another evidence of her stupidity; on the other hand, her want of charm, in view of Smith's well-known frivolousness, was a great recommendation. Her shortsighted eyes would swim with pity for a poor mouse in a trap, and she had been seen once by some boys on her knees in the wet grass helping a toad in difficulties. If it's true, as some German fellow has said, that without phosphorus there is no thought, it is still more true that there is no kindness of heart without a certain amount of imagination. She had some. She had even more than is necessary to understand suffering and to be moved by pity. She fell in love under circumstances that leave no room for doubt in the matter; for you need imagination to form a notion of beauty at all, and still more to discover your ideal in an unfamiliar shape.

"How this aptitude came to her, what it did feed upon, is an inscrutable mystery. She was born in the village, and had never been farther away from it than Colebrook or perhaps Darnford. She lived for four years with the Smiths. New Barns is an isolated farmhouse a mile away from the road, and she was content to look day after day at the same fields, hollows, rises; at the trees and the hedgerows; at the faces of the four men about the farm, always the same—day after day, month after month, year after year. She never showed a desire for conversation, and, as it seemed to me, she did not know how to smile. Sometimes of a fine Sunday afternoon she would put on her best dress, a pair of stout boots, a large gray hat trimmed with a black feather (I've seen her in that finery), seize an absurdly slender parasol, climb over two stiles, tramp over three fields and along two hundred yards of road—never farther. There stood Foster's cottage. She would help her mother to give their tea to the younger children, wash up the crockery, kiss the little ones, and go back to the farm. That was all. All the rest, all the change, all the relaxation. She never seemed to wish for anything more. And then she fell in love. She fell in love silently, obstinately—perhaps helplessly. It came slowly, but when it came it worked like a powerful spell; it was love as the ancients understood it: an irresistible and fateful impulse—a possession! Yes, it was in her to become haunted and possessed by a face, by a presence, fatally, as though she had been a pagan worshiper of form under a joyous sky—and to be awakened at last from that mysterious forgetfulness of self, from that enchantment, from that transport, by a fear resembling the unaccountable terror of a brute. . . ."

With the sun hanging low on its western limit, the expanse of the grasslands framed in the counterscarps of the rising ground took on a gorgeous and somber aspect. A sense of penetrating sadness, like that inspired by a grave strain of music, disengaged itself from the silence of the fields. The men we met walked past, slow, unsmiling, with downcast eyes, as if the melancholy of an overburdened earth had weighted their feet, bowed their shoulders, borne down their glances.

"Yes," said the doctor to my remark, "one would think the earth is under a curse, since of all her children these that cling to her the closest are uncouth in body and as leaden of gait as if their very hearts were loaded with chains. But here on this same road you might have seen amongst these heavy men a being lithe, supple and long-limbed, straight like a pine, with something striving upwards in his appearance as though the heart within him had been buoyant. Perhaps it was only the force of the contrast, but when he was passing one of these villagers here, the soles of his feet did not seem to me to touch the dust of the road. He vaulted over the stiles, paced these slopes with a long elastic stride that made him noticeable at a great distance, and had lustrous black eyes. He was so different from the mankind around that, with his freedom of movement, his soft—a little startled—glance, his olive complexion and graceful bearing, his humanity suggested to me the nature of a woodland creature. He came from there."

The doctor pointed with his whip, and from the summit of the descent seen over the rolling tops of the trees in a park by the side of the road, appeared the level sea far below us, like the floor of an immense edifice inlaid with bands of dark ripple, with still trails of glitter, ending in a belt of glassy water at the foot of the sky. The light blur of smoke, from an invisible steamer, faded on the great clearness of the horizon like the mist of a breath on a mirror; and, inshore, the white sails of a coaster, with the appearance of disentangling themselves slowly from under the branches, floated clear of the foliage of the trees.

"Shipwrecked in the bay?" I said.

"Yes; he was a castaway. A poor emigrant from Central Europe bound to America and washed ashore here in a storm. And for him, who knew nothing of the earth, England was an undiscovered country. It was some time before he learned its name; and for all I know he might have expected to find wild beasts or wild men here, when, crawling in the dark over the sea wall, he rolled down the other side into a dyke, where it was another miracle he didn't get drowned. But he struggled instinctively like an animal under a net, and this blind struggle threw him out into a field. He must have been, indeed, of a tougher fiber than he looked to withstand without expiring such buffetings, the violence of his exertions, and so much fear. Later on, in his broken English that resembled curiously the speech of a young child, he told me himself that he put his trust in God, believing he was no longer in this world. And truly—he would add—how was he to know? He fought his way against the rain and the gale on all fours, and crawled at last among some sheep huddled close under the lee of a hedge. They ran off in all directions, bleating in the darkness, and he welcomed the first familiar sound he heard on these shores. It must have been two in the morning then. And this is all we know of the manner of his landing, though he did not arrive unattended by any means. Only his grisly company did not begin to come ashore till much later in the day. . . ."

The doctor gathered the reins, clicked his tongue; we trotted down the hill. Then turning, almost directly, a sharp corner into High Street, we rattled over the stones and were home.

Late in the evening Kennedy, breaking a spell of moodiness that had come over him, returned to the story. Smoking his pipe, he paced the long room from end to end. A reading lamp concentrated all its light upon the papers on his desk; and, sitting by the open window, I saw, after the windless, scorching day, the frigid splendor of a hazy sea lying motionless under the moon. Not a whisper, not a splash, not a stir of the shingle, not a footstep, not a sigh came up from the earth below—never a sign of life but the scent of climbing jasmine; and Kennedy's voice, speaking behind me, passed through the wide casement, to vanish outside in a chill and sumptuous stillness.

". . . The relations of shipwrecks in the olden times tell us of much suffering. Often the castaways were only saved from drowning to die miserably from starvation on a barren coast; others suffered violent death or else slavery, passing through years of precarious existence with people to whom their strangeness was an object of suspicion, dislike or fear. We read about these things, and they are very pitiful. It is indeed hard upon a man to find himself a lost stranger, helpless, incomprehensible, and of a mysterious origin, in some obscure corner of the earth. Yet amongst all the adventurers shipwrecked in all the wild parts of the world, there is not one, it seems to me, that ever had to suffer a fate so simply tragic as the man I am speaking of, the most innocent of adventurers cast out by the sea in the bight of this bay, almost within sight from this very window.

"He did not know the name of his ship. Indeed, in the course of time we discovered he did not even know that ships had names—'like Christian people'; and when, one day, from the top of Talfourd Hill, he beheld the sea lying open to his view, his eyes roamed afar, lost in an air of wild surprise, as though he had never seen such a sight before. And probably he had not. As far as I could make out, he had been hustled together with many others on board an emigrant ship at the mouth of the Elbe, too bewildered to take note of his surroundings, too weary to see anything, too anxious to care. They were driven below into the 'tween-deck and battened down from the very start. It was a low timber dwelling—he would say—with wooden beams overhead, like the houses in his country, but you went into it down a ladder. It was very large, very cold, damp and somber, with places in the manner of wooden boxes where people had to sleep one above another, and it kept on rocking all ways at once all the time. He crept into one of these boxes and lay down there in the clothes in which he had left his home many days before, keeping his bundle and his stick by his side. People groaned, children cried, water dripped, the lights went out, the walls of the place creaked, and everything was being shaken so that in one's little box one dared not lift one's head. He had lost touch with his only companion (a young man from the same valley, he said), and all the time a great noise of wind went on outside and heavy blows fell—boom! boom! An awful sickness overcame him, even to the point of making him neglect his prayers. Besides, one could not tell whether it was morning or evening. It seemed always to be night in that place.

"Before that he had been traveling a long, long time on the iron track. He looked out of the window, which had a wonderfully clear glass in it, and the trees, the houses, the fields, and the long roads seemed to fly round and round about him till his head swam. He gave me to understand that he had on his passage beheld uncounted multitudes of people—whole nations—all dressed in such clothes as the rich wear. Once he was made to get out of the carriage, and slept through a night on a bench in a house of bricks with his bundle under his head; and once for many hours he had to sit on a floor of flat stones, dozing, with his knees up and with his bundle between his feet. There was a roof over him, which seemed made of glass, and was so high that the tallest mountain pine he had ever seen would have had room to grow under it. Steam machines rolled in at one end and out at the other. People swarmed more than you can see on a feast day round the miraculous Holy Image in the yard of the Carmelite Convent down in the plains where, before he left his home, he drove his mother in a wooden cart—a pious old woman who wanted to offer prayers and make a vow for his safety. He could not give me an idea of how large and lofty and full of noise and smoke and gloom, and clang of iron, the place was, but someone had told him it was called Berlin. Then they rang a bell, and another steam machine came, in and again he was taken on and on through a land that wearied his eyes by its flatness without a single bit of a hill to be seen anywhere. One more night he spent shut up in a building like a good stable with a litter of straw on the floor, guarding his bundle amongst a lot of men, of whom not one could understand a single word he said. In the morning they were all led down to the stony shores of an extremely broad muddy river, flowing not between hills but between houses that seemed immense. There was a steam machine that went on the water, and they all stood upon it packed tight, only now there were with them many women and children who made much noise. A cold rain fell, the wind blew in his face; he was wet through, and his teeth chattered. He and the young man from the same valley took each other by the hand.

"They thought they were being taken to America straight away, but suddenly the steam machine bumped against the side of a thing like a great house on the water. The walls were smooth and black, and there uprose, growing from the roof as it were, bare trees in the shape of crosses, extremely high. That's how it appeared to him then, for he had never seen a ship before. This was the ship that was going to swim all the way to America. Voices shouted, everything swayed; there was a ladder dipping up and down. He went up on his hands and knees in mortal fear of falling into the water below, which made a great splashing. He got separated from his companion, and when he descended into the bottom of that ship his heart seemed to melt suddenly within him.

"It was then also, as he told me, that he lost contact for good and all with one of those three men who the summer before had been going about through all the little towns in the foothills of his country. They would arrive on market days driving in a peasant's cart, and would set up an office in an inn or some other Jew's house. There were three of them, of whom one with a long beard looked venerable; and they had red cloth collars round their necks and gold lace on their sleeves like Government officials. They sat proudly behind a long table; and in the next room, so that the common people shouldn't hear, they kept a cunning telegraph machine, through which they could talk to the Emperor of America. The fathers hung about the door, but the young men of the mountains would crowd up to the table asking many questions, for there was work to be got all the year round at three dollars a day in America, and no military service to do.

"But the American Kaiser would not take everybody. Oh, no! He himself had great difficulty in getting accepted, and the venerable man in uniform had to go out of the room several times to work the telegraph on his behalf. The American Kaiser engaged him at last at three dollars, he being young and strong. However, many able young men backed out, afraid of the great distance; besides, those only who had some money could be taken. There were some who sold their huts and their land because it cost a lot of money to get to America; but then, once there, you had three dollars a day, and if you were clever you could find places where true gold could be picked up on the ground. His father's house was getting over-full. Two of his brothers were married and had children. He promised to send money home from America by post twice a year. His father sold an old cow, a pair of piebald mountain ponies of his own raising, and a cleared plot of fair pasture land on the sunny slope of a pineclad pass to a Jew innkeeper, in order to pay the people of the ship that took men to America to get rich in a short time.

"He must have been a real adventurer at heart, for how many of the greatest enterprises in the conquest of the earth had for their beginning just such a bargaining away of the paternal cow for the mirage or true gold far away! I have been telling you more or less in my own words what I learned fragmentarily in the course of two or three years, during which I seldom missed an opportunity of a friendly chat with him. He told me this story of his adventure with many flashes of white teeth and lively glances of black eyes, at first in a sort of anxious baby-talk, then, as he acquired the language, with great fluency, but always with that singing, soft, and at the same time vibrating intonation that instilled a strangely penetrating power into the sound of the most familiar English words, as if they had been the words of an unearthly language. And he always would come to an end, with many emphatic shakes of his head, upon that awful sensation of his heart melting within him directly he set foot on board that ship. Afterwards there seemed to come for him a period of blank ignorance, at any rate as to facts. No doubt he must have been abominably seasick and abominably unhappy—this soft and passionate adventurer, taken thus out of his knowledge, and feeling bitterly as he lay in his emigrant bunk his utter loneliness; for his was a highly sensitive nature. The next thing we know of him for certain is that he had been hiding in Hammond's pig-pound by the side of the road to Norton, six miles, as the crow flies, from the sea. Of these experiences he was unwilling to speak: they seemed to have seared into his soul a somber sort of wonder and indignation. Through the rumors of the countryside, which lasted for a good many days after his arrival, we know that the fishermen of West Colebrook had been disturbed and startled by heavy knocks against the walls of weatherboard cottages, and by a voice crying piercingly strange words in the night. Several of them turned out even, but, no doubt, he had fled in sudden alarm at their rough angry tones hailing each other in the darkness. A sort of frenzy must have helped him up the steep Norton hill. It was he, no doubt, who early the following morning had been seen lying (in a swoon, I should say) on the roadside grass by the Brenzett carrier, who actually got down to have a nearer look, but drew back, intimidated by the perfect immobility, and by something queer in the aspect of that tramp, sleeping so still under the showers. As the day advanced, some children came dashing into school at Norton in such a fright that the schoolmistress went out and spoke indignantly to a 'horrid-looking man' on the road. He edged away, hanging his head, for a few steps, and then suddenly ran off with extraordinary fleetness. The driver of Mr. Bradley's milk cart made no secret of it that he had lashed with his whip at a hairy sort of gypsy fellow who, jumping up at a turn of the road by the Vents, made a snatch at the pony's bridle. And he caught him a good one, too, right over the face, he said, that made him drop down in the mud a jolly sight quicker than he had jumped up; but it was a good half a mile before he could stop the pony. Maybe that in his desperate endeavors to get help, and in his need to get in touch with someone, the poor devil had tried to stop the cart. Also three boys confessed afterwards to throwing stones at a funny tramp, knocking about all wet and muddy, and, it seemed, very drunk, in the narrow deep lane by the limekilns. All this was the talk of three villages for days; but we have Mrs. Finn's (the wife of Smith's wagoner) unimpeachable testimony that she saw him get over the low wall of Hammond's pig-pound and lurch straight at her, babbling aloud in a voice that was enough to make one die of fright. Having the baby with her in a perambulator, Mrs. Finn called out to him to go away, and as he persisted in coming nearer, she hit him courageously with her umbrella over the head, and, without once looking back, ran like the wind with the perambulator as far as the first house in the village. She stopped then, out of breath, and spoke to old Lewis, hammering there at a heap of stones; and the old chap, taking off his immense black wire goggles, got up on his shaky legs to look where she pointed. Together they followed with their eyes the figure of the man running over a field; they saw him fall down, pick himself up, and run on again, staggering and waving his long arms above his head, in the direction of the New Barns Farm. From that moment he is plainly in the toils of his obscure and touching destiny. There is no doubt after this of what happened to him. All is certain now: Mrs. Smith's intense terror; Amy Foster's stolid conviction held against the other's nervous attack, that the man 'meant no harm'; Smith's exasperation (on his return from Darnford Market) at finding the dog barking himself into a fit, the back door locked, his wife in hysterics; and all for an unfortunate dirty tramp, supposed to be even then lurking in his stackyard. Was he? He would teach him to frighten women.

"Smith is notoriously hot-tempered, but the sight of some nondescript and miry creature sitting cross-legged amongst a lot of loose straw, and swinging itself to and fro like a bear in a cage, made him pause. Then this tramp stood up silently before him, one mass of mud and filth from head to foot. Smith, alone amongst his stacks with this apparition, in the stormy twilight ringing with the infuriated barking of the dog, felt the dread of an inexplicable strangeness. But when that being, parting with his black hands the long matted locks that hung before his face, as you part the two halves of a curtain, looked out at him with glistening, wild, black-and-white eyes, the weirdness of this silent encounter fairly staggered him. He has admitted since (for the story has been a legitimate subject of conversation about here for years) that he made more than one step backwards. Then a sudden burst of rapid, senseless speech persuaded him at once that he had to do with an escaped lunatic. In fact, that impression never wore off completely. Smith has not in his heart given up his secret conviction of the man's essential insanity to this very day.

"As the creature approached him, jabbering in a most discomposing manner, Smith (unaware that he was being addressed as 'gracious lord,' and adjured in God's name to afford food and shelter) kept on speaking firmly but gently to it, and retreating all the time into the other yard. At last, watching his chance, by a sudden charge he bundled him headlong into the wood-lodge, and instantly shot the bolt. Thereupon he wiped his brow, though the day was cold. He had done his duty to the community by shutting up a wandering and probably dangerous maniac. Smith isn't a hard man at all, but he had room in his brain only for that one idea of lunacy. He was not imaginative enough to ask himself whether the man might not be perishing with cold and hunger. Meantime, at first, the maniac made a great deal of noise in the lodge. Mrs. Smith was screaming upstairs, where she had locked herself in her bedroom; but Amy Foster sobbed piteously at the kitchen door, wringing her hands and muttering, 'Don't! don't!' I daresay Smith had a rough time of it that evening with one noise and another, and this insane, disturbing voice crying obstinately through the door only added to his irritation. He couldn't possibly have connected this troublesome lunatic with the sinking of a ship in Eastbay, of which there had been a rumor in the Darnford market place. And I dare say the man inside had been very near to insanity on that night. Before his excitement collapsed and he became unconscious he was throwing himself violently about in the dark, rolling on some dirty sacks, and biting his fists with rage, cold, hunger, amazement, and despair.

"He was a mountaineer of the eastern range of the Carpathians, and the vessel sunk the night before in Eastbay was the Hamburg emigrant ship *Herzogin Sophia-Dorothea*, of appalling memory.

"A few months later we could read in the papers the accounts of the bogus 'Emigration Agencies' among the Slavic peasantry in the more remote provinces of Austria. The object of these scoundrels was to get hold of the poor ignorant people's homesteads, and they were in league with the local usurers. They exported their victims through Hamburg mostly. As to the ship, I had watched her out of this very window, reaching close-hauled under short canvas into the bay on a dark, threatening afternoon. She came to an anchor, correctly by the chart, off the Brenzett Coastguard station. I remember before the night fell looking out again at the outlines of her spars and rigging that stood out dark and pointed on a background of ragged, slaty clouds like another and a slighter spire to the left of the Brenzett churchtower. In the evening the wind rose. At midnight I could hear in my bed the terrific gusts and the sounds of a driving deluge.

"About that time the Coastguardmen thought they saw the lights of a steamer over the anchoring ground. In a moment they vanished; but it is clear that another vessel of some sort had tried for shelter in the bay on that awful, blind night, had rammed the German ship amidships ('a breach' —as one of the divers told me afterwards—'that you could sail a Thames barge through'), and then had gone out either scatheless or damaged, who shall say; but had gone out, unknown, unseen, and fatal, to perish mysteriously at sea. Of her nothing ever came to light, and yet the hue and cry that was raised all over the world would have found her out if she had been in existence anywhere on the face of the waters.

"A completeness without a clue, and a stealthy silence as of a neatly executed crime, characterize this murderous disaster, which, as you may remember, had its gruesome celebrity. The wind would have prevented the loudest outcries from reaching the shore; there had been evidently no time for signals of distress. It was death without any sort of fuss. The Hamburg ship, filling all at once, capsized as she sank, and at daylight there was not even the end of a spar to be seen above water. She was missed, of course, and at first the Coastguardmen surmised that she had either dragged her anchor or parted her cable sometime during the night, and had been blown out to sea. Then, after the tide turned, the wreck must have shifted a little and released some of the bodies, because a child—a little fair-haired child in a red frock—came ashore abreast of the Martello tower. By the afternoon you could see along three miles of beach dark figures with bare legs dashing in and out of the tumbling foam, and rough-looking men, women with hard faces, children, mostly fair-haired, were being carried, stiff and dripping, on stretchers, on wattles, on ladders, in a long procession past the door of the 'Ship Inn,' to be laid out in a row under the north wall of the Brenzett Church.

"Officially, the body of the little girl in the red frock is the first thing that came ashore from that ship. But I have patients amongst the seafaring population of West Colebrook, and, unofficially, I am informed that very early that morning two brothers, who went down to look after their cobble hauled up on the beach, found a good way from Brenzett, an ordinary ship's hencoop, lying high and dry on the shore, with eleven drowned ducks inside. Their families ate the birds, and the hencoop was split into firewood with a hatchet. It is possible that a man (supposing he happened to be on deck at the time of the accident) might have floated ashore on that hencoop. He might. I admit it is improbable, but there was the man—and for days, nay, for weeks—it didn't enter our heads that we had amongst us the only living soul that had escaped from that disaster. The man himself, even when he learned to speak intelligibly, could tell us very little. He remembered he had felt better (after the ship had anchored, I suppose), and that the darkness, the wind, and the rain took his breath away. This looks as if he had been on deck sometime during that night. But we mustn't forget he had been taken out of his knowledge, that he had been seasick and battened down below for four days, that he had no general notion of a ship or of the sea, and therefore could have no definite idea of what was happening to him. The rain, the wind, the darkness he knew; he understood the bleating of the sheep, and he remembered the pain of his wretchedness and misery, his heart-broken astonishment that it was neither seen nor understood, his dismay at finding all the men angry and all the women fierce. He had approached them as a beggar, it is true, he said; but in his country, even if they gave nothing, they spoke gently to beggars. The children in his country were not taught to throw stones at those who asked for compassion. Smith's strategy overcame him completely. The wood-lodge presented the horrible aspect of a dungeon. What would be done to him next? . . . No wonder that Amy Foster appeared to his eyes with the aureole of an angel of light. The girl had not been able to sleep for thinking of the poor man, and in the morning, before the Smiths were up, she slipped out across the back yard. Holding the door of the wood-lodge ajar, she looked in and extended to him half a loaf of white bread—'such bread as the rich eat in my country,' he used to say.

"At this he got up slowly from amongst all sorts of rubbish, stiff, hungry, trembling, miserable, and doubtful. 'Can you eat this?' she asked in her soft and timid voice. He must have taken her for a 'gracious lady.' He devoured ferociously, and tears were falling on the crust. Suddenly he dropped the bread, seized her wrist, and imprinted a kiss on her hand. She was not frightened. Through his forlorn condition she had observed that he was good-looking. She shut the door and walked back slowly to the kitchen. Much later on, she told Mrs. Smith, who shuddered at the bare idea of being touched by that creature.

"Through this act of impulsive pity he was brought back again within the pale of human relations with his new surroundings. He never forgot it—never.

"That very same morning old Mr. Swaffer (Smith's nearest neighbor) came over to give his advice, and ended by carrying him off. He stood, unsteady on his legs, meek, and caked over in half-dried mud, while the two men talked around him in an incomprehensible tongue. Mrs. Smith had refused to come downstairs till the madman was off the premises; Amy Foster, far from within the dark kitchen, watched through the open back door; and he obeyed the signs that were made to him to the best of his ability. But Smith was full of mistrust. 'Mind, sir! It may be all his cunning,' he cried repeatedly in a tone of warning. When Mr. Swaffer started the mare, the deplorable being sitting humbly by his side, through weakness, nearly fell out over the back of the high two-wheeled cart. Swaffer took him straight home. And it is then that I come upon the scene.

"I was called in by the simple process of the old man beckoning to me with his forefinger over the gate of his house as I happened to be driving past. I got down, of course.

" 'I've got something here,' he mumbled, leading way to an outhouse at a little distance from his other farm buildings.

"It was there that I saw him first, in a long, low room taken upon the space of that sort of coach house. It was bare and whitewashed, with a small square aperture glazed with one cracked, dusty pane at its further end. He was lying on his back upon a straw pallet; they had given him a couple of horse blankets, and he seemed to have spent the remainder of his strength in the exertion of cleaning himself. He was almost speechless; his quick breathing under the blankets pulled up to his chin, his glittering, restless black eyes reminded me of a wild bird caught in a snare. While I was examining him, old Swaffer stood silently by the door, passing the tips of his fingers along his shaven upper lip. I gave some directions, promised to send a bottle of medicine, and naturally made some inquiries.

" 'Smith caught him in the stackyard at New Barns,' said the old chap in his deliberate, unmoved manner, and as if the other had been indeed a sort of wild animal. 'That's how I came by him. Quite a curiosity, isn't he? Now tell me, doctor—you've been all over the world—don't you think that's a bit of a Hindu we've got hold of here?'

"I was greatly surprised. His long black hair scattered over the straw bolster contrasted with the olive pallor of his face. It occurred to me he might be a Basque. It didn't necessarily follow that he should understand Spanish; but I tried him with the few words I know, and also with some French. The whispered sounds I caught by bending my ear to his lips puzzled me utterly. That afternoon the young ladies from the rectory (one of them read Goethe with a dictionary, and the other had struggled with Dante for years), coming to see Miss Swaffer, tried their German and Italian on him from the doorway. They retreated, just the least bit scared by the flood of passionate speech which, turning on his pallet, he let out at them. They admitted that the sound was pleasant, soft, musical—but, in conjunction with his looks perhaps, it was startling—so excitable, so utterly unlike anything one had ever heard. The village boys climbed up the bank to have a peep through the little square aperture. Everybody was wondering what Mr. Swaffer would do with him.

"He simply kept him.

"Swaffer would be called eccentric were he not so much respected. They will tell you that Mr. Swaffer sits up as late as ten o'clock at night to read books, and they will tell you also that he can write a check for two hundred pounds without thinking twice about it. He himself would tell you that the Swaffers had owned land between this and Darnford for these three hundred years. He must be eighty-five today, but he does not look a bit older than when I first came here. He is a great breeder of sheep, and deals extensively in cattle. He attends market days for miles around in every sort of weather, and drives sitting bowed low over the reins, his lank gray hair curling over the collar of his warm coat, and with a green plaid rug round his legs. The calmness of advanced age gives a solemnity to his manner. He is clean-shaved; his lips are thin and sensitive; something rigid and monachal in the set of his features lends a certain elevation to the character of his face. He has been known to drive miles in the rain to see a new kind of rose in somebody's garden, or a monstrous cabbage grown by a cottager. He loves to hear tell of or to be shown something that he calls 'outlandish.' Perhaps it was just that outlandishness of the man which influenced old Swaffer. Perhaps it was only an inexplicable caprice. All I know is that at the end of three weeks I caught sight of Smith's lunatic digging in Swaffer's kitchen garden. They had found out he could use a spade. He dug barefooted.

"His black hair flowed over his shoulders. I suppose it was Swaffer who had given him the striped old cotton shirt; but he wore still the national brown cloth trousers (in which he had been washed ashore) fitting to the leg almost like tights; was belted with a broad leather belt studded with little brass discs; and had never yet ventured into the village. The land he looked upon seemed to him kept neatly, like the grounds round a land-owner's house; the size of the cart horses struck him with astonishment; the roads resembled garden walks, and the aspect of the people, especially on

Sundays, spoke of opulence. He wondered what made them so hard-hearted and their children so bold. He got his food at the back door, car-ried it in both hands, carefully, to his outhous⸱ and, sitting alone on his pallet, would make the sign of the cross before he began. Beside the same pallet, kneeling in the early darkness of the short days, he recited aloud the Lord's Prayer before he slept. Whenever he saw old Swaffer he would bow with veneration from the waist, and stand erect while the old man, with his fingers over his upper lip, surveyed him silently. He bowed also to Miss Swaffer, who kept house frugally for her father—a broad-shouldered, big-boned woman of forty-five, with the pocket of her dress full of keys, and a gray, steady eye. She was Church—as people said (while her father was one of the trustees of the Baptist Chapel)—and wore a little steel cross at her waist. She dressed severely in black, in memory of one of the innumerable Bradleys of the neighborhood, to whom she had been engaged some twenty-five years ago—a young farmer who broke his neck out hunting on the eve of the wedding day. She had the unmoved counte-nance of the deaf, spoke very seldom, and her lips, thin like her father's, astonished one sometimes by a mysteriously ironic curl.

"These were the people to whom he owed allegiance, and an over-whelming loneliness seemed to fall from the leaden sky of that winter without sunshine. All the faces were sad. He could talk to no one, and had no hope of ever understanding anybody. It was as if these had been the faces of people from the other world—dead people—he used to tell me years afterwards. Upon my word, I wonder he did not go mad. He didn't know where he was. Somewhere very far from his mountains—somewhere over the water. Was this America, he wondered?

"If it hadn't been for the steel cross at Miss Swaffer's belt he would not, he confessed, have known whether he was in a Christian country at all. He used to cast stealthy glances at it, and feel comforted. There was nothing here the same as in his country! The earth and the water were different; there were no images of the Redeemer by the roadside. The very grass was different, and the trees. All the trees but the three old Norway pines on the bit of lawn before Swaffer's house, and these reminded him of his country. He had been detected once, after dusk, with his forehead against the trunk of one of them, sobbing, and talking to himself. They had been like brothers to him at that time, he affirmed. Everything else was strange. Conceive you the kind of an existence overshadowed, oppressed, by the everyday material appearances, as if by the visions of a nightmare. At night, when he could not sleep he kept on thinking of the girl who gave him the first piece of bread he had eaten in this foreign land. She had been neither fierce nor angry, nor frightened. Her face he remembered as the only comprehensible face amongst all these faces that were as closed, as mysterious, and as mute as the faces of the dead who are possessed of a knowledge beyond the comprehension of the living. I wonder whether the memory of her compassion prevented him from cutting his throat. But there! I suppose I am an old sentimentalist, and forget the instinctive love of life which it takes all the strength of an uncommon despair to overcome.

"He did the work which was given him with an intelligence which surprised old Swaffer. By and by it was discovered that he could help at the plowing, could milk the cows, feed the bullocks in the cattle-yard, and was of some use with the sheep. He began to pick up words, too, very fast; and suddenly, one fine morning in spring, he rescued from an untimely death a grandchild of old Swaffer.

"Swaffer's younger daughter is married to Willcox, a solicitor and the town clerk of Colebrook. Regularly twice a year they come to stay with the old man for a few days. Their only child, a little girl not three years old at the time, ran out of the house alone in her little white pinafore, and, toddling across the grass of a terraced garden, pitched herself over a low wall headfirst into the horsepond in the yard below.

"Our man was out with the wagoner and the plow in the field nearest to the house, and as he was leading the team round to begin a fresh furrow, he saw, through the gap of a gate, what for anybody else would have been a mere flutter of something white. But he had straight-glancing, quick, far-reaching eyes, that only seemed to flinch and lose their amazing power before the immensity of the sea. He was bare-footed, and looking as outlandish as the heart of Swaffer could desire. Leaving the horses on the turn, to the inexpressible disgust of the wagoner he bounded off, going over the plowed ground in long leaps, and suddenly appeared before the mother, thrust the child into her arms, and strode away.

"The pond was not very deep; but still, if he had not had such good eyes, the child would have perished—miserably suffocated in the foot or so of sticky mud at the bottom. Old Swaffer walked out slowly into the field, waited till the plow came over to his side, had a good look at him, and without saying a word went back to the house. But from that time they laid out his meals on the kitchen table; and at first, Miss Swaffer, all in black and with an inscrutable face, would come and stand in the doorway of the living room to see him make a big sign of the cross before he fell to. I believe that from that day, too, Swaffer began to pay him regular wages.

"I can't follow step by step his development. He cut his hair short, was seen in the village and along the road going to and fro to his work like any other man. Children ceased to shout after him. He became aware of social differences, but remained for a long time surprised at the bare poverty of the churches among so much wealth. He couldn't understand either why they were kept shut up on weekdays. There was nothing to steal in them. Was it to keep people from praying too often? The rectory took much notice of him about that time, and I believe the young ladies attempted to prepare the ground for his conversion. They could not, however, break him of his habit of crossing himself, but he went so far as to take off the string with a couple of brass medals the size of a sixpence, a tiny metal cross, and a square sort of scapulary which he wore round his neck. He hung them on the wall by the side of his bed, and he was still to be heard every evening reciting the Lord's Prayer, in incomprehensible words and in a slow, fervent tone, as he had heard his old father do at the head of all the kneeling family, big and little, on every evening of his life. And though he wore corduroys at work, and a slop-made pepper-and-salt suit on Sundays, strangers would turn round to look after him on the road. His foreignness had a peculiar and indelible stamp. At last people became used to seeing him. But they never became used to him. His rapid, skimming walk; his swarthy complexion; his hat cocked on the left ear; his habit, on warm evenings, of wearing his coat over one shoulder, like a hussar's dolman; his manner of leaping over the stiles, not as a feat of agility, but in the ordinary course of progression—all these peculiarities were, as one may say, so many causes of scorn and offense to the inhabitants of the village. They wouldn't in their dinner hour lie flat on their backs on the grass to stare at the sky. Neither did they go about the fields screaming dismal tunes. Many times have I heard his high-pitched voice from behind the ridge of some sloping sheepwalk, a voice light and soaring, like a lark's, but with a melancholy human note, over our fields that hear only the song of birds. And I would be startled myself. Ah! He was different; innocent of heart, and full of good will, which nobody wanted, this castaway, that, like a man transplanted into another planet, was separated by an immense space from his past and by an immense ignorance from his future. His quick, fervent utterance positively shocked everybody. 'An excitable devil,' they called him. One evening, in the taproom of the Coach and Horses (having drunk some whisky), he upset them all by singing a love song of his country. They hooted him down, and he was pained; but Preble, the lame wheelwright, and Vincent, the fat blacksmith, and the other notables, too, wanted to drink their evening beer in peace. On another occasion he tried to show them how to dance. The dust rose in clouds from the sanded floor; he leaped straight up amongst the deal tables, struck his heels together, squatted on one heel in front of old Preble, shooting out the other leg, uttered wild and exulting cries, jumped up to whirl on one foot, snapping his fingers above his head—and a strange carter who was having a drink in there began to swear, and cleared out his half-pint in his hand into the bar. But when suddenly he sprang upon a table and continued to dance among the glasses, the landlord interfered. He didn't want any 'acrobat tricks in the taproom.' They laid their hands on him. Having had a glass or two, Mr. Swaffer's foreigner tried to expostulate: was ejected forcibly: got a black eye.

"I believe he felt the hostility of his human surroundings. But he was tough—tough in spirit, too, as well as in body. Only the memory of the sea frightened him, with that vague terror that is left by a bad dream. His home was far away; and he did not want now to go to America. I had often explained to him that there is no place on earth where true gold can be found lying ready and to be got for the trouble of the picking up. How, then, he asked, could he ever return home with empty hands when there had been sold a cow, two ponies, and a bit of land to pay for his going? His eyes would fill with tears, and, averting them from the immense shimmer of the sea, he would throw himself face down on the grass. But sometimes, cocking his hat with a little conquering air, he would defy my wisdom. He had found his bit of true gold. That was Amy Foster's heart; which was 'a golden heart, and soft to people's misery,' he would say in the accents of overwhelming conviction.

"He was called Yanko. He had explained that this meant Little John; but as he would also repeat very often that he was a mountaineer (some word sounding in the dialect of his country like Goorall) he got it for his surname. And this is the only trace of him that the succeeding ages may find in the marriage register of the parish. There it stands—Yanko Goorall—in the rector's handwriting. The crooked cross made by the castaway, a cross whose tracing no doubt seemed to him the most solemn part of the whole ceremony, is all that remains now to perpetuate the memory of his name.

"His courtship had lasted some time—ever since he got his precarious footing in the community. It began by his buying for Amy Foster a green satin ribbon in Darnford. This was what you did in his country. You bought a ribbon at a Jew's stall on a fair-day. I don't suppose the girl knew what to do with it, but he seemed to think that his honorable intentions could not be mistaken.

"It was only when he declared his purpose to get married that I fully understood how, for a hundred futile and inappreciable reasons, how—shall I say odious?—he was to all the countryside. Every old woman in the village was up in arms. Smith, coming upon him near the farm, promised to break his head for him if he found him about again. But he twisted his little black mustache with such a bellicose air and rolled such big, black fierce eyes at Smith that this promise came to nothing. Smith, however, told the girl that she must be mad to take up with a man who was surely wrong in his head. All the same, when she heard him in the gloaming whistle from beyond the orchard a couple of bars of a weird and mournful tune, she would drop whatever she had in her hand—she would leave Mrs. Smith in the middle of a sentence—and she would run out to his call. Mrs. Smith called her a shameless hussy. She answered nothing. She said nothing at all to anybody, and went on her way as if she had been deaf. She and I alone in all the land, I fancy, could see his very real beauty. He was very good-looking, and most graceful in his bearing, with that something wild as of a woodland creature in his aspect. Her mother moaned over her dismally whenever the girl came to see her on her day out. The father was surly, but pretended not to know; and Mrs. Finn once told her plainly that 'this man, my dear, will do you some harm some day yet.' And so it went on. They could be seen on the roads, she tramping stolidly in her finery—gray dress, black feather, stout boots, prominent white cotton gloves that caught your eye a hundred yards away; and he, his coat slung picturesquely over one shoulder, pacing by her side, gallant of bearing and casting tender glances upon the girl with the golden heart. I wonder whether he saw how plain she was. Perhaps among types so different from what he had ever seen, he had not the power to judge; or perhaps he was seduced by the divine quality of her pity.

"Yanko was in great trouble meantime. In his country you get an old man for an ambassador in marriage affairs. He did not know how to proceed. However, one day in the midst of sheep in a field (he was now Swaffer's under-shepherd with Foster) he took off his hat to the father and declared himself humbly. 'I daresay she's fool enough to marry you,' was all Foster said. 'And then,' he used to relate, 'he puts his hat on his head, looks black at me as if he wanted to cut my throat, whistles the dog, and off he goes, leaving me to do the work.' The Fosters, of course, didn't like to lose the wages the girl earned: Amy used to give all her money to her mother. But there was in Foster a very genuine aversion to that match. He contended that the fellow was very good with sheep, but was not fit for any girl to marry. For one thing, he used to go along the hedges muttering to himself like a dam' fool; and then, these foreigners behave very queerly to women sometimes. And perhaps he would want to carry her off somewhere—or run off himself. It was not safe. He preached it to his daughter that the fellow might ill-use her in some way. She made no answer. It was, they said in the village, as if the man had done something to her. People discussed the matter. It was quite an excitement, and the two went on 'walking out' together in the face of opposition. Then something unexpected happened.

"I don't know whether old Swaffer ever understood how much he was regarded in the light of a father by his foreign retainer. Anyway the relation was curiously feudal. So when Yanko asked formally for an interview—'and the Miss, too' (he called the severe, deaf Miss Swaffer simply *Miss*)—it was to obtain their permission to marry. Swaffer heard him unmoved, dismissed him by a nod, and then shouted the intelligence into Miss Swaffer's best ear. She showed no surprise, and only remarked grimly, in a veiled blank voice, 'He certainly won't get any other girl to marry him.'

"It is Miss Swaffer who has all the credit for the munificence: but in a very few days it came out that Mr. Swaffer had presented Yanko with a cottage (the cottage you've seen this morning) and something like an acre of ground—had made it over to him in absolute property. Willcox expedited the deed, and I remember him telling me he had a great pleasure in making it ready. It recited: 'In consideration of saving the life of my beloved grandchild, Bertha Willcox.'

"Of course, after that no power on earth could prevent them from getting married.

"Her infatuation endured. People saw her going out to meet him in the evening. She stared with unblinking, fascinated eyes up the road where he was expected to appear, walking freely, with a swing from the hip, and humming one of the love tunes of his country. When the boy was born, he got elevated at the 'Coach and Horses,' assayed again a song and a dance, and was again ejected. People expressed their commiseration for a woman married to that jack-in-the-box. He didn't care. There was a man now (he told me boastfully) to whom he could sing and talk in the language of his country, and show how to dance by and by.

"But I don't know. To me he appeared to have grown less springy of step, heavier in body, less keen of eye. Imagination, no doubt; but it seems to me now as if the net of fate had been drawn closer round him already.

"One day I met him on the footpath over the Talfourd Hill. He told me that 'women were funny.' I had heard already of domestic differences. People were saying that Amy Foster was beginning to find out what sort of man she had married. He looked upon the sea with indifferent, unseeing eyes. His wife had snatched the child out of his arms one day as he sat on the doorstep crooning to it a song such as the mothers sing to babies in his mountains. She seemed to think he was doing it some harm. Women are funny. And she had objected to him praying aloud in the evening. Why? He expected the boy to repeat the prayer aloud after him by and by, as he used to do after his old father when he was a child—in his own country. And I discovered he longed for their boy to grow up so that he could have a man to talk with in that language that to our ears sounded so disturbing, so passionate, and so bizarre. Why his wife should dislike the idea he couldn't tell. But that would pass, he said. And tilting his head knowingly, he tapped his breastbone to indicate that she had a good heart: not hard, not fierce, open to compassion, charitable to the poor!

"I walked away thoughtfully; I wondered whether his difference, his strangeness, were not penetrating with repulsion that dull nature they had begun by irresistibly attracting. I wondered. . . ."

The doctor came to the window and looked out at the frigid splendor of the sea, immense in the haze, as if enclosing all the earth with all the hearts lost among the passions of love and fear.

"Physiologically, now," he said, turning away abruptly, "it was possible. It was possible."

He remained silent. Then went on—

"At all events, the next time I saw him he was ill—lung trouble. He was tough, but I dare say he was not acclimatized as well as I had supposed. It was a bad winter; and, of course, these mountaineers do get fits of homesickness; and a state of depression would make him vulnerable. He was lying half dressed on a couch downstairs.

"A table covered with a dark oilcloth took up all the middle of the little room. There was a wicker cradle on the floor, a kettle spouting steam on the hob, and some child's linen lay drying on the fender. The room was warm, but the door opens right into the garden, as you noticed perhaps.

"He was very feverish, and kept on muttering to himself. She sat on a chair and looked at him fixedly across the table with her brown, blurred eyes. 'Why don't you have him upstairs?' I asked. With a start and a confused stammer she said, 'Oh! ah! I couldn't sit with him upstairs, sir.'

"I gave her certain directions; and going outside, I said again that he ought to be in bed upstairs. She wrung her hands. 'I couldn't. I couldn't. He keeps on saying something—I don't know what.' With the memory of all the talk against the man that had been dinned into her ears, I looked at her narrowly. I looked into her shortsighted eyes, at her dumb eyes that once in her life had seen an enticing shape, but seemed, staring at me, to see nothing at all now. But I saw she was uneasy.

"'What's the matter with him?' she asked in a sort of vacant trepidation. 'He doesn't look very ill. I never did see anybody look like this before. . . .'

"'Do you think,' I asked indignantly, 'he is shamming?'

"'I can't help it, sir,' she said, stolidly. And suddenly she clapped her hands and looked right and left. 'And there's the baby. I am so frightened. He wanted me just now to give him the baby. I can't understand what he says to it.'

"'Can't you ask a neighbor to come in tonight?' I asked.

"'Please, sir, nobody seems to care to come,' she muttered, dully resigned all at once.

"I impressed upon her the necessity of the greatest care, and then had to go. There was a good deal of sickness that winter. 'Oh, I hope he won't talk!' she exclaimed softly just as I was going away.

"I don't know how it is I did not see—but I didn't. And yet, turning in my trap, I saw her lingering before the door, very still, and as if meditating a flight up the miry road.

"Towards the night his fever increased.

"He tossed, moaned, and now and then muttered a complaint. And she sat with the table between her and the couch, watching every movement and every sound, with the terror, the unreasonable terror, of that man she could not understand creeping over her. She had drawn the wicker cradle close to her feet. There was nothing in her now but the maternal instinct and that unaccountable fear.

"Suddenly coming to himself, parched, he demanded a drink of water. She did not move. She had not understood, though he may have thought he was speaking in English. He waited, looking at her, burning with fever, amazed at her silence and immobility, and then he shouted impatiently, 'Water! Give me water!'

"She jumped to her feet, snatched up the child, and stood still. He spoke to her, and his passionate remonstrances only increased her fear of that strange man. I believe he spoke to her for a long time, entreating, wondering, pleading, ordering, I suppose. She says she bore it as long as she could. And then a gust of rage came over him.

"He sat up and called out terribly one word—some word. Then he got up as though he hadn't been ill at all, she says. And as in fevered dismay, indignation, and wonder he tried to get to her round the table, she simply opened the door and ran out with the child in her arms. She heard him call twice after her down the road in a terrible voice—and fled. . . . Ah! but you should have seen stirring behind the dull, blurred glance of those eyes the specter of the fear which had hunted her on that night three miles and a half to the door of Foster's cottage! I did the next day.

"And it was I who found him lying face down and his body in a puddle, just outside the little wicker gate.

"I had been called out that night to an urgent case in the village, and on my way home at daybreak passed by the cottage. The door stood open. My man helped me to carry him in. We laid him on the couch. The lamp smoked, the fire was out, the chill of the stormy night oozed from the cheerless yellow paper on the wall. 'Amy!' I called aloud, and my voice seemed to lose itself in the emptiness of this tiny house as if I had cried in a desert. He opened his eyes. 'Gone!' he said, distinctly. 'I had only asked for water—only for a little water. . . .'

"He was muddy. I covered him up and stood waiting in silence, catching a painfully gasped word now and then. They were no longer in his own language. The fever had left him, taking with it the heat of life. And with his panting breast and lustrous eyes he reminded me again of a wild creature under the net; of a bird caught in a snare. She had left him. She had left him—sick—helpless—thirsty. The spear of the hunter had entered his very soul. 'Why?' he cried, in the penetrating and indignant voice of a man calling to a responsible Maker. A gust of wind and a swish of rain answered.

"And as I turned away to shut the door he pronounced the word 'Merciful!' and expired.

"Eventually I certified heart failure as the immediate cause of death. His heart must have indeed failed him, or else he might have stood this night of storm and exposure, too. I closed his eyes and drove away. Not very far from the cottage I met Foster walking sturdily between the dripping hedges with his collie at his heels.

" 'Do you know where your daughter is?' I asked.

" 'Don't I!' he cried. 'I am going to talk to him a bit. Frightening a poor woman like this.'

" 'He won't frighten her any more,' I said. 'He is dead.'

"He struck with his stick at the mud.

" 'And there's the child.'

"Then, after thinking deeply for a while—

" 'I don't know that it isn't for the best.'

"That's what he said. And she says nothing at all now. Not a word of him. Never. Is his image as utterly gone from her mind as his lithe and striding figure, his caroling voice are gone from our fields? He is no longer before her eyes to excite her imagination into a passion of love or fear; and his memory seems to have vanished from her dull brain as a shadow passes away upon a white screen. She lives in the cottage and works for Miss Swaffer. She is Amy Foster for everybody, and the child is 'Amy Foster's boy.' She calls him Johnny—which means Little John.

"It is impossible to say whether this name recalls anything to her. Does she ever think of the past? I have seen her hanging over the boy's cot in a very passion of maternal tenderness. The little fellow was lying on his back, a little frightened at me, but very still, with his big black eyes, with his fluttered air of a bird in a snare. And looking at him I seemed to see again the other one—the father, cast out mysteriously by the sea to perish in the supreme disaster of loneliness and despair."

DINO BUZZATI

The Killing of the Dragon

IN May 1902 a peasant of the Count Gerol, one Giosuè Longo, who often hunted in the mountains, reported having seen in the valley of Secca a great ugly beast that seemed to be a dragon. At Palissano, the last village of the valley, there had been for centuries the legend that among certain arid gorges one of the monsters yet lived. But nobody had ever taken the tale seriously. This time, however, the common sense of Longo, the precision of his account, the particulars of the adventure many times repeated without the least variation, all indicated that there had to be some truth in it; and so the Count decided to go and see. Indeed, he scarcely expected a dragon; but among those uninhabited gorges there might be some great serpent of a rare species yet surviving.

His companions for the expedition were the Governor of the province, Quinto Andronico, with his beautiful and intrepid wife Maria, the naturalist Professor Inghirami and his colleague Fusti, specially versed in the art of embalming. For some time the worn and sceptical Governor had been aware that his wife cherished considerable feeling for Gerol, but he did not greatly concern himself about it. When Maria proposed that they should go with the Count on the dragon hunt, he consented willingly enough. He did not have the least jealousy of the man Martino, nor the least envy of the Count Gerol, for being so much younger, handsomer, stronger, more audacious, and richer than he.

The two carriages left the city shortly after midnight, escorted by eight mounted huntsmen, and toward six in the morning had reached the village of Palissano. The Count, the beautiful Maria, and the two naturalists were sleeping. Andronico, the only one awake, ordered the carriage to stop in front of the house of an old acquaintance, a certain Taddei, a physician. A moment later, roused by the coachman, the doctor, drugged by sleep, appeared at a second-story window. Andronico, directly below, greeted him jovially, explained the object of the expedition, and then waited for the laugh that would come after such talk of a dragon. But Dr. Taddei shook his head.

"If I were in your shoes, I wouldn't go," he said flatly.

"Why? Do you think there's nothing in it? That it's all just talk?"

"I don't know," the doctor replied. "Personally, I believe there may be a dragon, even though I've never seen it. But I wouldn't get myself into this mess. It's a thing of ill omen."

"Ill omen? Would you really maintain, Taddei, that you believe that?"

"I am old, my dear Governor," the other said, "and I have seen such cases. Perhaps this now is only a tale, but, again, it may be true. If I were in your shoes, I wouldn't fool with it. Besides, the way is hard to find, it's all rotten mountains full of landslips, and a breath of wind is enough to bring the Crack of Doom, and there's not a trickle of water. Let it alone, Governor. Instead, go up the Crocetta"—and he indicated a round grassy mountain above the village—"and there you'll find all the hares you want."

He was silent a moment, then added: "I wouldn't go there, for a fact. One time I heard say, but it's useless, you would start laughing—"

"Why should I laugh?" demanded Andronico. "Tell me—go ahead and tell me."

"All right, some say that the dragon sends forth smoke, that this smoke is poisonous, and just a little will kill you."

Despite his promise, Andronico burst out laughing.

"I've always known you were archaic," he wound up, "cranky and archaic. But this beats all. You are mediaeval, my dear Taddei. Well, so long until tonight—and with the head of the dragon!"

He made a gesture of salute, got back into the carriage, and gave the command to proceed. Giosuè Longo, who was one of the huntsmen and knew the road, took the head of the convoy.

"What was that old fellow shaking his head about?" demanded the beautiful Maria, who meanwhile had waked up.

"Nothing," replied Andronico, "He's just good old Taddei, who in his spare time is also a veterinarian. We were just talking of hoof-and-mouth disease."

"And the dragon?" asked the Count, who was sitting in front. "Did you ask if he knows anything about the dragon?"

"No, to tell the truth," the Governor replied, "I didn't want to get laughed at. I just said that we'd come for a little hunting, that's all."

With the sun now up, the sleepiness of the party vanished, the horses stepped more briskly, and the coachmen began to sing.

"He was our family doctor, Taddei was. Long back," the Governor began, "he had a magnificent practice. But one fine day, I don't know for what delusion of love, he retired into the country. Then he had another misfortune, and holes up, up here. One more piece of bad luck, and who knows how he will end. Maybe he'll turn into some kind of dragon himself!"

"What nonsense!" said Maria, a little irritated. "Always this stuff about the dragon. It's getting to be a bore, this harping on the dragon. You haven't talked about anything else since we left."

"But you are the one who wanted to come," her husband retorted with ironical sweetness. "And then, how could you hear our talk if you were really asleep? Were you faking, maybe?"

Maria did not answer, but disturbed, looked out the carriage window. She stared at the mountains, which grew higher, more and more precipitous, and more arid. At the end of the valley appeared a chaotic succession of peaks, generally conical in form, naked of trees or grass, yellowish in color, of an unparalleled desolation. Struck by the sun, they glittered with a light powerful and unremitting.

It was about nine when the carriages stopped at the end of the road. The hunters, stepping from the carriage, realized that they were now in the heart of those sinister mountains. Viewed close up, they seemed made of rock rotting and crumbling into earth, from peak to base ready for a landslip or rock-fall.

"Well, here the trail begins," said Longo, pointing to the marks of human passage which went up to the lip of a little valley.

So they moved on, and in three quarters of an hour reached the Burel, where the dragon had been seen.

"Did you bring the water?" Andronico asked the huntsmen.

"There are four flasks, and two more of wine, Excellency," one of them answered him. "That's enough, I guess—"

It was strange. Now that they were far from the city, closed in by these mountains, the notion of the dragon did not seem so absurd. The company looked about them without finding any comfort. Yellowish crests, where nothing had ever grown, little valleys twisting off to the sides to hide quickly their own meanderings—all was an abandoned world.

Without a word, they resumed the track. The hunters went first with the rifles, the culverins, and the other hardware of a hunt; then came Maria, last the two naturalists. Luckily, the track was still in shade; among those yellow slopes the sun would have been an affliction.

Even the little valley that led to the Burel was narrow and torturous; there was no stream at the bottom; there were no shrubs or grass on the sides, only rock-fall and rubble. There was no song of bird or water, only the solitary susurrus of gravel.

As the company thus proceeded, there came into view from below, overtaking them, a young fellow with a dead goat on his shoulders. "He's going to the dragon," said Longo, and said it with the greatest naturalness, with no air of waggery. The villagers of Palissano, he explained, were very superstitious, and every day sent a goat to the Burel, to placate the monster. The offering was carried, in turn, by the young men of the village. Woe if the monster should make its voice heard. There would be bad luck.

"And every day the dragon eats the goat?" teased Count Gerol.

"The next morning they don't find anything, that's sure."

"Not even the bones?"

"No, not even the bones. It goes to eat it inside the cave."

"Couldn't it be that somebody from the village eats it?" asked the Governor. "They all know the track up there. Has anybody ever really seen the dragon take the goat?"

"I don't know, Excellency," replied the huntsman.

The young man with the goat had meanwhile caught up with them.

"Say, young fellow!" said Count Gerol, with his tone of authority. "How much do you want for that goat?"

"I can't sell it, Signor," the fellow answered.

"Not even for ten scudos?"

"Well, for ten scudos . . ." the young man allowed. "That means I could go get another one." And he deposited the animal on the ground.

Andronico asked the Count: "What use will the goat be to you? You won't want to eat it, I hope."

"You'll see, you'll see what it's for," said the other, evasively.

One of the huntsmen took the goat on his shoulders, the young fellow from Palissano headed back down toward the village, as fast as he could, evidently to get another goat for the dragon, and the company resumed the march.

After less than an hour, they had arrived. The valley opened abruptly into a wide, wild circle, the Burel, a kind of ampitheater surrounded by walls of earth and crumbling rock, yellow-pink in color. In the very middle, at the summit of a hump of rubble, was a black hole: the lair of the dragon.

"It's there," said Longo. They stopped a little way off, on a gravelly terrace that offered a fine observation point, some ten meters above the level of the cave and almost opposite it. The terrace, overhanging its own walls of support, had the additional advantage of not being accessible from below. Maria could stay here in perfect safety.

They fell silent, listening. There was nothing except the infinite silence of the mountains, accented now and then by some whispering slip of gravel. Now to the right, now to the left, some cornice of earth would suddenly break, and then trickles of little stones begin to slip down, to come, after a little, sadly to rest. Thus the landscape wore an air of ruin perennial and continuous: mountains abandoned by God, they undid themselves, it seemed, moment to moment.

"What if the dragon doesn't come out today?" demanded Quinto Andronico.

"I have the goat," retorted Gerol. "You forget I have the goat."

What he meant was clear. The creature would be the bait to lure the monster from his cave. They began the preparations. Two huntsmen, with considerable difficulty, clambered up some twenty meters above the entrance of the cave to be ready to hurl stones down if need came. Another went to deposit the goat on the gravel-bank, not far from the cave. Others established themselves behind boulders, with the culverins and rifles. Andronico stayed where he was; he had come only to watch.

The beautiful Maria was quiet. In her, all enterprise had faded. With what relief she would now have turned back. But she did not dare to confide this to a soul. Her gaze moved over the surrounding walls, the old and new rock-falls, the pilasters of red earth that seemed ready, at any moment, to collapse. Her husband, the Count Gerol, the two naturalists, the huntsmen—they seemed few, so few, against that solitude.

The dead goat now being in place before the cave, they settled down to waiting. It was now a little past ten, and the sun had completely invested the Burel, flooding it with intense heat. Burning waves rebounded from one wall to the other. To protect the Governor and his wife, the huntsmen rigged up a kind of canopy from the coverings of the carriage; but Maria, no matter how much she drank, could not quench her thirst.

"No!" suddenly cried Count Gerol from the gravel-bank down there, where he stood on a boulder, carbine in hand, a metal mace at his belt.

They all shivered, and held their breath, aware that something alive was about to issue from the cave.

"The dragon! The dragon!" shouted two or three of the huntsmen, whether with joy or dismay it was not certain.

With the quivering sway of a serpent, the creature emerged to the light. Well, there it was, the monster of the legends, whose voice alone could make a whole village tremble!

"Oh, how ugly!" cried Maria, with evident relief, having expected something much worse.

"Buck up, buck up!" a huntsman shouted, for his joke.

And all resumed their accustomed self-certitude.

"It looks like a little *ceratosaurus!*" said Professor Inghirami, who had regained enough ease of soul for the problems of science.

In fact, it didn't seem tremendous, the monster, little longer than two meters, with a head like a crocodile, though shorter, the exaggerated neck of a lizard, the thorax somewhat swollen, the tail short, a kind of soft cresting along the spine. More apt than the modesty of dimension to allay fear were, however, the retarded movement, the earthy color of parchment (with some greenish streaks), the generally flaccid appearance of the body. The whole effect was of great age. If it was a dragon, it was one gone decrepit, near the very verge of life.

"Take that!" taunted one of the huntsmen above the mouth of the cave. And he hurled a rock down at the beast.

The rock came down straight as a plumb-line and, with precision, found the skull of the dragon. There was a dull *toc*, as from a gourd. Maria felt a shiver of repulsion.

The stroke was strong, but insufficient. After remaining, for a moment or two, immobile, as though stunned, the reptile began to sway the neck and head from side to side, in a movement of pain. The jaws opened and closed with mechanical regularity, exposing a row of sharp teeth, but no voice came out. Then the dragon moved down across the gravel toward the goat.

"That made you groggy, eh!" laughed the Count, who had suddenly lost his hauteur. He seemed taken by a joyous excitement, already tasting the slaughter.

A blast from one of the culverins, fired from some thirty meters off, missed the target. The detonation, shattering the stagnant air, woke sad reverberations among the walls, down which innumerable little slides of earth began.

Almost immediately the second culverin was fired. The slug hit the monster in one of the hind paws, from which, suddenly, a little rivulet of blood gushed.

"Look at him dance!" cried the beautiful Maria, taken, even she, by the cruel spectacle. At the spasm of the wound, the brute had, in fact, begun to turn back on itself, heaving up, with pitiful effort. The shattered paw swung behind, leaving on the gravel a streak of black fluid.

Finally the reptile managed to reach the goat and seized it with its teeth. It was on the point of retiring when Count Gerol, to exhibit his courage, set himself close, only a couple of meters off, and discharged his carbine into the head.

A sort of whistle escaped from the gullet of the monster. It seemed that it was trying to control itself, to repress its rage, not to allow forth all that voice leashed in its body—that some motive unknowable by the spectators induced it to silence. The slug of the carbine had entered an eye. The charge being delivered, Gerol stepped hastily back and waited for the dragon to drop stone-dead.

But the beast did not drop stone-dead. The life in its seemed as inextinguishable as fire in pitch. With the ball of lead in the eye, the monster calmly swallowed the goat, and the throat dilated like rubber as the enormous mouthful slipped slowly downward. Then it drew back to the base of the rocks and tried to clamber up the wall, beside the cave. Clumsily, it ascended, starting the loose earth under its paws, anxious to escape. The sky leaned clear and pale above, and the sun quickly dried the traces of blood.

"Like a cockroach in a pot," Governor Andronico murmured, speaking only to himself.

"What, what did you say?" his wife asked.

"Nothing, nothing," he said.

"Why doesn't it go back into the cave?" wondered Professor Inghirami, lucidly scouting every scientific aspect of the scene.

"It's afraid of being trapped there," suggested Fusti. "Besides, it must be stunned. And then how would you expect it to reason it out? A *ceratosaurus*. No, but it's not a *ceratosaurus*," said Fusti, correcting himself. "I have reconstructed several of them for museums, but they are different. Where are the stings of the tail?"

"It's holding them hidden," retorted Inghirami. "Look what a bloated belly. The tail is shrunk back under and you can't see it."

They were arguing there when one of the huntsmen, the one who had fired the second culverin, came running toward the terrace where Andronico stood, with the evident intention of making off.

"Where are you going? Where are you going?" shouted Gerol after him. "Stay at your place till we've finished."

"I'm going," the huntsman answered, positively. "I don't like this business. This isn't hunting—not this."

"What do you mean? Are you afraid? Is that what you mean?"

"No, sir, I'm not afraid."

"You are afraid, I tell you, if you don't hold your place."

"I'm not afraid. I tell you. You're the one that ought to be ashamed, sir count."

"Me ashamed!" And Martino Gerol began to curse him: "You filthy scoundrel, that's what you are! You're from Palissano I bet, you damned coward! Get on off before I teach you a lession."

Then, as he saw a second huntsman withdrawing, the Count again shouted: "And you, Beppi, where do you think you are going?"

"Me too, sir count, I'm going. I don't want to be mixed up in this mess."

"Cowards!" screamed Gerol. "Cowards, I'd make you pay for it, if I could just get at you."

"It's not being afraid, sir count," said the second huntsman. "It's not being afraid, sir count. But you'll see, it will come out bad!"

"I'll make you see right now!" And seizing a stone from the ground, the Count hurled it with all his force at the huntsman. But his aim missed.

There was a moment of pause, while the dragon clambered at the wall without being able to get up. The earth and stones slid down, drawing the beast with them, lower and lower, back where it had started. Except for that sound of disturbed stones, there was silence.

Then came the voice of Andronico. "Haven't we had enough of this?" he shouted at Gerol. "It's hellishly hot. Get the poor brute out of its misery, once and for all. Why do you want to torture it this way, even if it is a dragon?"

"Is it my fault?" demanded Gerol, irritably. "Don't you see, it won't die? With a bullet in the skull it's more alive than ever. . . ."

He stopped, suddenly aware that the young fellow they had met earlier was now at the lip of the gravel-bank with another goat on his shoulders. Bemused by the presence of these men, of these weapons, of those smears of blood, and above all by the cumbrous effort of the dragon to get up the rocks, the dragon he had never before seen out of the cave, he stood there, gawking at the strange scene.

"Hey, fellow!" yelled Gerol. "How much for that goat?"

"Nothing—I can't," the young fellow answered. "I can't give it to you, not even for its weight in gold." Then, staring at the bleeding monster, he demanded: "But what have you done to it?"

"We're here to settle things. You—you villagers—ought to be happy. From tomorrow it's over with the goats."

"Why over with the goats?"

"Tomorrow the dragon won't be here any more," said the Count, smiling.

"But you can't, you can't do it, I tell you!" the young fellow cried, terror-struck.

"And now you too start it!" Martino Gerol exclaimed. "Give me that goat, and quick!"

"No, I tell you," the other repeated stubbornly, retreating.

"For God's sake!" the Count yelled, and was on the youth, gave him a fist in the face, jerked the goat off his back, and threw him to the ground.

"You'll be sorry, I tell you, you'll be sorry for it, wait and see if you won't be sorry," threatened the youth, but in a low voice, picking himself up but not daring to avenge himself.

But Gerol had already turned his back on him.

The sun now came boiling down into the pot, and one could barely endure to keep the eyes open, so dazzling was the glitter of the yellow gravel, of the rocks, of the gravel again. There was nothing, absolutely nothing, where the sight might find ease.

Maria's thirst grew more and more intense, and to drink did no good. "God, what heat!" she wailed. Also, the sight of the Count began to annoy her.

Meanwhile, as though popped out of the earth, some ten men had appeared. Probably come from Palissano on the rumor that strangers had gone up to the Burel, they stood fixed, here and there, on the rim of the various crests of yellow earth, and stared with no motion.

"You've got a proper public now!" Andronico tried to bait Gerol, who was busy with two huntsmen around the goat.

The young Count lifted up his gaze until he was aware of those unidentified ones peering from the brows of the crests around. He made an expression of contempt and resumed his work.

The dragon had slid from the wall down to the gravel-bank, and lay stretched out, immobile except for the palpitation of the swollen belly.

"Ready!" cried one of the huntsmen, and with Gerol lifted the goat. They had slit the belly of the creature and inserted a charge of explosive connected with a fuse.

Then the Count was seen to advance intrepidly over the gravel-bank, to deposit, quite calmly, the goat on the gravel not more than ten meters from the dragon, and then to withdraw, unwinding the fuse.

They had to wait half an hour for the brute to move. The unidentified ones standing on the brows of the crests round about seemed statues; though they said nothing, not even among themselves, their gaze was a reprobation. Insensible to the sun that had now assumed its fullest power, they never shifted their gaze from the reptile, as though imploring it not to move.

But the dragon, struck in the spine by a carbine slug, suddenly turned, saw the goat, and slowly dragged itself there. It was in the act of stretching out its head to seize the prey when the Count lighted the fuse. The flash ran swiftly along the line, reached the goat, and set off the explosion.

The blast was not loud, much less than the report of the culverins, a sound dry but thick, like splitting a plank. But the body of the dragon was suddenly hurled back, and one saw that the belly was torn open. Again the head began that painful swaying from side to side, as though it were saying no, no, that it was not right, that they had been too cruel, that it was all hopeless.

The Count laughed with satisfaction, out this time alone.

"Oh, how awful! Enough!" cried the beautiful Maria, covering her face with her hands.

"Yes," her husband said, slowly, "I, too, think things will end badly."

The monster lay, apparently exhausted, in a pool of black blood. And from its sides issued two threads of dark smoke, one to the right and one to the left, two little heavy strands of smoke that could scarcely rise.

"Did you see?" demanded Inghirami of his colleague.

"Yes, I did," the other confirmed.

"Two breath-vents, as in the *Ceratosaurus*, the so-called *operculi hammeriani*."

"No," said Fusti. "It isn't a *Ceratosaurus*."

At this point. from behind the boulder where he had retired, Count Gerol advanced to finish off the monster. He was exactly in the middle of the hump of gravel and in the act of grasping his metal mace, when all spectators let forth a cry.

For an instant Gerol thought it a cry of triumph at the death of the dragon. Then he was aware that something was moving behind him. He turned in a flash, and saw—but how ridiculous!—saw two little creatures issue blundering from the cave then move rather quickly toward him. Two little unformed reptiles, not longer than a half meter, repeating in miniature the image of the dying dragon. Two little dragons, the offspring, driven, no doubt by hunger, from the cave.

It was a matter of seconds. The Count gave a beautiful exhibition of agility. "Take that! Take that!" he shouted joyously, whirling the iron club. And two strokes were enough. Wielded with extraordinary energy and decision, the mace struck, in turn, the little monsters, cracking the heads like bottles. Both went flabby, dead, from a distance looking somewhat like a couple of bagpipes.

Then the unidentified men, not uttering a sound, disappeared, running away down the channels of gravel. It was as though they fled a sudden danger. They fled without sound, not starting any earth-falls, not turning their heads even an instant toward the cave of the dragon, disappearing, as they had come, in mystery.

The dragon now moved; it seemed that it would simply never manage to die. Dragging itself, slow as a snail, it approached its dead young, still emitting the two threads of smoke. Then, having reached them, it sank down on the gravel-bank, stretched out its neck with a painful retardation, and began, very gently, to lick the two little dead monsters, perhaps with the hope of bringing them back to life.

Finally, the dragon seemed to collect its last force, and as it had not done previously, lifted its head vertically toward the sky; then from its throat came, softly at first, but with progressive power, an indescribable cry, a voice never yet heard in the world, neither animal nor human, so charged with hate that even Count Gerol stopped stock still, paralyzed with horror.

Now it could be understood why the thing had not wanted to go back into its den, where it might well have found safety, why it had not earlier uttered any roar, limiting itself to mere sibilance. The dragon had thought of its offspring, and to save them had rejected its own safety: If it had, indeed, sought refuge in the cave, the men might have followed it in and discovered the young; and if it had raised its voice, the little beasts might have come out to see why. Only now that it had seen them die, the monster could utter that hellish howl.

The dragon invoked help and implored vengeance for its children. But of whom? Of the mountains perhaps, arid and unpeopled? Of the sky without bird or cloud? Of the men who had been torturing it? Of some demon, perhaps? The howl pierced the very walls of rock and the dome of the sky; it filled the whole world. It seemed impossible that nobody would answer, even if there was now no good reason—it seemed simply impossible.

"Who will it call?" demanded Andronico, trying vainly to keep a tone of jest in his voice. "Who is it calling? There isn't anybody to come, is there?"

"Oh, won't he die soon!" said the woman.

But the dragon wouldn't decide to die, although the Count, caught by the mania to finish it off, was firing at it with the carbine. *Tam! Tam!* It was useless. The dragon was caressing with its tongue the little dead beasts; and a whitish fluid was issuing from the unhurt eye.

"The saurian!" exclaimed Professor Fusti. "Look, it's crying."

The Governor said: "It's late. Enough, Martino, it's late, it's time to go."

Seven times the voice of the monster was raised to the sky, and the cliffs and sky resounded. On the seventh time, it seemed that the cry would never end; then, suddenly, it was extinguished, dropped abruptly, was lost in the silence.

In the mortal quiet that ensued a coughing began. Covered with dust, his face transformed by fatigue, emotion, and sweat, Count Martino threw his carbine aside, among the stones, and moved across the hump of rubble, coughing, pressing a hand to his chest.

"What's this now?" demanded Andronico, his face gone grave with a presentiment of evil. "What have you done to yourself?"

"Nothing," returned Gerol, forcing his tone to levity. "It's just that some of that smoke got into me."

"What smoke?"

Gerol did not answer, but made a gesture toward the dragon. The monster lay immoblie, the head extended in abandonment among the stones; it would have been said to be dead, except for those two thin plumes of smoke.

"It looks finished," said Andronico.

So indeed it seemed. The obstinate life was coming out of the mouth of the dragon.

Nobody had answered its cry, in all the world nobody had been moved. The mountains yet remained immobile, even the little earth-slides seemed to be reabsorbed; the sky was clear, and without the slightest trace of a cloud; the sun was westering. Nothing, neither brute nor spirit, had hastened to avenge the slaughter. It had been man who wiped out that last, residual stain from the earth; it had been man, the astute and powerful, who everywhere establishes wise laws to maintain order, man the blameless who exhausts himself for progress, and may not concede the survival of any dragon, not even in the desolate mountains. It had been man who killed it, and recrimination would be stupid.

What man had done was just, and precisely in conformity with law. Even so, it seemed impossible that no one had responded to that last outcry of the dragon. Andronico, as well as his wife and the huntsmen, wanted nothing now but to flee; even the naturalists renounced the embalming to get off as soon as possible.

The men of the village had disappeared, as with presentiment of evil. The shadows ascended the crumbling walls. From the body of the dragon, that parchment-like carcass, there lifted, without ceasing, the two threads of smoke to entwine sluggishly in the stagnant air. All seemed finished, a sad thing, a thing to forget, nothing else.

But Count Gerol continued to cough, and cough. Exhausted, he sat on a boulder, near the friends who did not dare to speak to him. Even the intrepid Maria, from the other side, was staring at him. The only sound was those brief attacks of coughing. Vainly, Martino Gerol tried to control himself; a kind of fire was sinking into the depth of his lungs, lower and lower.

"I knew it," murmured Governor Andronico to his wife, who shivered a little. "I knew it would end badly."

MARCEL AYMÉ

Dermuche

HE had murdered a family of three in order to get possession of a gramophone record which he had coveted for several years. The fiery eloquence of counsel for the prosecution was unnecessary, and that of the defending counsel unavailing. He was unanimously condemned to have his head cut off, and not a voice was raised in sympathy, in the courtroom or elsewhere. Heavy-shouldered and bull-necked, he had a huge, flat face, all jaw and no forehead, with small, half-closed, dull-staring eyes. Even had there been a doubt as to his guilt, his brutish aspect would have caused any sensitive jury to condemn him. Throughout the trial he stayed motionless, seemingly indifferent and uncomprehending.

"Dermuche," asked the presiding judge, "are you sorry for what you did?"

"Well, yes and no, your Honor," said Dermuche. "I am, and then again, I'm not."

"Try to make yourself more clear. Do you feel any remorse?"

"Pardon, your Honor?"

"Don't you know what the word 'remorse' means? Have you no feeling of distress when you think of your victims?"

"I feel all right, your Honor, thanking you all the same."

Only at one moment during the trial did Dermuche display any interest, and this was when the prosecution produced the gramophone record. Leaning over the edge of the dock he gazed at it steadfastly, and when the gramophone, set in motion by the clerk, ground out the refrain, a smile of great gentleness passed over his dull, heavy face.

In the condemned cell he waited calmly for the day of execution, seemingly untroubled by the prospect. He never spoke of it to the warders entering the cell. Indeed, he had no desire to talk to them, and merely replied politely to the questions put to him. His sole occupation was to hum the magical refrain that had driven him to murder, and he knew it badly. His was a very slow memory, and perhaps it was his exasperation at being unable to recapture it which had taken him, on a September evening, to the modest villa in Nogent-sur-Mare. Three persons of small independent means lived in the villa, two old maids and an uncle, decorated with the Legion of Honor, who felt the cold. Every Sunday, at the end of the midday meal, the elder of the two sisters wound up the gramophone. In fine weather they kept the dining-room window open, and for three years Dermuche had known enchanted summers. Crouched at the foot of the villa wall he listened to that Sunday melody which during the ensuing week he sought to fix wholly in his memory, without ever being completely successful in doing so. But with the onset of autumn the uncle who felt the cold caused the window to be shut, and thereafter the music sounded only for persons of independent means. For three years in succession Dermuche had lived through the long months of deprivation, without music and without rapture. Little by little the refrain escaped him, diminishing day by day, until by the end of winter nothing was left of it but the longing. The fourth year he could not endure the thought of that long period of waiting, and so he broke into the villa. The police found him there next morning, listening to the song of the gramophone record in company with the three dead bodies.

For a month he had it by heart, but by the time the trial came on he had forgotten it again. Now, in the condemned cell, he gathered together the fragments restored to him by the playing of the record during the trial, but which every day became more uncertain. *Tum-tum-ti-tum,* hummed the condemned man from morning till night.

The prison chaplain visited Dermuche and found him filled with good will. He would have liked it better, however, if the poor wretch had shown himself more receptive, so that the words of consolation entered his heart. Dermuche listened with the docility of a tree, but neither his brief replies nor his expressionless face afforded any evidence that he was interested in his soul's salvation, or even that he possessed a soul. Nevertheless, one day in December, when he was talking of the Holy Virgin and the angels, the chaplain thought he caught a little gleam of light in those dull eyes—so fugitive, however, that he was not sure if he had really seen it. At the end of the interview Dermuche asked abruptly: "And the little Jesus, is he still alive?" The chaplain did not hesitate. No doubt he should have replied that the infant Jesus had once lived, but that, since he had died on the cross at the age of thirty-three, it was not possible to speak of him in the present tense. But Dermuche was so thick-headed that it was difficult to get him to understand. The fable of the infant Jesus was more within his range and might open his heart to the light of the sacred truths. The chaplain told the story of how the Son of God had elected to be born in a stable, between the ox and the ass.

"You see, Dermuche, it was to show that he loved the poor and had come for their sake. He might equally well have chosen to be born in a prison, among the most unhappy of men."

"Yes, sir, I see. In fact, Jesus might have been born in this cell I'm in, but he wouldn't have wanted to be born in a villa."

The chaplain contented himself with a wag of the head. Dermuche's logic was unassailable, but it was related rather too narrowly to his own particular case, and seemed unlikely to lead him into the way of repentance. Having thus nodded non-committally, the chaplain went on to tell him about the magi, the slaughter of innocents, the flight, and finally how the infant Jesus, when his beard was grown, had died crucified between two thieves to open the gates of heaven to mankind.

"Only think, Dermuche. The soul of the good thief must have been the first of all human souls to enter Paradise, and that was not due to accident, it was because God wished to show us what every sinner may expect of His mercy. For Him even the greatest crimes are no more than the accidents of life. . . ."

But for some time past Dermuche had not been following the chaplain's narrative, and the story of the good thief seemed to him as obscure as the miracle of the loaves and fishes.

"And so then little Jesus went back to his manger?"

He could think only of the infant Jesus. The chaplain left the cell reflecting that this murderer possessed no more understanding than a child. He even questioned whether Dermuche could be held responsible for his crime, and he prayed God to have mercy on him.

"A child's soul in a laborer's body. . . . He killed those three old people without malice, just as a child cuts open its doll, or pulls off its legs. A child that doesn't know its own strength. An unhappy child and nothing more. And the proof is that he believes in the infant Jesus."

A few days later, paying Dermuche another visit, the chaplain asked the warder who opened the cell door:

"What's that he's singing?"

The male voice of Dermuche, like a deep-toned bell, could be heard incessantly repeating, *tum-tum-ti-tum.*

"He never stops that *tum-tum-tum* of his," said the warder. "If only it sounded like something it wouldn't be so bad, but it isn't even a tune."

This apparent lightness of heart, on the part of a condemned man who had not yet come to terms with Heaven, was disturbing to the chaplain. He found Dermuche livelier than usual. His brutish face had an expression of gentle alertness, and through the half-closed lids there shone a gleam of laughter. Moreover, he was almost talkative.

"What's the weather like outside today, sir?"

"It's snowing, my son."

"Well, that doesn't matter. The snow won't stop him. A fat lot he cares about the snow."

Once again the chaplain talked of God's mercy and the light of repentance, but the condemned man constantly interrupted him with questions about the infant Jesus, so that his exhortations were without effect.

"Does little Jesus know everybody? Is little Jesus the boss in Paradise? Would you say, sir, that little Jesus likes music?"

The chaplain finally found himself unable to get a word in edgeways. As he turned towards the door Dermuche thrust into his hand a sheet of paper folded in four.

"It's my letter to little Jesus," he said with a smile.

The chaplain took it and read it a few minutes later.

"Dear little Jesus," the letter ran. "This is asking you a favor. My name is Dermuche. It will soon be Christmas. I know you don't mind about me doing those three old geezers in Nogent. You wouldn't have wanted to be born in the house of people like that. I'm not asking for anything here on earth, seeing it won't be long before I have my chips. All I ask is, when I get to Heaven can I have my gramophone record? Thanking you in advance, and good luck to you—Dermuche."

The priest was horrified by the letter, which revealed all too clearly how impervious the murderer was to the idea of repentance.

"It is true," he reflected, "that the man is an innocent possessing no more discernment than a newborn babe. The trust he places in the infant Jesus bears sufficient witness to his childlike simplicity. But when he appears at the Seat of Judgment with three murders on his conscience, and no vestige of repentance, even God will be able to do nothing for him. Yet his small soul is as pure as the waters of a spring."

That evening he went to the prison chapel, and after having prayed for Dermuche, placed his letter in the plaster cradle of the infant Jesus.

At dawn on the 24th December, Christmas Eve, a party of well-dressed gentlemen accompanied the warders into the condemned cell. Their eyes still heavy with sleep, stomachs rumbling and mouths suppressing yawns, they paused at a short distance from the bed, seeking in the pallid early light to make out the shape of a body stretched beneath the coverings. The blankets moved feebly and a faint wail came from the bed. The Public Prosecutor felt a shiver pass down his spine. The Governor of the prison straightened his black tie and moved apart from the group. Shooting his cuffs he sought a posture appropriate to the occasion, and with his head inclined forward, shoulders rounded and hands clasped in front of his fly-buttons, he said in a theatrical voice:

"You must be brave, Dermuche. Your appeal has failed."

Another wail answered him, louder and more insistent than the first, but Dermuche did not move. He seemed to be buried even to his hair, and nothing of him emerged from the blankets.

"Come, Dermuche, you mustn't keep us waiting," said the Governor. "Do show a little co-operation, just for once."

A warder moved forward to shake the condemned man. He bent over the bed, then straightened himself and turned to the Governor with an air of astonishment.

"Why, what's the matter?"

"I don't know, sir. The bedclothes are moving, and yet . . ."

A long wail of heart-rending poignancy came from the blankets. With an abrupt movement the warder stripped them off the bed and then uttered a sharp exclamation. The others, who had pressed forward, in their turn uttered a cry of stupefaction. In place of Dermuche, on the uncovered bed, lay an infant a few months old. It seemed pleased to find itself in the light, and gazed placidly smiling at the visitors.

"What does this mean?" shouted the Governor, turning to the chief warder. "Have you let the prisoner escape?"

"It's impossible, sir. I made my last round three-quarters of an hour ago, and I'm positive I saw Dermuche in his bed."

Purple with fury, the Governor abused his subordinates, threatening them with the direst sanctions. The chaplain, meanwhile, had sunk to his knees and was offering thanks to God, the Holy Virgin, St. Joseph, Providence and the infant Jesus. But no one paid any attention to him.

"God almighty," cried the Governor, bending over the child, "will you look at that? It's got the same tattoo-marks as Dermuche on its chest!"

The others leaned over in their turn. The child had two pictures tattooed on either side of is chest, a woman's head on one side and a dog's head on the other. Dermuche had had exactly the same, even to their relative size. The warders all confirmed it. There was a long silence.

"I am perhaps mistaken," said M. Leboeuf, the Public Prosecutor, "but the child seems to me to be as much like Dermuche as a child that age can be like a man of thirty-three. Look at the big head, the flat face, the low forehead, the small, slit-eyes and even the shape of the nose. Don't you agree?" And he turned to M. Bridon, counsel for the defense.

"There does certainly seem to be a resemblance," said M. Bridon.

"Dermuche had a brown birthmark on the back of one thigh," the chief warder said.

They examined the child's leg and found the same thing.

"Fetch me the condemned man's finger-prints," said the Governor. "We'll see how those compare."

The chief warder went off at the double. While they awaited his return the others sought to find some rational explanation for the metamorphosis of Dermuche, which none could any longer doubt. The Governor alone took no part in the conversation but paced nervously up and down the cell. When the infant, alarmed by the sound of voices, began to cry, he advanced to the bedside and said in a threatening voice:

"You wait, my lad. I'll give you something to cry about!"

M. Leboeuf, who had seated himself beside the child, looked up at him with an intrigued expression.

"Do you really think this is your murderer?" he asked.

"I hope so. In any case, we shall soon know."

Confronted by this exquisite miracle, the chaplain continued to give thanks to God, his eyes damp with tenderness as he gazed at the virtually divine infant lying between Leboeuf and the Governor. He wondered a little anxiously what was to happen now, but concluded with confidence, "It will be as if the infant Jesus decides."

When the comparison of finger-prints had confirmed the extraordinary metamorphosis the Governor gave a sigh of relief and rubbed his hands.

"Well, now let's get on with it," he said. "We've simply been wasting time. Come along, Dermuche. Come along."

A murmur of protest arose in the cell, and M. Bridon cried indignantly:

"You surely can't intend to execute a babe in arms! It would be a hideous thing to do, utterly monstrous. Even if we admit the fact of Dermuche's guilt, and that he deserved the death sentence, we have surely no need to plead the innocence of a newly born infant."

"I can't go into those details," answered the Governor. "Is this Dermuche, or isn't it? Did he murder three people in Nogent-sur-Marne? Was he condemned to death? The law applies to everyone and I don't want any trouble. The scaffold has been erected and the guillotine was set up more than an hour ago. This talk about the innocence of the newly born is merely tiresome. At that rate anyone could escape justice simply by turning themselves into an infant. It would be a bit too easy!"

The defending counsel, with a maternal gesture, had drawn the covers back over the dimpled body of his client. The infant, responding to the warmth, laughed and crowed with pleasure, and the Governor looked coldly at it, finding this manifestation of gaiety out of place.

"You note the cynicism," he said. "He means to brazen it out to the end."

"My dear Governor," said the chaplain, "is it possible that you cannot see in this episode the hand of God?"

"Perhaps, but that makes no difference. It's certainly nothing to do with me. It isn't God who gave me my job or who is responsible for my advancement. I've had my instructions, and I intend to carry them out." The Governor turned to the Public Prosecutor. "Don't you agree that I'm entirely right?"

M. Leboeuf took time for thought before giving his opinion.

"Undoubtedly your position is logically sound. It would be profoundly unjust for a murderer to be privileged to begin his life again instead of paying the just penalty of his crime. On the other hand, the execution of an infant is a rather ticklish matter. I think you would be wise to consult your superiors."

"I know them," said the Governor. "They'll be annoyed with me for putting them in an embarrassing position. However, I'll ring them up."

The high officials concerned had not yet arrived at the Ministry. The Governor had to ring up their homes. Being still only half awake they were not in the best of tempers. The metamorphosis of Dermuche seemed to them a treacherous stratagem aimed directly at themselves, and they were highly indignant. The fact remained, none the less, that the condemned man was now a babe in arms. But the times were harsh, and they feared for their advancement if they should be suspected of lenience. Having agreed among themselves they resolved that—"the fact that the murderer has somewhat shrunk beneath the burden of remorse, or from no matter what cause, can in no way be allowed to divert the course of Justice."

Accordingly the condemned man's toilet was proceeded with—that is to say, he was wrapped in one of the bed coverings and the soft down on the back of his neck was shaved off. The chaplain then took the precaution of baptising him. It was he who carried him in his arms to the machine erected in the prison courtyard.

As they returned from the place of execution he told counsel for the defense of Dermuche's letter to the infant Jesus.

"God could not allow a murderer entirely untouched by remorse to enter Paradise. But Dermuche had hope on his side, and his love of the infant Jesus. So God effaced his life as a sinner and restored him to the age of innocence."

"But if his life as a sinner was effaced, then Dermuche committed no crime and those people in Nogent were never murdered."

Wanting to be quite sure on this point, the Counsel immediately went to Nogent-sur-Marne. Upon arriving there he asked to be directed to the house where the crime had been committed, but no one had heard of any crime. He had no difficulty, however, in finding the house where the two Mademoiselles Bridaine lived with their uncle who suffered from the cold. The three old people received him at first with mistrust, and after being reassured, complained to him that that very night someone had stolen a gramophone record lying on the dining-room table.

THOMAS MANN

Disorder and Early Sorrow

THE principal dish at dinner had been croquettes made of turnip greens. So there follows a trifle, concocted out of one of those dessert powders we use nowadays, that taste like almond soap. Xaver, the youthful manservant, in his outgrown striped jacket, white woolen gloves, and yellow sandals, hands it round, and the "big folk" take this opportunity to remind their father, tactfully, that company is coming today.

The "big folk" are two, Ingrid and Bert. Ingrid is brown-eyed, eighteen, and perfectly delightful. She is on the eve of her exams, and will probably pass them, if only because she knows how to wind masters, and even headmasters, round her finger. She does not, however, mean to use her certificate once she gets it; having leanings towards the stage, on the ground of her ingratiating smile, her equally ingratiating voice, and a marked and irresistible talent for burlesque. Bert is blond and seventeen. He intends to get done with school somehow, anyhow, and fling himself into the arms of life. He will be a dancer, or a cabaret actor, possible even a waiter—but not a waiter anywhere else save at the Cairo, the night-club, whither he has once already taken flight, at five in the morning, and been brought back crestfallen. Bert bears a strong resemblance to the youthful manservant Xaver Kleinsgutl, of about the same age as himself; not because he looks common—in features he is strikingly like his father, Professor Cornelius—but by reason of an approximation of types, due in its turn to far-reaching compromises in matters of dress and bearing generally. Both lads wear their heavy hair very long on top, with a cursory parting in the middle, and give their heads the same characteristic toss to throw it off the forehead. When one of them leaves the house, by the garden gate, bareheaded in all weathers, in a blouse rakishly girt with a leather strap, and sheers off bent well over with his head on one side; or else mounts his push-bike—Xaver makes free with his employers', of both sexes, or even, in acutely irresponsible mood, with the Professor's own—Dr. Cornelius from his bedroom window cannot, for the life of him, tell whether he is looking at his son or his servant. Both, he thinks, look like young moujiks. And both are impassioned cigarette-smokers, though Bert has not the means to compete with Xaver, who smokes as many as thirty a day, of a brand named after a popular cinema star. The big folk call their father and mother "old folk"—not behind their backs, but as a form of address and in all affection: "Hullo, old folks," they will say; though Cornelius is only forty-seven years old and his wife eight years younger. And the Professor's parents, who lead in his household the humble and hesitant life of the really old, are on the big folk's lips the "ancients." As for the "little folk," Ellie and Snapper, who take their meals upstairs with blue-faced Ann—so-called because of her prevailing facial hue—Ellie and Snapper follow their mother's example and address their father by his first name, Abel. Unutterably comic it sounds, in its pert, confiding familiarity; particularly on the lips, in the sweet accents, of five-year-old Eleanor, who is the image of Frau Cornelius's baby pictures and whom the Professor loves above everything else in the world.

"Darling old thing," says Ingrid affably, laying her large but shapely hand on his, as he presides in proper middle-class style over the family table, with her on his left and the mother opposite: "Parent mine, may I ever so gently jog your memory, for you have probably forgotten: this is the afternoon we were to have our little jollification, our turkey-trot with eats to match. You haven't a thing to do but just bear up and not funk it; everything will be over by nine o'clock."

"Oh—ah!" says Cornelius, his face falling. "Good!" he goes on, and nods his head to show himself in harmony with the inevitable. "I only meant—is this really the day? Thursday, yes. How time flies! Well, what time are they coming?"

"Half past four they'll be dropping in, I should say," answers Ingrid, to whom her brother leaves the major role in all dealings with the father. Upstairs, while he is resting, he will hear scarcely anything, and from seven to eight he takes his walk. He can slip out by the terrace if he likes.

"Tut!" says Cornelius deprecatingly, as who should say: "You exaggerate." But Bert puts in: "It's the one evening in the week Wanja doesn't have to play. Any other night he'd have to leave by half past six, which would be painful for all concerned."

Wanja is Ivan Herzl, the celebrated young leading man at the Stadttheater. Bert and Ingrid are on intimate terms with him, they often visit him in his dressing-room and have tea. He is an artist of the modern school, who stands on the stage in strange and, to the Professor's mind, utterly affected dancing attitudes, and shrieks lamentably. To a professor of history, all highly repugnant; but Bert has entirely succumbed to Herzl's influence, blackens the lower rim of his eyelids—despite painful but fruitless scenes with the father—and with youthful carelessness of the ancestral anguish declares that not only will he take Herzl for his model if he becomes a dancer, but in case he turns out to be a waiter at the Cairo he means to walk precisely thus.

Cornelius slightly raises his brows and makes his son a little bow—indicative of the unassumingness and self-abnegation that befits his age. You could not call it a mocking bow or suggestive in any special sense. Bert may refer it to himself or equally to his so talented friend.

"Who else is coming?" next inquires the master of the house. They mention various people, names all more or less familiar, from the city, from the suburban colony, from Ingrid's school. They still have some telephoning to do, they say. They have to phone Max. This is Max Hergesell, an engineering student; Ingrid utters his name in the nasal drawl which according to her is the traditional intonation of all the Hergesells. She goes on to parody it in the most abandonedly funny and lifelike way, and the parents laugh until they nearly choke over the wretched trifle. For even in these times when something funny happens people have to laugh.

From time to time the telephone bell rings in the Professor's study, and the big folk run across, knowing it is their affair. Many people had to give up their telephones the last time the price rose, but so far the Corneliuses have been able to keep theirs, just as they have kept their villa, which was built before the war, by dint of the salary Cornelius draws as professor of history—a million marks, and more or less adequate to the chances and changes of postwar life. The house is comfortable, even elegant, though sadly in need of repairs that cannot be made for lack of materials, and at present disfigured by iron stoves with long pipes. Even so, it is still the proper setting of the upper middle class, though they themselves look odd enough in it, with their worn and turned clothing and altered way of life. The children, of course, know nothing else; to them it is normal and regular, they belong by birth to the "villa proletariat."

The problem of clothing troubles them not at all. They and their like have evolved a costume to fit the time, by poverty out of taste for innovation: in summer it consists of scarcely more than a belted linen smock and sandals. The middle-class parents find things rather more difficult.

The big folk's table-napkins hang over their chair-backs, they talk with their friends over the telephone. These friends are the invited guests who have rung up to accept or decline or arrange; and the conversation is carried on in the jargon of the clan, full of slang and high spirits, of which the old folk understand hardly a word. These consult together meantime about the hospitality to be offered to the impending guests. The Professor displays a middle-class ambitiousness: he wants to serve a sweet—or something that looks like a sweet—after the Italian salad and brown-bread sandwiches. But Frau Cornelius says that would be going too far. The guests would not expect it, she is sure—and the big folk, returning once more to their trifle, agree with her.

The mother of the family is of the same general type as Ingrid, though not so tall. She is languid; the fantastic difficulties of the housekeeping have broken and worn her. She really ought to go and take a cure, but feels incapable; the floor is always swaying under her feet, and everything seems upside down. She speaks of what is uppermost in her mind: the eggs, they simply must be bought today. Six thousand marks apiece they are, and just so many are to be had on this one day of the week at one single shop fifteen minutes' journey away. Whatever else they do, the big folk must go and fetch them immediately after luncheon, with Danny, their neighbor's son, who will soon be calling for them; and Xaver Kleinsgutl will don civilian garb and attend his young master and mistress. For no single household is allowed more than five eggs a week; therefore the young people will enter the shop singly, one after another, under assumed names, and thus wring twenty eggs from the shopkeeper for the Cornelius family. This enterprise is the sporting event of the week for all participants, not excepting the moujik Kleinsgutl, and most of all for Ingrid and Bert, who delight in misleading and mystifying their fellow-men and would revel in the performance even if it did not achieve one single egg. They adore impersonating fictitious characters; they love to sit in a bus and carry on long lifelike conversations in a dialect which they otherwise never speak, the most commonplace dialogue about politics and people and the price of food, while the whole bus listens open-mouthed to this incredibly ordinary prattle, though with a dark suspicion all the while that something is wrong somewhere. The conversation waxes ever more shameless, it enters into revolting detail about these people who do not exist. Ingrid can make her voice sound ever so common and twittering and shrill as she impersonates a shop-girl with an illegitimate child, said child being a son with sadistic tendencies, who lately out in the country treated a cow with such unnatural cruelty that no Christian could have borne to see it. Bert nearly explodes at her twittering, but restrains himself and displays a grisly sympathy; he and the unhappy shop-girl entering into a long, stupid, depraved, and shuddery conversation over the particular morbid cruelty involved; until an old gentleman opposite, sitting with his ticket folded between his index finger and his seal ring, can bear it no more and makes public protest against the nature of the themes these young folk are discussing with such particularity. He uses the Greek plural: "themata." Whereat Ingrid pretends to be dissolving in tears, and Bert behaves as though his wrath against the old gentleman was with difficulty being held in check and would probably burst out before long. He clenches his fists, he gnashes his teeth, he shakes from head to foot; and the unhappy old gentleman, whose intentions had been of the best, hastily leaves the bus at the next stop.

Such are the diversions of the big folk. The telephone plays a prominent part in them: they ring up any and everybody—members of government, opera singers, dignitaries of the Church—in the character of shop assistants, or perhaps as Lord or Lady Doolittle. They are only with difficulty persuaded that they have the wrong number. Once they emptied their parents' card-tray and distributed its contents among the neighbors' letter-boxes, wantonly, yet not without enough impish sense of the fitness of things to make it highly upsetting, God only knowing why certain people should have called where they did.

Xaver comes in to clear away, tossing the hair out of his eyes. Now that he has taken off his gloves you can see the yellow chain-ring on his left hand. And as the Professor finishes his watery eight-thousand-mark beer and lights a cigarette, the little folk can be heard scrambling down the stair, coming, by established custom, for their after-dinner call on Father and Mother. They storm the dining-room, after a struggle with the latch, clutched by both pairs of little hands at once; their clumsy small feet twinkle over the carpet, in red felt slippers with the socks falling down on them. With prattle and shoutings each makes for his own place: Snapper to Mother, to climb on her lap, boast of all he has eaten, and thump his fat little tum; Ellie to her Abel, so much hers because she is so very much his; because she consciously luxuriates in the deep tenderness—like all deep feeling, concealing a melancholy strain—with which he holds her small form embraced; in the love in his eyes as he kisses her little fairy hand or the sweet brow with its delicate tracery of tiny blue veins.

The little folk look like each other, with the strong undefined likeness of brother and sister. In clothing and hair-cut they are twins. Yet they are sharply distinguished after all, and quite on sex lines. It is a little Adam and a little Eve. Not only is Snapper the sturdier and more compact, he appears consciously to emphasize his four-year-old masculinity in speech, manner, and carriage, lifting his shoulders and letting the little arms hang down quite like a young American athlete, drawing down his mouth when he talks and seeking to give his voice a gruff and forthright ring. But all this masculinity is the result of effort rather than natively his. Born and brought up in these desolate, distracted times, he has been endowed by them with an unstable and hypersensitive nervous system and suffers greatly under life's disharmonies. He is prone to sudden anger and out-bursts of bitter tears, stamping his feet at every trifle; for this reason he is his mother's special nursling and care. His round, round eyes are chest-nut brown and already inclined to squint, so that he will need glasses in the near future. His little nose is long, the mouth small—the father's nose and mouth they are, more plainly than ever since the Professor shaved his pointed beard and goes smooth-faced. The pointed beard had become impossible—even professors must make some concession to the changing times.

But the little daughter sits on her father's knee, his Eleonorchen, his little Eve, so much more gracious a little being, so much sweeter-faced than her brother—and he holds his cigarette away from her while she fin-gers his glasses with her dainty wee hands. The lenses are divided for reading and distance, and each day they tease her curiosity afresh.

At bottom he suspects that his wife's partiality may have a firmer basis than his own: that Snapper's refractory masculinity perhaps is solider stuff than his own little girl's more explicit charm and grace. But the heart will not be commanded, that he knows; and once and for all his heart be-longs to the little one, as it has since the day she came, since the first time he saw her. Almost always when he holds her in his arms he remembers that first time: remembers the sunny room in the Women's Hospital, where Ellie first saw the light, twelve years after Bert was born. He remembers how he drew near, the mother smiling the while, and cautiously put aside the canopy of the diminutive bed that stood beside the large one. There lay the little miracle among the pillows: so well formed, so encompassed, as it were, with the harmony of sweet proportions, with little hands that even then, though so much tinier, were beautiful as now; with wide-open eyes blue as the sky and brighter than the sunshine—and almost in that very second he felt himself captured and held fast. This was love at first sight, love everlasting: a feeling unknown, unhoped for, unexpected—in so far as it could be a matter of conscious awareness; it took entire possession of him, and he understood, with joyous amazement, that this was for life.

But he understood more. He knows, does Dr. Cornelius, that there is something not quite right about this feeling, so unaware, so undreamed of, so involuntary. He has a shrewd suspicion that it is not by accident it has so utterly mastered him and bound itself up with his existence; that he had —even subconsciously—been preparing for it, or, more precisely, been prepared for it. There is, in short, something in him which at a given mo-ment was ready to issue in such a feeling; and this something, highly ex-traordinary to relate, is his essence and quality as a professor of history.

Dr. Cornelius, however, does not actually say this, even to himself; he merely realizes it, at odd times, and smiles a private smile. He knows that history professors do not love history because it is something that comes to pass, but only because it is something that *has* come to pass; that they hate a revolution like the present one because they feel it is lawless, incoherent, irrelevant—in a word, unhistoric; that their hearts belong to the coherent, disciplined, historic past. For the temper of timelessness, the temper of eternity—thus the scholar communes with himself when he takes his walk by the river before supper—that temper broods over the past; and it is a temper much better suited to the nervous system of a history professor than are the excesses of the present. The past is immortalized; that is to say, it is dead; and death is the root of all godliness and all abiding significance. Dr. Cornelius, walking alone in the dark, has a profound insight into this truth. It is this conservative instinct of his, his sense of the eternal, that has found in his love for his little daughter a way to save itself from the wounding inflicted by the times. For father love, and a little child on its mother's breast—are not these timeless, and thus very, very holy and beautiful? Yet Cornelius, pondering there in the dark, descries something not perfectly right and good in his love. Theoretically, in the interests of science, he admits it to himself. There is something ulterior about it, in the nature of it; that something is hostility, hostility against the history of today, which is still in the making and thus not history at all, in behalf of the genuine history that has already happened—that is to say, death. Yes, passing strange though all this is, yet it is true; true in a sense, that is. His devotion to this priceless little morsel of life and new growth has something to do with death, it clings to death as against life; and that is neither right nor beautiful—in a sense. Though only the most fanatical asceticism could be capable, on no other ground than such casual scientific perception, of tearing this purest and most precious of feelings out of his heart.

He holds his darling on his lap and her slim rosy legs hang down. He raises his brows as he talks to her, tenderly, with a half-teasing note of respect, and listens enchanted to her high, sweet little voice calling him Abel. He exchanges a look with the mother, who is caressing her Snapper and reading him a gentle lecture. He must be more reasonable, he must learn self-control; today again, under the manifold exasperations of life, he has given way to rage and behaved like a howling dervish. Cornelius casts a mistrustful glance at the big folk now and then, too; he thinks it not unlikely they are not unaware of those scientific preoccupations of his evening walks. If such be the case they do not show it. They stand there leaning their arms on their chair-backs and with a benevolence not untinctured with irony look on at the parental happiness.

The children's frocks are of a heavy, brick-red stuff, embroidered in modern "arty" style. They once belonged to Ingrid and Bert and are precisely alike, save that little knickers come out beneath Snapper's smock. And both have their hair bobbed. Snapper's is a streaky blond, inclined to turn dark. It is bristly and sticky and looks for all the world like a droll, badly fitting wig. But Ellie's is chestnut brown, glossy and fine as silk, as pleasing as her whole little personality. It covers her ears—and these ears are not a pair, one of them being the right size, the other distinctly too large. Her father will sometimes uncover this little abnormality and exclaim over it as though he had never noticed it before, which both makes Ellie giggle and covers her with shame. Her eyes are now golden brown, set far apart and with sweet gleams in them—such a clear and lovely look! The brows above are blond; the nose still unformed, with thick nostrils and almost circular holes; the mouth large and expressive, with a beautifully arching and mobile upper lip. When she laughs, dimples come in her cheeks and she shows her teeth like loosely strung pearls. So far she has lost but one tooth, which her father gently twisted out with his handkerchief after it had grown very wobbling. During this small operation she had paled and trembled very much. Her cheeks have the softness proper to her years, but they are not chubby; indeed, they are rather concave, due to her facial structure, with its somewhat prominent jaw. On one, close to the soft fall of her hair, is a downy freckle.

Ellie is not too well pleased with her looks—a sign that already she troubles about such things. Sadly she thinks it is best to admit it once for all, her face is "homely"; though the rest of her, "on the other hand," is not bad at all. She loves expressions like "on the other hand"; they sound choice and grown-up to her, and she likes to string them together, one after the other: "very likely," "probably," "after all." Snapper is self-critical too, though more in the moral sphere: he suffers from remorse for his attacks of rage and considers himself a tremendous sinner. He is quite certain that heaven is not for such as he; he is sure to go to "the bad place" when he dies, and no persuasions will convince him to the contrary—as that God sees the heart and gladly makes allowances. Obstinately he shakes his head, with the comic, crooked little peruke, and vows there is no place for him in heaven. When he has a cold he is immediately quite choked with mucus; rattles and rumbles from top to toe if you even look at him; his temperature flies up at once and he simply puffs. Nursy is pessimistic on the score of his constitution: such fat-blooded children as he might get a stroke any minute. Once she even thought she saw the moment at hand: Snapper had been in one of his berserker rages, and in the ensuing fit of penitence stood himself in the corner with his back to the room. Suddenly Nursy noticed that his face had gone all blue, far bluer, even, than her own. She raised the alarm, crying out that the child's all too rich blood had at length brought him to his final hour; and Snapper, to his vast astonishment, found himself, so far from being rebuked for evil-doing, encompassed in tenderness and anxiety—until it turned out that his color was not caused by apoplexy but by the distempering on the nursery wall, which had come off on his tear-wet face.

Nursy has come downstairs too, and stands by the door, sleek-haired, owl-eyed, with her hands folded over her white apron, and a severely dignified manner born of her limited intelligence. She is very proud of the care and training she gives her nurslings and declares that they are "enveloping wonderfully." She has had seventeen suppurated teeth lately removed from her jaws and been measured for a set of symmetrical yellow ones in dark rubber gums; these now embellish her peasant face. She is obsessed with the strange conviction that these teeth of hers are the subject of general conversation, that, as it were, the sparrows on the housetops chatter of them. "Everybody knows I've had a false set put in," she will say; "there has been a great deal of foolish talk about them." She is much given to dark hints and veiled innuendo: speaks, for instance, of a certain Dr. Bleifuss, whom every child knows, and "there are even some in the house who pretend to be him." All one can do with talk like this is charitably to pass it over in silence. But she teaches the children nursery rhymes: gems like:

> "Puff, puff, here comes the train
> Puff, puff, toot, toot,
> Away it goes again."

Or that gastronomical jingle, so suited, in its sparseness, to the times, and yet seemingly with a blitheness of its own:

> "Monday we begin the week,
> Tuesday there's a bone to pick.
> Wednesday we're half way through,
> Thursday what a great to-do!
> Friday we eat what fish we're able,
> Saturday we dance round the table.
> Sunday brings us pork and greens—
> Here's a feast for kings and queens!"

Also a certain four-line stanza with a romantic appeal, unutterable and unuttered:

> "Open the gate, open the gate
> And let the carriage drive in.
> Who is it in the carriage sits?
> A lordly sir with golden hair."

Or, finally that ballad about golden-haired Marianne who sat on a, sat on a, sat on a stone, and combed out her, combed out her, combed out her hair; and about bloodthirsty Rudolph, who pulled out a, pulled out a, pulled out a knife—and his ensuing direful end. Ellie enunciates all these ballads charmingly, with her mobile little lips, and sings them in her sweet little voice—much better than Snapper. She does everything better than he does, and he pays her honest admiration and homage and obeys her in all things except when visited by one of his attacks. Sometimes she teaches him, instructs him upon the birds in the picture-book and tells him their proper names: "This is a chaffinch, Buddy, this is a bullfinch, this is a cowfinch." He has to repeat them after her. She gives him medical instruction too, teaches him the names of diseases, such as infammation of the lungs, infammation of the blood, infammation of the air. If he does not pay attention and cannot say the words after her, she stands him in the corner. Once she even boxed his ears, but was so ashamed that she stood herself in the corner for a long time. Yes, they are fast friends, two souls with but a single thought, and have all their adventures in common. They come home from a walk and relate as with one voice that they have seen two moollies and a teenty-weenty baby calf. They are on familiar terms with the kitchen, which consists of Xaver and the ladies Hinterhofer, two sisters once of the lower middle class who, in these evil days, are reduced to living "*au pair*" as the phrase goes and officiating as cook and housemaid for their board and keep. The little ones have a feeling that Xaver and the Hinterhofers are on much the same footing with their father and mother as they are themselves. At least sometimes, when they have been scolded, they go downstairs and announce that the master and mistress are cross. But playing with the servants lacks charm compared with the joys of playing upstairs. The kitchen could never rise to the height of the games their father can invent. For instance, there is "four gentlemen taking a walk." When they play it Abel will crook his knees until he is the same height with themselves and go walking with them, hand in hand. They never get enough of this sport; they could walk round and round the dining-room a whole day on end, five gentlemen in all, counting the diminished Abel.

Then there is the thrilling cushion game. One of the children, usually Ellie, seats herself, unbeknownst to Abel, in his seat at table. Still as a mouse she awaits his coming. He draws near with his head in the air, descanting in loud, clear tones upon the surpassing comfort of his chair; and sits down on top of Ellie. "What's this, what's this?" says he. And bounces about, deaf to the smothered giggles exploding behind him. "Why have they put a cushion in my chair? And what a queer, hard, awkward-shaped cushion it is!" he goes on. "Frightfully uncomfortable to sit on!" And keeps pushing and bouncing about more and more on the astonishing cushion and clutching behind him into the rapturous giggling and squeaking, until at last he turns round, and the game ends with a magnificent climax of discovery and recognition. They might go through all this a hundred times without diminishing by an iota its power to thrill.

Today is no time for such joys. The imminent festivity disturbs the atmosphere, and besides there is work to be done, and, above all, the eggs to be got. Ellie has just time to recite "Puff, puff," and Cornelius to discover that her ears are not mates, when they are interrupted by the arrival of Danny, come to fetch Bert and Ingrid. Gaver, meantime, has exchanged his striped livery for an ordinary coat, in which he looks rather rough-and-ready, though as brisk and attractive as ever. So then Nursy and the children ascend to the upper regions, the Professor with draws to his study to read, as always after dinner, and his wife bends her energies upon the sandwiches and salad that must be prepared. And she has another errand as well. Before the young people arrive she has to take her shopping-basket and dash into town on her bicycle, to turn into provisions a sum of money she has in hand, which she dares not keep lest it lose all value.

Cornelius reads, leaning back in his chair, with his cigar between his middle and index fingers. First he reads Macaulay on the origin of the English public debt at the end of the seventeenth century; then an article in a French periodical on the rapid increase in the Spanish debt towards the end of the sixteenth. Both these for his lecture on the morrow. He intends to compare the astonishing prosperity which accompanied the phenomenon in England with its fatal effects a hundred years earlier in Spain, and to analyse the ethical and psychological grounds of the difference in results. For that will give him a chance to refer back from the England of William III, which is the actual subject in hand, to the time of Phillip II and the Counter-Reformation, which is his own special field. He has already written a valuable work on this period; it is much cited and got him his professorship. While his cigar burns down and gets strong, he excogitates a few pensive sentences in a key of gentle melancholy, to be delivered before his class next day: about the practically hopeless struggle carried on by the belated Philip against the whole trend of history: against the new, the kingdom-disrupting power of the Germanic ideal of freedom and individual liberty. And about the persistent, futile struggle of the aristocracy, condemned by God and rejected of man, against the forces of progress and change. He savors his sentences; keeps on polishing them while he puts back the books he has been using; then goes upstairs for the usual pause in his day's work, the hour with drawn blinds and closed eyes, which he so imperatively needs. But today, he recalls, he will rest under disturbed conditions, amid the bustle of preparations for the feast. He smiles to find his heart giving a mild flutter at the thought. Disjointed phrases on the theme of black-clad Philip and his times mingle with a confused consciousness that they will soon be dancing down below. For five minutes or so he falls asleep.

As he lies and rests he can hear the sound of the garden gate and the repeated ringing at the bell. Each time a little pang goes through him, of excitement and suspense, at the thought that the young people have begun to fill the floor below. And each time he smiles at himself again—though even his smile is slightly nervous, is tinged with the pleasurable anticipations people always feel before a party. At half past four—it is already dark—he gets up and washes at the washstand. The basin has been out of repair for two years. It is supposed to tip, but has broken away from its socket on one side and cannot be mended because there is nobody to mend it; neither replaced because no shop can supply another. So it has to be hung up above the vent and emptied by lifting in both hands and pouring out the water. Cornelius shakes his head over this basin, as he does several times a day—whenever, in fact, he has occasion to use it. He finishes his toilet with care, standing under the ceiling light to polish his glasses till they shine. Then he goes downstairs.

On his way to the dining-room he hears the gramophone already going, and the sound of voices. He puts on a polite, society air; at his tongue's end is the phrase he means to utter: "Pray don't let me disturb you," as he passes directly into the dining-room for his tea. "Pray don't let me disturb you"—it seems to him precisely the *mot juste;* towards the guests cordial and considerate, for himself a very bulwark.

The lower floor is lighted up, all the bulbs in the chandelier are burning save one that has burned out. Cornelius pauses on a lower step and surveys the entrance hall. It looks pleasant and cosy in the bright light, with its copy of Marées over the brick chimney-piece, its wainscoted walls—wainscoted in soft wood—and red-carpeted floor, where the guests stand in groups, chatting, each with his tea-cup and slice of bread-and-butter spread with anchovy paste. There is a festal haze, faint scents of hair and clothing and human breath come to him across the room, it is all characteristic and familiar and highly evocative. The door into the dressing-room is open, guests are still arriving.

A large group of people is rather bewildering at first sight. The Professor takes in only the general scene. He does not see Ingrid, who is standing just at the foot of the steps, in a dark silk frock with a pleated collar falling softly over the shoulders, and bare arms. She smiles up at him, nodding and showing her lovely teeth.

"Rested?" she asks, for his private ear. With a quite unwarranted start he recognizes her, and she presents some of her friends.

"May I introduce Herr Zuber?" she says. "And this is Fräulein Plaichinger."

Herr Zuber is insignificant. But Fräulein Plaichinger is a perfect Germania, blond and voluptuous, arrayed in floating draperies. She has a snub nose, and answers the Professor's salutation in the high, shrill pipe so many stout women have.

"Delighted to meet you," he says. "How nice of you to come! A class-mate of Ingrid's, I suppose?"

And Herr Zuber is a golfing partner of Ingrid's. He is in business; he works in his uncle's brewery. Cornelius makes a few jokes about the thin-ness of the beer and professes to believe that Herr Zuber could easily do something about the quality if he would. "But pray don't let me disturb you," he goes on, and turns towards the dining-room.

"There comes Max," says Ingrid. "Max, you sweep, what do you mean by rolling up at this time of day?" For such is the way they talk to each other, offensively to an older ear; of social forms, of hospitable warmth, there is no faintest trace. They all call each other by their first names.

A young man comes up to them out of the dressing-room and makes his bow; he has an expanse of white shirt-front and a little black string tie. He is as pretty as a picture, dark, with rosy cheeks, clean-shaven of course, but with just a sketch of side-whisker. Not a ridiculous or flashy beauty, not like a gypsy fiddler, but just charming to look at, in a winning, well-bred way, with kind dark eyes. He even wears his dinner-jacket a little awkwardly.

"Please don't scold me, Cornelia," he says; "it's the idiotic lectures." And Ingrid presents him to her father as Herr Hergesell.

Well, and so this is Herr Hergesell. He knows his manners, does Herr Hergesell, and thanks the master of the house quite ingratiatingly for his invitation as they shake hands. "I certainly seem to have missed the bus," says he jocosely. "Of course I have lectures today up to four o'clock; I would have; and after that I had to go home to change." Then he talks about his pumps, with which he has just been struggling in the dressing-room.

"I brought them with me in a bag," he goes on. "Mustn't tramp all over the carpet in our brogues—it's not done. Well, I was ass enough not to fetch along a shoe-horn, and I find I simply can't get in! What a sell! They are the tightest I've ever had, the numbers don't tell you a thing, and all the leather today is just cast iron. It's not leather at all. My poor finger"—he confidingly displays a redened digit and once more characterizes the whole thing as a "sell," and a putrid sell into the bargain. He really does talk just as Ingrid said he did, with a peculiar nasal drawl, not affectedly in the least, but merely because that is the way of all the Hergesells.

Dr. Cornelius says it is very careless of them not to keep a shoe-horn in the cloak-room and displays proper sympathy with the mangled finger. "But now you *really* must not let me disturb you any longer," he goes on. "*Auf wiedersehen!*" And he crosses the hall into the dining-room.

There are guests there too, drinking tea; the family table is pulled out. But the Professor goes at once to his own little upholstered corner with the electric light bulb above it—the nook where he usually drinks his tea.

His wife is sitting there talking with Bert and two other young men, one of them Herzl, whom Cornelius knows and greets; the other a typical "Wandervogel" named Möller, a youth who obviously neither owns nor cares to own the correct evening dress of the middle classes (in fact, there is no such thing any more), nor to ape the manners of a gentleman (and, in fact, there is no such thing any more either). He has a wilderness of hair, horn spectacles, and a long neck, and wears golf stockings and a belted blouse. His regular occupation, the Professor learns, is banking, but he is by way of being an amateur folk-lorist and collects folk-songs from all localities and in all languages. He sings them, too, and at Ingrid's command has brought his guitar; it is hanging in the dressing-room in an oil-cloth case. Herzl, the actor, is small and slight, but he has a strong growth of black beard, as you can tell by the thick coat of powder on his cheeks. His eyes are larger than life, with a deep and melancholy glow. He has put on rouge besides the powder—those dull carmine high-lights on the cheeks can be nothing but a cosmetic. "Queer," thinks the Professor. "You would think a man would be one thing or the other—not melancholic and use face paint at the same time. It's a psychological contradiction. How can a melancholy man rouge? But here we have a perfect illustration of the abnormality of the artist soul-form. It can make possible a contradiction like this—perhaps it even consists in the contradiction. All very interesting—and no reason whatever for not being polite to him. Politeness is a primitive convention—and legitimate. . . . Do take some lemon, Herr Hofschauspieler!"

Court actors and court theaters—there are no such things any more, really. But Herzl relishes the sound of the title, notwithstanding he is a revolutionary artist. This must be another contradiction inherent in his soul-form; so, at least, the Professor assumes, and he is probably right. The flattery he is guilty of is a sort of atonement for his previous hard thoughts about the rouge.

"Thank you so much—it's really too good of you, sir," says Herzl, quite embarrassed. He is so overcome that he almost stammers; only his perfect enunciation saves him. His whole bearing towards his hostess and the master of the house is exaggeratedly polite. It is almost as though he had a bad conscience in respect of his rouge; as though an inward compulsion had driven him to put it on, but now, seeing it through the Professor's eyes, he disapproves of it himself, and thinks, by an air of humility toward the whole of unrouged society, to mitigate its effect.

They drink their tea and chat: about Möller's folk-songs, about Basque folk-songs and Spanish folk-songs; from which they pass to the new production of *Don Carlos* at the Stadttheater, in which Herzl plays the title-role. He talks about his own rendering of the part and says he hopes his conception of the character has unity. They go on to criticize the rest of the cast, the setting, and the production as a whole; and Cornelius is struck, rather painfully, to find the conversation trending towards his own special province, back to Spain and the Counter-Reformation. He has done nothing at all to give it this turn, he is perfectly innocent, and hopes it does not look as though he had sought an occasion to play the professor. He wonders, and falls silent, feeling relieved when the little folk come up to the table. Ellie and Snapper have on their blue velvet Sunday frocks; they are permitted to partake in the festivities up to bed-time. They look shy and large-eyed as they say how-do-you-do to the strangers and, under pressure, repeat their names and ages. Herr Möller does nothing but gaze at them solemnly, but Herzl is simply ravished. He rolls his eyes up to heaven and puts his hands over his mouth; he positively blesses them. It all, no doubt, comes from his heart, but he is so addicted to theatrical methods of making an impression and getting an effect that both words and behaviour ring frightfully false. And even his enthusiasm for the little folk looks too much like part of his general craving to make up for the rouge on his cheeks.

The tea-table has meanwhile emptied of guests, and dancing is going on in the hall. The children run off, the Professor prepares to retire. "Go and enjoy yourselves," he says to Möller and Herzl, who have sprung from their chairs as he rises from his. They shake hands and he withdraws into his study, his peaceful kingdom, where he lets down the blinds, turns on the desk lamp, and sits down to his work.

It is work which can be done, if necessary, under disturbed conditions: nothing but a few letters and a few notes. Of course, Cornelius's mind wanders. Vague impressions float through it: Herr Hergesell's refractory pumps, the high pipe in that plump body of the Plaichinger female. As he writes, or leans back in his chair and stares into space, his thoughts go back to Herr Möller's collection of Basque folk-songs, to Herzl's posings and humility, to "his" Carlos and the court of Philip II. There is something strange, he thinks, about conversations. They are so ductile, they will flow of their own accord in the direction of one's dominating interest. Often and often he has seen this happen. And while he is thinking, he is listening to the sounds next door—rather subdued, he finds them. He hears only voices, no sound of footsteps. The dancers do not glide or circle round the room; they merely walk about over the carpet, which does not hamper their movements in the least. Their way of holding each other is quite different and strange, and they move to the strains of the gramophone, to the weird music of the new world. He concentrates on the music and makes out that it is a jazz-band record, with various percussion instruments and the clack and clatter of castanets, which, however, are not even faintly suggestive of Spain, but merely jazz like the rest. No, not Spain. . . . His thoughts are back at their old round.

Half an hour goes by. It occurs to him it would be no more than friendly to go and contribute a box of cigarettes to the festivities next door.

Too bad to ask the young people to smoke their own—though they have probably never thought of it. He goes into the empty dining-room, and takes a box from his supply in the cupboard: not the best ones, nor yet the brand he himself prefers, but a certain long, thin kind he is not averse to getting rid of—after all, they are nothing but youngsters. He takes the box into the hall, holds it up with a smile, and deposits it on the mantel-shelf. After which he gives a look round and returns to his own room.

There comes a lull in dance and music. The guests stand about the room in groups or round the table at the window or are seated in a circle by the fireplace. Even the built-in stairs, with their worn velvet carpet, are crowded with young folk as in an amphitheater: Max Hergesell is there, leaning back with one elbow on the step above and gesticulating with his free hand as he talks to the shrill, voluptuous Plaichinger. The floor of the hall is nearly empty, save just in the center: there, directly beneath the chandelier, the two little ones in their blue velvet frocks clutch each other in an awkward embrace and twirl silently round and round, oblivious of all else. Cornelius, as he passes, strokes their hair, with a friendly word; it does not distract them from their small solemn pre-occupation. But at his own door he turns to glance round and sees young Hergesell push himself off the stair by his elbow—probably because he noticed the Professor. He comes down into the arena, takes Ellie out of her brother's arms, and dances with her himself. It looks very comic, with-out the music, and he crouches down just as Cornelius does when he goes walking with the four gentlemen, holding the fluttered Ellie as though she were grown up and talking little "shimmying" steps. Everybody watches with huge enjoyment, the gramophone is put on again, dancing becomes general. The Professor stands and looks, with his hand on the door-knob. He nods and laughs; when he finally shuts himself into his study the me-chanical smile still lingers on his lips.

Again he turns over pages by his desk lamp, takes notes, attends to a few simple matters. After a while he notices that the guests have forsaken the entrance hall for his wife's drawing-room, into which there is a door from his own study as well. He hears their voices and the sounds of a guitar being tuned. Herr Möller, it seems, is to sing—and does so. He twangs the strings of his instrument and sings in a powerful bass a ballad in a strange tongue, possibly Swedish. The Professor does not succeed in identifying it, though he listens attentively to the end, after which there is great ap-plause. The sound is deadened by the portière that hangs over the dividing door. The young bank-clerk begins another song. Cornelius goes softly in.

It is half-dark in the drawing-room; the only light is from the shaded standard lamp, beneath which Möller sits, on the divan, with his legs crossed, picking his strings. His audience is grouped easily about; as there are not enough seats, some stand, and more, among them many young ladies, are simply sitting on the floor with their hands clasped round their knees or even with their legs stretched out before them. Hergesell sits thus, in his dinner jacket, next the piano, with Fräulein Plaichinger beside him. Frau Cornelius is holding both children on her lap as she sits in her easy-chair opposite the singer. Snapper, the Boeotian, begins to talk loud and clear in the middle of the song and has to be intimidated with hushings and finger-shakings. Never, never would Ellie allow herself to be guilty of such conduct. She sits there daintily erect and still on her mother's knee. The Professor tries to catch her eye and exchange a private signal with his little girl; but she does not see him. Neither does she seem to be looking at the singer. Her gaze is directed lower down.

Möller sings the "joli tambour":

> "Sire, mon roi, donnez-moi votre
> fille—"

They are all enchanted. "How good!" Hergesell is heard to say, in the odd, nasally condescending Hergesell tone. The next one is a beggar ballad, to a tune composed by young Möller himself; it elicits a storm of applause:

> "Gypsy lassie a-goin' to the fair,
> Huzza!
> Gypsy laddie a-goin' to be there—
> Huzza, diddlety umpty dido!"

Laughter and high spirits, sheer reckless hilarity, reigns after this jovial ballad. "Frightfully good!" Hergesell comments again, as before. Follows another popular song, this time a Hungarian one; Möller sings it in its own outlandish tongue, and most effectively. The Professor applauds with ostentation. It warms his heart and does him good, this outcropping of artistic, historic, and cultural elements all amongst the shimmying. He goes up to young Möller and congratulates him, talks about the songs and their sources, and Möller promises to lend him a certain annotated book of folk songs. Cornelius is the more cordial because all the time, as fathers do, he has been comparing the parts and achievements of this young stranger with those of his own son, and being gnawed by envy and chagrin. This young Möller, he is thinking, is a capable bank-clerk (though about Möller's capacity he knows nothing whatever) and has this special gift besides, which must have taken talent and energy to cultivate. "And here is my poor Bert, who knows nothing and can do nothing and thinks of nothing except playing the clown, without even talent for that!" He tries to be just; he tells himself that, after all, Bert has innate refinement; that probably there is a good deal more to him than there is to the successful Möller; that perhaps he has even something of the poet in him, and his dancing and table-waiting are due to mere boyish folly and the distraught times. But paternal envy and pessimism win the upper hand; when Möller begins another song, Dr. Cornelius goes back to his room.

He works as before, with divided attention, at this and that, while it gets on for seven o'clock. Then he remembers a letter he may just as well write, a short letter and not very important, but letter-writing is wonderful for the way it takes up the time, and it is almost half past when he has finished. A half past eight the Italian salad will be served; so now is the prescribed moment for the Professor to go out into the wintry darkness to post his letters and take his daily quantum of fresh air and exercise. They are dancing again, and he will have to pass through the hall to get his hat and coat; but they are used to him now, he need not stop and beg them not to be disturbed. He lays away his papers, takes up the letters he has written, and goes out. But he sees his wife sitting near the door of his room and pauses a little by her easy-chair.

She is watching the dancing. Now and then the big folk or some of their guests stop to speak to her; the party is at its height, and there are more onlookers than these two: blue-faced Ann is standing at the bottom of the stairs, in all the dignity of her limitations. She is waiting for the children, who simply cannot get their fill of these unwonted festivities, and watching over Snapper, lest his all too rich blood be churned to the danger-point by too much twirling round. And not only the nursery but the kitchen takes an interest: Xaver and the two ladies Hinterhofer are standing by the pantry door looking on with relish. Fräulein Walburga, the elder of the two sunken sisters (the culinary section—she objects to being called a cook), is a whimsical, good-natured sort, brown-eyed, wearing glasses with thick circular lenses; the nose-piece is wound with a bit of rag to keep it from pressing on her nose. Fräulein Cecilia is younger, though not so precisely young either. Her bearing is as self-assertive as usual, this being her way of sustaining her dignity as a former member of the middle class. For Fräulein Cecilia feels acutely her descent into the ranks of domestic service. She positively declines to wear a cap or other badge of servitude, and her hardest trial is on the Wednesday evening when she has to serve the dinner while Xaver has his afternoon out. She hands the dishes with averted face and elevated nose—a fallen queen; and so distressing is it to behold her degradation that one evening when the little folk happened to be at table and saw her they both with one accord burst into tears. Such anguish is unknown to young Xaver. He enjoys serving and does it with an ease born of practice as well as talent, for he was once a "piccolo." But otherwise he is a thorough-paced good-for-nothing and windbag—with quite distinct traits of character of his own, as his long-suffering employers are always ready to concede, but perfectly impossible and a bag of wind for all that. One must just take him as he is, they think, and not expect figs from thistles. He is the child and product of the disrupted times, a perfect specimen of his generation, follower of the revolution, Bolshevist sympathizer.

The Professor's name for him is the "minute-man," because he is always to be counted on in any sudden crisis, if only it address his sense of humor or love of novelty, and will display therein amazing readiness and resource. But he utterly lacks a sense of duty and can as little be trained to the performance of the daily round and common task as some kinds of dog can be taught to jump over a stick. It goes so plainly against the grain that criticism is disarmed. One becomes resigned. On grounds that appealed to him as unusual and amusing he would be ready to turn out of his bed at any hour of the night. But he simply cannot get up before eight in the morning, he cannot do it, he will not jump over the stick. Yet all day long the evidence of this free and untrammelled existence, the sound of his mouth-organ, his joyous whistle, or his raucous but expressive voice lifted in song, rises to the hearing of the world above-stairs; and the smoke of his cigarettes fills the pantry. While the Hinterhofer ladies work he stands and looks on. Of a morning while the Professor is breakfasting, he tears the leaf off the study calendar—but does not lift a finger to dust the room. Dr. Cornelius has often told him to leave the calendar alone, for he tends to tear off two leaves at a time and thus to add to the general confusion. But young Xaver appears to find joy in this activity, and will not be deprived of it.

Again, he is fond of children, a winning trait. He will throw himself into games with the little folk in the garden, make and mend their toys with great ingenuity, even read aloud from their books—and very droll it sounds in his thick-lipped pronunciation. With his whole soul he loves the cinema; after an evening spent there he inclines to melancholy and yearning and talking to himself. Vague hopes stir in him that some day he may make his fortune in that gay world and belong to it by rights—hopes based on his shock of hair and his physical agility and daring. He likes to climb the ash tree in the front garden, mounting branch by branch to the very top and frightening everybody to death who sees him. Once there he lights a cigarette and smokes it as he sways to and fro, keeping a look-out for a cinema director who might chance to come along and engage him.

If he changed his striped jacket for mufti, he might easily dance with the others and no one would notice the difference. For the big folk's friends are rather anomalous in their clothing: evening dress is worn by a few, but it is by no means the rule. There is quite a sprinkling of guests, both male and female, in the same general style as Möller the ballad-singer. The Professor is familiar with the circumstances of most of this young generation he is watching as he stands beside his wife's chair; he has heard them spoken of by name. They are students at the high school or at the School of Applied Art; they lead, at least the masculine portion, that precarious and scrambling existence which is purely the product of the time. There is a tall, pale, spindling youth, the son of a dentist, who lives by speculation. From all the Professor hears, he is a perfect Aladdin. He keeps a car, treats his friends to champagne suppers, and showers presents upon them on every occasion, costly little trifles in mother-of-pearl and gold. So today he has brought gifts to the young givers of the feast: for Bert a gold lead-pencil, and for Ingrid a pair of ear-rings of barbaric size, great gold circlets that fortunately do not have to go through the little ear-lobe, but are fastened over it by means of a clip. The big folk come laughing to their parents to display these trophies; and the parents shake their heads even while they admire—Aladdin bowing over and over from afar.

The young people appear to be absorbed in their dancing—if the performance they are carrying out with so much still concentration can be called dancing. They stride across the carpet, slowly, according to some unfathomable prescript, strangely embraced; in the newest attitude, tummy advanced and shoulders high, waggling the hips. They do not get tired, because nobody could. There is no such thing as heightened color or heaving bosoms. Two girls may dance together or two young men—it is all the same. They move to the exotic strains of the gramophone, played with the loudest needles to procure the maximum of sound: shimmies, foxtrots, one-steps, double foxes, African shimmies, Java dances, and Creole polkas, the wild musky melodies follow one another, now furious, now languishing, a monotonous Negro program in unfamiliar rhythm, to a clacking, clashing, and strumming orchestral accompaniment.

"What is that record?" Cornelius inquires of Ingrid, as she passes him by in the arms of the pale young speculator, with reference to the piece then playing, whose alternate languors and furies he finds comparatively pleasing and showing a certain resourcefulness in detail.

"*Prince of Pappenheim*: 'Console thee, dearest child,' " she answers, and smiles pleasantly back at him with her white teeth.

The cigarette smoke wreathes beneath the chandelier. The air is blue with a festal haze compact of sweet and thrilling ingredients that stir the blood with memories of green-sick pains and are particularly poignant to those whose youth—like the Professor's own—has been over-sensitive. . . . The little folk are still on the floor. They are allowed to stop up until eight, so great is their delight in the party. The guests have got used to their presence; in their own way, they have their place in the doings of the evening. They have separated, anyhow: Snapper revolves all alone in the middle of the carpet, in his little blue velvet smock, while Ellie is running after one of the dancing couples, trying to hold the man fast by his coat. It is Max Hergesell and Fräulein Plaichinger. They dance well, it is a pleasure to watch them. One has to admit that these mad modern dances, when the right people dance them, are not so bad after all—they have something quite taking. Young Hergesell is a capital leader, dances according to rule, yet with individuality. So it looks. With what aplomb can he walk backwards—when space permits! And he knows how to be graceful standing still in a crowd. And his partner supports him well, being unsuspectedly lithe and buoyant, as fat people often are. They look at each other, they are talking, paying no heed to Ellie, though others are smiling to see the child's persistence. Dr. Cornelius tries to catch up his little sweetheart as she passes and draw her to him. But Ellie sludes him, almost peevishly; her dear Abel is nothing to her now. She braces her little arms against his chest and turns her face away with a persecuted look. Then escapes to follow her fancy once more.

The Professor feels an involuntary twinge. Uppermost in his heart is hatred for this party, with its power to intoxicate and estrange his darling child. His love for her—that not quite disinterested, not quite unexceptionable love of his—is easily wounded. He wears a mechanical smile, but his eyes have clouded, and he stares fixedly at a point in the carpet, between the dancers' feet.

"The children ought to go to bed," he tells his wife. But she pleads for another quarter of an hour; she has promised already, and they do love it so! He smiles again and shakes his head, stands so a moment and then goes across to the cloak-room, which is full of coats and hats and scarves and overshoes. He has trouble in rummaging out his own coat, and Max Hergesell comes out of the hall, wiping his brow.

"Going out, sir?" he asks, in Hergesellian accents, dutifully helping the older man on with his coat. "Silly business this, with my pumps," he says. "They pinch like hell. The brutes are simply too tight for me, quite apart from the bad leather. They press just here on the ball of my great toe"—he stands on one foot and holds the other in his hand—"it's simply unbearable. There's nothing for it but to take them off; my brogues will have to do the business. . . . Oh, let me help you, sir."

"Thanks," says Cornelius. "Don't trouble. Get rid of your own tormentors. . . . Oh, thanks very much!" For Hergesell has gone on one knee to snap the fasteners of his snow-boots.

Once more the Professor expresses his gratitude; he is pleased and touched by so much sincere respect and youthful readiness to serve. "Go and enjoy yourself," he counsels. "Change your shoes and make up for what you have been suffering. Nobody can dance in shoes that pinch. Goodbye, I must be off to get a breath of fresh air."

"I'm going to dance with Ellie now," calls Hergesell after him. "She'll be a first-rate dancer when she grows up, and that I'll swear to."

"Think so?" Cornelius answers, already half out. "Well, you are a connoisseur, I'm sure. Don't get curvature of the spine with stooping."

He nods again and goes. "Fine lad," he thinks as he shuts the door. "Student of engineering. Knows what he's bound for, got a good clear head, and so well set up and pleasant too." And again paternal envy rises as he compares his poor Bert's status with this young man's, which he puts in the rosiest light that his son's may look the darker. Thus he sets out on his evening walk.

He goes up the avenue, crosses the bridge, and walks along the bank on the other side as far as the next bridge but one. The air is wet and cold, with a little snow now and then. He turns up his coat-collar and slips the crook of his cane over the arm behind his back. Now and then he ventilates his lungs with a long deep breath of the night air. As usual when he walks, his mind reverts to his professional preoccupations, he thinks about his lectures and the things he means to say tomorrow about Philip's struggle against the Germanic revolution, things steeped in melancholy and penetratingly just. Above all just, he thinks. For in one's dealings with the young it behooves one to display the scientific spirit, to exhibit the principles of enlightenment—not only for purposes of mental discipline, but on the human and individual side, in order not to wound them or indirectly offend their political sensibilities; particularly in these days, when there is so much tinder in the air, opinions are so frightfully split up and chaotic, and you may so easily incur attacks from one party or the other, or even give rise to scandal, by taking sides on a point of history. "And taking sides is unhistoric anyhow," so he muses. "Only justice, only impartiality is historic." And could not, properly considered, be otherwise. . . . For justice can have nothing of youthful fire and blithe, fresh, loyal conviction. It is by nature melancholy. And, being so, has secret affinity with the lost cause and the forlorn hope rather than with the fresh and blithe and loyal—perhaps this affinity is its very essence and without it it would not exist at all! . . . "And is there then no such thing as justice?" the Professor asks himself, and ponders the question so deeply that he absently post his letters in the next box and turns round to go home. This thought of his is unsettling and disturbing to the scientific mind—but is it not after all itself scientific, psychological, conscientious, and therefore to be accepted without prejudice, no matter how upsetting? In the midst of which musings Dr. Cornelius finds himself back at his own door.

On the outer threshold stands Xaver, and seems to be looking for him.

"Herr Professor," says Xaver, tossing back his hair, "go upstairs to Ellie straight off. She's in a bad way."

"What's the matter?" asks Cornelius in alarm. "Is she ill?"

"No-o, not to say ill," answers Xaver. "She's just in a bad way and crying fit to bust her little heart. It's along o' that chap with the shirt-front that danced with her—Herr Hergesell. She couldn't be got to go upstairs peaceably, not at no price at all, and she's b'en crying bucketfuls."

"Nonsense," says the Professor, who has entered and is tossing off his things in the cloak-room. He says no more; opens the glass door and without a glance at the guests turns swiftly to the stairs. Takes them two at a time, crosses the upper hall and the small room leading into the nursery. Xaver follows at his heels, but stops at the nursery door.

A bright light still burns within, showing the gay frieze that runs all round the room, the large row of shelves heaped with a confusion of toys, the rocking-horse on his swaying platform, with red-varnished nostrils and raised hoofs. On the linoleum lie other toys—building blocks, railway trains, a little trumpet. The two white cribs stand not far apart, Ellie's in the window corner, Snapper's out in the room.

Snapper is asleep. He has said his prayers in loud, ringing tones, prompted by Nurse, and gone off at once into vehement, profound, and rosy slumber—from which a cannon-ball fired at close range could not rouse him. He lies with both fists flung back on the pillows on either side of the tousled head with its funny crooked little slumber-tossed wig.

A circle of females surrounds Ellie's bed: not only blue-faced Ann is there, but the Hinterhofer ladies too, talking to each other and to her. They make way as the Professor comes up and reveal the child sitting all pale among her pillows, sobbing and weeping more bitterly than he has ever seen her sob and weep in her life. Her lovely little hands lie on the coverlet in front of her, the nightgown with its narrow lace border has slipped down from her shoulder—such a thin, birdlike little shoulder—and the sweet head Cornelius loves so well, set on the neck like a flower on its stalk, her head is on one side, with the eyes rolled up to the corner between wall and ceiling above her head. For there she seems to envisage the anguish of her heart and even to nod to it—either on purpose or because her head wobbles as her body is shaken with the violence of her sobs. Her eyes rain down tears. The bow-shaped lips are parted, like a little *mater dolorosa's*, and from them issue long, low wails that in nothing resemble the unnecessary and exasperating shrieks of a naughty child, but rise from the deep extremity of her heart and wake in the Professor's own a sympathy that is well-nigh intolerable. He has never seen his darling so before. His feelings find immediate vent in an attack on the ladies Hinterhofer.

"What about the supper?" he asks sharply. "There must be a great deal to do. Is my wife being left to do it alone?"

For the acute sensibilities of the former middle class this is quite enough. The ladies withdraw in righteous indignation, and Xaver Kleingutl jeers at them as they pass out. Having been born to low life instead of achieving it, he never loses a chance to mock at their fallen state.

"Childie, childie," murmurs Cornelius, and sitting down by the crib enfolds the anguished Ellie in his arms. "What is the trouble with my darling?"

She bedews his face with her tears.

"Abel . . . Abel . . ." she stammers between sobs. "Why—isn't Max —my brother? Max ought to be—my brother!"

Alas, alas! What mischance is this? Is this what the party has wrought, with its fatal atmosphere? Cornelius glances helplessly up at blue-faced Ann standing there in all the dignity of her limitations with her hands before her on her apron. She purses up her mouth and makes a long face. "It's pretty young," she says, "for the female instincts to be showing up."

"Hold your tongue," snaps Cornelius, in his agony. He has this much to be thankful for, that Ellie does not turn from him now; s.1e does not push him away as she did downstairs, but clings to him in her need, while she reiterates her absurd, bewildered prayer that Max might be her brother, or with a fresh burst of desire demands to be taken downstairs so that he can dance with her again. But Max, of course, is dancing with Fräulein Plaichinger, that behemoth who is his rightful partner and has every claim upon him; whereas Ellie—never, thinks the Professor, his heart torn with the violence of his pity, never has she looked so tiny and birdlike as now, when she nestles to him shaken with sobs and all unaware of what is happening in her little soul. No, she does not know. She does not comprehend that her suffering is on account of Fräulein Plaichinger, fat, overgrown, and utterly within her rights in dancing with Max Hergesell, whereas Ellie may only do it once, by way of a joke, although she is incomparably the more charming of the two. Yet it would be quite mad to reproach young Hergesell with the state of affairs or to make fantastic demands upon him. No, Ellie's suffering is without help or healing and must be covered up. Yet just as it is without understanding, so it is also without restraint—and that is what makes it so horribly painful. Xaver and blue-faced Ann do not feel this pain, it does not affect them—either because of native callousness or because they accept it as the way of nature. But the Professor's fatherly heart is quite torn by it, and by a distressful horror of this passion, so hopeless and so absurd.

Of no avail to hold forth to poor Ellie on the subject of the perfectly good little brother she already has. She only casts a distraught and scornful glance over at the other crib, where Snapper lies vehemently slumbering, and with fresh tears calls again for Max. Of no avail either the promise of a long, long walk tomorrow, all five gentlemen, round and round the dining-room table; or a dramatic description of the thrilling cushion games they will play. No, she will listen to none of all this, nor to lying down and going to sleep. She will not sleep, she will sit bolt upright and suffer. . . . But on a sudden they stop and listen, Abel and Ellie; listen to something miraculous that is coming to pass, that is approaching by strides, two strides, to the nursery door, that now overwhelmingly appears. . . .

It is Xaver's work, not a doubt of that. He has not remained by the door where he stood to gloat over the ejection of the Hinterhofers. No, he has bestirred himself, taken a notion; likewise steps to carry it out. Downstairs he has gone, twitched Herr Hergesell's sleeve, and made a thick-lipped request. So here they both are. Xaver, having done his part, remains by the door; but Max Hergesell comes up to Ellie's crib; in his dinner-jacket, with his sketchy side-whisker and charming black eyes; obviously quite pleased with his role of swan knight and fairy prince, as one who should say: "See, here am I, now all losses are restored and sorrows end."

Cornelius is almost as much overcome as Ellie herself.

"Just look," he says feebly, "look who's here. This is uncommonly good of you, Herr Hergesell."

"Not a bit of it," says Hergesell. "Why shouldn't I come to say good-night to my fair partner?"

And he approaches the bars of the crib, behind which Ellie sits struck mute. She smiles blissfully through her tears. A funny, high little note that is half a sigh of relief comes from her lips, then she looks dumbly up at her swan knight with her golden-brown eyes—tear-swollen though they are, so much more beautiful than the fat Plaichinger's. She does not put up her arms. Her joy, like her grief, is without understanding; but she does not do that. The lovely little hands lie quiet on the coverlet, and Max Hergesell stands with his arms leaning over the rail as on a balcony.

"And now," he says smartly, "she need not 'sit the livelong night and weep upon her bed'!" He looks at the Professor to make sure he is receiving due credit for the quotation. "Ha ha!" he laughs, "she's beginning young. 'Console thee, dearest child!' Never mind, you're all right! Just as you are you'll be wonderful! You've only got to grow up. . . . And you'll lie down and go to sleep like a good girl, now I've come to say good-night? And not cry any more, little Lorelei?"

Ellie looks up at him, transfigured. One birdlike shoulder is bare; the Professor draws the lace-trimmed nighty over it. There comes into his mind a sentimental story he once read about a dying child who longs to see a clown he had once, with unforgettable ecstasy, beheld in a circus. And they bring the clown to the bedside marvellously arrayed, embroidered before and behind with silver butterflies; and the child dies happy. Max Hergesell is not embroidered, and Ellie, thank God, is not going to die, she has only "been in a bad way." But, after all, the effect is the same. Young Hergesell leans over the bars of the crib and rattles on, more for the father's ear than the child's, but Ellie does not know that—and the father's feelings towards him are a most singular mixture of thankfulness, embarrassment, and hatred.

"Good night, little Lorelei," says Hergesell, and gives her his hand through the bars. Her pretty, soft, white little hand is swallowed up in the grasp of his big, strong, red one. "Sleep well," he says, "and sweet dreams! But don't dream about me—God forbid! Not at your age—ha ha!" And then the fairy clown's visit is at an end. Cornelius accompanies him to the door. "No, no, positively, no thanks called for, don't mention it," he large-heartedly protests; and Xaver goes downstairs with him, to help serve the Italian salad.

But Dr. Cornelius returns to Ellie, who is now lying down, with her cheek pressed into her flat little pillow.

"Well, wasn't that lovely?" he says as he smooths the covers. She nods, with one last little sob. For a quarter of an hour he sits beside her and watches while she falls asleep in her turn, beside the little brother who found the right way so much earlier than she. Her silky brown hair takes the enchanting fall it always does when she sleeps; deep, deep lie the lashes over the eyes that late so abundantly poured forth their sorrow; the angelic mouth with its bowed upper lip is peacefully relaxed and a little open. Only now and then comes a belated catch in her slow breathing.

And her small hands, like pink and white flowers, lie so quietly, one on the coverlet, the other on the pillow by her face—Dr. Cornelius, gazing, feels his heart melt with tenderness as with strong wine.

"How good," he thinks, "that she breathes in oblivion with every breath she draws! That in childhood each night is a deep, wide gulf between one day and the next. Tomorrow, beyond all doubt, young Hergesell will be a pale shadow, powerless to darken her little heart. Tomorrow, forgetful of all but present joy, she will walk with Abel and Snapper, all five gentlemen, round and round the table, will play the ever-thrilling cushion game."

Heaven be praised for that!

Fiction and Human Experience: How Four Stories Came to Be Written

WHEN we read a piece of fiction, we move from our actual world, the world where we, as people, live, into a world of imagination. But that world of imagination has been created by the writer out of the actual world in which he, as a person, lives. So there are three worlds involved here, our actual world, the writer's actual world, and the world which he has created for us. The world that the writer has created is what we want to savor and enjoy, but we cannot deeply appreciate it unless we comprehend its relevance to the other two worlds, the writer's world and our world.

A story, if it is a good story, is more than a little mechanical contrivance of words and events, more than a clever trick the writer has learned to do to amuse others or make an honest penny. It is an attempt, however modest and limited, to make sense of experience, to understand how things hang meaningfully together. Therefore, in our attempt to read fiction more fully and enjoy it more deeply, it may be of use to see what four writers have to say of the origins of their four stories. If what they have to say can suggest to us how the individual story grew out of the personal world of the writer, then we can see more clearly how the created world of fiction relates to the world of actuality, including our own particular personal one, whatever that may be. For in the end what our imagination craves is not a flight from actuality, but an illumination of it, a new vision of it.

As their comments indicate, the last thing any of our four writers had in mind to tell us is "How to Write a Short Story." Writers, even moderately good writers anyway, are not concerned with rules and formulas as such. As Eudora Welty says, "each story is going to open up a different prospect and pose a new problem," and the important question is always "How do I write *this* story?"—or to adjust the question to the needs of the reader of this book: "How do I read *this* story?"

Every serious writer regards each of his stories as a process of discovery: there is a vital experience with roots, more or less obscure, in his own experience which has to be brought into clarity and full meaning. Thus every story represents the author's effort to make sense of his world. By realizing this, we free our own imaginations to enter more fully the created world of fiction. For it becomes plain that the writer's effort to write his story is closely parallel to our effort to make sense of our own process of daily living. And if we enter the world of fiction with this realization, we can also see how the created world of fiction relates to our own personal, day-to-day worlds.

We have already noted that none of the four accounts to follow makes much reference to technical questions. All four writers, we may be sure, would admit the fact that there are technical problems, that such things as exposition and denouement are parts of plot, and so on. Most of them would probably concede that the analytic study of fiction is a worthwhile endeavor and may lead to a fuller understanding of fiction, and would concede further that for such a process we need certain dry technical terms, with more or less fixed meanings. But all of them would emphasize the difference between the analytic process, with which we have been so often concerned in this book, and the creative process.

The analytic process is concerned with breaking fiction down into the component parts—plot, theme, character, exposition, atmosphere, and so on. The creative process is concerned with bringing things together; but we may add that, in general, *what it brings together is not even the same kind of elements that critical analysis distinguishes.* The writer does not say, "I shall put this plot with that theme," or this character with that atmosphere, or anything of the sort. He is not, in the end, trying to put things "together" at all. He is trying to attain to what Eudora Welty calls a "vision"—a vision of people alive and moving in a meaningful way in a certain world that we recognize as real and yet a world dominated by a certain feeling characteristic of the story. It is, too, a vision which must find its substance, finally, in words if it is to be shared with others and be, in fact, a story.

In the preceding paragraph, we said that the analytic process is concerned with breaking fiction into its component parts; but the good reader, of course, puts them back together again. The analysis is for the sake of better understanding, so that when the parts once more come together, they form a richer and more meaningful whole. The good reader ultimately attains to a sort of "vision" too. But we shall have more to say about the justification of fictional analysis a little later in this introduction.

Attaining to the vision depends on some free movement of mind, on letting the mind go loose, so that one thing leads to another, at random as it were. But this kind of association has, in the end, to be a responsible kind of irresponsibility. Logic has to develop in it, and meaning from it; or, to state the matter another way, as logic and meaning come clearer in the process, the vision will in its subsequent stages, more and more manifest them and develop them.

Of ten things, or a thousand, that come into the writer's head, only one may be useful—only one may latch on to the emerging line of logic and meaning. Therefore, as the items come into his head, from whatever source, memory or imagination or outside suggestion, the writer's power of veto is constantly being exercised. In exercising his veto the writer may be very critical and conscious, and may argue out with himself the reasons for rejecting a thing; or he may simply feel in his bones that something is wrong, and chuck it. Usually, as the logic and meaning in the developing story are discovered the writer grows surer and surer in his veto. Sometimes, however, he may have fooled himself. He may think he knows the logic and knows the meaning, and then finds that all the time, at another level, there has been developing another logic and another meaning. We know, for instance, that in certain famous pieces of fiction, the writer had, in the very middle of the process, changed his whole conception of, say, a character, even switching a piece of dialogue from one person to another, or transferring an action. The writer might, for example, be aware that the "feel" of the story demanded such a thing to be done or said at a certain point, and yet might not know until late in the process of composition just which character should say or do the thing.

If this discussion, for all its brevity, is a fair account of the creative process, then what becomes of our worry about technical matters and our attempts at analysis? Nothing becomes of them. They remain important for the story itself. The story exists in itself and has its own architecture, no matter whether the author was consciously "working" it out or not. As for the awareness of technical matters, a writer may hope in his business of composition that the technical considerations will be completely absorbed into his whole way of thinking and feeling. When on the football field a man takes a pass and sees three tacklers coming, he doesn't stop and review the fundamentals of broken field running. If he does stop to make the review, he is very apt to be in the hospital and the score is apt to look very bad. The player wants to be in motion, with the fundamentals safely stowed away in his nerve centers, where they belong. So with the writer;

he wants the technique absorbed into himself, and deeply related to all the other considerations of his story. It is just because the general principles of technique can be so thoroughly absorbed into the personal manner of a writer that we so often find among good writers little individualities of technique, their special way of doing things, from the way of putting sentences together to the handling of exposition. We recognise the personal touch, the "signature" of style.

But how does a writer get his technique absorbed? One may learn instinctively from trial and error. One may think consciously about one's own process of trial and error. One may think about the work of other writers in the hope that this study will enter into one's own unconscious processes of creation and modify them. There is no other possible way.

No doubt the total absorption of technical considerations into the process of composition is the ideal situation for a writer. But a writer never lives very long, if ever, in an ideal situation, and so when the going gets rough he may very well have to stop and reflect quite consciously on technical questions. He may have to ask himself such questions as: "Shall I put this piece of exposition in now?"—or, "Shall I rewrite this passage describing the room because the atmosphere is not in keeping with my story?" —or, "Will the very contrast be effective?" He may not argue the reasons. He may not even put the question into words. But he has to make a conscious decision. If it is merely shutting his eyes and taking a plunge, he has to be aware even of that and of the risk he is taking.

Two of the writers presented here, Katherine Anne Porter and John Cheever, do not speak of technical questions at all—yet both are accomplished technicians. Instead, one of them is thinking, in a peculiarly fascinating way, of the deep, far-off origins in the world of childhood of a particular story; and the other, though with a passing look at such deep origins in his reference to an inherited family puritanism, is thinking primarily of a more immediate associative process. But the other two, Eudora Welty and Robert Penn Warren, do touch on technical questions— though not on such questions taken in isolation.

Eudora Welty tells us how she had a story in her head for a long time but couldn't get it to work until she happened to go to a certain place; then, when she thought of the story as happening in this place, with its strange atmosphere, the story came clear and could get itself written. Her discussion provides a very nice instance of how that quality which we technically called atmosphere is related to the way in which at least one story came into being.

In Miss Welty's discussion of her story, the question of atmosphere leads her to another technical consideration: point of view. The change of scene for the story leads, she tells us, to a new conception of how the story should be told. First, it led to the putting of the stranger into the story to look at the heroine, to give a kind of mirror for our knowledge of her.

Second, it led to a new conception of how the whole story should be looked at—but that had best be left to the author's own words when we come to her discussion.

As for "Blackberry Winter," the writer tells us how, after the story had begun in certain casual recollections, he stumbled on a pattern which could be developed, that is, could be used as a kind of guide-line in thinking about the other things that subsequently came into consciousness. He also says that he had a kind of pattern for the denouement long before he got to the actual writing of the end, or even knew what would happen there. That is, he had some sense of the structure of the story at that point, and a feeling associated with the structure, before he had a precise content.

A story may start from anything, from the death cry heard distantly by Katherine Anne Porter on a summer day, when she was a child in Texas, from a character observed or imagined, from an episode seen or an anecdote heard, from a feeling that seems to come from nowhere and is seeking an objective mooring in actuality, from the atmosphere of a place which seems to yearn for some special thing to happen there, from an historical event, from a family affection or hatred, from an idea, or from a moral conviction. It may stem from anything that will start the imagination on its characteristic job of putting things concretely together in a movement toward meaning—no, not putting them together, but creating a world in which they can grow naturally together in a movement toward meaning.

EUDORA WELTY

No Place for You, My Love

THEY were strangers to each other, both fairly well strangers to the place, now seated side by side at luncheon— a party combined in a free-and-easy way when the friends he and she were with recognized each other across Galatoire's. The time was a Sunday in summer—those hours of afternoon that seem Time Out in New Orleans.

The moment he saw her little blunt, fair face, he thought that here was a woman who was having an affair. It was one of those odd meetings when such an impact is felt that it has to be translated at once into some sort of speculation.

With a married man, most likely, he supposed, slipping quickly into a groove—he was long married—and feeling more conventional, then, in his curiosity as she sat there, leaning her cheek on her hand, looking no further before her than the flowers on the table, and wearing that hat.

He did not like her hat, any more than he liked tropical flowers. It was the wrong hat for her, thought this Eastern businessman who had no interest whatever in women's clothes and no eye for them; he thought the unaccustomed thing crossly.

It must stick out all over me, she thought, so people think they can love me or hate me just by looking at me. How did it leave us—the old, safe, slow way people used to know of learning how one another feels, and the privilege that went with it of shying away if it seemed best? People in love like me, I suppose, give away the short cuts to everybody's secrets.

Something, though, he decided, had been settled about her predicament—for the time being, anyway; the parties to it were all still alive, no doubt. Nevertheless, her predicament was the only one he felt so sure of here, like the only recognizable shadow in that restaurant, where mirrors and fans were busy agitating the light, as the very local talk drawled across and agitated the peace. The shadow lay between her fingers, between her little square hand and her cheek, like something always best carried about the person. Then suddenly, as she took her hand down, the secret fact was still there—it lighted her. It was a bold and full light, shot up under the brim of that hat, as close to them all as the flowers in the center of the table.

Did he dream of making her disloyal to that hopelessness that he saw very well she'd been cultivating down here? He knew very well that he did not. What they amounted to was two Northerners keeping each other company. She glanced up at the big gold clock on the wall and smiled. He didn't smile back. She had that naïve face that he associated, for no good reason, with the Middle West—because it said "Show me," perhaps. It was a serious, now-watch-out-everybody face, which orphaned her entirely in the company of these Southerners. He guessed her age, as he could not guess theirs: thirty-two. He himself was further along.

Of all human moods, deliberate imperviousness may be the most quickly communicated—it may be the most successful, most fatal signal of all. And two people can indulge in imperviousness as well as in anything else. "You're not very hungry either," he said.

The blades of fan shadows came down over their two heads, as he saw inadvertently in the mirror, with himself smiling at her now like a villain. His remark sounded dominant and rude enough for everybody present to listen back a moment; it even sounded like an answer to a question she might have just asked him. The other women glanced at him. The Southern look—Southern mask—of life-is-a-dream irony, which could turn to pure challenge at the drop of a hat, he could wish well away. He liked naïveté better.

"I find the heat down here depressing," she said, with the heart of Ohio in her voice.

"Well—I'm in somewhat of a temper about it, too," he said.

They looked with grateful dignity at each other.

"I have a car here, just down the street," he said to her as the luncheon party was rising to leave, all the others wanting to get back to their houses and sleep. "If it's all right with— Have you ever driven down south of here?"

Out on Bourbon Street, in the bath of July, she asked at his shoulder, "South of New Orleans? I didn't know there was any south to *here*. Does it just go on and on?" She laughed, and adjusted the exasperating hat to her head in a different way. It was more than frivolous, it was conspicuous, with some sort of glitter or flitter tied in a band around the straw and hanging down.

"That's what I'm going to show you."

"Oh—you've been there?"

"No!"

His voice rang out over the uneven, narrow sidewalk and dropped back from the walls. The flaked-off, colored houses were spotted like the hides of beasts faded and shy, and were hot as a wall of growth that seemed to breathe flower-like down onto them as they walked to the car parked there.

"It's just that it couldn't be any worse—we'll see."

"All right, then," she said. "We will."

So, their actions reduced to amiability, they settled into the car—a faded-red Ford convertible with a rather threadbare canvas top, which had been standing in the sun for all those lunch hours.

"It's rented," he explained. "I asked to have the top put down, and was told I'd lost my mind."

"It's out of this world. *Degrading* heat," she said and added, "Doesn't matter."

The stranger in New Orleans always sets out to leave it as though following the clue in a maze. They were threading through the narrow and one-way streets, past the pale-violet bloom of tired squares, the brown steeples and statutes, the balcony with the live and probably famous black monkey dipping along the railing as over a ballroom floor, past the grill-work and the lattice-work to all the iron swans painted flesh color on the front steps of bungalows outlying.

Driving, he spread his new map and put his finger down on it. At the intersection marked Arabi, where their road led out of the tangle and he took it, a small Negro seated beneath a black umbrella astride a box chalked "Shou Shine" lifted his pink-and-black hand and waved them languidly good-by. She didn't miss it, and waved back.

Below New Orleans there was a raging of insects from both sides of the concrete highway, not quite together, like the playing of separated marching bands. The river and the levee were still on her side, waste and jungle and some occasional settlements on his—poor houses. Families bigger than housefuls thronged the yards. His nodding, driving head would veer from side to side, looking and almost lowering. As time passed and the distance from New Orleans grew, girls ever darker and younger were disposing themselves over the porches and the porch steps, with jet-black hair pulled high, and ragged palm-leaf fans rising and falling like rafts of butterflies. The children running forth were nearly always naked ones.

She watched the road. Crayfish constantly crossed in front of the wheels, looking grim and bonneted, in a great hurry.

"How the Old Woman Got Home," she murmured to herself.

He pointed, as it flew by, at a saucepan full of cut zinnias which stood waiting on the open lid of a mailbox at the roadside, with a little note tied onto the handle.

They rode mostly in silence. The sun bore down. They met fishermen and other men bent on some local pursuits, some in sulphur-colored pants, walking and riding; met wagons, trucks, boats in trucks, autos, boats on top of autos—all coming to meet them, as though something of high moment were doing back where the car came from, and he and she were determined to miss it. There was nearly always a man lying with his shoes off in the bed of any truck otherwise empty—with the raw, red look of a man sleeping in the daytime, being jolted about as he slept. Then there was a sort of dead man's land, where nobody came. He loosened his collar and tie. By rushing through the heat at high speed, they brought themselves the effect of fans turned onto their cheeks. Clearing alternated with jungle and canebrake like something tried, tried again. Little shell roads led off on both sides; now and then a road of planks led into the yellow-green.

"Like a dance floor in there." She pointed.

He informed her, "In there's your oil, I think."

There were thousands, millions of mosquitoes and gnats—a universe of them, and on the increase.

A family of eight or nine people on foot strung along the road in the same direction the car was going, beating themselves with the wild palmettos. Heels, shoulders, knees, breasts, back of the heads, elbows, hands, were touched in turn—like some game, each playing it with himself.

He struck himself on the forehead, and increased their speed. (His wife would not be at her most charitable if he came bringing malaria home to the family.)

More and more crayfish and other shell creatures littered their path, scuttling or dragging. These little samples, little jokes of creation, persisted and sometimes perished, the more of them the deeper down the road went. Terrapins and turtles came up steadily over the horizons of the ditches.

Back there in the margins were worse—crawling hides you could not penetrate with bullets or quite believe, grins that had come down from the primeval mud.

"Wake up." Her Northern nudge was very timely on his arm. They had veered toward the side of the road. Still driving fast, he spread his map.

Like a misplaced sunrise, the light of the river flowed up; they were mounting the levee on a little shell road.

"Shall we cross here?" he asked politely.

He might have been keeping track over years and miles of how long they could keep that tiny ferry waiting. Now skidding down the levee's flank, they were the last-minute car, the last possible car that could squeeze on. Under the sparse shade of one willow tree, the small, amateurish-looking boat slapped the water, as, expertly, he wedged on board.

"Tell him we put him on hub cap!" shouted one of the numerous olive-skinned, dark-eyed young boys standing dressed up in bright shirts at the railing, hugging each other with delight that that last straw was on board. Another boy drew his affectionate initials in the dust of the door on her side.

She opened the door and stepped out, and, after only a moment's standing at bay, started up a little iron stairway. She appeared above the car, on the tiny bridge beneath the captain's window and the whistle.

From there, while the boat still delayed in what seemed a trance—as if it were too full to attempt the start—she could see the panlike deck below, separated by its rusty rim from the tilting, polished water.

The passengers walking and jostling about there appeared oddly amateurish, too—too amateur travelers. They were having such a good time. They all knew each other. Beer was being passed around in cans, bets were being loudly settled and new bets made, about local and special subjects on which they all doted. One red-haired man in a burst of wildness even tried to give away his truckload oi shrimp to a man on the other side of the boat— nearly all the trucks were full of shrimp—causing taunts and then protests of "They good! They good!" from the giver. The young boys leaned on each other thinking of what next, rolling their eyes absently.

A radio pricked the air behind her. Looking like a great tomcat just above her head, the captain was digesting the news of a fine stolen automobile.

At last a tremendous explosion burst—the whistle. Everything shuddered in outline from the sound, everybody said something—everybody else.

They started with no perceptible motion, but her hat blew off. It went spiraling to the deck below, where he, thank heaven, sprang out of the car and picked it up. Everybody looked frankly up at her now, holding her hands to her head.

The little willow tree receded as its shade was taken away. The heat was like something falling on her head. She held the hot rail before her. It was like riding a stove. Her shoulders dropping, her hair flying, her skirt buffeted by the sudden strong wind, she stood there, thinking they all must see that with her entire self all she did was wait. Her set hands, with the bag that hung from her wrist and rocked back and forth—all three seemed objects bleaching there, belonging to no one; she could not feel a thing in the skin of her face; perhaps she was crying, and not knowing it. She could look down and see him just below her, his black shadow, her hat, and his black hair. His hair in the wind looked unreasonably long and rippling. Little did he know that from here it had a red undergleam like an animal's. When she looked up and outward, a vortex of light drove through and over the brown waves like a star in the water.

He did after all bring the retrieved hat up the stairs to her. She took it back—useless—and held it to her skirt. What they were saying below was more polite than their searchlight faces.

"Where you think he come from, that man?"

"I bet he come from Lafitte."

"Lafitte? What you bet, eh?"—all crouched in the shade of trucks, squatting and laughing.

Now his shadow fell partly across her; the boat had jolted into some other strand of current. Her shaded arm and shaded hand felt pulled out from the blaze of light and water, and she hoped humbly for more shade for her head. It had seemed so natural to climb up and stand in the sun.

The boys had a surprise—an alligator on board. One of them pulled it by a chain around the deck, between the cars and trucks, like a toy—a hide that could walk. He thought, Well they had to catch one sometime. It's Sunday afternoon. So they have him on board now, riding him across the Mississippi River. . . . The playfulness of it beset everybody on the ferry. The hoarseness of the boat whistle, commenting briefly, seemed part of the general appreciation.

"Who want to rassle him? Who want to, eh?" two boys cried, looking up. A boy with shrimp-colored arms capered from side to side, pretending to have been bitten.

What was there so hilarious about jaws that could bite? And what danger was there once in this repulsiveness—so that the last worldly evidence of some old heroic horror of the dragon had to be paraded in capture before the eyes of country clowns?

He noticed that she looked at the alligator without flinching at all. Her distance was set—the number of feet and inches between herself and it mattered to her.

Perhaps her measuring coolness was to him what his bodily shade was to her, while they stood pat up there riding the river, which felt like the sea and looked like the earth under them—full of the red-brown earth, charged with it. Ahead of the boat it was like an exposed vein of ore. The river seemed to swell in the vast middle with the curve of the earth. The sun rolled under them. As if in memory of the size of things, uprooted trees were drawn across their path, sawing at the air and tumbling one over the other.

When they reached the other side, they felt that they had been racing around an arena in their chariot, among lions. The whistle took and shook the stairs as they went down. The young boys, looking taller, had taken out colored combs and were combing their wet hair back in solemn pompadour above their radiant foreheads. They had been bathing in the river themselves not long before.

The cars and trucks, then the foot passengers and the alligator, waddling like a child to school, all disembarked and wound up the weed-sprung levee.

Both respectable and merciful, their hides, she thought, forcing herself to dwell on the alligator as she looked back. Deliver us all from the naked in heart. (As she had been told.)

When they regained their paved road, he heard her give a little sigh and saw her turn her straw-colored head to look back once more. Now that she rode with her hat in her lap, her earrings were conspicuous too. A little metal ball set with small pale stones danced beside each square, faintly downy cheek.

Had she felt a wish for someone else to be riding with them? He thought it was more likely that she would wish for her husband if she had one (his wife's voice) than for the lover in whom he believed. Whatever people liked to think, situations (if not scenes) were usually three-way—there was somebody else always. The one who didn't—couldn't—understand the two made the formidable third.

He glanced down at the map flapping on the seat between them, up at his wristwatch, out at the road. Out there was the incredible brightness of four o'clock.

On this side of the river, the road ran beneath the brow of the levee and followed it. Here was a heat that ran deeper and brighter and more intense than all the rest—its nerve. The road grew one with the heat as it was one with the unseen river. Dead snakes stretched across the concrete like markers—inlaid mosaic bands, dry as feathers, which their tires licked at intervals that began to seem clocklike.

No, the heat faced them—it was ahead. They could see it waving at them, shaken in the air above the white of the road, always at a certain distance ahead, shimmering finely as a cloth, with running edges of green and gold, fire and azure.

"It's never anything like this in Syracuse," he said.

"Or in Toledo, either," she replied with dry lips.

They were driving through greater waste down here, through fewer and even more insignificant towns. There was water under everything. Even where a screen of jungle had been left to stand, splashes could be heard from under the trees. In the vast open, sometimes boats moved inch by inch through what appeared endless meadows of rubbery flowers.

Her eyes overcome with brightness and size, she felt a panic rise, as sudden as nausea. Just how far below questions and answers, concealment and revelation, they were running now—that was still a new question, with a power of its own, waiting. How dear—how costly—could this ride be?

"It looks to me like your road can't go much further," she remarked cheerfully. "Just over there, it's all water."

"Time out," he said, and with that he turned the car into a sudden road of white shells that rushed at them narrowly out of the left.

They bolted over a cattle guard, where some rayed and crested purple flowers burst out of the vines in the ditch, and rolled onto a long, narrow, green, mowed clearing: a churchyard. A paved track ran between two short rows of raised tombs, all neatly white-washed and now brilliant as faces against the vast flushed sky.

The track was the width of the car with a few inches to spare. He passed between the tombs slowly but in the manner of a feat. Names took their places on the walls slowly at a level with the eye, names as near as the eyes of a person stopping in conversation, and as far away in origin, and in all their music and dead longing, as Spain. At intervals were set packed bouquets of zinnias, oleanders, and some kind of purple flowers, all quite fresh, in fruit jars, like nice welcomes on bureaus.

They moved on into an open plot beyond, of violent-green grass, spread before the green-and-white frame church with worked flower beds around it, flowerless poinsettias growing up to the windowsills. Beyond was a house, and left on the doorstep of the house a fresh-caught catfish the size of a baby—a fish wearing whiskers and bleeding. On a clothesline in the yard, a priest's black gown on a hanger hung airing, swaying at man's height, in a vague, trainlike, lady-like sweep along an evening breath that might otherwise have seemed imaginary from the unseen, felt river.

With the motor cut off, with the raging of the insects about them, they sat looking out at the green and white and black and red and pink as they leaned against the sides of the car.

"What is your wife like?" she asked. His right hand came up and spread—iron, wooden, manicured. She lifted her eyes to his face. He looked at her like that hand.

Then he lit a cigarette, and the portrait, and the righthand testimonial it made, were blown away. She smiled, herself as unaffected as by some stage performance; and he was annoyed in the cemetery. They did not risk going on to her husband—if she had one.

Under the supporting posts of the priest's house, where a boat was, solid ground ended and palmettos and water hyacinths could not wait to begin; suddenly the rays of the sun, from behind the car, reached that lowness and struck the flowers. The priest came out onto the porch in his underwear, stared at the car a moment as if he wondered what time it was, then collected his robe off the line and his fish off the doorstep and returned inside. Vespers was next, for him.

After backing out between the tombs he drove on still south, in the sunset. They caught up with an old man walking in a sprightly way in their direction, all by himself, wearing a clean bright shirt printed with a pair of palm trees fanning green over his chest. It might better be a big colored woman's shirt, but she didn't have it. He flagged the car with gestures like hoops.

"You're coming to the end of the road," the old man told them. He pointed ahead, tipped his hat to the lady, and pointed again. "End of the road." They didn't understand that he meant, "Take me."

They drove on. "If we do go any further, it'll have to be by water—is that it?" he asked her, hesitating at this odd point.

"You know better than I do," she replied politely.

The road had for some time ceased to be paved; it was made of shells. It was leading into a small, sparse settlement like the others a few miles back, but with even more of the camp about it. On the lip of the clearing, directly before a green willow blaze with the sunset gone behind it, the row of houses and shacks faced out on broad, colored, moving water that stretched to reach the horizon and looked like an arm of the sea. The houses on their shaggy posts, patchily built, some with plank runways instead of steps, were flimsy and alike, and not much bigger than the boats tied up at the landing.

"Venice," she heard him announce, and he dropped the crackling map in her lap.

They coasted down the brief remainder. The end of the road—she could not remember ever seeing a road simply end—was a spoon shape, with a tree stump in the bowl to turn around by.

Around it, he stopped the car, and they stepped out, feeling put down in the midst of a sudden vast pause or subduement that was like a yawn. They made their way on foot toward the water, where at an idle-looking landing men in twos and threes stood with their backs to them.

The nearness of darkness, the still uncut trees, bright water partly under a sheet of flowers, shacks, silence, dark shapes of boats tied up, then the first sounds of people just on the other side of thin walls—all this reached them. Mounds of shells like day-old snow, pink-tinted, lay around a central shack with a beer sign on it. An old man up on the porch there sat holding an open newspaper, with a fat white goose sitting opposite him on the floor. Below, in the now shadowless and sunless open, another old man, with a colored pencil bright under his hat brim, was late mending a sail.

When she looked clear around, thinking they had a fire burning somewhere now, out of the heat had risen the full moon. Just beyond the trees, enormous, tangerine-colored, it was going solidly up. Other lights just striking into view, looking farther distant, showed moss shapes hanging, or slipped and broke matchlike on the water that so encroached upon the rim of ground they were standing on.

There was a touch at her arm—his, accidental.

"We're at the jumping-off place," he said.

She laughed, having thought his hand was a bat, while her eyes rushed downward toward a great pale drift of water hyacinths—still partly open, flushed and yet moonlit, level with her feet—through which paths of water for the boats had been hacked. She drew her hands up to her face under the brim of her hat; her own cheeks felt like the hyacinths to her, all her skin still full of too much light and sky, exposed. The harsh vesper bell was ringing.

"I believe there must be something wrong with me, that I came on this excursion to begin with," she said, as if he had already said this and she were merely in hopeful, willing, maddening agreement with him.

He took hold of her arm, and said, "Oh, come on—I see we can get something to drink here, at least."

But there was a beating, muffled sound from over the darkening water. One more boat was coming in, making its way through the tenacious, tough, dark flower traps, by the shaken light of what first appeared to be torches. He and she waited for the boat, as if on each other's patience. As if borne in on a mist of twilight or a breath, a horde of mosquitoes and gnats came singing and striking at them first. The boat bumped, men laughed. Somebody was offering somebody else some shrimp.

Then he might have cocked his dark city head down at her; she did not look up at him, only turned when he did. Now the shell mounds, like the shacks and trees, were solid purple. Lights had appeared in the not-quite-true window squares. A narrow neon sign, the lone sign, had come out in bright blush on the beer shack's roof: "Baba's Place." A light was on on the porch.

The barnlike interior was brightly lit and unpainted, looking not quite finished, with a partition dividing this room from what lay behind. One of the four cardplayers at a table in the middle of the floor was the newspaper reader; the paper was in his pants pocket. Midway along the partition was a bar, in the form of a pass-through to the other room, with a varnished, second-hand fretwork overhang. They crossed the floor and sat, alone there, on wooden stools. An eruption of humorous signs, newspaper cut-outs and cartoons, razor-blade cards, and personal messages of significance to the owner or his friends decorated the overhang, framing where Baba should have been but wasn't.

Through there came a smell of garlic and cloves and red pepper, a blast of hot cloud escaped from a cauldron they could see now on a stove at the back of the other room. A massive back, presumably female, with a twist of gray hair on top, stood with a ladle akimbo. A young man joined her and with his fingers stole something out of the pot and ate it. At Baba's they were boiling shrimp.

When he got ready to wait on them, Baba strolled out to the counter, young, black-headed, and in very good humor.

"Coldest beer you've got. And food—What will you have?"

"Nothing for me, thank you," she said. "I'm not sure I could eat, after all."

"Well, I could," he said, shoving his jaw out. Baba smiled. "I want a good solid ham sandwich."

"I could have asked him for some water," she said, after he had gone.

While they sat waiting, it seemed very quiet. The bubbling of the shrimp, the distant laughing of Baba, and the slap of cards, like the beating of moths on the screens, seemed to come in fits and starts. The steady breathing they heard came from a big rough dog asleep in the corner. But it was bright. Electric lights were strung riotously over the room from a kind of spider web of old wires in the rafters. One of the written messages tacked before them read, "Joe! At the boyy!!" It looked very yellow, older than Baba's Place. Outside, the world was pure dark.

Two little boys, almost alike, almost the same size, and just cleaned up, dived into the room with a double bang of the screen door, and circled around the card game. They ran their hands into the men's pockets.

"Nickel for some pop!"

"Nickel for some pop!"

"Go 'way and let me play, you!"

They circled around and shrieked at the dog, ran under the lid of the counter and raced through the kitchen and back, and hung over the stools at the bar. One child had a live lizard on his shirt, clinging like a breast pin—like lapis lazuli.

Bringing in a strong odor of geranium talcum, some men had come in now—all in bright shirts. They drew near the counter, or stood and watched the game.

When Baba came out bringing the beer and sandwich, "Could I have some water?" she greeted him.

Baba laughed at everybody. She decided the woman back there must be Baba's mother.

Beside her, he was drinking his beer and eating his sandwich—ham, cheese, tomato, pickle, and mustard. Before he finished, one of the men who had come in beckoned from across the room. It was the old man in the palmtree shirt.

She lifted her head to watch him leave her, and was looked at, from all over the room. As a minute passed, no cards were laid down. In a far-off way, like accepting the light from Arcturus, she accepted it that she was more beautiful or perhaps more fragile than the women they saw every day of their lives. It was just this thought coming into a woman's face, and at this hour, that seemed familiar to them.

Baba was smiling. He had set an opened, frosted brown bottle before her on the counter, and a thick sandwich, and stood looking at her. Baba made her eat some supper, for what she was.

"What the old fellow wanted," said he when he came back at last, "was to have a friend of his apologize. Seems church is just out. Seems the friend made a remark coming in just now. His pals told him there was a lady present."

"I see you bought him a beer," she said.

"Well, the old man looked like he wanted *something*."

All at once the juke box interrupted from back in the corner, with the same old song as anywhere. The half-dozen slot machines along the wall were suddenly all run to like Maypoles, and thrown into action—taken over by further battalions of little boys.

There were three little boys to each slot machine. The local custom appeared to be that one pulled the lever for the friend he was holding up to put the nickel in, while the third covered the pictures with the flat of his hand as they fell into place, so as to surprise them all if anything happened.

The dog lay sleeping on in front of the raging juke box, his ribs working fast as a concertina's. At the side of the room a man with a cap on his white thatch was trying his best to open a side screen door, but it was stuck fast. It was he who had come in with the remark considered ribald; now he was trying to get out the other way. Moths as thick as ingots were trying to get in. The card players broke into shouts of derision, then joy, then tired derision among themselves; they might have been here all afternoon—they were the only ones not cleaned up and shaved. The original pair of little boys ran in once more, with the hyphenated bang. They got nickels this time, then were brushed away from the table like mosquitoes, and they rushed under the counter and on to the cauldron behind, clinging to Baba's mother there. The evening was at the threshold.

They were quite unnoticed now. He was eating another sandwich, and she, having finished part of hers, was fanning her face with her hat. Baba had lifted the flap of the counter and come out into the room. Behind his head there was a sign lettered in orange crayon: "Shrimp Dance Sun. PM." That was tonight, still to be.

And suddenly she made a move to slide down from her stool, maybe wishing to walk out into that nowhere down the front steps to be cool a moment. But he had hold of her hand. He got down from his stool, and, patiently, reversing her hand in his own—just as she had had the look of being about to give up, faint—began moving her, leading her. They were dancing.

"I get to thinking this is what we get—what you and I deserve," she whispered, looking past his shoulder into the room. "And all the time, it's real. It's a real place—away off down here . . ."

They danced gratefully, formally, to some song carried on in what must be the local patois, while no one paid any attention as long as they were together, and the children poured the family nickels steadily into the slot machines, walloping the handles down with regular crashes and troubling nobody with winning.

She said rapidly, as they began moving together too well, "One of those clippings was an account of a shooting right here. I guess they're proud of it. And that awful knife Baba was carrying . . . I wonder what he called me," she whispered in his ear.

"Who?"

"The one who apologized to you."

If they had ever been going to overstep themselves, it would be now as he held her closer and turned her, when she became aware that he could not help but see the bruise at her temple. It would not be six inches from his eyes. She felt it come out like an evil star. (Let it pay him back, then, for the hand he had stuck in her face when she'd tried once to be sympathetic, when she'd asked about his wife.) They danced on still as the record changed, after standing wordless and motionless, linked together in the middle of the room, for the moment between.

Then, they were like a matched team—like professional, Spanish dancers wearing masks—while the slow piece was playing.

Surely even those immune from the world, for the time being, need the touch of one another, or all is lost. Their arms encircling each other, their bodies circling the odorous, just-nailed-down floor, they were, at last, imperviousness in motion. They had found it, and had almost missed it: they had had to dance. They were what their separate hearts desired that day, for themselves and each other.

They were so good together that once she looked up and half smiled. "For whose benefit did we have to show off?"

Like people in love, they had a superstition about themselves almost as soon as they came out on the floor, and dared not think the words "happy" or "unhappy," which might strike them, one or the other, like lightning.

In the thickening heat they danced on while Baba himself sang with the mosquito-voiced singer in the chorus of "*Moi pas l'aimez ça*," enumerating the *ça*'s with a hot shrimp between his fingers. He was counting over the platters the old woman now set on the counter, each heaped with shrimp in their shells boiled to iridescence, like mounds of honeysuckle flowers.

The goose wandered in from the back room under the lid of the counter and hitched itself around the floor among the table legs and people's legs, never seeing that it was neatly avoided by two dancers—

who nevertheless vaguely thought of this goose as learned, having earlier heard an old man read to it. The children called it Mimi, and lured it away. The old thatched man was again drunkenly trying to get out by the stuck side door; now he gave it a kick, but was prevailed on to remain. The sleeping dog shuddered and snored.

It was left up to the dancers to provide nickels for the juke box; Baba kept a drawerful for every use. They had grown fond of all the selections by now. This was the music you heard out of the distance at night—out of the roadside taverns you fled past, around the late corners in cities half asleep, drifting up from the carnival over the hill, with one odd little strain always managing to repeat itself. This seemed a homey place.

Bathed in sweat, and feeling the false coolness that it brings, they stood finally on the porch in the lapping night air for a moment before leaving. The first arrivals of the girls were coming up the steps under the porch light—all flowered fronts, their black pompadours giving out breathlike feelers from sheer abundance. Where they'd resprinkled it since church, the talcum shone like mica on their downy arms. Smelling solidly of geranium, they filed across the porch with short steps and fingers joined, just timed to turn their smiles loose inside the room. He held the door open for them.

"Ready to go?" he asked her.

Going back, the ride was wordless, quiet except for the motor and the insects driving themselves against the car. The windshield was soon blinded. The headlights pulled in two other spinning storms, cones of flying things that, it seemed, might ignite at the last minute. He stopped the car and got out to clean the windshield thoroughly with his brisk, angry motions of driving. Dust lay thick and cratered on the roadside scrub. Under the now ash-white moon, the world traveled through very faint stars— very many slow stars, very high, very low.

It was a strange land, amphibious—and whether water-covered or grown with jungle or robbed entirely of water and trees, as now, it had the same loneliness. He regarded the great sweep—like steppes, like moors, like deserts (all of which were imaginary to him); but more than it was like any likeness, it was South. The vast, thin, wide-thrown, pale, unfocused star-sky, with its veils of lightning adrift, hung over this land as it hung over the open sea. Standing out in the night alone, he was struck as powerfully with recognition of the extremity of this place as if all other bearings had vanished—as if snow had suddenly started to fall.

He climbed back inside and drove. When he moved to slap furiously at his shirtsleeves, she shivered in the hot, licking night wind that their speed was making. Once the car lights picked out two people—a Negro couple, sitting on two facing chairs in the yard outside their lonely cabin—half undressed, each battling for self against the hot night, with long white rags in endless, scarflike motions.

In peopleless open places there were lakes of dust, smudge fires burning at their hearts. Cows stood in untended rings around them, motionless in the heat, in the night—their horns standing up sharp against that glow.

At length, he stopped the car again, and this time he put his arm under her shoulder and kissed her—not knowing ever whether gently or harshly. It was the loss of that distinction that told him this was now. Then their faces touched unkissing, unmoving, dark, for a length of time. The heat came inside the car and wrapped them still, and the mosquitoes had begun to coat their arms and even their eyelids.

Later, crossing a large open distance, he saw at the same time two fires. He had the feeling that they had been riding for a long time across a face— great, wide, and upturned. In its eyes and open mouth were those fires they had had glimpses of, where the cattle had drawn together: a face, a head, far down here in the South—south of South, below it. A whole giant body sprawled downward then, on and on, always, constant as a constellation or an angel. Flaming and perhaps falling, he thought.

She appeared to be sound asleep, lying back flat as a child, with her hat in her lap. He drove on with her profile beside his, behind his, for he bent forward to drive faster. The earrings she wore twinkled with their rushing motion in an almost regular beat. They might have spoken like tongues. He looked straight before him and drove on, at a speed that, for the rented, overheated, not at all new Ford car, was demoniac.

It seemed often now that a barnlike shape flashed by, roof and all outlined in lonely neon—a movie house at a cross roads. The long white flat road itself, since they had followed it to the end and turned around to come back, seemed able, this far up, to pull them home.

A thing is incredible, if ever, only after it is told—returned to the world it came out of. For their different reasons, he thought, neither of them would tell this (unless something was dragged out of them): that, strangers, they had ridden down into a strange land together and were getting safely back—by a slight margin, perhaps, but margin enough. Over the levee wall now, like an aurora borealis, the sky of New Orleans, across the river, was flickering gently. This time they crossed by bridge, high above everything, merging into a long light-stream of cars turned cityward.

For a time afterward he was lost in the streets, turning almost at random with the noisy traffic until he found his bearings. When he stopped the car at the next sign and leaned forward frowning to make it out, she sat up straight on her side. It was Arabi. He turned the car right around.

"We're all right now," he muttered, allowing himself a cigarette.

Something that must have been with them all along suddenly, then, was not. In a moment, tall as panic, it rose, cried like a human, and dropped back.

"I never got my water," she said.

She gave him the name of her hotel, he drove her there, and he said good night on the sidewalk. They shook hands.

"Forgive . . . " For, just in time, he saw she expected it of him.

And that was just what she did, forgive him. Indeed, had she waked in time from a deep sleep, she would have told him her story. She disappeared through the revolving door, with a gesture of smoothing her hair, and he thought a figure in the lobby strolled to meet her. He got back in the car and sat there.

He was not leaving for Syracuse until early in the morning. At length, he recalled the reason; his wife had recommended that he stay where he was this extra day so that she could entertain some old, unmarried college friends without him underfoot.

As he started up the car, he recognized in the smell of exhausted, body-warm air in the streets, in which the flow of drink was an inextricable part, the signal that the New Orleans evening was just beginning. In Dickie Grogan's, as he passed, the well-known Josefina at her organ was charging up and down with *"Clair de Lune."* As he drove the little Ford safely to its garage, he remembered for the first time in years when he was young and brash, a student in New York, and the shriek and horror and unholy smother of the subway had its original meaning for him as the lilt and expectation of love.

EUDORA WELTY

How I Write

"HOW do I write my stories?" is a blessedly open question. For the writer it is forever in the course of being studied through doing and new doing, and wouldn't last very long as a matter of self-observation, which could very well turn him to stone. Apart from what he's learned about his separate stories, out of passion, the renewable passion, of doing each in the smallest part better (at least nearer the way he wants it), he may or may not be a good judge of his work in the altogether. To him if a story is good enough to be called finished, as far as he can see, it is detached on the dot from the hand that wrote it, and the luster goes with it; what *is* attached is the new story. "How I wrote," past tense, may be seen into from this detachment, but not with the same insight—that too is gone, displaced. Looking backward can't compete with looking forward with the story in progress—that invites and absorbs and uses every grain of his insight, and his love and wits and curiosity and strength of purpose. "How do I write *this* story?" is really the question, the vital question; but its findings can be set down only in terms of the story's own—terms of fiction. (At least, ordinarily. Story writing and an independently operating power of critical analysis are separate gifts, like spelling and playing the flute, and one person proficient in both has been doubly endowed. But even he can't rise and do both at the same time.)

I feel myself that any *generalization* about writing is remote from anything I have managed to learn about it. I believe I can make one wide one, and others must have often nailed it down, but I shall have to hold my blow till I get there. The only things I feel I really know well are stuck to the stories, part of the animal. The main lesson I've learned from work so far is the simple one that each story is going to open up a different prospect and pose a new problem; no story bears on another or helps another, even if the writing mind had room for help and the wish that it would come. Help would be a blight. I could add that it's hard for me to think that a writer's stories are a unified whole in any respect except perhaps their lyric quality. I don't believe they are written in any typical, predictable, logically developing, or even chronological way (for all that a good writer's stories are, to the reader, so immediately identifiable as his)—or in any way that after enough solid tries guarantees him a certain measure of excellence, safety (spare the word!), or delight.

I do have the feeling that all stories by one writer tend to spring from the same source within him. However they differ in subject or approach, however they vary in excellence or fluctuate in their power to alter the mind or mood or move the heart, all of one writer's stories must take on their quality, carry their signature, because of one characteristic, lyrical impulse of his mind—the impulse to praise, to love, to call up, to prophesy. But then what countless stories share a common source! All writers write out of the same few, few and eternal—love, pity, terror do not change.

Sources of stories could be examined with less confusion, perhaps, not in the subjective terms of emotion, but through finding what in the outside world leads back to those emotions most directly and tautly and specifically. The surest clue is the pull on the line, the "inspiration," the outside signal that has startled or moved the creative mind to complicity and brought the story to active being: the irresistible, the magnetic, the alarming (pleasurable or disturbing), the overwhelming person, place, or thing.

Surely, for the writer this is the world where stories come from, and where their origins are living reference plain to his eyes. The dark changes of the mind and heart, where all in the world is constantly *becoming* something—the poetic, the moral, the passionate, hence the *shaping* idea—are not mapped and plotted yet, except as psychiatry has applied the healing or tidying hand, and their being so would make no change in their processes, or their climates, or their way of life and death (any more than a map hung on the wall changes the world); or schedule or pigeonhole or allot or substitute or predict the mysteries rushing unsubmissively through them by the minute; or explain a single work of art that came out the other side. The artist at work functions, while whoever likes to may explain how he does it (or failing that, why)—without, however, the least power of prevention or prophecy or even cure—for some alarmists say that literature has come out of a disease of society, as if stamping out the housefly would stop it, and I've heard there's another critic who says writing is nothing but the death wish. (Exactly where in all this *standards* come in I don't know.)

It is of course the *way* of writing that gives a story, however humble, its whole distinction and glory—something learned, and learned each writer for himself, by dint of each story's unique challenge and his work that rises to meet it—work scrupulous, questioning, unprecedented, ungeneralized, uncharted, and his own. It is the changeable outside world and the learnable way of writing that are the different quotients. Always different, always differing, from writer to writer and story to story, they are—or so I believe—most intimately connected with each other.

Like a good many other writers, I am myself touched off by place. The place where I am and the place I know, and other places that familiarity with and love for my own make strange and lovely and enlightening to look into, are what set me to writing my stories. To such writers I suppose place opens a door in the mind, either spontaneously or through beating it down, attrition. The impression of place as revealing something is an indelible one—which of course is not to say it isn't highly personal and very likely distorted. The imagination further and further informs and populates the impression according to present mood, intensification of feeling, beat of memory, accretion of idea, and by the blessing of being located —contained—a story so changed is now capable of being written.

The connection of this to what's called regional writing is clear but not much more informing; it does mean a lot of writers behave the same way. Regional writing itself has old deep roots; it is not the big root itself. Place is surely one of the most simple and obvious and direct sources of the short story, and one of the most ancient—as it is of lyric poetry—and, if I may presume to speak freely here for other regional writers too, the connection of story to place can go for ever so long not even conscious in the mind, because taken for granted. The regional writer's vision is as surely made of the local clay as any mud pie of his childhood was, and it's still the act of the imagination that makes the feast; only in the case of any art the feast is real, for the act of the imagination gives vision the substance and makes it last.

After we see the connection between our place and our writing, has anything changed for us? We aren't admonished in any way we weren't admonished already by pride of work, surely? Yes, something *has* changed for us; we learn that. I am the proud partisan I am of regional writing because this connection between place and story *is* deep, *does* take time, and its claims on us are deep; they, like our own minds' responsibilities, are for us to find out. To be a regional writer is not like belonging to a club or a political party; it is nothing you can take credit for—it's an endowment, but more than that. It's a touchstone when you write, and shows up, before anything else does, truth and mistakes. In a way place is your honor as it is your wisdom, and would make you responsible to it for what you put down for the truth.

Whatever the story a reader takes up, the road from origin on isn't any the plainer for the simplicity of the start. Sometimes a reader thinks he is "supposed" to see in a story (I judge from letters from readers when they can't find it in mine) a sort of plant-from-seed development, rising in the end to a perfect Christmas tree of symmetry, branch, and ornament, with a star at the top for neatness. The reader of more willing imagination, who has specified for something else, may find the branchings not what he's expecting either, and the fulfillment not a perfect match, not at all to the letter of the promise—rather to a degree—(and to a degree of pleasure) mysterious. This is one of the short story's finest attributes. The analyst, should the story come under his eye, may miss this gentle shock and this pleasure too, for he's picked up the story at once by its heels (as if it had swallowed a button) and is examining the writing as his own process in reverse, as though a story (or any system of feeling) could be the more accessible to understanding for being hung upside down. "Sweet Analytics, 'tis thou hast ravish'd me!"

Analysis, to speak generally, has to travel backwards; the path it goes, while paved with good intentions, is an ever-narrowing one, whose goal is the vanishing point, beyond which only "influences" lie. But writing, bound in the opposite direction, works further and further always into the open. The choices get freer and wider, apparently, as with everything else that has a life and moves. "This story promises me fear and joy and so I write it" has been the writer's honest beginning. Dr. Faustus, the critic, coming to the end of his trail, may call out the starting point he's found, but the writer long ago knew the starting point for what it was to him—the jumping off place. If they coincide, it's a coincidence. I think the writer's out-bound choices seem obstructive sometimes to analysts simply because they wouldn't be there if they weren't plain evidence that they were to the writer inevitable choices, not arguable; impelled, not manipulated; that they came with an arrow inside them. Indeed they have been *fiction's* choices: one-way and fateful; strict as art, obliged as feeling, powerful in their authenticity though for slightest illusion's sake; and reasonable (in the out-of-fiction sense) only last, and by the grace of, again, coincidence—always to be welcomed and shown consideration, but never to be courted or flattered.

Certainly a story and its analysis are not the mirror opposites of each other, for all their running off in opposite directions. Criticism can be an art too and may go deeper than its object, and more times around; it may pick up a story and waltz with it, so that it's never the same. In any case it's not a reflection. But I think that's exactly why it cannot be *used* as one, whoever holds it up, even the curious author; why it's a mistake to think you can stalk back a story by analysis's footprints and even dream that's the original coming through the woods. Besides the difference in the direction of the two, there's the difference in speeds, when one has fury; but the main difference is in world-surround. One surround is a vision and the other is a pattern for good visions (which—who knows!—fashion may have tweaked a little) or the nicest, carefullest black-and-white tracing that a breath of life would do for. Each, either, or neither may be a masterpiece of construction; but the products are not to be confused.

The story is a vision; while it's being written, all choices must be its choices, and as these multiply upon one another, their field is growing too. The choices remain inevitable, in fact, through moving in a growing maze of possibilities that the writer, far from being dismayed at his presence on unknown ground (which might frighten him as a critic) has learned to be grateful for, and excited by. The fiction writer has learned (and here is my generalization) that it is the very existence, the very multitude and clamor and threat and lure of *possibility*—all possibilities his work calls up for itself as it goes—that guide his story most delicately. In the act of writing he finds, if no explanation outside fiction for what he is doing, or the need of it, no mystery about it either. What he does know is the word comes surest out of too much, not too little—just as the most exacting and sometimes the simplest-appearing work is brought off (when it does not fail) on the sharp edge of experiment, not in dim, reneging safety. He is not at the end yet, but it was for this he left all he knew behind, at the jumping off place, when he started this new story.

II

I made the remark above that I believed the changeable outside world and the learnable way of writing are connected with each other. I think it is this connection that can be specifically looked at in any story, but maybe a regional story could give us the easiest time. I offer here the clearest example I could find among my own stories of the working point I am hoping to make, since place not only suggested how to write the story but repudiated a way I had already tried it.

What happened was that I was invited to drive with a friend down south of New Orleans one summer day, to see that country for the first (and only) time, and when I got back home I realized that without being aware of it at the time I had treated a story, which I was working on then, to my ride, and it had come into my head in an altogether new form. I set to work and wrote the new version from scratch, which resulted in my throwing away the first and using the second. I learned all the specific detail of this story from the ride, though I should add that the story in neither version had any personal connection with myself and there was no conscious "gathering of material" on a pleasant holiday.

As first written, the story told, from the inside, of a girl in a claustrophobic predicament: she was caught fast in the over-familiar, monotonous life of her small town, and immobilized further by a hopeless and inarticulate love, which she had to pretend was something else. This happens all the time. As a result of my ride I extracted her. But she had been well sealed inside her world, by nature and circumstance both, and even more closely by my knowing her too well (the story had gone on too long) and too confidently. Before I could prize her loose, I had to take a primary step of getting outside her mind. I made her a girl from the Middle West— she'd been what I knew best, a Southerner, before. I kept outside her by taking glimpses of her through the curious eyes of a stranger: instead of the half-dozen characters (I knew them too well too) from the first version, I put in one single new one—a man whom I brought into the story *to be* a stranger. I had double-locked the doors behind me—you never dream the essentials can be simple again, within one story.

But the vital thing that happened to the story came from writing, as I began the work. My first realization of what it was came when I looked back and recognized that country (the once-submerged, strange land of "south from South" that had so stamped itself upon my imagination) as the image to me of the story's predicament come to life. This pointed out to me, as I wrote into the story, where the real point of view belonged. Once I was outside, I saw *it* was outside—suspended, hung in the air between the two people, fished alive from the surrounding scene, where as it carried the story along it revealed itself (I hoped) as more real, more essential, than the characters were or had any cause to be. In effect there'd come to be a sort of third character present— an identity, rather: the relationship between the two and between the two and the world. It was what grew up between them meeting as strangers, went on the trip with them, nodded back and forth from one to the other—listening, watching, persuading or denying them, enlarging or diminishing them, forgetful sometimes of who they were or what they were doing here, helping or betraying them along. Its role was that of hypnosis—it was what a relationship *does*, be it however brief, tentative, potential, happy or sinister, ordinary or extraordinary. I wanted to suggest that its being took shape as the strange, compulsive journey itself, was palpable as its climate and mood, the heat of the day—but was its spirit too, a spirit that held territory—what's seen fleeting past by two vulnerable people who might seize hands on the run. There are times in the story when I say neither "she felt" nor "he felt" but "they felt." All this is something that *doesn't* happen all the time. It merely could, or almost could, as here.

This is to grant that I rode out of the old story on the back of the girl and then threw away the girl; but I saved the story, for entirely different as the second version was, it was what I wanted to say. My subject was out in the open, provided at the same time with a place to happen and a way to say it was happening. All I had had to do was recognize it, which I did a little late.

Anyone who has visited the actual scene of this story has a chance of recognizing it when he meets it here, for the story is visual and the place is out of the ordinary. The connection between a story and its setting may not always be so plain. A reader may not see the slightest excuse for a given story after a personal inspection of the scene that called it up; the chances are good that he may not recognize it at all, and about 100 per cent that he will feel he would certainly have written something of a different sort himself. The point is, of course, that no matter whether the "likeness" is there for all to see or not, the place, once entered into the writer's mind in a story, is, in the course of writing the story, *functional.*

I wanted to make it seen and believed what was to me, in my story's grip, literally apparent—that secret and shadow are taken away in this country by the merciless light that prevails there, by the river that is like an exposed vein of ore, the road that descends as one with the heat—its nerve (these are all terms in the story), and that the heat is also a visual illusion, shimmering and dancing over the waste that stretches ahead. I was writing of a real place; but doing so in order to write about my subject. I was writing of exposure, and the shock of the world; in the end I tried to make the story's inside outside and then throw away the shell.

The vain courting of imperviousness in the face of exposure is this little story's plot. Deliver us all from the naked in heart, the girl thinks (this is what I kept of her). "So strangeness gently steels us," I read today in a poem of Richard Wilbur's. Riding down together into strange country is danger, a play at danger, secretly poetic, and the characters, in attempting it as a mutual feat, admit nothing to each other except the wicked heat and its comical inconvenience; the only time they will yield or touch is while they are dancing in the crowd that to them is comically unlikely (hence insulating, non-conducting) or taking a kiss outside time. Nevertheless it happens that they go along aware, from moment to moment, as one: as my third character, the straining, hallucinatory eyes and ears, the roused up sentient being of that place. Exposure begins in intuition and has its end in showing the heart that has expected, while it dreads, that exposure. Writing it as I'd done before as a story of concealment, in terms of the

hermetic and the familiar, had somehow resulted in my effective concealment of what I meant to say.

(I might say, for what interest it has here, that the original image of
the story's first version came from an object—a grandiose, dusty, empty
punch bowl of cut glass surrounded by its ring of cups, standing typically
in the poor, small-town hardware store window where such things go un-
sold for ever, surrounded by the axes and halters and tin mailboxes and
shotguns of the country trade. Even as I write it's still provocative to me—
as it is probably, also, still there in the window, still $13.75.)

In my second effort to show the story happen, the place had suggested
to me that something demoniac was called for—the speed of the ride pitted
against the danger of an easy or ignorant or tempting sympathy, too pressing, too acute, in the face of an inimical world, the heat that in itself
drives on the driver. Something wilder than ordinary communication between well-disposed strangers, and more ruthless and more tender than
their automatic, saving ironies and graces, I felt, and do so often feel, has
to come up against a world like that.

I did my best to merge, rather to identify, the abstract with the concrete, it being so happily possible in this story—however the possibilities
may have been realized—where setting, characters, mood, and method of
writing all appeared parts of the same thing and subject to related laws
and conditionings. I cut out some odd sentences that occurred, not because
they were odd—for the story is that—but because they would tantalize
some cooling explanations out of the mind if they stayed in. The story
had to be self-evident and hold its speed—which I think of as racing, though
it may not seem so to the reader. Above all I had no wish to sound mystical,
but I did expect to sound mysterious now and then, if I could: this was
a circumstantial, realistic story in which the reality *was* mystery. The cry
that rose up at the story's end was, I hope unmistakably, the cry of the
fading relationship—personal, individual, psychic—admitted in order to be
denied, a cry that the characters were first able (and prone) to listen to,
and then able in part to ignore. The cry was authentic to my story and
so I didn't care if it did seem a little odd: the end of a journey *can* set up
a cry, the shallowest provocation to sympathy and loves does hate to
give up the ghost. A relationship of the most fleeting kind has the power
inherent to loom like a genie—to become vocative at the last, as it has
already become present and taken up room; as it has spread out as a destination however makeshift; as it has, more faintly, more sparsely, glimmered
and rushed by in the dark and dust outside. Relationship *is* a pervading
and changing mystery; it is not words that make it so in life, but words
have to make it so in a story. Brutal or lovely, the mystery waits for people
wherever they go, whatever extreme they run to. I had got back at the
end of the new story to suggesting what I had started with at the begin-

ning of the old, but there was no question in my mind which story was nearer the mark.

This may not reflect very well on the brightness of the author; it may only serve to prove that for some writers a story has to rescue itself. This may be so, but I think it might show too what alone in the actual writing process may have interest for others besides the writer: that subject, method, form, style, all wait upon—indeed hang upon—a sort of double thunderclap at the author's ears: the break of the living world upon what is stirring inside the mind, and the answering impulse that in a moment of high consciousness fuses impact and image and fires them off together. There really never was a sound, but the impact is always recognizable, granting the author's sensitivity and sense, and if the impulse so projected is to some degree fulfilled it may give some pleasure out of reason to writer and reader. The living world remains just the same as it always was, and luckily enough for the story, among other things, for it can test and talk back to the story any day in the week.

JOHN CHEEVER

Goodbye, My Brother

WE are a family that has always been very close in spirit. Our father was drowned in a sailing accident when we were young, and our mother has always stressed the fact that our familial relationships have a kind of permanence that we will never meet with again. I don't think about the family much, but when I remember its members and the coast where they lived and the sea salt that I think is in our blood, I am happy to recall that I am a Pommeroy—that I have the nose, the coloring, and the promise of longevity—and that while we are not a distinguished family, we enjoy the illusion, when we are together, that the Pommeroys are unique. I don't say any of this because I'm interested in family history or because this sense of uniqueness is deep or important to me but in order to advance the point that we are loyal to one another in spite of our differences, and that any rupture in this loyalty is a source of confusion and pain.

We are four children; there is my sister Diana and the three men—Chaddy, Lawrence, and myself. Like most families in which the children are out of their twenties, we have been separated by business, marriage, and war. Helen and I live on Long Island now, with our four children. I teach in a secondary school, and I am past the age where I expect to be made headmaster—or principal, as we say—but I respect the work. Chaddy, who has done better than the rest of us, lives in Manhattan, with Odette and their children. Mother lives in Philadelphia, and Diana, since her divorce, has been living in France, but she comes back to the States in the summer to spend a month at Laud's Head. Laud's Head is a summer place on the shore of one of the Massachusetts islands. We used to have a cottage there, and in the twenties our father built the big house. It stands on a cliff above the sea and, excepting St. Tropez and some of the Apennine villages, it is my favorite place in the world. We each have an equity in the place and we contribute some money to help keep it going.

Our youngest brother, Lawrence, who is a lawyer, got a job with a Cleveland firm after the war, and none of us saw him for four years. When he decided to leave Cleveland and go to work for a firm in Albany, he wrote Mother that he would, between jobs, spend ten days at Laud's Head, with his wife and their two children. This was when I had planned to take my vacation—I had been teaching summer school—and Helen and Chaddy and Odette and Diana were all going to be there, so the family would be together. Lawrence is the member of the family with whom the rest of us have least in common. We have never seen a great deal of him, and I suppose that's why we still call him Tifty—a nickname he was given when he was a child, because when he came down the hall toward the dining room for breakfast, his slippers made a noise that sounded like "Tifty, tifty, tifty." That's what Father called him, and so did everyone else. When he grew older, Diana sometimes used to call him Little Jesus, and Mother often called him The Croaker. We had disliked Lawrence, but we looked forward to his return with a mixture of apprehension and loyalty, and with some of the joy and delight of reclaiming a brother.

Lawrence crossed over from the mainland on the four-o'clock boat one afternoon late in the summer, and Chaddy and I went down to meet him. The arrivals and departures of the summer ferry have all the outward signs that suggest a voyage—whistles, bells, hand trucks, reunions, and the smell of brine—but it is a voyage of no import, and when I watched the boat come into the blue harbor that afternoon and thought that it was completing a voyage of import, I realized that I had hit on exactly the kind of observation that Lawrence would have made. We looked for his face behind the windshields as the cars drove off the boat, and we had no trouble in recognizing him. And we ran over and shook his hand and clumsily kissed his wife and the children. "Tifty!" Chaddy shouted. "Tifty!" It is difficult to judge changes in the appearance of a brother, but both Chaddy and I agreed, as we drove back to Laud's Head, that Lawrence still looked very young. He got to the house first, and we took the suitcases out of his car. When I came in, he was standing in the living room, talking with Mother and Diana. They were in their best clothes and all their jewelry, and they were welcoming him extravagantly, but even then, when everyone was endeavoring to seem most affectionate and at a time when these endeavors come easiest, I was aware of a faint tension in the room. Thinking about this as I carried Lawrence's heavy suitcases up the stairs, I realized that our dislikes are as deeply ingrained as our better passions, and I remembered that once, twenty-five years ago, when I had hit Lawrence on the head with a rock, he had picked himself up and gone directly to our father to complain.

I carried the suitcases up to the third floor, where Ruth, Lawrence's wife, had begun to settle her family. She is a thin girl, and she seemed very tired from the journey, but when I asked her if she didn't want me to bring a drink upstairs to her, she said she didn't think she did.

When I got downstairs, Lawrence wasn't around, but the others were all ready for cocktails, and we decided to go ahead. Lawrence is the only member of the family who has never enjoyed drinking. We took our cocktails onto the terrace, so that we could see the bluffs and the sea and the islands in the east, and the return of Lawrence and his wife, their presence in the house, seemed to refresh our responses to the familiar view; it was as if the pleasure they would take in the sweep and the color of that coast, after such a long absence, had been imparted to us. While we were there, Lawrence came up the path from the beach.

"Isn't the beach fabulous, Tifty?" Mother asked. "Isn't it fabulous to be back? Will you have a Martini?"

"I don't care," Lawrence said. "Whiskey, gin—I don't care what I drink. Give me a little rum."

"We don't have any *rum*," Mother said. It was the first note of asperity. She has taught us never to be indecisive, never to reply as Lawrence had. Beyond this, she is deeply concerned with the propriety of her house, and anything irregular by her standards, like drinking straight rum or bringing a beer can to the dinner table, excites in her a conflict that she cannot, even with her capacious sense of humor, surmount. She sensed the asperity and worked to repair it. "Would you like some Irish, Tifty dear?" she said. "Isn't Irish what you've always liked? There's some Irish on the sideboard. Why don't you get yourself some Irish?" Lawrence said that he didn't care. He poured himself a Martini, and then Ruth came down and we went in to dinner.

In spite of the fact that we had, through waiting for Lawrence, drunk too much before dinner, we were all anxious to put our best foot forward and to enjoy a peaceful time. Mother is a small woman whose face is still a striking reminder of how pretty she must have been, and whose conversation is unusually light, but she talked that evening about a soil-reclamation project that is going on up-island. Diana is as pretty as Mother must have been; she is an animated and lovely woman who likes to talk about the dissolute friends that she has made in France, but she talked that night about the school in Switzerland where she had left her two children. I could see that the dinner had been planned to please Lawrence. It was not too rich, and there was nothing to make him worry about extravagance.

After supper, when we went back onto the terrace, the clouds held that kind of light that looks like blood, and I was glad that Lawrence had such a lurid sunset for his homecoming. When we had been out there a few minutes, a man named Edward Chester came to get Diana. She had met him in France, or on the boat home, and he was staying for ten days at the inn in the village. He was introduced to Lawrence and Ruth, and then he and Diana left.

"Is that the one she's sleeping with now?" Lawrence asked.

"What a horrid thing to say!" Helen said.

"You ought to apologize for that, Tifty," Chaddy said.

"I don't know," Mother said tiredly. "I don't know, Tifty. Diana is in a position to do whatever she wants, and I don't ask sordid questions. She's my only daughter. I don't see her often."

"Is she going back to France?"

"She's going back the week after next."

Lawrence and Ruth were sitting at the edge of the terrace, not in the chairs, not in the circle of chairs. With his mouth set, my brother looked to me then like a Puritan cleric. Sometimes, when I try to understand his frame of mind, I think of the beginnings of our family in this country, and his disapproval of Diana and her lovers reminded me of this. The branch of the Pommeroys to which we belong was founded by a minister who was eulogized by Cotton Mather for his untiring abjuration of the Devil. The Pommeroys were ministers until the middle of the nineteenth century, and the harshness of their thought—man is full of misery, and all earthly beauty is lustful and corrupt—has been preserved in books and sermons. The temper of our family changed somewhat and became more light-hearted, but when I was of school age, I can remember a cousinage of old men and women who seemed to hark back to the dark days of the ministry and to be animated by perpetual guilt and the deification of the scourge. If you are raised in this atmosphere—and in a sense we were—I think it is a trial of the spirit to reject its habits of guilt, self-denial, taciturnity, and penitence, and it seemed to me to have been a trial of the spirit in which Lawrence had succumbed.

"Is that Cassiopeia?" Odette asked.

"No, dear," Chaddy said. "That isn't Cassiopeia."

"Who was Cassiopeia?" Odette said.

"She was the wife of Cepheus and the mother of Andromeda," I said.

"The cook is a Giants fan," Chaddy said. "She'll give you even money that they win the pennant."

It had grown so dark that we could see the passage of light through the sky from the lighthouse at Cape Herion. In the dark below the cliff, the continual detonations of the surf sounded. And then, as she often does when it is getting dark and she has drunk too much before dinner, Mother began to talk about the improvements and additions that would someday be made on the house, the wings and bathrooms and gardens.

"This house will be in the sea in five years," Lawrence said.

"Tifty the Croaker," Chaddy said.

"Don't call me Tifty," Lawrence said.

"Little Jesus," Chaddy said.

"The sea wall is badly cracked," Lawrence said. "I looked at it this afternoon. You had it repaired four years ago, and it cost eight thousand dollars. You can't do that every four years."

"Please, Tifty," Mother said.

"Facts are facts," Lawrence said, "and it's a damned-fool idea to build a house at the edge of a cliff on a sinking coastline. In my lifetime, half the garden has washed away and there's four feet of water where we used to have a bathhouse."

"Let's have a very *general* conversation," Mother said bitterly. "Let's talk about politics or the boat-club dance."

"As a matter of fact," Lawrence said, "the house is probably in some danger now. If you had an unusually high sea, a hurricane sea, the wall would crumble and the house would go. We could all be drowned."

"I can't *bear* it," Mother said. She went into the pantry and came back with a full glass of gin.

I have grown too old now to think that I can judge the sentiments of others, but I was conscious of the tension between Lawrence and Mother, and I knew some of the history of it. Lawrence couldn't have been more than sixteen years old when he decided that Mother was frivolous, mischievous, destructive, and overly strong. When he had determined this, he decided to separate himself from her. He was at boarding school then, and I remember that he did not come home for Christmas. He spent Christmas with a friend. He came home very seldom after he had made his unfavorable judgment on Mother, and when he did come home, he always tried, in his conversation, to remind her of his estrangement. When he married Ruth, he did not tell Mother. He did not tell her when his children were born. But in spite of these principled and lengthy exertions he seemed, unlike the rest of us, never to have enjoyed any separation, and when they are together, you feel at once a tension, an unclearness.

And it was unfortunate, in a way, that Mother should have picked that night to get drunk. It's her privilege, and she doesn't get drunk often, and fortunately she wasn't bellicose, but we were all conscious of what was happening. As she quietly drank her gin, she seemed sadly to be parting from us; she seemed to be in the throes of travel. Then her mood changed from travel to injury, and the few remarks she made were petulant and irrelevant. When her glass was nearly empty, she stared angrily at the dark air in front of her nose, moving her head a little, like a fighter. I knew that there was not room in her mind then for all the injuries that were crowding into it. Her children were stupid, her husband was drowned, her servants were thieves, and the chair she sat in was uncomfortable. Suddenly she put down her empty glass and interrupted Chaddy, who was talking about baseball. "I know one *thing*," she said hoarsely. "I know that if there is an afterlife, I'm going to have a very different kind of family. I'm going to have nothing but fabulously rich, witty, and enchanting children." She got up and, starting for the door, nearly fell. Chaddy caught her and helped her up the stairs. I could hear their tender good nights, and then Chaddy came back. I thought that Lawrence by now would be tired from his journey and his return, but he remained on the terrace, as if he were waiting to see the final malfeasance, and the rest of us left him there and went swimming in the dark.

When I woke the next morning, or half woke, I could hear the sound of someone rolling the tennis court. It is a fainter and a deeper sound than the iron buoy bells off the point—an unrhythmic iron chiming—that belongs in my mind to the beginnings of a summer day, a good portent. When I went downstairs, Lawrence's two kids were in the living room, dressed in ornate cowboy suits. They are frightened and skinny children. They told me their father was rolling the tennis court but that they did not want to go out because they had seen a snake under the doorstep. I explained to them that their cousins—all the other children—ate breakfast in the kitchen and that they'd better run along in there. At this announcement, the boy began to cry. Then his sister joined him. They cried as if to go in the kitchen and eat would destroy their most precious rights. I told them to sit down with me. Lawrence came in, and I asked him if he wanted to play some tennis. He said no, thanks, although he thought he might play some singles with Chaddy. He was in the right here, because both he and Chaddy play better tennis than I, and he did play some singles with Chaddy after breakfast, but later on, when the others came down to play family doubles, Lawrence disappeared. This made me cross—unreasonably so, I suppose—but we play darned interesting family doubles and he could have played in a set for the sake of courtesy.

Late in the morning, when I came up from the court alone, I saw Tifty on the terrace, prying up a shingle from the wall with his jackknife. "What's the matter, Lawrence?" I said. "Termites?" There are termites in the wood and they've given us a lot of trouble.

He pointed out to me, at the base of each row of shingles, a faint blue line of carpenter's chalk. "This house is about twenty-two years old," he said. "These shingles are about two hundred years old. Dad must have bought shingles from all the farms around here when he built the place, to make it look venerable. You can still see the carpenter's chalk put down where these antiques were nailed into place."

It was true about the shingles, although I had forgotten it. When the house was built, our father, or his architect, had ordered it covered with lichened and weather-beaten shingles. I didn't follow Lawrence's reasons for thinking that this was scandalous.

"And look at these doors," Lawrence said. "Look at these doors and window frames." I followed him over to a big Dutch door that opens onto the terrace and looked at it. It was a relatively new door, but someone had worked hard to conceal its newness. The surface had been deeply scored with some metal implement, and white paint had been rubbed into the incisions to imitate brine, lichen, and weather rot. "Imagine spending thousands of dollars to make a sound house look like a wreck," Lawrence said. "Imagine the frame of mind this implies. Imagine wanting to live so much in the past that you'll pay men carpenters' wages to disfigure your front door." Then I remembered Lawrence's sensitivity to time and his sentiments and opinions about our feelings for the past. I had heard him say, years ago, that we and our friends and our part of the nation, finding ourselves unable to cope with the problems of the present, had, like a wretched adult, turned back to what we supposed was a happier and a simpler time, and that our taste for reconstruction and candlelight was a measure of this irremediable failure. The faint blue line of chalk had reminded him of these ideas, the scarified door had reinforced them, and now clue after clue presented itself to him—the stern light at the door, the bulk of the chimney, the width of the floorboards and the pieces set into them to resemble pegs. While Lawrence was lecturing me on these frailties, the others came up from the court. As soon as Mother saw Lawrence, she responded, and I saw that there was little hope of any rapport between the matriarch and the changeling. She took Chaddy's arm. "Let's go swimming and have Martinis on the beach," she said. "Let's have a *fabulous* morning."

The sea that morning was a solid color, like verd stone. Everyone went to the beach but Tifty and Ruth. "I don't mind *him*," Mother said. She was excited, and she tipped her glass and spilled some gin into the sand. "I don't mind *him*. It doesn't matter to me how *rude* and *horrid* and *gloomy* he is, but what I can't bear are the faces of his wretched little children, those fabulously unhappy little children." With the height of the cliff between us, everyone talked wrathfully about Lawrence, about how he had grown worse instead of better, how unlike the rest of us he was, how he endeavored to spoil every pleasure. We drank our gin; the abuse seemed to reach a crescendo, and then, one by one, we went swimming in the solid green water. But when we came out no one mentioned Lawrence unkindly; the line of abusive conversation had been cut, as if swimming had the cleansing force claimed for baptism. We dried our hands and lighted cigarettes, and if Lawrence was mentioned, it was only to suggest, kindly, something that might please him. Wouldn't he like to sail to Barin's cove, or go fishing?

And now I remember that while Lawrence was visiting us, we went swimming oftener than we usually do, and I think there was a reason for this. When the irritability that accumulated as a result of his company began to lessen our patience, not only with Lawrence but with one another, we would all go swimming and shed our animus in the cold water. I can see the family now, smarting from Lawrence's rebukes as they sat on the sand, and I can see them wading and diving and surface-diving and hear in their voices the restoration of patience and the rediscovery of inexhaustible good will. If Lawrence noticed this change—this illusion of purification—I suppose that he would have found in the vocabulary of psychiatry, or the mythology of the Atlantic, some circumspect name for it, but I don't think he noticed the change. He neglected to name the curative powers of the open sea, but it was one of the few chances for diminution that he missed.

The cook we had that year was a Polish woman named Anna Ostrovick, a summer cook. She was first-rate—a big, fat, hearty, industrious woman who took her work very seriously. She liked to cook and to have the food she cooked appreciated and eaten, and whenever we saw her, she always urged us to eat. She cooked hot bread—crescents and brioches—for breakfast two or three times a week, and she would bring these into the dining room herself and say, "Eat, eat, eat!" When the maid took the serving dishes back into the pantry, we could sometimes hear Anna, who was standing there, say, "Good! They eat." She fed the garbage man, the milkman, and the gardener. "Eat!" she told them. "Eat, eat!" On Thursday afternoons, she went to the movies with the maid, but she didn't enjoy the movies, because the actors were all so thin. She would sit in the dark theater for an hour and a half watching the screen anxiously for the appearance of someone who had enjoyed his food. Bette Davis merely left with Anna the impression of a woman who has not eaten well. "They are all so skinny," she would say when she left the movies. In the evenings, after she had gorged all of us, and washed the pots and pans, she would collect the table scraps and go out to feed the creation. We had a few chickens that year, and although they would have roosted by then, she would dump food into their trough and urge the sleeping fowl to eat. She fed the songbirds in the orchard and the chipmunks in the yard. Her appearance at the edge of the garden and her urgent voice—we could hear her calling "Eat, eat, eat"—had become, like the sunset gun at the boat club and the passage of light from Cape Herion, attached to that hour. "Eat, eat, eat," we could hear Anna say. "Eat, eat . . ." Then it would be dark.

When Lawrence had been there three days, Anna called me into the kitchen. "You tell your mother," she said, "that *he* doesn't come into my kitchen. If *he* comes into my kitchen all the time, I go. *He* is always coming into my kitchen to tell me what a sad woman I am. He is always telling me that I work too hard and that I don't get paid enough and that I should belong to a union with vacations. Ha! He is so skinny but he is always coming into my kitchen when I am busy to pity me, but I am as good as him, I am as good as *anybody*, and I do not have to have people like that getting into my way all the time and feeling sorry for me. I am a famous and a wonderful cook and I have jobs everywhere and the only reason I come here to work this summer is because I was never before on an island, but I can have other jobs tomorrow, and if he is always coming into my kitchen to pity me, you tell your mother I am going. I am as good as *anybody* and I do not have to have that skinny all the time telling how poor I am."

I was pleased to find that the cook was on our side, but I felt that the situation was delicate. If Mother asked Lawrence to stay out of the kitchen, he would make a grievance out of the request. He could make a grievance out of anything, and it sometimes seemed that as he sat darkly at the dinner table, every word of disparagement, wherever it was aimed, came home to him. I didn't mention the cook's complaint to anyone, but somehow there wasn't any more trouble from that quarter.

The next cause for contention that I had from Lawrence came over our backgammon games.

When we are at Laud's Head, we play a lot of backgammon. At eight o'clock, after we have drunk our coffee, we usually get out the board. In a way, it is one of our pleasantest hours. The lamps in the room are still unlighted, Anna can be seen in the dark garden, and in the sky above her head there are continents of shadow and fire. Mother turns on the light and rattles the dice as a signal. We usually play three games apiece, each with the others. We play for money, and you can win or lose a hundred dollars on a game, but the stakes are usually much lower. I think that Lawrence used to play—I can't remember—but he doesn't play any more. He doesn't gamble. This is not because he is poor or because he has any principles about gambling but because he thinks the game is foolish and a waste of time. He was ready enough, however, to waste his time watching the rest of us play. Night after night, when the game began, he pulled a chair up beside the board, and watched the checkers and the dice. His expression was scornful, and yet he watched carefully. I wondered why he watched us night after night, and, through watching his face, I think that I may have found out.

Lawrence doesn't gamble, so he can't understand the excitement of winning and losing money. He has forgotten how to play the game, I think, so that its complex odds can't interest him. His observations were bound to include the facts that backgammon is an idle game and a game of chance, and that the board, marked with points, was a symbol of our worthlessness. And since he doesn't understand gambling or the odds of the game, I thought that what interested him must be the members of his family. One night when I was playing with Odette—I had won thirty-seven dollars from Mother and Chaddy—I think I saw what was going on in his mind.

Odette has black hair and black eyes. She is careful never to expose her white skin to the sun for long, so the striking contrast of blackness and pallor is not changed in the summer. She needs and deserves admiration—it is the element that contents her—and she will flirt, unseriously, with any man. Her shoulders were bare that night, her dress was cut to show the division of her breasts and to show her breasts when she leaned over the board to play. She kept losing and flirting and making her losses seem like a part of the flirtation. Chaddy was in the other room. She lost three games, and when the third game ended, she fell back on the sofa and, looking at me squarely, said something about going out on the dunes to settle the score. Lawrence heard her. I looked at Lawrence. He seemed shocked and gratified at the same time, as if he had suspected all along that we were not playing for anything so insubstantial as money. I may be wrong, of course, but I think that Lawrence felt that in watching our backgammon he was observing the progress of a mordant tragedy in which the money we won and lost served as a symbol for more vital forfeits. It is like Lawrence to try to read significance and finality into every gesture that we make, and it is certain of Lawrence that when he finds the inner logic to our conduct, it will be sordid.

Chaddy came in to play with me. Chaddy and I have never liked to lose to each other. When we were younger, we used to be forbidden to play games together, because they always ended in a fight. We think we know each other's mettle intimately. I think he is prudent; he thinks I am foolish. There is always bad blood when we play anything—tennis or backgammon or softball or bridge—and it does seem at times as if we were playing for the possession of each other's liberties. When I lose to Chaddy, I can't sleep. All this is only half the truth of our competitive relationship, but it was the half-truth that would be discernible to Lawrence, and his presence at the table made me so self-conscious that I lost two games. I tried not to seem angry when I got up from the board. Lawrence was watching me. I went out onto the terrace to suffer there in the dark the anger I always feel when I lose to Chaddy.

When I came back into the room, Chaddy and Mother were playing. Lawrence was still watching. By his lights, Odette had lost her virtue to me, I had lost my self-esteem to Chaddy, and now I wondered what he saw in the present match. He watched raptly, as if the opaque checkers and the marked board served for an exchange of critical power. How dramatic the board, in its ring of light, and the quiet players and the crash of the sea outside must have seemed to him! Here was spiritual cannibalism made visible; here, under his nose, were the symbols of the rapacious use human beings make of one another.

Mother plays a shrewd, an ardent, and an interfering game. She always has her hands in her opponent's board. When she plays with Chaddy, who is her favorite, she plays intently. Lawrence would have noticed this. Mother is a sentimental woman. Her heart is good and easily moved by tears and frailty, a characteristic that, like her handsome nose, has not been changed at all by age. Grief in another provokes her deeply, and she seems at times to be trying to divine in Chaddy some grief, some loss, that she can succor and redress, and so re-establish the relationship that she enjoyed with him when he was sickly and young. She loves defending the weak and the child-like, and now that we are old, she misses it. The world of debts and business, men and war, hunting and fishing has on her an exacerbating effect. (When Father drowned, she threw away his fly rods and his guns.) She has lectured us all endlessly on self-reliance, but when we come back to her for comfort and for help—particularly Chaddy—she seems to feel most like herself. I suppose Lawrence thought that the old woman and her son were playing for each other's soul.

She lost. "Oh *dear*," she said. She looked stricken and bereaved, as she always does when she loses. "Get me my glasses, get me my checkbook, get me something to drink." Lawrence got up at last and stretched his legs. He looked at us all bleakly. The wind and the sea had risen, and I thought that if he heard the waves, he must hear them only as a dark answer to all his dark questions; that he would think that the tide had expunged the embers of our picnic fires. The company of a lie is unbearable, and he seemed like the embodiment of a lie. I couldn't explain to him the simple and intense pleasures of playing for money, and it seemed to me hideously wrong that he should have sat at the edge of the board and concluded that we were playing for one another's soul. He walked restlessly around the room two or three times and then, as usual, gave us a parting shot. "I should think you'd go crazy," he said, "cooped up with one another like this, night after night. Come on, Ruth. I'm going to bed."

That night, I dreamed about Lawrence. I saw his plain face magnified into ugliness, and when I woke in the morning, I felt sick, as if I had suffered a great spiritual loss while I slept, like the loss of courage and heart. It was foolish to let myself be troubled by my brother. I needed a vacation. I needed to relax. At school, we live in one of the dormitories, we eat at the house table, and we never get away. I not only teach English winter and summer but I work in the principal's office and fire the pistol at track meets. I needed to get away from this and from every other form of anxiety, and I decided to avoid my brother. Early that day, I took Helen and the children sailing, and we stayed out until suppertime. The next day, we went on a picnic. Then I had to go to New York for a day, and when I got back, there was the costume dance at the boat club. Lawrence wasn't going to this, and it's a party where I always have a wonderful time.

The invitations that year said to come as you wish you were. After several conversations, Helen and I had decided what to wear. The thing she most wanted to be again, she said, was a bride, and so she decided to wear her wedding dress. I thought this was a good choice—sincere, light-hearted, and inexpensive. Her choice influenced mine, and I decided to wear an old football uniform. Mother decided to go as Jenny Lind, because there was an old Jenny Lind costume in the attic. The others decided to rent costumes, and when I went to New York, I got the clothes. Lawrence and Ruth didn't enter into any of this.

Helen was on the dance committee, and she spent most of Friday decorating the club. Diana and Chaddy and I went sailing. Most of the sailing that I do these days is in Manhasset, and I am used to setting a homeward course by the gasoline barge and the tin roofs of the boat shed, and it was a pleasure that afternoon, as we returned, to keep the bow on a white church spire in the village and to find even the inshore water green and clear. At the end of our sail, we stopped at the club to get Helen. The committee had been trying to give a submarine appearance to the ballroom, and the fact that they had nearly succeeded in accomplishing this illusion made Helen very happy. We drove back to Laud's Head. It had been a brilliant afternoon, but on the way home we could smell the east wind—the dark wind, as Lawrence would have said—coming in from the sea.

My wife, Helen, is thirty-eight, and her hair would be gray, I guess, if it were not dyed, but it is dyed an unobstrusive yellow—a faded color—and I think it becomes her. I mixed cocktails that night while she was dressing, and when I took a glass upstairs to her, I saw her for the first time since our marriage in her wedding dress. There would be no point in saying that she looked to me more beautiful than she did on our wedding day, but because I have grown older and have, I think, a greater depth of feeling, and because I could see in her face that night both youth and age, both her devotion to the young woman that she had been and the positions that she had yielded graciously to time, I think I have never been so deeply moved. I had already put on the football uniform, and the weight of it, the heaviness of the pants and the shoulder guards, had worked a change in me, as if in putting on these old clothes I had put off the reasonable anxieties and troubles of my life. It felt as if we had both returned to the years before our marriage, the years before the war.

The Collards had a big dinner party before the dance, and our family —excepting Lawrence and Ruth—went to this. We drove over to the club, through the fog, at about half past nine. The orchestra was playing a waltz. While I was checking my raincoat, someone hit me on the back. It was Chucky Ewing, and the funny thing was that Chucky had on a football uniform. This seemed comical as hell to both of us. We were laughing when we went down the hall to the dance floor. I stopped at the door to look at the party, and it was beautiful. The committee had hung fish nets all around the sides and over the high ceiling. The nets on the ceiling were filled with colored balloons. The light was soft and uneven, and the people —our friends and neighbors—dancing in the soft light to "Three O'Clock in the Morning" made a pretty picture. Then I noticed the number of women dressed in white, and I realized that they, like Helen, were wearing wedding dresses. Patsy Hewitt and Mrs. Gear and the Lackland girl waltzed by, dressed as brides. Then Pep Talcott came over to where Chucky and I were standing. He was dressed to be Henry VIII, but he told us that the Auerbach twins and Henry Barrett and Dwight MacGregor were all wearing football uniforms, and that by the last count there were ten brides on the floor.

This coincidence, this funny coincidence, kept everybody laughing, and made this one of the most lighthearted parties we've ever had at the club. At first I thought that the women had planned with one another to wear wedding dresses, but the ones that I danced with said it was a coincidence and I'm sure that Helen had made her decision alone. Everything went smoothly for me until a little before midnight. I saw Ruth standing at the edge of the floor. She was wearing a long red dress. It was all wrong. It wasn't in the spirit of the party at all. I danced with her, but no one cut in, and I was darned if I'd spend the rest of the night dancing with her and I asked her where Lawrence was. She said he was out on the dock, and I took her over to the bar and left her and went out to get Lawrence.

The east fog was thick and wet, and he was alone on the dock. He was not in costume. He had not even bothered to get himself up as a fisherman or a sailor. He looked particularly saturnine. The fog blew around us like a cold smoke. I wished that it had been a clear night, because the easterly fog seemed to play into my misanthropic brother's hands. And I knew that the buoys—the groaners and bells that we could hear then—would sound to him like half-human, half-drowned cries, although every sailor knows that buoys are necessary and reliable fixtures, and I knew that the foghorn at the lighthouse would mean wanderings and losses to him and that he could misconstrue the vivacity of the dance music. "Come on in, Tifty," I said, "and dance with your wife or get her some partners."

"Why should I?" he said. "Why should I?" And he walked to the window and looked in at the party. "Look at it," he said. "Look at that . . ."

Chucky Ewing had got hold of a balloon and was trying to organize a scrimmage line in the middle of the floor. The others were dancing a samba. And I knew that Lawrence was looking bleakly at the party as he had looked at the weather-beaten shingles on our house, as if he saw here an abuse and a distortion of time; as if in wanting to be brides and football players we exposed the fact that, the lights of youth having been put out in us, we had been unable to find other lights to go by and, destitute of faith and principle, had become foolish and sad. And that he was thinking this about so many kind and happy and generous people made me angry, made me feel for him such an unnatural abhorrence that I was ashamed, for he is my brother and a Pommeroy. I put my arm around his shoulders and tried to force him to come in, but he wouldn't.

I got back in time for the Grand March, and after the prizes had been given out for the best costumes, they let the balloons down. The room was hot, and someone opened the big doors onto the dock, and the easterly wind circled the room and went out, carrying across the dock and out onto the water most of the balloons. Chucky Ewing went running out after the balloons, and when he saw them pass the dock and settle on the water, he took off his football uniform and dove in. Then Eric Auerbach dove in and Lew Phillips dove in and I dove in, and you know how it is at a party after midnight when people start jumping into the water. We recovered most of the balloons and dried off and went on dancing, and we didn't get home until morning.

The next day was the day of the flower show. Mother and Helen and Odette all had entries. We had a pickup lunch, and Chaddy drove the women and children over to the show. I took a nap, and in the middle of the afternoon I got some trunks and a towel and, on leaving the house, passed Ruth in the laundry. She was washing clothes. I don't know why she should seem to have so much more work to do than anyone else, but she is always washing or ironing or mending clothes. She may have been taught, when she was young, to spend her time like this, or she may be at the mercy of an expiatory passion. She seems to scrub and iron with a penitential fervor, although I can't imagine what it is that she thinks she's done wrong. Her children were with her in the laundry. I offered to take them to the beach, but they didn't want to go.

It was late in August, and the wild grapes that grow profusely all over the island made the land wind smell of wine. There is a little grove of holly at the end of the path, and then you climb the dunes, where nothing grows but that coarse grass. I could hear the sea, and I remember thinking how Chaddy and I used to talk mystically about the sea. When we were young, we had decided that we could never live in the West because we would miss the sea. "It is very nice here," we used to say politely when we visited people in the mountains, "but we miss the Atlantic." We used to look down our noses at people from Iowa and Colorado who had been denied this revelation, and we scorned the Pacific. Now I could hear the waves, whose heaviness sounded like a reverberation, like a tumult, and it pleased me as it had pleased me when I was young, and it seemed to have a purgative force, as if it had cleared my memory of, among other things, the penitential image of Ruth in the laundry.

But Lawrence was on the beach. There he sat. I went in without speaking. The water was cold, and when I came out, I put on a shirt. I told him that I was going to walk up to Tanners Point, and he said that he would come with me. I tried to walk beside him. His legs are no longer than mine, but he always likes to stay a little ahead of his companion. Walking along behind him, looking at his bent head and his shoulders, I wondered what he could make of that landscape.

There were the dunes and cliffs and then, where they declined, there were some fields that had begun to turn from green to brown and yellow. The fields were used for pasturing sheep, and I guess Lawrence would have noticed that the soil was eroded and that the sheep would accelerate this decay. Beyond the fields there are a few coastal farms, with square and pleasant buildings, but Lawrence could have pointed out the hard lot of an island farmer. The sea, at our other side, was the open sea. We always tell guests that there, to the east, lies the coast of Portugal, and for Lawrence it would be an easy step from the coast of Portugal to the tyranny in Spain. The waves broke with a noise like a "hurrah, hurrah, hurrah," but to Lawrence they would say "*Vale, vale.*" I suppose it would have occurred to his baleful and incisive mind that the coast was terminal moraine, the edge of the prehistoric world, and it must have occurred to him that we walked along the edge of the known world in spirit as much as in fact. If he should otherwise have overlooked this, there were some Navy planes bombing an uninhabited island to remind him.

That beach is a vast and preternaturally clean and simple landscape. It is like a piece of the moon. The surf had pounded the floor solid, so it was easy walking, and everything left on the sand had been twice changed by the waves. There was the spine of a shell, a broomstick, part of a bottle and part of a brick, both of them milled and broken until they were nearly unrecognizable, and I suppose Lawrence's sad frame of mind—for he kept his head down—went from one broken thing to another. The company of his pessimism began to infuriate me, and I caught up with him and put a hand on his shoulder. "It's only a summer day, Tifty," I said. "It's only a summer day. What's the matter? Don't you like it here?"

"I don't like it here," he said blandly, without raising his eyes. "I'm going to sell my equity in the house to Chaddy. I didn't expect to have a good time. The only reason I came back was to say goodbye."

I let him get ahead again and I walked behind him, looking at his shoulders and thinking of all the goodbyes he had made. When Father drowned, he went to church and said goodbye to Father. It was only three years later that he concluded that Mother was frivolous and said goodbye to her. In his freshman year at college, he had been very good friends with his roommate, but the man drank too much, and at the beginning of the spring term Lawrence changed roommates and said good-bye to his friend. When he had been in college for two years, he concluded that the atmosphere was too sequestered and he said goodbye to Yale. He enrolled at Columbia and got his law degree there, but he found his first employer dishonest, and at the end of six months he said goodbye to a good job. He married Ruth in City Hall and said goodbye to the Protestant Episcopal Church; they went to live on a back street in Tuckahoe and said goodbye to the middle class. In 1938, he went to Washington to work as a government lawyer, saying goodbye to private enterprise, but after eight months in Washington he concluded that the Roosevelt administration was sentimental and he said goodbye to it. They left Washington for a suburb of Chicago, where he said goodbye to his neighbors, one by one, on counts of drunkenness, boorishness, and stupidity. He said goodbye to Chicago and went to Kansas; he said goodbye to Kansas and went to Cleveland. Now he had said goodbye to Cleveland and come East again, stopping at Laud's Head long enough to say goodbye to the sea.

It was elegiac and it was bigoted and narrow, it mistook circumspection for character, and I wanted to help him. "Come out of it," I said. "Come out of it, Tifty."

"Come out of what?"

"Come out of this gloominess. Come out of it. It's only a summer day. You're spoiling your own good time and you're spoiling everyone else's. We need a vacation, Tifty. I need one. I need to rest. We all do. And you've made everything tense and unpleasant. I only have two weeks in the year. Two weeks. I need to have a good time and so do all the others. We need to rest. You think that your pessimism is an advantage, but it's nothing but an unwillingness to grasp realities."

"What are the realities?" he said. "Diana is a foolish and a promiscuous woman. So is Odette. Mother is an alcoholic. If she doesn't discipline herself, she'll be in a hospital in a year or two. Chaddy is dishonest. He always has been. The house is going to fall into the sea." He looked at me and added, as an afterthought, "You're a fool."

"You're a gloomy son of a bitch," I said. "You're a gloomy son of a bitch."

"Get your fat face out of mine," he said. He walked along.

Then I picked up a root and, coming at his back—although I have never hit a man from the back before—I swung the root, heavy with sea water, behind me, and the momentum sped my arm and I gave him, my brother, a blow on the head that forced him to his knees on the sand, and I saw the blood come out and begin to darken his hair. Then I wished that he was dead, dead and about to be buried, not buried but about to be buried, because I did not want to be denied ceremony and decorum in putting him away, in putting him out of my consciousness, and I saw the rest of us —Chaddy and Mother and Diana and Helen—in mourning in the house on

Belvedere Street that was torn down twenty years ago, greeting our guests and our relatives at the door and answering their mannerly condolences with mannerly grief. Nothing decorous was lacking, so that even if he had been murdered on a beach, one would feel before the tiresome ceremony ended that he had come into the winter of his life and that it was a law of nature, and a beautiful one, that Tifty should be buried in the cold, cold ground.

He was still on his knees. I looked up and down. No one had seen us. The naked beach, like a piece of the moon, reached to invisibility. The spill of a wave, in a glancing run, shot up to where he knelt. I would still have liked to end him, but now I had begun to act like two men, the murderer and the Samaritan. With a swift roar, like hollowness made sound, a white wave reached him and encircled him, boiling over his shoulders, and I held him against the undertow. Then I led him to a higher place. The blood has spread all through his hair, so that it looked black. I took off my shirt and tore it to bind up his head. He was conscious, and I didn't think he was badly hurt. He didn't speak. Neither did I. Then I left him there.

I walked a little way down the beach and turned to watch him, and I was thinking of my own skin then. He had got to his feet and he seemed steady. The daylight was still clear, but on the sea wind fumes of brine were blowing in like a light fog, and when I had walked a little way from him, I could hardly see his dark figure in this obscurity. All down the beach I could see the heavy salt air blowing in. Then I turned my back on him, and as I got near to the house, I went swimming again, as I seem to have done after every encounter with Lawrence that summer.

When I got back to the house, I lay down on the terrace. The others came back. I could hear Mother defaming the flower arrangements that had won prizes. None of ours had won anything. Then the house quieted, as it always does at that hour. The children went into the kitchen to get supper and the others went upstairs to bathe. Then I heard Chaddy making cocktails, and the conversation about the flower-show judges was resumed. Then Mother cried, "Tifty! Tifty! Oh, Tifty!"

He stood in the door, looking half dead. He had taken off the bloody bandage and he held it in his hand. "My brother did this," he said. "My brother did it. He hit me with a stone—something—on the beach." His voice broke with self-pity. I thought he was going to cry. No one else spoke. "Where's Ruth?" he cried: "Where's Ruth? Where in hell is Ruth? I want her to start packing. I don't have any more time to waste here. I have important things to do. I have *important* things to do." And he went up the stairs.

They left for the mainland the next morning, taking the six o'clock boat. Mother got up to say goodbye, but she was the only one, and it is a harsh and an easy scene to imagine the matriarch and the changeling, looking at each other with a dismay that would seem like the powers of love reversed. I heard the children's voices and the car go down the drive, and I got up and went to the window, and what a morning that was! Jesus, what a morning! The wind was northerly. The air was clear. In the early heat, the roses in the garden smelled like strawberry jam. While I was dressing, I heard the boat whistle, first the warning signal and then the double blast, and I could see the good people on the top deck drinking coffee out of fragile paper cups, and Lawrence at the bow, saying to the sea, "*Thalassa, thalassa,*" while his timid and unhappy children watched the creation from the encirclement of their mother's arms. The buoys would toll mournfully for Lawrence, and while the grace of the light would make it an exertion not to throw out your arms and swear exultantly, Lawrence's eyes would trace the black sea as it fell astern; he would think of the bottom, dark and strange, where full fathom five our father lies.

Oh, what can you do with a man like that? What can you do? How can you dissuade his eye in a crowd from seeking out the cheek with acne, the infirm hand; how can you teach him to respond to the inestimable great-ness of the race, the harsh surface beauty of life; how can you put his finger for him on the obdurate truths before which fear and horror are powerless? The sea that morning was iridescent and dark. My wife and my sister were swimming—Diana and Helen—and I saw their uncovered heads, black and gold in the dark water. I saw them come out and I saw that they were naked, unshy, beautiful, and full of grace, and I watched the naked women walk out of the sea.

JOHN CHEEVER

What Happened

A few years ago I stayed with my family in a rented house on Martha's Vineyard until the second week in October. The Indian Summer was brilliant and still. We went unwillingly when the time came to go. We took the mid-morning boat to Wood's Hole and drove from a brilliant day at the sea into humid and overcast weather. South of Hartford it began to rain. We reached the apartment house in the east Fifties where we then lived just before dark. The city in the rain seemed particularly cavernous and noisy and the summer was definitely ended. Early the next morning I went to the room where I work. Before leaving the Vineyard I had begun a story, based on some notes made a year or two earlier in New Hampshire. The story described a family in a summer house who spent their evenings playing backgammon. It probably would have been called "The Backgammon Game." I meant to use the checkers, the board and the forfeits of a game to show that the relationships within a family can be extortionate. I was not sure of the story's conclusion but at the back of my mind was the idea that someone would lose his life over the board. I saw a canoe accident on a mountain lake. Reading the story over that morning I saw that, like some kinds of wine, it had not traveled. It was bad.

I come from a Puritanical family and I had been taught as a child that a moral lies beneath all human conduct and that the moral is always detrimental to man. I count among my relations people who feel that there is some inexpugnable nastiness at the heart of life and that love, friendship, Bourbon whisky, lights of all kinds—are merely the crudest deceptions. My aim as a writer has been to record a moderation of these attitudes—an escape from them if this seemed necessary—and in the backgammon story I had plainly failed. It was in essence precisely the kind of idle pessimism that I had hoped to enlighten. It was in the vein of one of my elderly uncles who never put a worm on a fish hook without stating that sooner or later we will all be corruption.

In order to occupy myself more cheerfully I looked over the notes I had made during the summer. I first came on a long description of train-sheds and ferry-boat landings—a song to the engines of love and death—but the substance of this was that these journeys were of no import—they were a kind of deception. A few pages after this I came on the description of a friend who, having lost the charms of youth and unable to find any new lights to go by, had begun to dwell on his football triumphs. This was connected to a scathing description of the house in the Vineyard where we had spent a pleasant summer. The house had not been old, but it had been sheathed with old shingles and the new wood of the doors had been scored and stained. The rooms were lighted with electric candles and I linked this crude sense of the past to my friend's failure to mature. The failure, my notes said, was national. We had failed to mature as a people and had turned back to dwell on old football triumphs, raftered ceilings, candlelight and open fires. There were some tearful notes on the sea, washing away the embers of our picnic fires, on the east wind—the dark wind—on the promiscuity of a beautiful young woman I know, on the hardships of island farming, on the jet planes that bombed an island off Gay Head, and a morose description of a walk on South Beach. The only cheerful notes in all this were two sentences about the pleasure I had taken one afternoon in watching my wife and another young lady walk out of the sea without any clothes on.

It is brief, but most journeys leave with us at least an illusion of improved perspective and there was a distance that morning between myself and my notes. I had spent the summer in excellent company and in a land-scape that I love, but there was no hint of this in the journal I had kept. The conflict in my feelings and my indignation at this division formed quickly in my mind the image of a despicable brother and I wrote: "Good-bye, My brother." The story moved quickly. Lawrence arrived on the is-land on a voyage of no import. I made the narrator fatuous since there was some ambiguity in my indignation. Laud's Head had the accommodating power of an imaginary landscape where you can pick and choose from a wide range of memory, putting in the smell of roses from a very different place and the ringing of a tennis-court roller that you heard years ago. The plan of the house was clear to me at once, although it was unlike any house that I had even seen. The terrace, the living-room, the staircase all appeared in order and when I pushed open the door from the pantry into the kitchen I seemed to find there a cook who had worked for my mother-in-law the year before the year before last. I had brought Lawrence home and taken him through his first night at Laud's Head before it was time for me to walk home for supper.

In the morning I unloaded onto Lawrence's shoulders my observations about backgammon. The story was moving then towards the boat club dance. Ten years ago at a costume ball in Minneapolis a man had worn a football uniform and his wife a wedding dress and this recollection fitted easily into place. The story was finished by Friday and I was happy for I know almost no pleasure greater than having a piece of fiction draw to-gether incidents as disparate as a dance in Minneapolis and a backgammon game in the mountains so that they relate to one another and confirm that feeling that life itself is creative process, that one thing is put purposefully upon another, that what is lost in one encounter is replenished in the next and that we possess some power to make sense of what takes place.

On Saturday I took a train to Philadelphia with a friend to see a foot-ball game. The story was still on my mind but when I thought back over what I had written, looking for weakness or crudeness, I felt assured. The football game was dull. It got cold. I began to feel uneasy at the half. We left in the middle of the fourth quarter. I had not worn a top-coat and I was shivering. Waiting in the cold for the train back to New York I saw the true worthlessness of my story, the scope of my self-deceptions, the flights and crash-landings of an unstable disposition and when the train came into the station I thought vaguely of throwing myself onto the tracks; but I went instead to the club car and drank some whisky. I have read the story since, and while I see that Lawrence lacks dimension and that the am-biguity will estrange some readers, it remains a reasonably exact account of my feelings after returning to Manhattan after a long summer on Martha's Vineyard.

KATHERINE ANNE PORTER

Noon Wine

Time: 1896–1905
Place: Small South Texas Farm

THE two grubby small boys with tow-colored hair who were digging among the ragweed in the front yard sat back on their heels and said, "Hello," when the tall bony man with straw-colored hair turned in at their gate. He did not pause at the gate; it had swung back, conveniently half open, long ago, and was now sunk so firmly on its broken hinges no one thought of trying to close it. He did not even glance at the small boys, much less give them good-day. He just clumped down his big square dusty shoes one after the other steadily, like a man following a plow, as if he knew the place well and knew where he was going and what he would find there. Rounding the right-hand corner of the house under the row of chinaberry trees, he walked up to the side porch where Mr. Thompson was pushing a big swing churn back and forth.

Mr. Thompson was a tough weather-beaten man with stiff black hair and a week's growth of black whiskers. He was a noisy proud man who held his neck so straight his whole face stood level with his Adam's apple, and the whiskers continued down his neck and disappeared into a black thatch under his open collar. The churn rumbled and swished like the belly of a trotting horse, and Mr. Thompson seemed somehow to be driving a horse with one hand, reining it in and urging it forward; and every now and then he turned halfway around and squirted a tremendous spit of tobacco juice out over the steps. The door stones were brown and gleaming with fresh tobacco juice. Mr. Thompson had been churning quite a while and he was tired of it. He was just fetching a mouthful of juice to squirt again when the stranger came around the corner and stopped. Mr. Thompson saw a narrow-chested man with blue eyes so pale they were almost white, looking and not looking at him from a long gaunt face, under white eyebrows. Mr. Thompson judged him to be another of these Irishmen, by his long upper lip.

"Howdy do, sir," said Mr. Thompson politely, swinging his churn.

"I need work," said the man, clearly enough but with some kind of foreign accent Mr. Thompson couldn't place. It wasn't Cajun and it wasn't Nigger and it wasn't Dutch, so it had him stumped. "You need a man here?"

Mr. Thompson gave the churn a great shove and it swung back and forth several times on its own momentum. He sat on the steps, shot his quid into the grass, and said, "Set down. Maybe we can make a deal. I been kinda lookin' round for somebody. I had two niggers but they got into a cutting scrape up the creek last week, one of 'em dead now and the other in the hoosegow at Cold Springs. Neither one of 'em worth killing, come right down to it. So it looks like I'd better get somebody. Where'd you work last?"

"North Dakota," said the man, folding himself down on the other end of the steps, but not as if he were tired. He folded up and settled down as if it would be a long time before he got up again. He never had looked at Mr. Thompson, but there wasn't anything sneaking in his eye, either. He didn't seem to be looking anywhere else. His eyes sat in his head and let things pass by them. They didn't seem to be expecting to see anything worth looking at. Mr. Thompson waited a long time for the man to say something more, but he had gone into a brown study.

"North Dakota," said Mr. Thompson, trying to remember where that was. "That's a right smart distance off, seems to me."

"I can do everything on farm," said the man; "cheap. I need work."

Mr. Thompson settled himself to get down to business. "My name's Thompson, Mr. Royal Earle Thompson," he said.

"I'm Mr. Helton," said the man, "Mr. Olaf Helton." He did not move.

"Well, now," said Mr. Thompson in his most carrying voice, "I guess we'd better talk turkey."

When Mr. Thompson expected to drive a bargain he always grew very hearty and jovial. There was nothing wrong with him except that he hated like the devil to pay wages. He said so himself. "You furnish grub and a shack," he said, "and then you got to pay 'em besides. It ain't right. Besides the wear and tear on your implements," he said, "they just let everything go to rack and ruin." So he began to laugh and shout his way through the deal.

"Now, what I want to know is, how much you fixing to gouge outa me?" he brayed, slapping his knee. After he had kept it up as long as he could, he quieted down, feeling a little sheepish, and cut himself a chew. Mr. Helton was staring out somewhere between the barn and the orchard, and seemed to be sleeping with his eyes open.

"I'm good worker," said Mr. Helton as from the tomb. "I get dollar a day."

Mr. Thompson was so shocked he forgot to start laughing again at the top of his voice until it was nearly too late to do any good. "Haw, haw," he bawled. "Why, for a dollar a day I'd hire out myself. What kinda work is it where they pay you a dollar a day?"

"Wheatfields, North Dakota," said Mr. Helton, not even smiling.

Mr. Thompson stopped laughing. "Well, this ain't any wheatfield by a long shot. This is more of a dairy farm," he said, feeling apologetic. "My wife, she was set on a dairy, she seemed to like working around with cows and calves, so I humored her. But it was a mistake," he said. "I got nearly everything to do, anyhow. My wife ain't very strong. She's sick today, that's a fact. She's been porely for the last few days. We plant a little feed, and a corn patch, and there's the orchard, and a few pigs and chickens, but our main hold is the cows. Now just speakin' as one man to another, there ain't any money in it. Now I can't give you no dollar a day because ackshally I don't make that much out of it. No, sir, we get along on a lot less than a dollar a day, I'd say, if we figger up everything in the long run. Now, I paid seven dollars a month to the two niggers, three-fifty each, and grub, but what I say is, one middlin'-good white man ekals a whole passel of niggers any day in the week, so I'll give you seven dollars and you eat at the table with us, and you'll be treated like a white man, as the feller says—"

"That's all right," said Mr. Helton. "I take it."

"Well, now I guess we'll call it a deal, hey?" Mr. Thompson jumped up as if he had remembered important business. "Now, you just take hold of that churn and give it a few swings, will you, while I ride to town on a coupla little errands. I ain't been able to leave the place all week. I guess you know what to do with butter after you get it, don't you?"

"I know," said Mr. Helton without turning his head. "I know butter business." He had a strange drawling voice, and even when he spoke only two words his voice waved slowly up and down and the emphasis was in the wrong place. Mr. Thompson wondered what kind of foreigner Mr. Helton could be.

"Now just where did you say you worked last?" he asked, as if he expected Mr. Helton to contradict himself.

"North Dakota," said Mr. Helton.

"Well, one place is good as another once you get used to it," said Mr. Thompson, amply. "You're a forriner, ain't you?"

"I'm a Swede," said Mr. Helton, beginning to swing the churn.

Mr. Thompson let forth a booming laugh, as if this was the best joke on somebody he'd ever heard. "Well, I'll be damned," he said at the top of his voice. "A Swede: well, now, I'm afraid you'll get pretty lonesome around here. I never seen any Swedes in this neck of the woods."

"That's all right," said Mr. Helton. He went on swinging the churn as if he had been working on the place for years.

"In fact, I might as well tell you, you're practically the first Swede I ever laid eyes on."

"That's all right," said Mr. Helton.

Mr. Thompson went into the front room where Mrs. Thompson was lying down, with the green shades drawn. She had a bowl of water by her on the table and a wet cloth over her eyes. She took the cloth off at the sound of Mr. Thompson's boots and said, "What's all the noise out there? Who is it?"

"Got a feller out there says he's a Swede, Ellie," said Mr. Thompson; "says he knows how to make butter."

"I hope it turns out to be the truth," said Mrs. Thompson. "Looks like my head never will get any better."

"Don't you worry," said Mr. Thompson. "You fret too much. Now I'm gointa ride into town and get a little order of groceries."

"Don't you linger, now, Mr. Thompson," said Mrs. Thompson. "Don't go to the hotel." She meant the saloon; the proprietor also had rooms for rent upstairs.

"Just a coupla little toddies," said Mr. Thompson, laughing loudly, "never hurt anybody."

"I never took a dram in my life," said Mrs. Thompson, "and what's more I never will."

"I wasn't talking about the womenfolks," said Mr. Thompson.

The sound of the swinging churn rocked Mrs. Thompson first into a gentle doze, then a deep drowse from which she waked suddenly knowing that the swinging had stopped a good while ago. She sat up shading her weak eyes from the flat strips of late summer sunlight between the sill and the lowered shades. There she was, thank God, still alive, with supper to cook but no churning on hand, and her head still bewildered, but easy. Slowly she realized she had been hearing a new sound even in her sleep. Somebody was playing a tune on the harmonica, not merely shrilling up and down making a sickening noise, but really playing a pretty tune, merry and sad.

She went out through the kitchen, stepped off the porch, and stood facing the east, shading her eyes. When her vision cleared and settled, she saw a long, pale-haired man in blue jeans sitting in the doorway of the hired man's shack, tilted back in a kitchen chair, blowing away at the harmonica with his eyes shut. Mrs. Thompson's heart fluttered and sank. Heavens, he looked lazy and worthless, he did, now. First a lot of no-count fiddling darkies and then a no-count white man. It was just like Mr. Thompson to take on that kind. She did wish he would be more considerate, and take a little trouble with his business. She wanted to believe in her husband, and there were too many times when she couldn't. She wanted to believe that tomorrow, or at least the day after, life, such a battle at best, was going to be better.

She walked past the shack without glancing aside, stepping carefully, bent at the waist because of the nagging pain in her side, and went to the springhouse, trying to harden her mind to speak very plainly to that new hired man if he had not done his work.

The milk house was only another shack of weather-beaten boards nailed together hastily years before because they needed a milk house; it was meant to be temporary, and it was; already shapeless, leaning this way and that over a perpetual cool trickle of water that fell from a little grot, almost choked with pallid ferns. No one else in the whole countryside had such a spring on his land. Mr. and Mrs. Thompson felt they had a fortune in that spring, if ever they got around to doing anything with it.

Rickety wooden shelves clung at hazard in the square around the small pool where the larger pails of milk and butter stood, fresh and sweet in the cold water. One hand supporting her flat, pained side, the other shading her eyes, Mrs. Thompson leaned over and peered into the pails. The cream had been skimmed and set aside, there was a rich roll of butter, the wooden molds and shallow pans had been scrubbed and scalded for the first time in who knows when, the barrel was full of buttermilk ready for the pigs and the weanling calves, the hard packed-dirt floor had been swept smooth. Mrs. Thompson straightened up again, smiling tenderly. She had been ready to scold him, a poor man who needed a job, who had just come there and who might not have been expected to do things properly at first. There was nothing she could do to make up for the injustice she had done him in her thoughts but to tell him how she appreciated his good clean work, finished already, in no time at all. She ventured near the door of the shack with her careful steps; Mr. Helton opened his eyes, stopped playing, and brought his chair down straight, but did not look at her, or get up. She was a little frail woman with long thick brown hair in a braid, a suffering patient mouth and diseased eyes which cried easily. She wove her fingers into an eyeshade, thumbs on temples, and, winking her tearful lids, said with a polite little manner, "Howdy do, sir. I'm Miz Thompson, and I wanted to tell you I think you did real well in the milk house. It's always been a hard place to keep."

He said, "That's all right," in a slow voice, without moving.

Mrs. Thompson waited a moment. "That's a pretty tune you're playing. Most folks don't seem to get much music out of a harmonica."

Mr. Helton sat humped over, long legs sprawling, his spine in a bow, running this thumb over the square mouth-stops; except for his moving hand he might have been asleep. The harmonica was a big shiny new one, and Mrs. Thompson, her gaze wandering about, counted five others, all good and expensive, standing in a row on the shelf beside his cot. "He must carry them around in his jumper pocket," she thought, and noted there was not a sign of any other possession lying about. "I see you're mighty fond of music," she said. "We used to have an old accordion, and Mr. Thompson could play it right smart, but the little boys broke it up."

Mr. Helton stood up rather suddenly, the chair clattered under him, his knees straightened though his shoulders did not, and he looked at the floor as if he were listening carefully. "You'd better set them harmonicas on a high shelf or they'll be after them. They're great hands for getting into things. I try to learn 'em, but it don't do much good."

Mr. Helton, in one wide gesture of his long arms, swept his harmonicas up against his chest, and from there transferred them in a row to the ledge where the roof joined to the wall. He pushed them back almost out of sight.

"That'll do, maybe," said Mrs. Thompson. "Now I wonder," she said, turning and closing her eyes helplessly against the stronger western light, "I wonder what became of them little tads. I can't keep up with them." She had a way of speaking about her children as if they were rather troublesome nephews on a prolonged visit.

"Down by the creek," said Mr. Helton, in his hollow voice. Mrs. Thompson, pausing confusedly, decided he had answered her question. He stood in silent patience, not exactly waiting for her to go, perhaps, but pretty plainly not waiting for anything else. Mrs. Thompson was perfectly accustomed to all kinds of men full of all kinds of cranky ways. The point was, to find out just how Mr. Helton's crankiness was different from any other man's, and then get used to it, and let him feel at home. Her father had been cranky, her brothers and uncles had all been set in their ways and none of them alike; and every hired man she'd ever seen had quirks and crotchets of his own. Now here was Mr. Helton, who was a Swede, who wouldn't talk, and who played the harmonica besides.

"They'll be needing something to eat," said Mrs. Thompson in a vague friendly way, "pretty soon. Now I wonder what I ought to be thinking about for supper? Now what do you like to eat, Mr. Helton? We always have plenty of good butter and milk and cream, that's a blessing. Mr. Thompson says we ought to sell all of it, but I say my family comes first." Her little face went all out of shape in a pained blind smile.

"I eat anything," said Mr. Helton, his words wandering up and down.

He *can't* talk, for one thing, thought Mrs. Thompson, it's a shame to keep at him when he don't know the language good. She took a slow step away from the shack, looking back over her shoulder. "We usually have cornbread except on Sundays," she told him. "I suppose in your part of the country you don't get much good cornbread."

Not a word from Mr. Helton. She saw from her eye-corner that he had sat down again, looking at his harmonica, chair tilted. She hoped he would remember it was getting near milking time. As she moved away, he started playing again, the same tune.

Milking time came and went. Mrs. Thompson saw Mr. Helton going back and forth between the cow barn and the milk house. He swung along in an easy lope, shoulders bent, head hanging, the big buckets balancing like a pair of scales at the ends of his bony arms. Mr. Thompson rode in from town sitting straighter than usual, chin in, a tow-sack full of supplies swung behind the saddle. After a trip to the barn, he came into the kitchen full of good will, and gave Mrs. Thompson a hearty smack on the cheek after dusting her face off with his tough whiskers. He had been to the hotel, that was plain. "Took a look around the premises, Ellie," he shouted. "That Swede sure is grinding out the labor. But he is the closest mouthed feller I ever met up with in all my days. Looks like he's scared he'll crack his jaw if he opens his front teeth."

Mrs. Thompson was stirring up a big bowl of buttermilk cornbroad. "You smell like a toper, Mr. Thompson," she said with perfect dignity. "I wish you'd get one of the little boys to bring me in an extra load of firewood. I'm thinking about baking a batch of cookies tomorrow."

Mr. Thompson, all at once smelling the liquor on his own breath, sneaked out, justly rebuked, and brought in the firewood himself. Arthur and Herbert, grubby from thatched head to toes, from skin to shirt, came stamping in yelling for supper. "Go wash your faces and comb your hair," said Mrs. Thompson, automatically. They retired to the porch. Each one put his hand under the pump and wet his forelock, combed it down with his fingers, and returned at once to the kitchen, where all the fair prospects of life were centered. Mrs. Thompson set an extra plate and commanded Arthur, the eldest, eight years old, to call Mr. Helton for supper.

Arthur, without moving from the spot, bawled like a bull calf, "Saaaaaay, Helllllllton, suuuuuupper's ready!" and added in a lower voice, "You big Swede!"

"Listen to me," said Mrs. Thompson, "that's no way to act. Now you go out there and ask him decent, or I'll get your daddy to give you a good licking."

Mr. Helton loomed, long and gloomy, in the doorway. "Sit right there," boomed Mr. Thompson, waving his arm. Mr. Helton swung his square shoes across the kitchen in two steps, slumped onto the bench and sat. Mr. Thompson occupied his chair at the head of the table, the two boys scrambled into place opposite Mr. Helton, and Mrs. Thompson sat at the end nearest the stove. Mrs. Thompson clasped her hands, bowed her head and said aloud hastily, "Lord, for all these and Thy other blessings we thank Thee in Jesus' name, amen," trying to finish before Herbert's dusty little paw reached the nearest dish. Otherwise she would be duty-bound to send him away from the table, and growing children need their meals. Mr. Thompson and Arthur always waited, but Herbert, aged six, was too young to take training yet.

Mr. and Mrs. Thompson tried to engage Mr. Helton in conversation, but it was a failure. They tried first the weather, and then the crops, and then the cows, but Mr. Helton simply did not reply. Mr. Thompson then told something funny he had seen in town. It was about some of the other old grangers at the hotel, friends of his, giving beer to a goat, and the goat's subsequent behavior. Mr. Helton did not seem to hear. Mrs. Thompson laughed dutifully, but she didn't think it was very funny. She had heard it often before, though Mr. Thompson, each time he told it, pretended it had happened that self-same day. It must have happened years ago if it ever happened at all, and it had never been a story that Mrs. Thompson thought suitable for mixed company. The whole thing came of Mr. Thompson's weakness for a dram too much now and then, though he voted for local option at every election. She passed the food to Mr. Helton, who took a helping of everything, but not much, not enough to keep him up to his full powers if he expected to go on working the way he had started.

At last he took a fair-sized piece of cornbread, wiped his plate up as clean as if it had been licked by a hound dog, stuffed his mouth full, and, still chewing, slid off the bench and started for the door.

"Good night, Mr. Helton," said Mrs. Thompson, and the other Thompsons took it up in a scattered chorus. "Good night, Mr. Helton!"

"Good night," said Mr. Helton's wavering voice grudgingly from the darkness.

"Gude not," said Arthur, imitating Mr. Helton.

"Gude not," said Herbert, the copy-cat.

"You don't do it right," said Arthur. "Now listen to me. Guuuuuude naht," and he ran a hollow scale in a luxury of successful impersonation. Herbert almost went into a fit with joy.

"Now you *stop* that," said Mrs. Thompson. "He can't help the way he talks. You ought to be ashamed of yourselves, both of you, making fun of a poor stranger like that. How'd you like to be a stranger in a strange land?"

"I'd like it," said Arthur. "I think it would be fun."

"They're both regular heathens, Ellie," said Mr. Thompson. "Just plain ignoramuses." He turned the face of awful fatherhood upon his young. "You're both going to get sent to school next year, and that'll knock some sense into you."

"I'm going to get sent to the 'formatory when I'm old enough," piped up Herbert. "That's where I'm goin'."

"Oh, you are, are you?' asked Mr. Thompson. "Who says so?"

"The Sunday School Superintendant," said Herbert, a bright boy showing off.

"You see?" said Mr. Thompson, staring at his wife. "What did I tell you?" He became a hurricane of wrath. "Get to bed, you two," he roared until his Adam's apple shuddered. "Get now before I take the hide off you!" They got, and shortly from their attic bedroom the sounds of scuffling and snorting and giggling and growling filled the house and shook the kitchen ceiling.

Mrs. Thompson held her head and said in a small uncertain voice,

"It's no use picking on them when they're so young and tender. I can't stand it."

"My goodness, Ellie," said Mr. Thompson, "we've got to raise 'em. We can't just let 'em grow up hog wild."

She went on in another tone. "That Mr. Helton seems all right, even if he can't be made to talk. Wonder how he comes to be so far from home."

"Like I said, he isn't no whamper-jaw," said Mr. Thompson, "but he sure knows how to lay out the work. I guess that's the main thing around here. Country's full of fellers trampin' round looking for work."

Mrs. Thompson was gathering up the dishes. She now gathered up Mr. Thompson's plate from under his chin. "To tell you the honest truth," she remarked, "I think it's a mighty good change to have a man round the place who knows how to work and keep his mouth shut. Means he'll keep out of our business. Not that we've got anything to hide, but it's convenient."

"That's a fact," said Mr. Thompson. "Haw, haw," he shouted suddenly. "Means you can do all the talking, huh?"

"The only thing," went on Mrs. Thompson, "is this: he don't eat hearty enough to suit me. I like to see a man set down and relish a good meal. My granma used to say it was no use putting dependence on a man who won't set down and make out his dinner. I hope it won't be that way this time."

"Tell *you* the truth, Ellie," said Mr. Thompson, picking his teeth with a fork and leaning back in the best of good humors, "I always thought your granma was a ter'ble ole fool. She'd just say the first thing that popped into her head and call it God's wisdom."

"My granma wasn't anybody's fool. Nine times out of ten she knew what she was talking about. I always say, the first thing you think is the best thing you can say."

"Well," said Mr. Thompson, going into another shout, "you're so reefined about that goat story, you just try speaking out in mixed comp'ny sometime! You just try it. S'pose you happened to be thinking about a hen and a rooster, hey? I reckon you'd shock the Babtist preacher!" He gave her a good pinch on her thin little rump. "No more meat on you than a rabbit," he said, fondly. "Now I like 'em cornfed."

Mrs. Thompson looked at him opened-eyed and blushed. She could see better by lamplight. "Why, Mr. Thompson, sometimes I think you're the evilest-minded man that ever lived." She took a handful of hair on the crown of his head and gave it a good, slow pull. "That's to show you how it feels, pinching so hard when you're supposed to be playing," she said, gently.

In spite of his situation in life, Mr. Thompson had never been able to outgrow his deep conviction that running a dairy and chasing after chickens was woman's work. He was fond of saying that he could plow a furrow, cut sorghum, shuck corn, handle a team, build a corn crib, as well as any man. Buying and selling, too, were man's work. Twice a week he drove the spring wagon to market with the fresh butter, a few eggs, fruits in their proper season, sold them, pocketed the change, and spent it as seemed best, being careful not to dig into Mrs. Thompson's pin money.

But from the first the cows worried him, coming up regularly twice a day to be milked, standing there reproaching him with their smug female faces. Calves worried him, fighting the rope and strangling themselves until their eyes bulged, trying to get at the teat. Wrestling with a calf unmanned him, like having to change a baby's diaper. Milk worried him, coming bitter sometimes, drying up, turning sour. Hens worried him, cackling, clucking, hatching out when you least expected it and leading their broods into the barnyard where the horses could step on them; dying of roup and wryneck and getting plagues of chicken lice; laying eggs all over God's creation so that half of them were spoiled before a man could find them, in spite of a rack of nests Mrs. Thompson had set out for them in the feed room. Hens were a blasted nuisance.

Slopping hogs was hired man's work, in Mr. Thompson's opinion. Killing hogs was a job for the boss, but scraping them and cutting them up was for the hired man again; and again woman's proper work was dressing meat, smoking, pickling, and making lard and sausage. All his carefully limited fields of activity were related somehow to Mr. Thompson's feeling for the appearance of things, his own appearance in the sight of God and man. "It don't *look* right," was his final reason for not doing anything he did not wish to do.

It was his dignity and his reputation that he cared about, and there were only a few kinds of work manly enough for Mr. Thompson to undertake with his own hands. Mrs. Thompson, to whom so many forms of work would have been becoming, had simply gone down on him early. He saw, after a while, how short-sighted it had been of him to expect much from Mrs. Thompson; he had fallen in love with her delicate waist and lace-trimmed petticoats and big blue eyes, and, though all those charms had disappeared, she had in the meantime become Ellie to him, not at all the same person as Miss Ellen Bridges, popular Sunday School teacher in the Mountain City First Baptist Church, but his dear wife, Ellie, who was not strong. Deprived as he was, however, of the main support in life which a man might expect in marriage, he had almost without knowing it resigned himself to failure. Head erect, a prompt payer of taxes, yearly subscriber to the preacher's salary, land owner and father of a family, employer, a hearty good fellow among men, Mr. Thompson knew, without putting it into words, that he had been going steadily down hill. God amighty, it did look like somebody around the place might take a rake in hand now and then and clear up the clutter around the barn and the kitchen steps. The wagon shed was so full of broken-down machinery and ragged harness and old wagon wheels and battered milk pails and rotting lumber you could hardly drive in there any more. Not a soul on the place would raise a hand to it, and as for him, he had all he could do with his regular work. He would sometimes in the slack season sit for hours worrying about it, squirting tobacco on the ragweeds growing in a thicket against the wood pile, wondering what a fellow could do, handicapped as he was. He looked forward to the boys growing up soon; he was going to put them through the mill just as his own father had done with him when he was a boy; they were going to learn how to take hold and run the place right. He wasn't going to overdo it, but those two boys were going to earn their salt, or he'd know why. Great big lubbers sitting around whittling! Mr. Thompson sometimes grew quite enraged with them, when imagining their possible future, big lubbers sitting around whittling or thinking about fishing trips. Well, he'd put a stop to that, mighty damn quick.

As the seasons passed, and Mr. Helton took hold more and more, Mr. Thompson began to relax in his mind a little. There seemed to be nothing the fellow couldn't do, all in the day's work and as a matter of course. He got up at five o'clock in the morning, boiled his own coffee and fried his own bacon and was out in the cow lot before Mr. Thompson had even begun to yawn, stretch, groan, roar and thump around looking for his jeans. He milked the cows, kept the milk house, and churned the butter; rounded the hens up and somehow persuaded them to lay in the nests, not under the house and behind the haystacks; he fed them regularly and they hatched out until you couldn't set a foot down for them. Little by little the piles of trash around the barns and house disappeared. He carried buttermilk and corn to the hogs, and curried cockleburs out of the horses' manes. He was gentle with the calves, if a little grim with the cows and hens; judging by his conduct, Mr. Helton had never heard of the difference between man's and woman's work on a farm.

In the second year, he showed Mr. Thompson the picture of a cheese press in a mail order catalogue, and said, "This is a good thing. You buy this, I make cheese." The press was bought and Mr. Helton did make cheese, and it was sold, along with the increased butter and the crates of eggs. Sometimes Mr. Thompson felt a little contemptuous of Mr. Helton's ways. It did seem kind of picayune for a man to go around picking up half a dozen ears of corn that had fallen off the wagon on the way from the field, gathering up fallen fruit to feed to the pigs, storing up old nails and stray parts of machinery, spending good time stamping a fancy pattern on the butter before it went to market. Mr. Thompson, sitting up high on the spring-wagon seat, with the decorated butter in a five-gallon lard can wrapped in wet towsack, driving to town, chirruping to the horses and snapping the reins over their backs, sometimes thought that Mr. Helton was a pretty meeching sort of fellow; but he never gave way to these feelings, he knew a good thing when he had it. It was a fact the hogs were in better shape and sold for more money. It was a fact that Mr. Thompson stopped buying feed, Mr. Helton managed the crops so well. When beef- and hog-slaughtering time came, Mr. Helton knew how to save the scraps that Mr. Thompson had thrown away, and wasn't above scraping guts and filling them with sausages that he made by his own methods. In all, Mr. Thompson had no grounds for complaint. In the third year, he raised Mr. Helton's wages, though Mr. Helton had not asked for a raise. The fourth year, when Mr. Thompson was not only out of debt but had a little cash in the bank, he raised Mr. Helton' wages again, two dollars and a half a month each time.

"The man's worth it, Ellie," said Mr. Thompson, in a glow of self- justification for his extravagance. "He's made this place pay, and I want him to know I appreciate it."

Mr. Helton's silence, the pallor of his eyebrows and hair, his long, glum jaw and eyes that refused to see anything, even the work under his hands, had grown perfectly familiar to the Thompsons. At first, Mrs. Thompson complained a little. "It's like sitting down at the table with a disembodied spirit," she said. "You'd think he'd find something to say, sooner or later."

"Let him alone," said Mr. Thompson. "When he gets ready to talk, he'll talk."

The years passed, and Mr. Helton never got ready to talk. After his work was finished for the day, he would come up from the barn or the milk house or the chicken house, swinging his lantern, his big shoes clumping like pony hoofs on the hard path. They, sitting in the kitchen in the winter, or on the back porch in summer, would hear him drag out his wooden chair, hear the creak of it tilted back, and then for a little while he would play his single tune on one or another of his harmonicas. The harmonicas were in different keys, some lower and sweeter than the others, but the same change- less tune went on, a strange tune, with sudden turns in it, night after night, and sometimes even in the afternoons when Mr. Helton sat down to catch his breath. At first the Thompsons liked it very much, and always stopped to listen. Later there came a time when they were fairly sick of it, and began to wish to each other that he would learn a new one. At last they did not hear it any more, it was as natural as the sound of the wind rising in the evenings, or the cows lowing, or their own voices.

Mrs. Thompson pondered now and then over Mr. Helton's soul. He didn't seem to be a church-goer, and worked straight through Sunday as if it were any common day of the week. "I think we ought to invite him to go to hear Dr. Martin," she told Mr. Thompson. "It isn't very Christian of us not to ask him. He's not a forward kind of man. He'd wait to be asked."

"Let him alone," said Mr. Thompson. "The way I look at it, his religion is every man's own business. Besides, he ain't got any Sunday clothes. He wouldn't want to go to church in them jeans and jumpers of his. I don't know what he does with his money. He certainly don't spend it foolishly."

Still, once the notion got into her head, Mrs. Thompson could not rest until she invited Mr. Helton to go to church with the family next Sunday. He was pitching hay into neat little piles in the field back of the orchard. Mrs. Thompson put on smoked glasses and a sunbonnet and walked all the way down there to speak to him. He stopped and leaned on his pitchfork, listening, and for a moment Mrs. Thompson was almost frightened at his face. The pale eyes seemed to glare past her, the eyebrows frowned, the long jaw hardened. "I got work," he said bluntly, and lifting his pitchfork he turned from her and began to toss the hay. Mrs. Thompson, her feelings hurt, walked back thinking that by now she should be used to Mr. Helton's ways, but it did seem like a man, even a foreigner, could be just a little polite when you gave him a Christian invitation. "He's not polite, that's the only thing I've got against him," she said to Mr. Thompson. "He just can't seem to behave like other people. You'd think he had a grudge against the world," she said. "I sometimes don't know what to make of it."

In the second year something had happened that made Mrs. Thompson uneasy, the kind of thing she could not put into words, hardly into thoughts, and if she had tried to explain to Mr. Thompson it would have sounded worse than it was, or not bad enough. It was that kind of queer thing that seems to be giving a warning, and yet, nearly always nothing comes of it. It was on a hot, still spring day, and Mrs. Thompson had been down to the garden patch to pull some new carrots and green onions and string beans for dinner. As she worked, sunbonnet low over her eyes, putting each kind of vegetable in a pile by itself in her basket, she noticed how neatly Mr. Helton weeded, and how rich the soil was. He had spread it all over with manure from the barns, and worked it in, in the fall, and the vegetables were coming up fine and full. She walked back under the nubbly little fig trees where the unpruned branches leaned almost to the ground, and the thick leaves made a cool screen. Mrs. Thompson was always looking for shade to save her eyes. So she, looking idly about, saw through the screen a sight that struck her as very strange. If it had been a noisy spectacle, it would have been quite natural. It was the silence that struck her. Mr. Helton was shaking Arthur by the shoulders, ferociously, his face most terribly fixed and pale. Arthur's head snapped back and forth and he had not stiffened in resistance, as he did when Mrs. Thompson tried to shake him. His eyes were rather frightened, but surprised, too, probably more surprised than anything else. Herbert stood by meekly, watching. Mr. Helton dropped Arthur, and seized Herbert, and shook him with the same methodical ferocity, the same face of hatred. Herbert's mouth crumpled as if he would cry, but he made no sound. Mr. Helton let him go, turned and strode into the shack, and the little boys ran, as if for their lives, without a word. They disappeared around the corner to the front of the house.

Mrs. Thompson took time to set her basket on the kitchen table, to push her sunbonnet back on her head and draw it forward again, to look in the stove and make certain the fire was going, before she followed the boys. They were sitting huddled together under a clump of chinaberry trees in plain sight of her bedroom window, as if it were a safe place they had discovered.

"What are you doing?" asked Mrs. Thompson.

They looked hang-dog from under their foreheads and Arthur mumbled, "Nothin'."

"Nothing *now*, you mean," said Mrs. Thompson, severely. "Well, I have plenty for you to do. Come right in here this minute and help me fix vegetables. This minute."

They scrambled up very eagerly and followed her close. Mrs. Thompson tried to imagine what they had been up to; she did not like the notion of Mr. Helton taking it on himself to correct her little boys, but she was afraid to ask them for reasons. They might tell her a lie, and she would have to overtake them in it, and whip them. Or she would have to pretend to believe them, and they would get in the habit of lying. Or they might tell her the truth, and it would be something she would have to whip them for. The very thought of it gave her a headache. She supposed she might ask Mr. Helton, but it was not her place to ask. She would wait and tell Mr. Thompson, and let him get at the bottom of it. While her mind ran on, she kept the little boys hopping. "Cut those carrot tops closer, Herbert, you're just being careless. Arthur, stop breaking up the beans so little. They're little enough already. Herbert, you go get an armload of wood. Arthur, you take these onions and wash them under the pump. Herbert, as soon as you're done here, you get a broom and sweep out this kitchen. Arthur, you get a shovel and take up the ashes. Stop picking your nose, Herbert. How often must I tell you? Arthur, you go look in the top drawer of my bureau, left-hand side, and bring me the vaseline for Herbert's nose. Herbert, come here to me. . . ."

They galloped through their chores, their animal spirits rose with activity, and shortly they were out in the front yard again, engaged in a wrestling match. They sprawled and fought, scrambled, clutched, rose and fell shouting, as aimlessly, noisily, montonously as two puppies. They imitated various animals, not a human sound from them, and their dirty faces were streaked with sweat. Mrs. Thompson, sitting at her window, watched them with baffled pride and tenderness, they were so sturdy and healthy and growing so fast; but uneasily, too, with her pained little smile and the tears rolling from her eyelids that clinched themselves against the sunlight. They were so idle and careless, as if they had no future in this world, and no immortal souls to save, and oh, what had they been up to that Mr. Helton had shaken them, with his face positively dangerous?

In the evening before supper, without a word to Mr. Thompson of the curious fear the sight had caused her, she told him that Mr. Helton had shaken the little boys for some reason. He stepped out to the shack and spoke to Mr. Helton. In five minutes he was back, glaring at his young. "He says them brats been fooling with his harmonicas, Ellie, blowing in them and getting them all dirty and full of spit and they don't play good."

"Did he say all that?" asked Mrs. Thompson. "It doesn't seem possible."

"Well, that's what he meant, anyhow," said Mr. Thompson. "He didn't say it just that way. But he acted pretty worked up about it."

"That's a shame," said Mrs. Thompson, "a perfect shame. Now we've got to do something so they'll remember they mustn't go into Mr. Helton's things."

"I'll tan their hides for them," said Mr. Thompson. "I'll take a calf rope to them if they don't look out."

"Maybe you'd better leave the whipping to me," said Mrs. Thompson. "You haven't got a light enough hand for children."

"That's just what's the matter with them now," shouted Mr. Thompson, "rotten spoiled and they'll wind up in the penitentiary. You don't half whip 'em. Just little love taps. My pa used to knock me down with a stick of stove wood or anything else that came handy."

"Well, that's not saying it's right," said Mrs. Thompson. "I don't hold with that way of raising children. It makes them run away from home. I've seen too much of it."

"I'll break every bone in 'em," said Mr. Thompson, simmering down, "if they don't mind you better and stop being so bull-headed."

"Leave the table and wash your face and hands," Mrs. Thompson commanded the boys, suddenly. They slunk out and dabbled at the pump and slunk in again, trying to makes themselves small. They had learned long ago that their mother always made them wash when there was trouble ahead. They looked at their plates. Mr. Thompson opened up on them.

"Well, now, what you got to say for yourselves about going into Mr. Helton's shack and ruining his harmonicas?"

The two little boys wilted, their faces drooped into the grieved hopeless lines of children's faces when they are brought to the terrible bar of blind adult justice; their eyes telegraphed each other in panic, "Now we're really going to catch a licking"; in despair, they dropped their buttered cornbread on their plates, their hands lagged on the edge of the table.

"I ought to break your ribs," said Mr. Thompson, "and I'm a good mind to do it."

"Yes, sir," whispered Arthur, faintly.

"Yes, sir," said Herbert, his lip trembling.

"Now, papa," said Mrs. Thompson in a warning tone. The children did not glance at her. They had no faith in her good will. She had betrayed them in the first place. There was no trusting her. Now she might save them and she might not. No use depending on her.

"Well, you ought to get a good thrashing. You deserve it, don't you, Arthur?"

Arthur hung his head. "Yes, sir."

"And the next time I catch either of you hanging around Mr. Helton's shack, I'm going to take the side off *both* of you, you hear me, Herbert?"

Herbert mumbled and choked, scattering his cornbread. "Yes, sir."

"Well, now sit up and eat your supper and not another word out of you," said Mr. Thompson, beginning on his own food. The little boys perked up somewhat and started chewing, but every time they looked around they met their parents' eyes, regarding them steadily. There was no telling when they would think of something new. The boys ate warily, trying not to be seen or heard, the cornbread sticking, the buttermilk gurgling, as it went down their gullets.

"And something else, Mr. Thompson," said Mrs. Thompson after a pause. "Tell Mr. Hlton he's to come straight to us when they bother him, and not to trouble shaking them himself. Tell him we'll look after that."

"They're so mean," answered Mr. Thompson, staring at them. "It's a wonder he don't just kill 'em off and be done with it." But there was something in the tone that told Arthur and Herbert that nothing more worth worrying about was going to happen this time. Heaving deep sighs, they sat up, reaching for the food nearest them.

"Listen," said Mrs. Thompson, suddenly. The little boys stopped eating. "Mr. Helton hasn't come for his supper. Arthur, go and tell Mr. Helton he's late for supper. Tell him nice, now."

Arthur, miserably depressed, slid out of his place and made for the door, without a word.

There were no miracles of fortune to be brought to pass on a small dairy farm. The Thompsons did not grow rich, but they kept out of the poor house, as Mr. Thompson was fond of saying, meaning he had got a little foothold in spite of Ellie's poor health, and unexpected weather, and strange declines in market prices, and his own mysterious handicaps which weighed him down. Mr. Helton was the hope and the prop of the family, and all the Thompsons became fond of him, or at any rate they ceased to regard him as in any way peculiar, and looked upon him, from a distance they did not know how to bridge, as a good man and a good friend. Mr. Helton went his way, worked, played his tune. Nine years passed. The boys grew up and learned to work. They could not remember the time when Ole Helton hadn't been there: a grouchy cuss, Brother Bones; Mr. Helton, the dairymaid; that Big Swede. If he had heard them, he might have been annoyed at some of the names they called him. But he did not hear them, and besides they meant no harm—or at least such harm as existed was all there, in the names; the boys referred to their father as the Old Man, or the Old Geezer, but not to his face. They lived through by main strength all the grimy, secret, oblique phases of growing up and got past the crisis safely if anyone does. Their parents could see they were good solid boys with hearts of gold in spite of their rough ways. Mr. Thompson was relieved to find that, without knowing how he had done it, he had succeeded in raising a set of boys who were not trifling whittlers. They were such good boys Mr. Thompson began to believe they were born that way, and that he had never spoken a harsh word to them in their lives, much less thrashed them. Herbert and Arthur never disputed his word.

Mr. Helton, his hair wet with sweat, plastered to his dripping forehead, his jumper streaked dark and light blue and clinging to his ribs, was chopping a little firewood. He chopped slowly, struck the ax into the end of the chopping log, and piled the wood up neatly. He then disappeared round the house into his shack, which shared with the wood pile a good shade from a row of mulberry trees. Mr. Thompson was lolling in a swing chair on the front porch, a place he had never liked. The chair was new, and Mrs. Thompson had wanted it on the front porch, though the side porch was the place for it, being cooler; and Mr. Thompson wanted to sit in the chair, so there he was. As soon as the new wore off of it, and Ellie's pride in it was exhausted, he would move it round to the side porch. Meantime the August heat was almost unbearable, the air so thick you could poke a hole in it. The dust was inches thick on everything, though Mr. Helton sprinkled the whole yard regularly every night. He even shot the hose upward and washed the tree tops and the roof of the house. They had laid waterpipes to the kitchen and an outside faucet. Mr. Thompson must have dozed, for he opened his eyes and shut his mouth just in time to save his face before a stranger who had driven up to the front gate. Mr. Thompson stood up, put on his hat, pulled up his jeans, and watched while the stranger tied his team, attached to a light spring wagon, to the hitching post. Mr. Thompson recognized the team and wagon. They were from a livery stable in Buda. While the stranger was opening the gate, a strong gate that Mr. Helton had built and set firmly on its hinges several years back, Mr. Thompson strolled down the path to greet him and find out what in God's world a man's business might be that would bring him out at this time of day, in all this dust and welter.

He wasn't exactly a fat man. He was more like a man who had been fat recently. His skin was baggy and his clothes were too big for him, and he somehow looked like a man who should be fat, ordinarily, but who might have just got over a spell of sickness. Mr. Thompson didn't take to his looks at all, he couldn't say why.

The stranger took off his hat. He said in a loud hearty voice, "Is this Mr. Thompson, Mr. Royal Earle Thompson?"

"That's my name," said Mr. Thompson, almost quietly, he was so taken aback by the free manner of the stranger.

"My name is Hatch," said the stranger, "Mr. Homer T. Hatch, and I've come to see you about buying a horse."

"I reckon you've been misdirected," said Mr. Thompson. "I haven't got a horse for sale. Usually if I've got anything like that to sell," he said, "I tell the neighbors and tack up a little sign on the gate."

The fat man opened his mouth and roared with joy, showing rabbit teeth brown as shoeleather. Mr. Thompson saw nothing to laugh at, for once. The stranger shouted, "That's just an old joke of mine." He caught one of his hands in the other and shook hands with himself heartily. "I always say something like that when I'm calling on a stranger, because I've noticed that when a feller says he's come to buy something nobody takes him for a suspicious character. You see? Haw, haw, haw."

His joviality made Mr. Thompson nervous, because the expression in the man's eyes didn't match the sounds he was making. "Haw, haw," laughed Mr. Thompson obligingly, still not seeing the joke. "Well, that's all wasted on me because I never take any man for a suspicious character 'til he shows hisself to be one. Says or does something," he explained. "Until that happens, one man's as good as another, so far's I'm concerned."

"Well," said the stranger, suddenly very sober and sensible, "I ain't come neither to buy nor sell. Fact is, I want to see you about something that's of interest to us both. Yes, sir, I'd like to have a little talk with you, and it won't cost you a cent."

"I guess that's fair enough," said Mr. Thompson, reluctantly. "Come on around the house where there's a little shade."

They went round and seated themselves on two stumps under a chinaberry tree.

"Yes, sir, Homer T. Hatch is my name and America is my nation," said the stranger. "I reckon you must know the name? I used to have a cousin named Jameson Hatch lived up the country a ways."

"Don't think I know the name," said Mr. Thompson. "There's some Hatchers settled somewhere around Mountain City."

"Don't know the old Hatch family," cried the man in deep concern. He seemed to be pitying Mr. Thompson's ignorance "Why, we came over from Georgia fifty years ago. Been here long yourself?"

"Just all my whole life," said Mr. Thompson, beginning to feel peevish. "And my pa and my grampap before me. Yes, sir, we've been right here all along. Anybody wants to find a Thompson knows where to look for him. My grampap immigrated in 1836."

"From Ireland, I reckon?" said the stranger.

"From Pennsylvania," said Mr. Thompson. "Now what makes you think we came from Ireland?"

The stranger opened his mouth and began to shout with merriment, and he shook hands with himself as if he hadn't met himself for a long time. "Well, what I always says is, a feller's got to come from *somewhere*, ain't he?"

While they were talking, Mr. Thompson kept glancing at the face near him. He certainly did remind Mr. Thompson of somebody, or maybe he really had seen the man himself somewhere. He couldn't just place the features. Mr. Thompson finally decided it was just that all rabbit-teethed men looked alike.

"That's right," acknowledged Mr. Thompson, rather sourly, "but what I always say is, Thompsons have been settled here for so long it don't make much difference any more *where* they come from. Now a course, this is the slack season, and we're all just laying round a little, but nevertheless we've all got our chores to do, and I don't want to hurry you, and so if you've come to see me on business maybe we'd better get down to it."

"As I said, it's not in a way, and again in a way it is," said the fat man. "Now I'm looking for a man named Helton, Mr. Olaf Eric Helton, from North Dakota, and I was told up around the country a ways that I might find him here, and I wouldn't mind having a little talk with him. No, siree, I sure wouldn't mind, if it's all the same to you."

"I never knew his middle name," said Mr. Thompson, "but Mr. Helton is right here, and been here now for going on nine years. He's a mighty steady man, and you can tell anybody I said so."

"I'm glad to hear that," said Mr. Homer T. Hatch. "I like to hear of a feller mending his ways and settling down. Now when I knew Mr. Helton he was pretty wild, yes, sir, wild is what he was, he didn't know his own mind atall. Well, now, it's going to be a great pleasure to me to meet up with an old friend and find him all settled down and doing well by hisself."

"We've all got to be young once," said Mr. Thompson. "It's like the measles, it breaks out all over you, and you're a nuisance to yourself and everybody else, but it don't last, and it usually don't leave no ill effects." He was so pleased with this notion he forgot and broke into a guffaw. The stranger folded his arms over his stomach and went into a kind of fit, roaring until he had tears in his eyes. Mr. Thompson stopped shouting and eyed the stranger uneasily. Now he liked a good laugh as well as any man, but there ought to be a little moderation. Now this feller laughed like a perfect lunatic, that was a fact. And he wasn't laughing because he really thought things were funny, either. He was laughing for reasons of his own. Mr. Thompson fell into a moody silence, and waited until Mr. Hatch settled down a little.

Mr. Hatch got out a very dirty blue cotton bandanna and wiped his eyes. "That joke just about caught me where I live," he said, almost apologetically. "Now I wish I could think up things as funny as that to say. It's a gift. It's . . ."

"If you want to speak to Mr. Helton, I'll go and round him up," said Mr. Thompson, making motions as if he might get up. "He may be in the milk house and he may be setting in his shack this time of day." It was drawing towards five o'clock. "It's right around the corner," he said.

"Oh, well, there ain't no special hurry," said Mr. Hatch. "I've been wanting to speak to him for a good long spell now and I guess a few minutes more won't make no difference. I just more wanted to locate him, like. That's all."

Mr. Thompson stopped beginning to stand up, and unbuttoned one more button of his shirt, and said, "Well, he's here, and he's this kind of man, that if he had any business with you he'd like to get it over. He don't dawdle, that's one thing you can say for him."

Mr. Hatch appeared to sulk a little at these words. He wiped his face with the bandanna and opened his mouth to speak, when round the house there came the music of Mr. Helton's harmonica. Mr. Thompson raised a finger. "There he is," said Mr. Thompson. "Now's your time."

Mr. Hatch cocked an ear towards the east side of the house and listened for a few seconds, a very strange expression on his face.

"I know that tune like I know the palm of my own hand," said Mr. Thompson, "but I never heard Mr. Helton say what it was."

"That's a kind of Scandahoovian song," said Mr. Hatch. "Where I come from they sing it a lot. In North Dakota, they sing it. It says something about starting out in the morning feeling so good you can't hardly stand it, so you drink up all your likker before noon. All the likker, y' understand, that you was saving for the noon lay-off. The words ain't much, but it's a pretty tune. It's a kind of drinking song." He sat there drooping a little, and Mr. Thompson didn't like his expression. It was a satisfied expression, but it was more like the cat that et the canary.

"So far as I know," said Mr. Thompson, "he ain't touched a drop since he's been on the place, and that's nine years this coming September. Yes, sir, nine years, so far as I know, he ain't wetted his whistle once. And that's more than I can say for myself," he said, meekly proud.

"Yes, that's a drinking song," said Mr. Hatch. "I used to play 'Little Brown Jug' on the fiddle when I was younger than I am now," he went on, "but this Helton, he just keeps it up. He just sits and plays it by himself."

"He's been playing it off and on for nine years right here on the place," said Mr. Thompson, feeling a little proprietary.

"And he was certainly singing it as well, fifteen years before that, in North Dakota," said Mr. Hatch. "He used to sit up in a straitjacket, prac-;ically, when he was in the asylum—"

"What's that you say?" said Mr. Thompson. "What's that?"

"Shucks, I didn't mean to tell you," said Mr. Hatch, a faint leer of regret in his drooping eyelids. "Shucks, that just slipped out. Funny, now I'd made up my mind I wouldn't say a word, because it would just make a lot of excitement, and what I say is, if a man has lived harmless and quiet for nine years it don't matter if he *is* loony, does it? So long's he keeps quiet and don't do nobody harm."

"You mean they had him in a straitjacket?" asked Mr. Thompson, uneasily. "In a lunatic asylum?"

"They sure did," said Mr. Hatch. "That's right where they had him, from time to time."

"They put my Aunt Ida in one of them things in the State asylum," said Mr. Thompson. "She got vi'lent, and they put her in one of these jackets with long sleeves and tied her to an iron ring in the wall, and Aunt Ida got so wild she broke a blood vessel and when they went to look after her she was dead. I'd think one of them things was dangerous."

"Mr. Helton used to sing his drinking song when he was in a straitjacket," said Mr. Hatch. "Nothing ever bothered him, except if you tried to make him talk. That bothered him, and he'd get vi'lent, like your Aunt Ida. He'd get vi'lent and then they'd put him in the jacket and go off and leave him, and he'd lay there perfickly contented, so far's you could see, singing his song. Then one night he just disappeared. Left, you might say, just went, and nobody ever saw hide or hair of him again. And then I come along and find him here," said Mr. Hatch, "all settled down and playing the same song."

"He never acted crazy to me," said Mr. Thompson. "He always acted like a sensible man, to me. He never got married, for one thing, and he works like a horse, and I bet he's got the first cent I paid him when he landed here, and he don't drink, and he never says a word, much less swear, and he don't waste time runnin' around Saturday nights, and if he's crazy," said Mr. Thompson, "why, I think I'll go crazy myself for a change."

"Haw, ha," said Mr Hatch, "heh, he, that's good! Ha, ha, ha, I hadn't thought of it jes like that. Yeah, that's right! Let's all go crazy and get rid of our wives and save our money, hey?" He smiled unpleasantly, showing his little rabbit teeth.

Mr. Thompson felt he was being misunderstood. He turned around and motioned toward the open window back of the honeysuckle trellis. "Let's move off down here a little," he said. "I oughta thought of that before." His visitor bothered Mr. Thompson. He had a way of taking the words out of Mr. Thompson's mouth, turning them around and mixing them up until Mr. Thompson didn't know himself what he had said. "My wife's not very strong," said Mr. Thompson. "She's been kind of invalid now goin' on fourteen years. It's mighty tough on a poor man, havin' sickness in the family. She had four operations," he said proudly, "one right after the other, but they didn't do any good. For five years handrunnin', I just turned every nickel I made over to the doctors. Upshot is, she's a mightly delicate woman."

"My old woman," said Mr. Homer T. Hatch, "had a back like a mule, yes, sir. That woman could have moved the barn with her bare hands if she'd ever took the notion. I used to say, it was a good thing she didn't know her own stren'th. She's dead now, though. That kind wear out quicker than the puny ones. I never had much use for a woman always complainin'. I'd get rid of her mighty quick, yes, sir, mighty quick. It's just as you say: a dead loss, keepin' one of 'em up."

This was not at all what Mr. Thompson had heard himself say; he had been trying to explain that a wife as expensive as his was a credit to a man. "She's a mighty reasonable woman," said Mr. Thompson, feeling baffled, "but I wouldn't answer for what she'd say or do if she found out we'd had a lunatic on the place all this time." They moved away from the window; Mr. Thompson took Mr. Hatch the front way, because if he went the back way they would have to pass Mr. Helton's shack. For some reason he didn't want the stranger to see or talk to Mr. Helton. It was strange, but that was the way Mr. Thompson felt.

Mr. Thompson sat down again, on the chopping log, offering his guest another tree stump. "Now, I mighta got upset myself at such a thing, once," said Mr. Thompson, "but now I *deefy* anything to get me lathered up." He cut himself an enormous plug of tobacco with his horn-handled pocketknife, and offered it to Mr. Hatch, who then produced his own plug and, opening a huge bowie knife with a long blade sharply whetted, cut off a large wad and put it in his mouth. They then compared plugs and both of them were astonished to see how different men's ideas of good chewing tobacco were.

"Now, for instance," said Mr. Hatch, "mine is lighter colored. That's because, for one thing, there ain't any sweetenin' in this plug. I like it dry, natural leaf, medium strong."

"A little sweetenin' don't do no harm so far as I'm concerned," said Mr. Thompson, "but it's got to be mighty little. But with me, now, I want a strong leaf, I want it heavy-cured, as the feller says. There's a man near here, named Williams, Mr. John Morgan Williams, who chews a plug— well, sir, it's black as your hat and soft as melted tar. It fairly drips with molasses, jus' plain molasses, and it chews like licorice. Now, I don't call that a good chew."

"One man's meat," said Mr. Hatch, "is another man's poison. Now, such a chew would simply gag me. I couldn't begin to put it in my mouth."

"Well," said Mr. Thompson, a tinge of apology in his voice, "I jus' barely tasted it myself, you might say. Just took a little piece in my mouth and spit it out again."

"I'm dead sure I couldn't even get that far," said Mr. Hatch. "I like a dry natural chew without any artificial flavorin' of any kind."

Mr. Thompson began to feel that Mr. Hatch was trying to make out he had the best judgment in tobacco, and was going to keep up the argument until he proved it. He began to feel seriously annoyed with the fat man. After all, who was he and where did he come from? Who was he to go around telling other people what kind of tobacco to chew?

"Artificial flavorin'," Mr. Hatch went on, doggedly, "is jes put in to cover up a cheap leaf and make a man think he's gettin' somethin' more than he *is* gettin'. Even a little sweetenin' is a sign of a cheap leaf, you can mark my words."

"I've always paid a fair price for my plug," said Mr. Thompson, stiffly. "I'm not a rich man and I don't go round settin' myself up for one, but I'll say this, when it comes to such things as tobacco, I buy the best on the market."

"Sweetenin', even a little," began Mr. Hatch, shifting his plug and squirting tobacco juice at a dry-looking little rose bush that was having a hard enough time as it was, standing all day in the blazing sun, its roots clenched in the baked earth, "is the sign of—"

"About this Mr. Helton, now," said Mr. Thompson, determinedly, "I don't see no reason to hold it against a man because he went loony once or twice in his lifetime and so I don't expect to take no steps about it. Not a step. I've got nothin' against the man, he's always treated me fair. They's things and people," he went on, " 'nough to drive any man loony. The wonder to me is, more men don't wind up in straitjackets, the way things are going these days and times."

"That's right," said Mr. Hatch, promptly, entirely too promptly, as if he were turning Mr. Thompson's meaning back on him. "You took the words right out of my mouth. There ain't every man in a straitjacket that ought to be there. Ha, ha, you're right all right. You got the idea."

Mr. Thompson sat silent and chewed steadily and stared at a spot on the ground about six feet away and felt a slow muffled resentment climbing from somewhere deep down in him, climbing and spreading all through him. What was this fellow driving at? What was he trying to say? It wasn't so much his words, but his looks and his way of talking: that droopy look in the eye, that tone of voice, as if he was trying to mortify Mr. Thompson about something. Mr. Thompson didn't like it, but he couldn't get hold of it either. He wanted to turn around and shove the fellow off the stump, but it wouldn't look reasonable. Suppose something happened to the fellow when he fell off the stump, just for instance, if he fell on the ax and cut himself, and then someone should ask Mr. Thompson why he shoved him, and what could a man say? It would look mighty funny, it would sound mighty strange to say, Well, him and me fell out over a plug of tobacco. He might just shove him anyhow and then tell people he was a fat man not used to the heat and while he was talking he got dizzy and fell off by himself, or something like that, and it wouldn't be the truth either, because it wasn't the heat and it wasn't the tobacco. Mr. Thompson made up his mind to get the fellow off the place pretty quick, without seeming to be anxious, and watch him sharp till he was out of sight. It doesn't pay to be friendly with strangers from another part of the country. They're always up to something, or they'd stay at home where they belong.

"And they's some people," said Mr. Hatch, "would jus' as soon have a loonatic around their house as not, they can't see no difference between them and anybody else. I always say, if that's the way a man feels, don't care who he associates with, why, why, that's his business, not mine. I don't wanta have a thing to do with it. Now back home in North Dakota, we don't feel that way. I'd like to a seen anybody hiring a loonatic there, aspecially after what he done."

"I didn't understand your home was North Dakota," said Mr. Thompson. "I thought you said Georgia."

"I've got a married sister in North Dakota," said Mr. Hatch, "married a Swede, but a white man if ever I saw one. So I say *we* because we got into a little business together out that way. And it seems like home, kind of."

"What did he do?" asked Mr. Thompson, feeling very uneasy again.

"Oh, nothin' to speak of," said Mr. Hatch, jovially, "jus' went loony one day in the hayfield and shoved a pitchfork right square through his brother, when they was makin' hay. They was goin' to execute him, but they found out he had went crazy with the heat, as the feller says, and so they put him in the asylum. That's all he done. Nothin' to get lathered up about, ha, ha, ha!" he said, and taking out his sharp knife he began to slice off a chew as carefully as if he were cutting cake.

"Well," said Mr. Thompson, "I don't deny that's news. Yes, sir, news. But I still say somethin' must have drove him to it. Some men make you feel like giving 'em a good killing just by lookin' at you. His brother may a been a mean ornery cuss."

"Brother was going to get married," said Mr. Hatch; "used to go courtin' his girl nights. Borrowed Mr. Helton's harmonica to give her a serenade one evenin', and lost it. Brand new harmonica."

"He thinks a heap of his harmonicas," said Mr. Thompson. "Only money he ever spends, now and then he buys hisself a new one. Must have a dozen in that shack, all kinds and sizes."

"Brother wouldn't buy him a new one," said Mr. Hatch, "so Mr. Helton just ups, and I says, and runs his pitchfork through his brother. Now you know he musta been crazy to get all worked up over a little thing like that."

"Sounds like it," said Mr. Thompson, reluctant to agree in anything with this intrusive and disagreeable fellow. He kept thinking he couldn't remember when he had taken such a dislike to a man on first sight.

"Seems to me you'd get pretty sick of hearin' the same tune year in, year out," said Mr. Hatch.

"Well, sometimes I think it wouldn't do no harm if he learned a new one," said Mr. Thompson, "but he don't, so there's nothin' to be done about it. It's a pretty good tune, though."

"One of the Scandahoovians told me what it meant, that's how I come to know," said Mr. Hatch. "Especially that part about getting so gay you jus' go ahead and drink up all the likker you got on hand before noon. It seems like up in them Swede countries a man carries a bottle of wine around with him as a matter of course, at least that's the way I understood it. Those fellers will tell you anything, though—" He broke off and spat.

The idea of drinking any kind of liqour in this heat made Mr. Thompson dizzy. The idea of anybody feeling good on a day like this, for instance, made him tired. He felt he was really suffering from the heat. The fat man looked as if he had grown to the stump; he slumped there in his damp, dark clothes too big for him, his belly slack in his pants, his wide black felt hat pushed off his narrow forehead red with prickly heat. A bottle of good cold beer, now, would be a help, thought Mr. Thompson, remembering the four bottles sitting deep in the pool at the springhouse, and his dry tongue squirmed in his mouth. He wasn't going to offer this man anything, though, not even a drop of water. He wasn't even going to chew any more tobacco with him. He shot out his quid suddenly, and wiped his mouth on the back of his hand, and studied the head near him attentively. The man was no good, and he was there for no good, but what was he up to? Mr. Thompson made up his mind he'd give him a little more time to get his business, whatever it was, with Mr. Helton over, and then if he didn't get off the place he'd kick him off.

Mr. Hatch, as if he suspected Mr. Thompson's thoughts, turned his eyes, wicked and pig-like, on Mr. Thompson. "Fact is," he said, as if he had made up his mind about something, "I might need your help in the little matter I've got on hand, but it won't cost you any trouble. Now, this Mr. Helton here, like I tell you, he's a dangerous escaped loonatic, you might say. Now fact is, in the last twelve years or so I musta rounded up twenty-odd escaped loonatics, besides a couple of escaped convicts that I just run into by accident, like. I don't make a business of it, but if there's a reward, and there usually is a reward, of course, I get it. It amounts to a tidy little sum in the long run, but that ain't the main question. Fact is, I'm for law and order, I don't like to see lawbreakers and loonatics at large. It ain't the place for them. Now I reckon you're bound to agree with me on that, aren't you?"

Mr. Thompson said, "Well, circumstances alters cases, as the feller says. Now, what I know of Mr. Helton, he ain't dangerous, as I told you."

Something serious was going to happen, Mr. Thompson could see that. He stopped thinking about it. He'd just let this fellow shoot off his head and then see what could be done about it. Without thinking he got out his knife and plug and started to cut a chew, then remembered himself and put them back in his pocket.

"The law," said Mr. Hatch, "is solidly behind me. Now this Mr. Helton, he's been one of my toughest cases. He's kept my record from being practically one hundred per cent. I knew him before he went loony, and I know the fam'ly, so I undertook to help out rounding him up. Well, sir, he was gone slick as a whistle, for all we knew the man was as good as dead long while ago. Now we never might have caught up with him, but do you know what he did? Well, sir, about two weeks ago his old mother gets a letter from him, and in that letter, what do you reckon she found? Well, it was a check on that little bank in town for eight hundred and fifty dollars, just like that; the letter wasn't nothing much, just said he was sending her a few little savings, she might need something, but there it was, name, postmark, date, everything. The old woman practically lost her mind with joy. She's gettin' childish, and it looked like she kinda forgot that her only living son killed his brother and went loony. Mr. Helton said he was getting along all right, and for her not to tell nobody. Well, natchally, she couldn't keep it to herself, with that check to cash and everything. So that's how I come to know." His feelings got the better of him. "You coulda knocked me down with a feather." He shook hands with himself and rocked, wagging his head, going "Heh, heh," in his throat. Mr. Thompson felt the corners of his mouth turning down. Why, the dirty low-down hound, sneaking around spying into other people's business like that. Collecting blood money, that's what it was! Let him talk!

"Yea, well, that musta been a surprise all right," he said, trying to hold his voice even. "I'd say a surprise."

"Well, siree," said Mr. Hatch, "the more I got to thinking about it, the more I just come to the conclusion that I'd better look into the matter a little, and so I talked to the old woman. She's pretty decrepit, now, half blind and all, but she was all for taking the first train out and going to see her son. I put it up to her square—how she was too feeble for the trip, and all. So, just as a favor to her, I told her for my expenses I'd come down and see Mr. Helton and bring her back all the news about him. She gave me a new shirt she made herself by hand, and a big Swedish kind of cake to bring to him, but I musta mislaid them along the road somewhere. It don't reely matter, though, he prob'ly ain't in any state of mind to appreciate 'em."

Mr. Thompson sat up and turning round on the log looked at Mr. Hatch and asked as quietly as he could, "And now what are you aiming to do? That's the question."

Mr. Hatch slouched up to his feet and shook himself. "Well, I come all prepared for a little scuffle," he said. "I got the handcuffs," he said, "but

I don't want no violence if I can help it. I didn't want to say nothing around the countryside, making an uproar. I figured the two of us could overpower him." He reached into his big inside pocket and pulled them out. Handcuffs, for God's sake, thought Mr. Thompson. Coming round on a peaceable afternoon worrying a man, making trouble, and fishing handcuffs out of his pocket on a decent family homestead, as if it was all in the day's work.

Mr. Thompson, his head buzzing, got up too. "Well," he said, roundly, "I want to tell you I think you've got a mighty sorry job on hand, you sure must be hard up for something to do, and now I want to give you a good piece of advice. You just drop the idea that you're going to come here and make trouble for Mr. Helton, and the quicker you drive that hired rig away from my front gate the better I'll be satisfied."

Mr. Hatch put one handcuff in his outside pocket, the other dangling down. He pulled his hat down over his eyes, and reminded Mr. Thompson of a sheriff, somehow. He didn't seem in the least nervous, and didn't take up Mr. Thompson's words. He said, "Now listen just a minute, it ain't reasonable to suppose that a man like yourself is going to stand in the way of getting an escaped loonatic back to the asylum where he belongs. Now I know it's enough to throw you off, coming sudden like this, but fact is I counted on your being a respectable man and helping me out to see that justice is done. Now a course, if you won't help, I'll have to look around for help somewheres else. It won't look very good to your neighbors that you was harboring an escaped loonatic who killed his own brother, and then you refused to give him up. It will look mighty funny."

Mr. Thompson knew almost before he heard the words that it would look funny. It would put him in a mighty awkward position. He said, "But I've been trying to tell you all along that the man ain't loony now. He's been perfectly harmless for nine years. He's—he's—"

Mr. Thompson couldn't think how to describe how it was with Mr. Helton. "Why, he's been like one of the family," he said, "the best standby a man ever had." Mr. Thompson tried to see his way out. It was a fact Mr. Helton might go loony again any minute, and now this fellow talking around the country would put Mr. Thompson in a fix. It was a terrible position. He couldn't think of any way out. "You're crazy," Mr. Thompson roared suddenly, "you're the crazy one around here, you're crazier than he ever was! You get off this place or I'll handcuff you and turn you over to the law. You're trespassing," shouted Mr. Thompson. "Get out of here before I knock you down!"

He took a step towards the fat man, who backed off, shrinking, "Try it, try it, go ahead!" and then something happened that Mr. Thompson tried hard afterwards to piece together in his mind, and in fact it never did come straight. He saw the fat man with his long bowie knife in his hand, he saw Mr. Helton come round the corner on the run, his long jaw dropped, his arms swinging, his eyes wild. Mr. Helton came in between them, fists doubled up, then stopped short, glaring at the fat man, his big frame seemed to collapse, he trembled like a shied horse; and then the fat man drove at him, knife in one hand, handcuffs in the other. Mr. Thompson saw it coming, he saw the blade going into Mr. Helton's stomach, he knew he had the ax out of the log in his own hands, felt his arms go up over his head and bring the ax down on Mr. Hatch's head as if he were stunning a beef.

Mrs. Thompson had been listening uneasily for some time to the voices going on, one of them strange to her, but she was too tired at first to get up and come out to see what was going on. The confused shouting that rose so suddenly brought her up to her feet and out across the front porch without her slippers, hair half-braided. Shading her eyes, she saw first Mr. Helton, running all stooped over through the orchard, running like a man with dogs after him; and Mr. Thompson supporting himself on the ax handle was leaning over shaking by the shoulder a man Mrs. Thompson had never seen, who lay doubled up with the top of his head smashed and the blood running away in a greasy-looking puddle. Mr. Thompson without taking his hand from the man's shoulder, said in a thick voice, "He killed Mr. Helton, he killed him, I saw him do it. I had to knock him out," he called loudly, "but he won't come to."

Mrs. Thompson said in a faint scream, "Why, yonder goes Mr. Helton," and she pointed. Mrs. Thompson sat down slowly against the side of the house and began to slide forward on her face; she felt as if she were drowning, she couldn't rise to the top somehow, and her only thought was she was glad the boys were not there, they were out, fishing at Halifax, oh, God, she was glad the boys were not there.

Mr. and Mrs. Thompson drove up to their barn about sunset. Mr. Thompson handed the reins to his wife, got out to open the big door, and Mrs. Thompson guided old Jim in under the roof. The buggy was gray with dust and age, Mrs. Thompson's face was gray with dust and weariness, and Mr. Thompson's face, as he stood at the horse's head and began unhitching, was gray except for the dark blue of his freshly shaven jaws and chin, gray and blue and caved in, but patient, like a dead man's face.

Mrs. Thompson stepped down to the hard packed manure of the barn floor, and shook out her light flower-sprigged dress. She wore her smoked glasses, and her wide shady leghorn hat with the wreath of exhausted pink and blue forget-me-nots hid her forehead, fixed in a knot of distress.

The horse hung his head, raised a huge sigh and flexed his stiffened legs. Mr. Thompson's words came up muffled and hollow. "Poor ole Jim," he said, clearing his throat, "he looks pretty sunk in the ribs. I guess he's had a hard week." He lifted the harness up in one piece, slid it off and Jim walked out of the shafts halting a little. "Well, this is the last time,"

Mr. Thompson said, still talking to Jim. "Now you can get a good rest."

Mrs. Thompson closed her eyes behind her smoked glasses. The last time, and high time, and they should never have gone at all. She did not need her glasses any more, now the good darkness was coming down again, but her eyes ran full of tears steadily, though she was not crying, and she felt better with the glasses, safer, hidden away behind them. She took out her handkerchief with her hands shaking as they had been shaking ever since *that day*, and blew her nose. She said, "I see the boys have lighted the lamps. I hope they've started the stove going."

She stepped along the rough path holding her thin dress and starched petticoats around her, feeling her way between the sharp small stones, leaving the barn because she could hardly bear to be near Mr. Thompson, advancing slowly towards the house because she dreaded going there. Life was all one dread, the faces of her neighbors, of her boys, of her husband, the face of the whole world, the shape of her own house in the darkness, the very smell of the grass and the trees were horrible to her. There was no place to go, only one thing to do, bear it somehow—but how? She asked herself that question often. How was she going to keep on living now? Why had she lived at all? She wished now she had died one of those times when she had been so sick, instead of living on for this.

The boys were in the kitchen; Herbert was looking at the funny pictures from last Sunday's newspapers, the Katzenjammer Kids and Happy Hooligan. His chin was in his hands and his elbows on the table, and he was really reading and looking at the pictures, but his face was unhappy. Arthur was building the fire, adding kindling a stick at a time, watching it catch and blaze. His face was heavier and darker than Herbert's, but he was a little sullen by nature; Mrs. Thompson thought, he takes things harder, too. Arthur said, "Hello, Momma," and went on with his work. Herbert swept the papers together and moved over on the bench. They were big boys—fifteen and seventeen, and Arthur as tall as his father. Mrs. Thompson sat down beside Herbert, taking off her hat. She said, "I guess you're hungry. We were late today. We went the Log Hollow road, it's rougher than ever." Her pale mouth drooped with a sad fold on either side.

"I guess you saw the Mannings, then," said Herbert.

"Yes, and the Fergusons, and the Allbrights, and that new family McClellan."

"Anybody say anything?" asked Herbert.

"Nothing much, you know how it's been all along, some of them keeps saying, yes, they know it was a clear case and a fair trial and they say how glad they are your papa came out so well, and all that, some of 'em do, anyhow, but it looks like they don't really take sides with him. I'm about wore out," she said, the tears rolling again from under her dark glasses. "I don't know what good it does, but your papa can't seem to rest unless he's telling how it happened. I don't know."

"I don't think it does any good, not a speck," said Arthur, moving away from the stove. "It just keeps the whole question stirred up in people's minds. Everybody will go round telling what he heard, and the whole thing is going to get worse mixed up than ever. It just makes matters worse. I wish you could get Papa to stop driving round the country talking like that."

"Your papa knows best," said Mrs. Thompson. "You oughtn't to criticize him. He's got enough to put up with without that."

Arthur said nothing, his jaw stubborn. Mr. Thompson came in, his eyes hollowed out and dead-looking, his thick hands gray white and seamed from washing them clean every day before he started out to see the neighbors to tell them his side of the story. He was wearing his Sunday clothes, a thick pepper-and-salt-colored suit with a black string tie.

Mrs. Thompson stood up, her head swimming. "Now you-all get out of the kitchen, it's too hot in here and I need room. I'll get us a little bite of supper, if you'll just get out and give me some room."

They went as if they were glad to go, the boys outside, Mr. Thompson into his bedroom. She heard him groaning to himself as he took off his shoes, and heard the bed creak as he lay down. Mrs. Thompson opened the icebox and felt the sweet coldness flow out of it; she had never expected to have an icebox, much less did she hope to afford to keep it filled with ice. It still seemed like a miracle, after two or three years. There was the food, cold and clean, all ready to be warmed over. She would never have had that icebox if Mr. Helton hadn't happened along one day, just by the strangest luck; so saving, and so managing, so good, thought Mrs. Thompson, her heart swelling until she feared she would faint again, standing there with the door open and leaning her head upon it. She simply could not bear to remember Mr. Helton, with his long sad face and silent ways, who had always been so quiet and harmless, who had worked so hard and helped Mr. Thompson so much, running through the hot fields and woods, being hunted like a mad dog, everybody turning out with ropes and guns and sticks to catch and tie him. Oh, God, said Mrs. Thompson in a long dry moan, kneeling before the icebox and fumbling inside for the dishes, even if they did pile mattresses all over the jail floor and against the walls, and five men there to hold him to keep him from hurting himself any more, he was already hurt too badly, he couldn't have lived anyway. Mr. Barbee, the sheriff, told her about it. He said, well, they didn't aim to harm him but they had to catch him, he was crazy as a loon; he picked up rocks and tried to brain every man that got near him. He had two harmonicas in his jumper pocket, said the sheriff, but they fell out in the scuffle, and Mr. Helton tried to pick 'em up again, and that's when they finally got him. "They *had* to be rough, Miz Thompson, he fought like a wildcat." Yes, thought Mrs. Thompson, again with the same bitterness, of course, they had to be rough. They always have to be rough. Mr. Thompson can't argue with a man and get him off the place peaceably; no, she thought, standing up and shutting the icebox, he has to kill somebody, he has to be a murderer and ruin his boys' lives and cause Mr. Helton to be killed like a mad dog.

Her thoughts stopped with a little soundless explosion, cleared and began again. The rest of Mr. Helton's harmonicas were still in the shack, his tune ran in Mrs. Thompson's head at certain times of the day. She missed it in the evenings. It seemed so strange she had never known the name of that song, nor what it meant, until after Mr. Helton was gone. Mrs. Thompson, trembling in the knees, took a drink of water at the sink and poured the red beans into the baking dish, and began to roll the pieces of chicken in flour to fry them. There was a time, she said to herself, when I thought I had neighbors and friends, there was a time when we could hold up our heads, there was a time when my husband hadn't killed a man and I could tell the truth to anybody about anything.

Mr. Thompson, turning on his bed, figured that he had done all he could, he'd just try to let the matter rest from now on. His lawyer, Mr. Burleigh, had told him right at the beginning, "Now you keep calm and collected. You've got a fine case, even if you haven't got witnesses. Your wife must sit in court, she'll be a powerful argument with the jury. You just plead not guilty and I'll do the rest. The trial is going to be a mere formality, you haven't got a thing to worry about. You'll be clean out of this before you know it." And to make talk Mr. Burleigh had got to telling about all the men he knew around the country who for one reason or another had been forced to kill somebody, always in self-defense, and there just wasn't anything to it at all. He even told about how his own father in the old days had shot and killed a man just for setting foot inside his gate when he told him not to. "Sure, I shot the scoundrel," said Mr. Burleigh's father, "in self-defense; I *told* him I'd shoot him if he set his foot in my yard, and he did, and I did." There had been bad blood between them for years, Mr. Burleigh said, and his father had waited a long time to catch the other fellow in the wrong, and when he did he certainly made the most of his opportunity.

"But Mr. Hatch, as I told you," Mr. Thompson had said, "made a pass at Mr. Helton with his bowie knife. That's why I took a hand."

"All the better," said Mr. Burleigh. "That stranger hadn't any right coming to your house on such an errand. Why, hell," said Mr. Burleigh, "that wasn't even manslaughter you committed. So now you just hold your horses and keep your shirt on. And don't say one word without I tell you."

Wasn't even manslaughter. Mr. Thompson had to cover Mr. Hatch with a piece of wagon canvas and ride to town to tell the sheriff. It had been hard on Ellie. When they got back, the sheriff and the coroner and two deputies, they found her sitting beside the road, on a low bridge over a gulley, about half a mile from the place. He had taken her up behind his saddle and got her back to the house. He had already told the sheriff that his wife had witnessed the whole business, and now he had time, getting her to her room and in bed, to tell her what to say if they asked anything. He had left out the part about Mr. Helton being crazy all along, but it came out at the trial. By Mr. Burleigh's advice Mr. Thompson had pretended to be perfectly ignorant; Mr. Hatch hadn't said a word about that. Mr. Thompson pretended to believe that Mr. Hatch had just come looking for Mr. Helton to settle old scores, and the two members of Mr. Hatch's family who had come down to try to get Mr. Thompson convicted didn't get anywhere at all. It hadn't been much of a trial, Mr. Burleigh saw to that. He had charged a reasonable fee, and Mr. Thompson had paid him and felt grateful, but after it was over Mr. Burleigh didn't seem pleased to see him when he got to dropping into the office to talk it over, telling him things that had slipped his mind at first: trying to explain what an ornery low hound Mr. Hatch had been, anyhow. Mr. Burleigh seemed to have lost his interest; he looked sour and upset when he saw Mr. Thompson at the door. Mr. Thompson kept saying to himself that he'd got off, all right, just as Mr. Burleigh had predicted, but, but—and it was right there that Mr. Thompson's mind stuck, squirming like an angleworm on a fishhook: he had killed Mr. Hatch, and he was a murderer. That was the truth about himself that Mr. Thompson couldn't grasp, even when he said the word to himself. Why, he had not even once *thought* of killing anybody, much less Mr. Hatch, and if Mr. Helton hadn't come out so unexpectedly, hearing the row, why, then—but then, Mr. Helton had come on the run that way to help him. What he couldn't understand was what happened next. He had seen Mr. Hatch go after Mr. Helton with the knife, he had seen the point, blade up, go into Mr. Helton's stomach and slice up like you slice a hog, but when they finally caught Mr. Helton there wasn't a knife scratch on him. Mr. Thompson knew he had the ax in his own hands and felt himself lifting it, but he couldn't remember hitting Mr. Hatch. He couldn't remember it. He couldn't. He remembered only that he had been determined to stop Mr. Hatch from cutting Mr. Helton. If he was given a chance he could explain the whole matter. At the trial they hadn't let him talk. They just asked questions and he answered yes or no, and they never did get to the core of the matter. Since the trial, now, every day for a week he had washed and shaved and put on his best clothes and had taken Ellie with him to tell every neighbor he had that he never killed Mr. Hatch on purpose, and what good did it do? Nobody believed him. Even when he turned to Ellie and said, "You was there, you saw it, didn't you?" and Ellie spoke up, saying, "Yes, that's the truth. Mr. Thompson was trying to save

Mr. Helton's life," and he added, "If you don't believe me, you can believe my wife. She won't lie," Mr. Thompson saw something in all their faces that disheartened him, made him feel empty and tired out. They didn't believe he was not a murderer.

Even Ellie never said anything to comfort him. He hoped she would say finally, "I remember now, Mr. Thompson, I really did come round the corner in time to see everything. It's not a lie, Mr. Thompson. Don't you worry." But as they drove together in silence, with the days still hot and dry, shortening for fall, day after day, the buggy jolting in the ruts, she said nothing; they grew to dread the sight of another house, and the people in it: all houses looked alike now, and the people—old neighbors or new—had the same expression when Mr. Thompson told them why he had come and began his story. Their eyes looked as if someone had pinched the eyeball at the back; they shriveled and the light went out of them. Some of them sat with fixed tight smiles trying to be friendly. "Yes, Mr. Thompson, we know how you must feel. It must be terrible for you, Mrs. Thompson. Yes, you know, I've about come to the point where I believe in such a thing as killing in self-defense. Why, certainly, we believe you, Mr. Thompson, why shouldn't we believe you? Didn't you have a perfectly fair and above-board trial? Well, now, natchally, Mr. Thompson, we think you done right."

Mr. Thompson was satisfied they didn't think so. Sometimes the air around him was so thick with their blame he fought and pushed with his fists, and the sweat broke out all over him, he shouted his story in a dust-choked voice, he would fairly bellow at last: "My wife, here, you know her, she was there, she saw and heard it all, if you don't believe me, ask her, she won't lie!" and Mrs. Thompson, with her hands knotted together, aching, her chin trembling, would never fail to say: "Yes, that's right, that's the truth—"

The last straw had been laid on today, Mr. Thompson decided. Tom Allbright, an old beau of Ellie's, why, he had squired Ellie around a whole summer, had come out to meet them when they drove up, and standing there bareheaded had stopped them from getting out. He had looked past them with an embarrassed frown on his face, telling them his wife's sister was there with a raft of young ones, and the house was pretty full and everything upset, or he'd ask them to come in. "We've been thinking of trying to get up to your place one of these days," said Mr. Allbright, moving away trying to look busy, "we've been mighty occupied up here of late." So they had to say, "Well, we just happened to be driving this way," and go on. "The Allbrights," said Mrs. Thompson, "always was fair-weather friends." "They look out for number one, that's a fact," said Mr. Thompson. But it was cold comfort to them both.

Finally Mrs. Thompson had given up. "Let's go home," she said. "Old Jim's tired and thirsty, and we've gone far enough."

Mr. Thompson said, "Well, while we're out this way, we might as well stop at the McClellans'." They drove in, and asked a little cotton-haired boy if his mamma and papa were at home. Mr. Thompson wanted to see them. The little boy stood gazing with his mouth open, then galloped into the house shouting, "Mommer, Popper, come out hyah. That man that kilt Mr. Hatch has come ter see yer!"

The man came out in his sock feet, with one gallus up, the other broken and dangling, and said, "Light down, Mr. Thompson, and come in. The ole woman's washing, but she'll git here." Mrs. Thompson, feeling her way, stepped down and sat in a broken rocking-chair on the porch that sagged under her feet. The woman of the house, barefooted, in a calico wrapper, sat on the edge of the porch, her fat sallow face full of curiosity. Mr. Thompson began, "Well, as I reckon you happen to know, I've had some strange troubles lately, and, as the feller says, it's not the kind of trouble that happens to a man every day in the year, and there's some things I don't want no misunderstanding about in the neighbors' minds, so—" He halted and stumbled forward, and the two listening faces took on a mean look, a greedy, despising look, a look that said plain as day, "My, you must be a purty sorry feller to come round worrying about what *we* think, *we* know you wouldn't be here if you had anybody else to turn to—my, I wouldn't lower myself that much, myself." Mr. Thompson was ashamed of himself, he was suddenly in a rage, he'd like to knock their dirty skunk heads together, the low-down white trash—but he held himself down and went on to the end. "My wife will tell you," he said, and this was the hardest place, because Ellie always without moving a muscle seemed to stiffen as if somebody had threatened to hit her; "ask my wife, she won't lie."

"It's true, I saw it—"

"Well, now," said the man, drily, scratching his ribs inside his shirt, "that sholy is too bad. Well, now, I kaint see what we've got to do with all this here, however. I kaint see no good reason for us to git mixed up in these murder matters, I shore kaint. Which ever way you look at it, it ain't none of my business. However, it's mighty nice of you-all to come around and give us the straight of it, fur we've heerd some mighty queer yarns about it, mighty queer, I golly you couldn't hardly make head ner tail of it."

"Evvybody goin' round shootin' they heads off," said the woman. "Now we don't hold with killin'; the Bible says—"

"Shet yer trap," said the man, "and keep it shet 'r I'll shet it fer yer. Now it shore looks like to me—"

"We mustn't linger," said Mrs. Thompson, unclasping her hands. "We've lingered too long now. It's getting late, and we've far to go." Mr. Thompson took the hint and followed her. The man and the woman lolled against their rickety porch poles and watched them go.

Now lying on his bed, Mr. Thompson knew the end had come. Now, this minute, lying in the bed where he had slept with Ellie for eighteen years; under this roof where he had laid the shingles when he was waiting to get married; there as he was with his whiskers already sprouting since his shave that morning; with his fingers feeling his bony chin, Mr. Thompson felt he was a dead man. He was dead to his other life, he had got to the end of something without knowing why, and he had to make a fresh start, he did not know how. Something different was going to begin, he didn't know what. It was in some way not his business. He didn't feel he was going to have much to do with it. He got up, aching, hollow, and went out to the kitchen where Mrs. Thompson was just taking up the supper.

"Call the boys," said Mrs. Thompson. They had been down to the barn, and Arthur put out the lantern before hanging it on a nail near the door. Mr. Thompson didn't like their silence. They had hardly said a word about anything to him since that day. They seemed to avoid him, they ran the place together as if he wasn't there, and attended to everything without asking him for any advice. "What you boys been up to?" he asked, trying to be hearty. "Finishing your chores?"

"No, sir," said Arthur, "there ain't much to do. Just greasing some axles." Herbert said nothing. Mrs. Thompson bowed her head: "For these and all Thy blessings. . . . Amen," she whispered weakly, and the Thompsons sat there with their eyes down and their faces sorrowful, as if they were at a funeral.

Every time he shut his eyes, trying to sleep, Mr. Thompson's mind started up and began to run like a rabbit. It jumped from one thing to another, trying to pick up a trail here or there that would straighten out what had happened that day he killed Mr. Hatch. Try as he might, Mr. Thompson's mind would not go anywhere that it had not already been, he could not see anything but what he had seen once, and he knew that was not right. If he had not seen straight that first time, then everything about his killing Mr. Hatch was wrong from start to finish, and there was nothing more to be done about it, he might just as well give up. It still seemed to him that he had done, maybe not the right thing, but the only thing he could do, that day, but had he? *Did he have to kill Mr. Hatch?* He had never seen a man he hated more, the minute he laid eyes on him. He knew in his bones the fellow was there for trouble. What seemed so funny now was this: Why hadn't he just told Mr. Hatch to get out before he ever even got in?

Mrs. Thompson, her arms crossed on her breast, was lying beside him, perfectly still, but she seemed awake, somehow. "Asleep, Ellie?"

After all, he might have got rid of him peaceably, or maybe he might have had to overpower him and put those handcuffs on him and turn him over to the sheriff for disturbing the peace. The most they could have done was to lock Mr. Hatch up while he cooled off for a few days, or fine him a little something. He would try to think of things he might have said to Mr. Hatch. Why, let's see, I could just have said, Now look here, Mr. Hatch, I want to talk to you as man to man. But his brain would go empty. What could he have said or done? But if he *could* have done anything else almost except kill Mr. Hatch, then nothing would have happened to Mr. Helton. Mr. Thompson hardly ever thought of Mr. Helton. His mind just skipped over him and went on. If he stopped to think about Mr. Helton he'd never in God's world get anywhere. He tried to imagine how it might all have been, this very night even, if Mr. Helton were still safe and sound out in his shack playing his tune about feeling so good in the morning, drinking up all the wine so you'd feel even better; and Mr. Hatch safe in jail somewhere, mad as hops, maybe, but out of harm's way and ready to listen to reason and to repent of his meanness, the dirty, yellow-livered hound coming around persecuting an innocent man and ruining a whole family that never harmed him! Mr. Thompson felt the veins of his forehead start up, his fists clutched as if they seized an ax handle, the sweat broke out on him, he bounded up from the bed with a yell smothered in his throat, and Ellie started up after him, crying out, "Oh, oh, don't! Don't! Don't!" as if she were having a nightmare. He stood shaking until his bones rattled in him, crying hoarsely, "Light the lamp, light the lamp, Ellie."

Instead, Mrs. Thompson gave a shrill weak scream, almost the same scream he had heard on that day she came around the house when he was standing there with the ax in his hand. He could not see her in the dark, but she was on the bed, rolling violently. He felt for her in horror, and his groping hands found her arms, up, and her own hands pulling her hair straight out from her head, her neck strained back, and the tight screams strangling her. He shouted out for Arthur, for Herbert. "Your mother!" he bawled, his voice cracking. As he held Mrs. Thompson's arms, the boys came tumbling in, Arthur with the lamp above his head. By this light Mr. Thompson saw Mrs. Thompson's eyes, wide open, staring dreadfully at him, the tears pouring. She sat up at sight of the boys, and held out one arm towards them, the hand wagging in a crazy circle, then dropped on her back again, and suddenly went limp. Arthur set the lamp on the table and turned on Mrs. Thompson. "She's scared," he said, "she's scared to death." His face was in a knot of rage, his fists were doubled up, he faced his father as if he meant to strike him. Mr. Thompson's jaw fell, he was so surprised he stepped back from the bed. Herbert went to the other side. They stood on each side of Mrs. Thompson and watched Mr. Thompson as if he were a dangerous wild beast. "What did you do to her?" shouted Arthur, in a grown man's voice. "You touch her again and I'll blow your heart out!" Herbert was pale and his cheek twitched, but he was on Arthur's side; he would do what he could to help Arthur.

Mr. Thompson had no fight left in him. His knees bent as he stood, his chest collapsed. "Why, Arthur," he said, his words crumbling and his breath coming short. "She's fainted again. Get the ammonia." Arthur did not move. Herbert brought the bottle, and handed it, shrinking, to his father.

Mr. Thompson held it under Mrs. Thompson's nose. He poured a little in the palm of his hand and rubbed it on her forehead. She gasped and opened her eyes and turned her head away from him. Herbert began a doleful hopeless sniffling. "Mamma," he kept saying, "Mamma, don't die."

"I'm all right," Mrs. Thompson said. "Now don't you worry around. Now Herbert, you mustn't do that. I'm all right." She closed her eyes. Mr. Thompson began pulling on his best pants; he put on his socks and shoes. The boys sat on each side of the bed, watching Mrs. Thompson's face. Mr. Thompson put on his shirt and coat. He said, "I reckon I'll ride over and get the doctor. Don't look like all this fainting is a good sign. Now you just keep watch until I get back." They listened, but said nothing. He said, "Don't you get any notions in your head. I never did your mother any harm in my life, on purpose." He went out, and, looking back, saw Herbert staring at him from under his brows, like a stranger. "You'll know how to look after her," said Mr. Thompson.

Mr. Thompson went through the kitchen. There he lighted the lantern, took a thin pad of scratch paper and a stub pencil from the shelf where the boys kept their schoolbooks. He swung the lantern on his arm and reached into the cupboard where he kept the guns. The shotgun was there to his hand, primed and ready, a man never knows when he may need a shotgun. He went out of the house without looking around, or looking back when he had left it, passed his barn without seeing it, and struck out to the farthest end of his fields, which ran for half a mile to the east. So many blows had been struck at Mr. Thompson and from so many directions he couldn't stop any more to find out where he was hit. He walked on, over plowed ground and over meadow, going through barbed wire fences cautiously, putting his gun through first; he could almost see in the dark, now his eyes were used to it. Finally he came to the last fence; here he sat down, back against a post, lantern at his side, and, with the pad on his knee, moistened the stub pencil and began to write:

"Before Almighty God, the great judge of all before who I am about to appear, I do hereby solemnly swear that I did not take the life of Mr. Homer T. Hatch on purpose. It was done in defense of Mr. Helton. I did not aim to hit him with the ax but only to keep him off Mr. Helton. He aimed a blow at Mr. Helton who was not looking for it. It was my belief at the time that Mr. Hatch would of taken the life of Mr. Helton if I did not interfere. I have told all this to the judge and the jury and they let me off but nobody believes it. This is the only way I can prove I am not a cold blooded murderer like everybody seems to think. If I had been in Mr. Helton's place he would of done the same for me. I still think I done the only thing there was to do. My wife—"

Mr. Thompson stopped here to think a while. He wet the pencil point with the tip of his tongue and marked out the last two words. He sat a while blacking out the words until he had made a neat oblong patch where they had been, and started again:

"It was Mr. Homer T. Hatch who came to do wrong to a harmless man. He caused all this trouble and he deserved to die but I am sorry it was me who had to kill him."

He licked the point of his pencil again, and signed his full name carefully, folded the paper and put it in his outside pocket. Taking off his right shoe and sock, he set the butt of the shotgun along the ground with the twin barrels pointed towards his head. It was very awkward. He thought about this a little, leaning his head against the gun mouth. He was trembling and his head was drumming until he was deaf and blind, but he lay down flat on the earth on his side, drew the barrel under his chin and fumbled for the trigger with his great toe. That way he could work it.

KATHERINE ANNE PORTER

"Noon Wine": The Sources

THIS short novel, "Noon Wine" exists so fully and wholly in its own right in my mind, that when I attempt to trace its growth from the beginning, to follow all the clues to their sources in my memory, I am dismayed; because I am confronted with my own life, the whole society in which I was born and brought up, and the facts of it. My aim is to find the truth in it, and to this end my imagination works and re-works its recollections in a constant search for meanings. Yet in this endless remembering which surely must be the main occupation of the writer, events are changed, reshaped, interpreted again and again in different ways, and this is right and natural because it is the intention of the writer to write fiction, after all—real fiction, not a *roman à clef*, or a thinly disguised personal confession which better belongs to the psychoanalyst's séance. By the time I wrote "Noon Wine" it had become "real" to me almost in the sense that I felt not as if I had made that story out of my own memory of real events and imagined consequences, but as if I were quite simply reporting events I had heard or witnessed. This is not in the least true: the story is fiction; but it is made up of thousands of things that did happen to living human beings in a certain part of the country, at a certain time of my life, things that are still remembered by others as single incidents; not as I remembered them, floating and moving with their separate life and reality, meeting and parting and mingling in my thoughts until they established their relationship. I could see and feel very clearly that all these events, episodes—hardly that, sometimes, but just mere glimpses and flashes here and there of lives strange or moving or astonishing to me—were forming a story, almost of themselves, it seemed; out of their apparent incoherence, unrelatedness, they grouped and clung in my mind in a form that gave a meaning to the whole that the individual parts had lacked. So I feel that this story is "true" in the way that a work of fiction should be true, created out of all the scattered particles of life I was able to absorb and combine and to shape into a living new being.

But why did this particular set of memories and early impressions combine in just this way to make this particular story? I do not in the least know. And though it is quite true that I intended to write fiction, this story wove itself in my mind for years before I ever intended to write it; there were many other stories going on in my head at once, some of them evolved and were written, more were not. Why? This to me is the most interesting question, because I am sure there is an answer, but nobody knows it yet.

When the moment came to write this story, I knew it; and I had to make quite a number of practical arrangements to get the time free for it, without fear of interruptions. I wrote it as it stands except for a few pen corrections in just seven days of trance-like absorption in a small room in an inn in rural Pennsylvania, from the early evening of November 7 to November 14, 1936. Yet I had written the central part, the scene between Mr. Hatch and Mr. Thompson, which leads up to the murder, in Basel, Switzerland, in the summer of 1932.

I had returned from Europe only fifteen days before I went to the inn in Pennsylvania: this was the end, as it turned out, of my living abroad, except for short visits back to Paris, Brittany, Rome, Belgium: but meantime I had, at a time of great awareness and active energy, spent nearly fourteen years of my life out of this country: in Mexico, Bermuda, various parts of Europe, but mostly by choice, Paris. Of my life in these places I felt then, and feel now, that it was all entirely right, timely, appropriate, exactly where I should have been and what doing at that very time. I did not feel exactly at home; I knew where home was; but the time had come for me to see the world for myself, and so I did, almost as naturally as a bird taking off on his new wingfeathers. In Europe, things were not so strange; sometimes I had a pleasant sense of having here and there touched home-base; if I was not at home, I was sometimes with friends. And all the time, I was making notes on stories—stories of my own place, my South—for my part of Texas was peopled almost entirely by Southerners from Virginia, Tennessee, the Carolinas, Kentucky—and I was almost instinctively living in a sustained state of mind and feeling, quietly and secretly, comparing one thing with another, always remembering and re-membering; and all sorts of things were falling into their proper places, taking on their natural shapes and sizes, and going back and back clearly into right perspective—right for me as artist, I simply mean to say; and it was like breathing—I did not have consciously to urge myself to think about it. So my time in Europe served me in a way I had not dreamed of, even, besides its own charm and goodness; it gave me back my past and my own house and my own people—the native land of my heart.

This summer country of my childhood, this space and memory is filled with landscapes shimmering in light and color, moving with sounds and shapes I hardly ever describe or put in my stories in so many words; they form only the living background of what I am trying to tell, so fa-miliar to my characters they would hardly notice them; the sound of mourning doves in the live-oaks, the childish voices of parrots chattering on every back porch in the little town, the hoverings of buzzards in the high blue air—all the life of that soft blackland farming country, full of fruits and flowers and birds, with good hunting and good fishing; with plenty of water, many little and big rivers. I shall name just a few of the rivers I remember—the San Antonio, the San Marcos, the Trinity, the Neuces, the Rio Grande, the Colorado, and the small clear branch of the Colorado—full of colored pebbles—Indian Creek, the place where I was born. The colors and tastes all had their smells, as the sounds have now their echoes: the bitter whiff of air over a sprawl of animal skeleton after the buzzards were gone; the smells and flavors of roses and melons, and peach bloom and ripe peaches, of cape jessamine in hedges blooming like popcorn, and the sickly sweetness of chinaberry florets; of honeysuckle in great swags on a trellised gallery; heavy tomatoes dead ripe and warm with the midday sun, eaten there, at the vine; the delicious milky green corn, and savory hot corn bread eaten with still-warm sweet milk; and the clinging brackish smell of the muddy little ponds where we caught, and boiled crawfish—in a discarded lard can—and ate them, then and there, we children, in the company of an old Negro who had once been my grand-parents' slave, as I have told in another story. He was by our time only a servant, and a cantankerous old cuss very sure of his place in the household.

Uncle Jimbilly, for that was his name, was not the only one who knew exactly where he stood, and just about how far he could go in maintaining the right, privileges, exemptions of his status so long as he performed its duties. At this point, I want to give a rather generalized view of the society of that time and place as I remember it, and as talks with my elders since confirm it. (Not long ago I planned to visit a very wonderful old lady who was a girlhood friend of my mother. I wrote to my sister that I could not think of being a burden to Miss Cora, and would therefore stop at the little hotel in town and call on her. And my sister wrote back air-mail on the very day saying: "For God's sake, don't mention the word hotel to Miss Cora—she'll think you've lost your raising!") The elders all talked and behaved as if the final word had gone out long ago on manners, morality, religion, even politics: nothing was ever to change, they said, and even as they spoke, everything was changing, sliding, disappearing. This had been happening in fact ever since they were born; the greatest change, the fatal dividing change in this country, the war between the states, was taking place even as most of my father's generation were coming into the world. But it was the grandparents who still ruled in daily life; and they showed plainly in acts, words, and even looks—an enormously handsome generation they seemed to have been I remember—all those wonderful high noses with a diamond shaped bony structure in the bridge!—the presence of good society, very well based on traditional Christian beliefs. These beliefs were mainly Protestant but not yet petty middle-class puritanism: there remained still an element fairly high stepping and wide gestured in its personal conduct. The petty middle class of fundamentalists who saw no difference between wine-drinking, dancing, card-playing, and adultery, had not yet got altogether the upper hand—in fact, never did except in certain limited areas; but it was making a brave try. It was not really a democratic society; if everybody had his place, sometimes very narrowly defined, at least he knew where it was, and so did everybody else. So too, the higher laws of morality and religion were defined; if a man offended against the one, or sinned against the other, he knew it, and so did his neighbors, and they called everything by its right name.

This firm view applied also to social standing. A man who had humble ancestors had a hard time getting away from them and rising in the world. If he prospered and took to leisurely ways of living, he was merely "getting above his raising." If he managed to marry into one of the good old families, he had simply "outmarried himself." If he went away and made a success somewhere else, when he returned for a visit he was still only "that Jimmerson boy who went No'th." There is—was, perhaps I should say—a whole level of society of the South where it was common knowledge that the mother's family outranked the father's by half, at least. This might be based on nothing more tangible than that the mother's family came from Richmond or Charleston, while the father's may have started out somewhere from Pennsylvania, or to have got bogged down one time or another in Arkansas. If they turned out well, the children of these matches were allowed their mother's status, for good family must never be denied, but father remained a member of the Plain People to the end. Yet there was nothing against any one hinting at better lineage, and a family past more dignified than the present, no matter how humble his present circumstances, nor how little proof he could offer for his claim. Aspiration to higher and better things was natural to all men, and a sign of proper respect for true blood and birth. Pride and hope may be denied to no one.

In this society of my childhood there were all sorts of tender ways of feeling and thinking, subtle understanding between people in matters of ritual and ceremony; I think in the main a civilized society, and yet, with the underlying, perpetual ominous presence of violence; violence potential that broke through the smooth surface almost without warning, or maybe just without warning to children one learned later to know the signs. There were old cruel customs, the feud, for one, gradually dying out among the good families, never in fact prevalent among them—the men of that class fought duels, and abided—in theory at least—on the outcome; and country life, ranch life, was rough, in Texas, at least. I remember tall bearded booted men striding about with clanking spurs; and carrying loaded pistols inside their shirts next to their ribs, even to church. It was quite matter of course that you opened a closet door in a bedroom and stared down into the cold eyes of shotguns and rifles, stacked there because there was no more room in the gun closet. In the summer, in that sweet smelling flowery country, we children with our father or some grown-up in charge, spent long afternoons on a range, shooting at fixed targets or clay pigeons with the ordinary domestic firearms, pistols, rifles of several calibers, shotguns single and double. I never fired a shotgun, but I knew the sounds and could name any round of fire I heard, even at great distances.

Some one asked me once where I had ever heard that conversation in "Noon Wine" between two men about chewing tobacco—that apparently aimless talk between Mr. Hatch and Mr. Thompson which barely masks hatred and is leading towards a murder. It seems that I *must* have heard something of the sort somewhere, some time or another; I do not in the least remember it. But that whole countryside was full of tobacco-chewing men, whittling men, hard-working farming men perched on fences with their high heels caught on a rail, or squatting on their toes, gossiping idly and comfortably for hours at a time. I often wondered what they found to say to each other, day in day out year after year; but I should never have dared go near enough to listen profitably; yet I surely picked up something that came back whole and free as air that summer in Basel, Switzerland when I thought I was studying only the life of Erasmus and the Reformation. And I have seen them, many a time, take out their razor-sharp long-bladed knives and slice a "chew" as delicately and precisely as if they were cutting a cake. These knives were so keen, often I have watched my father, shelling pecans for me, cut off the ends of the hard shells in a slow circular single gesture; then split them down the sides in four strips and bring out the nut meat whole. This fascinated me, but it did not occur to me to come near the knife, or offer to touch it. In our country life, in summers, we were surrounded by sharpened blades—hatchets, axes, plough-shares, carving knives, bowie knives, straight razors. We were taught so early to avoid all these, I do not remember ever being tempted to take one in my hand. Living as we did among loaded guns and dangerous cutting edges, four wild, adventurous children always getting hurt in odd ways, we none of us were ever injured seriously. The worst thing that happened was, my elder sister got a broken collar bone from a fall, not as you might expect from a horse, for we almost lived on horseback, but from a three-foot fall off a fence where she had climbed to get a better view of a battle between two bulls. But these sharp blades slicing tobacco—did I remember it because it was an unusual sight? I think not. I must have seen it, as I remember it, dozens of times—but one day I really *saw* it: and it became part of Mr. Thompson's hallucinated vision when he killed Mr. Hatch, and afterward could not live without justifying himself.

There is an early memory, not the first, but certainly before my third year, always connected with this story, "Noon Wine"; it is the source, if there could be only one. I was a very small child. I know this by the re-membered vastness of the world around me, the giant heights of grown-up people; a chair something to be scaled like a mountain; a table top to be peered over on tiptoe. It was late summer and near sunset, for the sky was a clear green-blue with long streaks of burning rose in it, and the air was full of the mournful sound of swooping bats. I was all alone in a wide grassy plain—it was the lawn on the east side of the house—and I was in that state of instinctive bliss which children only know, when there came like a blow of thunder echoing and rolling in that green sky, the explosion of a shotgun, not very far away; for it shook the air. There followed at once a high, thin, long-drawn scream, a sound I had never heard, but I knew what it was—it was the sound of death in the voice of a man. How did I know it was a shotgun? How should I not have known? How did I know it was death? We are born knowing death.

Let me examine this memory a little, which though it is of an actual event, is like a remembered dream; but then all my childhood is that; and if in parts of this story I am trying to tell you, I use poetic terms, it is be-cause in such terms do I remember many things, and the feeling is valid, it cannot be left out, or denied.

In the first place, could I have been alone when this happened? It is most unlikely. I was one of four children, brought up in a houseful of adults of ripening age; a grandmother, a father, several Negro servants, among them two aged, former slaves; visiting relatives, uncles, aunts, cousins; grandmother's other grandchildren older than we, with always an ill-identified old soul or two, male or female, who seemed to be guests but helped out with stray chores. The house, which seemed so huge to me, was probably barely adequate to the population it accommodated; but of one thing I am certain—nobody was ever alone except for the most neces-sary privacies, and certainly no child at any time. Children had no necessary privacies. We were watched and herded and monitored and followed and spied upon and corrected and lectured and scolded (and kissed, let's be just, loved tenderly, and prayed over!) all day, every day, through the endless years of childhood—endless, but where did they go? So the evidence all points to the fact that I was not, could not have been, bodily speaking, alone in that few seconds when for the first time I heard the sound of murder. Who was with me? What did she say—for it was certainly one of the care-taking women around the house. Could I have known by instinct, of which I am so certain now, or did some one speak words I cannot remember which nonetheless told me what had happened? There is nothing more to tell, all speculations are useless; this memory is a spot of clear light and color and sound, of immense, mysterious illumination of feeling against a horizon of total darkness.

Yet, was it the next day? next summer? In that same place, that grassy shady yard, in broad daylight I watched a poor little funeral procession creeping over the stony ridge of the near horizon, the dusty road out of town which led also to the cemetery. The hearse was just a spring wagon decently roofed and curtained with black oil cloth, poverty indeed, and some members of our household gathered on the front gallery to watch it pass, said, "Poor Pink Hodges—old man A——got him just like he said he would." Had it been Pink Hodges, then, I had heard screaming death in the blissful sunset? And who was old man A, whose name I do not remember, and what became of him, I wonder? I'll never know. I remember only that the air of our house was full of pity for Pink Hodges, for his harmlessness, his helplessness, "so pitiful, poor thing," they said; and, "It's just not right," they said. But what did they do to bring old man A——to justice, or at least a sense of his evil? Nothing, I am afraid. I began to ask all sorts of questions, and was silenced invariably by some elder who told me I was too young to understand such things.

Yet here I am coming to something quite clear, of which I am entirely certain. It happened in my ninth year, and again in that summer house in the little town near the farm, with the yard full of roses and irises and honeysuckle and hackberry trees, and the vegetable garden and the cow barn in back. It was already beginning to seem not so spacious to me; it went on dwindling year by year to the measure of my growing up.

One hot moist day after a great thunderstorm and heavy long rain, I saw a strange horse and buggy standing at the front gate. Neighbors and kin in the whole countryside knew each other's equipages as well as they did their own, and this outfit was not only strange, but not right; don't ask me why. It was not a good horse, and the buggy was not good, either. There was something wrong with the whole thing, and I went full of curiosity to see why such strangers as would drive such a horse and buggy would be calling on my grandmother. (At this point say anything you please about the snobbism of children and dogs. It is real. As real as the snobbism of their parents and owners, and much more keen and direct.)

I stood just outside the living room door, unnoticed for a moment by my Grandmother, who was sitting rather stiffly, with an odd expression on her face: a doubtful smiling mouth, brows knitted in painful inquiry. She was a woman called upon for decisions, many decisions every day, wielding justice among her unruly family. Once she struck, justly or unjustly, she dared not retract—the whole pack would have torn her in pieces. They did not want justice in any case, but revenge, each in his own favor. But this situation had nothing to do with her family, and there she sat, worried, undecided. I had never seen her so, and it dismayed me.

Then I saw first a poor sad pale beaten-looking woman in a faded cotton print dress and a wretched little straw hat with a wreath of wilted forget-me-nots. She looked as if she had never eaten a good dinner, or slept in a comfortable bed, the mark of life-starvation was all over her. Her hands were twisted tight in her lap and she was looking down at them in shame. Her eyes were covered with dark glasses. While I stared at her, I heard the man sitting near her almost shouting in a coarse, roughened voice: "I swear, it was in self-defense! His life or mine! If you don't believe me, ask my wife here. She saw it. My wife won't lie!" Every time he repeated these words, without lifting her head or moving, she would say in a low voice, "Yes, that's right. I saw it."

In that moment, or in another moment later as this memory sank in and worked in my feelings and understanding, it was quite clear to me, and seems now to have been clear from the first, that he expected her to lie, was indeed forcing her to tell a lie; that she did it unwillingly and unlovingly in bitter resignation to the double disgrace of her husband's crime and her own sin; and that he, stupid, dishonest, soiled as he was, was imploring her as his only hope, somehow to make his lie a truth.

I used this scene in "Noon Wine," but the man in real life was not lean and gaunt and blindly, foolishly proud, like Mr. Thompson; no, he was just a great loose-faced, blabbing man full of guilt and fear, and he was bawling at my grandmother, his eyes bloodshot with drink and tears, "Lady, if you don't believe me, ask my wife! She won't lie!" At this point my grandmother noticed my presence and sent me away with a look we children knew well and never dreamed of disobeying. But I heard part of the story later, when my grandmother said to my father, with an unfamiliar coldness in her voice, for she had made her decision about this affair, too: "I was never asked to condone a murder before. Something new." My father said, "Yes, and a cold-blooded murder too if ever there was one."

So, there was the dreary tale of violence again, this time with the killer out on bail, going the rounds of the countryside with his wretched wife, telling his side of it—whatever it was; I never knew the end. In the meantime, in one summer or another, certainly before my eleventh year, for that year we left that country for good, I had two other memorable glimpses. My father and I were driving from the farm to town, when we met with a tall black-whiskered man on horseback, sitting so straight his chin was level with his Adam's apple, dressed in clean mended blue denims, shirt open at the throat, a big devil-may-care black felt hat on the side of his head. He gave us a lordly gesture of greeting, caused his fine black horse to curvet and prance a little, and rode on, grandly. I asked my father who that could be, and he said, "That's Ralph Thomas, the proudest man in seven counties." I said, "What is he proud of?" And my father said, "I suppose the horse. It's a very fine horse," in a good-humored, joking tone, which made the poor man quite ridiculous, and yet not funny, but sad in some way I could not understand.

On another of these journeys I saw a bony, awkward, tired-looking man, tilted in a kitchen chair against the wall of his comfortless shack, set back from the road under the thin shade of hackberry trees, a thatch of bleached-looking hair between his eyebrows, blowing away at a doleful tune on his harmonica, in the hot dull cricket-whirring summer day: the very living image of loneliness. I was struck with pity for this stranger, his eyes closed against the alien scene, consoling himself with such poor music. I was told he was someone's Swedish hired man.

In time—when? how? Pink Hodges, whom I never knew except in the sound of his death-cry, merged with my glimpse of the Swedish hired man to become the eternal Victim; the fat bullying whining man in my grandmother's living room became the Killer. But nothing can remain so simple as that, this was only a beginning. Helton too, the Victim in my story, is also a murderer, with the dubious innocence of the madman; but no less a shedder of blood. Everyone in this story contributes, one way or another directly, or indirectly, to murder, or death by violence; even the two young sons of Mr. Thompson who turn on him in their fright and ignorance and side with their mother, who does not need them; they are guiltless, for they meant no harm, and they do not know what they have contributed to; indeed in their innocence they believe they are doing, not only right, but the only thing they could possibly do in the situation as they understand it: they must defend their mother. . . .

And here I am brought to a pause, for almost without knowing it, I have begun to write about these characters in a story of mine as though they were real persons exactly as I have shown them. And these fragments of memory on which the story is based now seem to have a random look; they nowhere contain in themselves, together or separately, the story I finally wrote out of them; a story of the most painful moral and emotional confusions, in which every one concerned, yes, in his crooked way, even Mr. Hatch, is trying to do right.

It is only in the varying levels of quality in the individual nature that we are able finally more or less to measure the degree of virtue in each man. Mr. Thompson's motives are most certainly mixed, yet not ignoble; he helps some one who helps him in turn; while acting in defense of what he sees as the good in his own life, the thing worth trying to save at almost any cost, he is trying at the same time to defend another life—the life of Mr. Helton, who has proved himself the bringer of good, the present help, the true friend. Mr. Helton would have done as much for me, Mr. Thompson says, and he is right. Yet he hated Mr. Hatch on sight, wished to injure him before he had a reason: could it not be a sign of virtue in Mr. Thompson that he surmised and resisted at first glance the evil in Mr. Hatch? The whole countryside, let us remember, for this is most important, the relations of a man to his society, agrees with Mr. Burleigh the lawyer, and the jury and the judge that Mr. Thompson's deed was justifiable homicide: but this did not, as his neighbors confirmed, make it any less a murder. Mr. Thompson was not an evil man, he was only a poor sinner doing his best according to his lights, lights somewhat dimmed by his natural aptitude for Pride and Sloth. He still had his virtues, even if he did not quite know what they were, and so gave himself credit for some few that he had not.

But Hatch was the doomed man, evil by nature, a lover and do-er of evil, who did no good thing for any one, not even, in the long run, himself. He was evil in the most dangerous, irremediable way: one who works safely within the law, and has reasoned himself into believing that his motives, if not good, are at least no worse than any one else's: for he believes quite simply and naturally that the motives of others are no better than his own; and putting aside all nonsense about good, he will always be found on the side of custom and common sense and the letter of the law. When challenged he has his defense pat and ready, and there is nothing much wrong with it—it only lacks human decency, of which he has no conception beyond a faint hearsay. Mr. Helton is, by his madness, beyond good and evil, his own victim as well as the victim of others. Mrs. Thompson is a woman of the sort produced in numbers in that time, that place, that code: so trained to the practice of her prescribed womanly vocation of virtue as such—manifest, unrelenting, sacrificial, stupifying—she has almost lost her human qualities, and her spiritual courage and insight, to boot. She commits the, to her, dreadful unforgivable sin of lying; moreover, lying to shield a criminal, even if that criminal is her own husband. Having done this, to the infinite damage, as she sees it, of her own soul (as well as her self-respect which is founded on her feeling of irreproachability) she lacks the courage and the love to see her sin through to its final good purpose; to commit it with her whole heart and with perfect acceptance of her guilt; to say to her husband the words that might have saved them both, soul and body—might have, I say only. I do not know and shall never know. Mrs. Thompson was not that robust a character, and this story, given all, must end as it does end . . . there is nothing in any of these beings tough enough to work the miracle of redemption in them.

Suppose I imagine now that I really saw all of these persons in the flesh at one time or another? I saw what I have told you, a few mere flashes of a glimpse here and there, one time or another; but I do know why I remembered them, and why in my memory they slowly took on their separate lives in a story. It it because there radiated from each one of those glimpses of strangers some element, some quality that arrested my attention at a vital moment of my own growth, and caused me, a child, to stop short and look outward, away from myself; to look at another human being with that attention and wonder and speculation which ordinarily, and very naturally, I think, a child lavishes only on himself. Is it not almost the sole end of civilized education of all sorts to teach us to be more and more highly, sensitively conscious of the reality of the existence, the essential being, of others, those around us so very like us and yet so bafflingly, so mysteriously different? I do not know whether my impressions were on the instant, as I now believe, or did they draw to their magnet gradually with time and confirming experience? That man on the fine horse, with his straight back, straight neck, shabby and unshaven, riding like a cavalry officer, "the proudest man in seven counties—" I saw him no doubt as my father saw him, absurd, fatuous, but with some human claim on respect and not to be laughed at, for all his simple vanity.

The woman I have called Mrs. Thompson—I never knew her name— showed me for the first time I am certain the face of pure shame; humiliation so nearly absolute it could not have been more frightening if she had grovelled in the floor; and I knew that whatever the cause, it was mortal and beyond help. In that bawling sweating man with the loose mouth and staring eyes, I saw the fear that is moral cowardice and I knew he was lying. In that yellow-haired, long-legged man playing his harmonica I felt almost the first glimmer of understanding and sympathy for any suffering not physical. Most certainly I had already done my share of weeping over lost or dying pets, or beside some one I loved who was very sick, or my own pains and accidents; but *this* was a spiritual enlightenment, some tenderness, some first wakening of charity in my self-centered heart. I am using here some very old fashioned noble words in their prime sense. They have perfect freshness and reality to me, they are the irreplaceable names of Realities. I know well what they mean, and I need them here to describe as well as I am able what happens to a child when the human feelings and the moral sense and the sense of charity are unfolding, and are touched once and for all in that first time when the soul is prepared for them; and I know that the all-important things in that way have all taken place long and long before we know the words for them.

ROBERT PENN WARREN

Blackberry Winter

IT was getting into June and past eight o'clock in the morning, but there was a fire—even if it wasn't a big fire, just a fire of chunks—on the hearth of the big stone fireplace in the living room. I was standing on the hearth, almost into the chimney, hunched over the fire, working my bare toes slowly on the warm stone. I relished the heat which made the skin of my bare legs warp and creep and tingle, even as I called to my mother, who was somewhere back in the dining room or kitchen, and said: "But it's June, I don't have to put them on!"

"You put them on if you are going out," she called.

I tried to assess the degree of authority and conviction in the tone, but at that distance it was hard to decide. I tried to analyze the tone, and then I thought what a fool I had been to start out the back door and let her see that I was barefoot. If I had gone out the front door or the side door she would never have known, not till dinner time anyway, and by then the day would have been half gone and I would have been all over the farm to see what the storm had done and down to the creek to see the flood. But it had never crossed my mind that they would try to stop you from going barefoot in June, no matter if there had been a gully-washer and a cold spell.

Nobody had ever tried to stop me in June as long as I could remember, and when you are nine years old, what you remember seems forever; for you remember everything and everything is important and stands big and full and fills up Time and is so solid that you can walk around and around it like a tree and look at it. You are aware that time passes, that there is a movement in time, but that is not what Time is. Time is not a movement, a flowing, a wind then, but is, rather, a kind of climate in which things are, and when a thing happens it begins to live and keeps on living and stands solid in Time like the tree that you can walk around. And if there is a movement, the movement is not Time itself, no more than a breeze is climate, for all the breeze does is to shake a little the leaves on the tree which is alive and solid. When you are nine, you know that there are things that you don't know, but you know that when you know something you know it. You know how a thing has been and you know that you can go barefoot in June. You do not understand that voice from back in the kitchen which says that you cannot go barefoot outdoors and run to see what has happened and rub your feet over the wet shivery grass and make the perfect mark of your foot in the smooth, creamy, red mud and then muse upon it as though you had suddenly come upon that single mark on the glistening auroral beach of the world. You have never seen a beach, but you have read the book and how the footprint was there.

The voice had said what it had said, and I looked savagely at the black stockings and the strong, scuffed brown shoes which I had brought from my closet as far as the hearth rug. I called once more, "But it's June," and waited.

"It's June," the voice replied from far away, "but it's blackberry winter."

I had lifted my head to reply to that, to make one more test of what was in that tone, when I happened to see the man.

The fireplace in the living room was at the end; for the stone chimney was built, as in so many of the farmhouses in Tennessee, at the end of a gable, and there was a window on each side of the chimney. Out of the window on the north side of the fireplace I could see the man. When I saw the man I did not call out what I had intended, but, engrossed by the strangeness of the sight, watched him, still far off, come along the path by the edge of the woods.

What was strange was that there should be a man there at all. That path went along the yard fence, between the fence and the woods which came right down to the yard, and then on back past the chicken runs and on by the woods until it was lost to sight where the woods bulged out and cut off the back field. There the path disappeared into the woods. It led on back, I knew, through the woods and to the swamp, skirted the swamp where the big trees gave way to sycamores and water oaks and willows and tangled cane, and then led on to the river. Nobody ever went back there except people who wanted to gig frogs in the swamp or to fish in the river or to hunt in the woods, and those people, if they didn't have a standing permission from my father, always stopped to ask permission to cross the farm. But the man whom I now saw wasn't, I could tell even at that distance, a sportsman. And what would a sportsman have been doing down there after a storm? Besides, he was coming from the river, and nobody had gone down there that morning. I knew that for a fact, because if anybody had passed, certainly if a stranger had passed, the dogs would have made a racket and would have been out on him. But this man was coming up from the river and had come up through the woods. I suddenly had a vision of him moving up the grassy path in the woods, in the green twilight under the big trees, not making any sound on the path, while now and then, like drops off the eaves, a big drop of water would fall from a leaf or bough and strike a stiff oak leaf lower down with a small, hollow sound like a drop of water hitting tin. That sound, in the silence of the woods, would be very significant.

When you are a boy and stand in the stillness of woods, which can be so still that your heart almost stops beating and makes you want to stand there in the green twilight until you feel your very feet sinking into and clutching the earth like roots and your body breathing slow through its pores like the leaves—when you stand there and wait for the next drop to drop with its small, flat sound to a lower leaf, that sound seems to measure out something, to put an end to something, to begin something, and you cannot wait for it to happen and are afraid it will not happen, and then when it has happened, you are waiting again, almost afraid.

But the man whom I saw coming through the woods in my mind's eye did not pause and wait, growing into the ground and breathing with the enormous, soundless breathing of the leaves. Instead, I saw him moving in the green twilight inside my head as he was moving at that very moment along the path by the edge of the woods, coming toward the house. He was moving steadily, but not fast, with his shoulders hunched a little and his head thrust forward, like a man who has come a long way and has a long way to go. I shut my eyes for a couple of seconds, thinking that when I opened them he would not be there at all. There was no place for him to have come from, and there was no reason for him to come where he was coming, toward our house. But I opened my eyes, and there he was, and he was coming steadily along the side of the woods. He was not yet even with the back chicken yard.

"Mama," I called.

"You put them on," the voice said.

"There's a man coming," I called, "out back."

She did not reply to that, and I guessed that she had gone to the kitchen window to look. She would be looking at the man and wondering who he was and what he wanted, the way you always do in the country, and if I went back there now she would not notice right off whether or not I was barefoot. So I went back to the kitchen.

She was standing by the window. "I don't recognize him," she said, not looking around at me.

"Where could he be coming from?" I asked.

"I don't know," she said.

"What would he be doing down at the river? At night? In the storm?"

She studied the figure out the window, then said, "Oh, I reckon maybe he cut across from the Dunbar place."

That was, I realized, a perfectly rational explanation. He had not been down at the river in the storm, at night. He had come over this morning. You could cut across from the Dunbar place if you didn't mind breaking through a lot of elder and sassafras and blackberry bushes which had about taken over the old cross path, which nobody ever used any more. That satisfied me for a moment, but only for a moment. "Mama," I asked, "What would he be doing over at the Dunbar place last night?"

Then she looked at me, and I knew I had made a mistake, for she was looking at my bare feet. "You haven't got your shoes on," she said.

But I was saved by the dogs. That instant there was a bark which I recognized as Sam, the collie, and then a heavier, churning kind of bark which was Bully, and I saw a streak of white as Bully tore round the corner of the back porch and headed out for the man. Bully was a big, bone-white bull dog, the kind of dog that they used to call a farm bull dog but that you don't see any more, heavy chested and heavy headed, but with pretty long legs. He could take a fence as light as a hound. He had just cleared the white paling fence toward the woods when my mother ran out to the back porch and began calling, "Here you, Bully! Here you!"

Bully stopped in the path, waiting for the man, but he gave a few more of those deep, gargling, savage barks that reminded you of something down a stone-lined well. The red clay mud, I saw, was splashed up over his white chest and looked exciting, like blood.

The man, however, had not stopped walking even when Bully took the fence and started at him. He had kept right on coming. All he had done was to switch a little paper parcel which he carried from the right hand to the left, and then reach into his pants pocket to get something. Then I saw the glitter and knew that he had a knife in his hand, probably the kind of mean knife just made for devilment and nothing else, with a blade as long as the blade of a frog-sticker, which will snap out ready when you press a button in the handle. That knife must have had a button in the handle, or else how could he have had the blade out glittering so quick and with just one hand?

Pulling his knife against the dogs was a funny thing to do, for Bully was a big, powerful brute and fast, and Sam was all right. If those dogs had meant business, they might have knocked him down and ripped him before he got a stroke in. He ought to have picked up a heavy stick, something to take a swipe at them with and something which they could see and respect when they came at him. But he apparently did not know much about dogs. He just held the knife blade close against the right leg, low down, and kept on moving down the path.

Then my mother had called, and Bully had stopped. So the man let the blade of the knife snap back into the handle, and dropped it into his pocket, and kept on coming. Many women would have been afraid with the strange man who they knew had that knife in his pocket. That is, if they were alone in the house with nobody but a nine-year-old boy. And my mother was alone, for my father had gone off, and Dellie, the cook, was down at her cabin because she wasn't feeling well. But my mother wasn't afraid. She wasn't a big woman, but she was clear and brisk about everything she did and looked everybody and everything right in the eye from her own blue eyes in her tanned face. She had been the first woman in the county to ride a horse astride (that was back when she was a girl and long before I was born), and I have seen her snatch up a pump gun and go out and knock a chicken hawk out of the air like a busted skeet when he came over her chicken yard. She was a steady and self-reliant woman, and when I think of her now after all the years she has been dead, I think of her brown hands, not big, but somewhat square for a woman's hands, with square-cut nails. They looked, as a matter of fact, more like a young boy's hands than a grown woman's. But back then it never crossed my mind that she would ever be dead.

She stood on the back porch and watched the man enter the back gate, where the dogs (Bully had leaped back into the yard) were dancing and muttering and giving sidelong glances back to my mother to see if she meant what she had said. The man walked right by the dogs, almost brushing them, and didn't pay them any attention. I could see now that he wore old khaki pants, and a dark wool coat with stripes in it, and a gray felt hat. He had on a gray shirt with blue stripes in it, and no tie. But I could see a tie, blue and reddish, sticking in his side coat-pocket. Everything was wrong about what he wore. He ought to have been wearing blue jeans or overalls, and a straw hat or an old black felt hat, and the coat, granting that he might have been wearing a wool coat and not a jumper, ought not to have had those stripes. Those clothes, despite the fact that they were old enough and dirty enough for any tramp, didn't belong there in our back yard, coming down the path, in Middle Tennessee, miles away from any big town, and even a mile off the pike.

When he got almost to the steps, without having said anything, my mother, very matter-of-factly, said, "Good morning."

"Good morning," he said, and stopped and looked her over. He did not take off his hat, and under the brim you could see the perfectly unmemorable face, which wasn't old and wasn't young, or thick or thin. It was grayish and covered with about three days of stubble. The eyes were a kind of nondescript, muddy hazel, or something like that, rather bloodshot. His teeth, when he opened his mouth, showed yellow and uneven. A couple of them had been knocked out. You knew that they had been knocked out, because there was a scar, not very old, there on the lower lip just beneath the gap.

"Are you hunting work?" my mother asked him.

"Yes," he said—not "yes, mam"—and still did not take off his hat.

"I don't know about my husband, for he isn't here," she said, and didn't mind a bit telling the tramp, or whoever he was, with the mean knife in his pocket, that no man was around, "but I can give you a few things to do. The storm has drowned a lot of my chicks. Three coops of them. You can gather them up and bury them. Bury them deep so the dogs won't get at them. In the woods. And fix the coops the wind blew over. And down yonder beyond that pen by the edge of the woods are some drowned poults. They got out and I couldn't get them in. Even after it started to rain hard. Poults haven't got any sense."

"What are them things—poults?" he demanded, and spat on the brick walk. He rubbed his foot over the spot, and I saw that he wore a black, pointed-toe low shoe, all cracked and broken. It was a crazy kind of shoe to be wearing in the country.

"Oh, they're young turkeys," my mother was saying. "And they haven't got any sense. I oughtn't to try to raise them around here with so many chickens, anyway. They don't thrive near chickens, even in separate pens. And I won't give up my chickens." Then she stopped herself and resumed briskly on the note of business. "When you finish that, you can fix my flower beds. A lot of trash and mud and gravel has washed down. Maybe you can save some of my flowers if you are careful."

"Flowers," the man said, in a low, impersonal voice which seemed to have a wealth of meaning, but a meaning which I could not fathom. As I think back on it, it probably was not pure contempt. Rather, it was a kind of impersonal and distant marveling that he should be on the verge of grubbing in a flower bed. He said the word, and then looked off across the yard.

"Yes, flowers," my mother replied with some asperity, as though she would have nothing said or implied against flowers. "And they were very fine this year." Then she stopped and looked at the man. "Are you hungry?" she demanded.

"Yeah," he said.

"I'll fix you something," she said, "before you get started." She turned to me. "Show him where he can wash up," she commanded, and went into the house.

I took the man to the end of the porch where a pump was and where a couple of wash pans sat on a low shelf for people to use before they went into the house. I stood there while he laid down his little parcel wrapped in newspaper and took off his hat and looked around for a nail to hang it on. He poured the water and plunged his hands into it. They were big hands, and strong looking, but they did not have the creases and the earth-color of the hands of men who work outdoors. But they were dirty, with black dirt ground into the skin and under the nails. After he had washed his hands, he poured another basin of water and washed his face. He dried his face, and with the towel still dangling in his grasp, stepped over to the mirror on the house wall. He rubbed one hand over the stubble on his face. Then he carefully inspected his face, turning first one side and then the other, and stepped back and settled his striped coat down on his shoulders. He had the movements of a man who had just dressed up to go to church or a party—the way he settled his coat and smoothed it and scanned himself in the mirror.

Then he caught my glance on him. He glared at me for an instant out of the bloodshot eyes, then demanded in a low, harsh voice, "What you looking at?"

"Nothing," I managed to say, and stepped back a step from him.

He flung the towel down, crumpled, on the shelf, and went toward the kitchen door and entered without knocking.

My mother said something to him which I could not catch. I started to go in again, then thought about my bare feet, and decided to go back of the chicken yard, where the man would have to come to pick up the dead chicks. I hung around behind the chicken house until he came out.

He moved across the chicken yard with a fastidious, not quite finicking motion, looking down at the curdled mud flecked with bits of chicken-droppings. The mud curled up over the soles of his black shoes. I stood back from him some six feet and watched him pick up the first of the drowned chicks. He held it up by one foot and inspected it.

There is nothing deader looking than a drowned chick. The feet curl in that feeble, empty way which back when I was a boy, even if I was a country boy who did not mind hog-killing or frog-gigging, made me feel hollow in the stomach. Instead of looking plump and fluffy, the body is stringy and limp with the fluff plastered to it, and the neck is long and loose like a little string of rag. And the eyes have that bluish membrane over them which makes you think of a very old man who is sick about to die.

The man stood there and inspected the chick. Then he looked all around as though he didn't know what to do with it.

"There's a great big old basket in the shed," I said, and pointed to the shed attached to the chicken house.

He inspected me as though he had just discovered my presence, and moved toward the shed.

"There's a spade there, too," I added.

He got the basket and began to pick up the other chicks, picking each one up slowly by a foot and then flinging it into the basket with a nasty, snapping motion. Now and then he would look at me out of the bloodshot eyes. Every time he seemed on the verge of saying something, but he did not. Perhaps he was building up to say something to me, but I did not wait that long. His way of looking at me made me so uncomfortable that I left the chicken yard.

Besides, I had just remembered that the creek was in flood, over the bridge, and that people were down there watching it. So I cut across the farm toward the creek. When I got to the big tobacco field I saw that it had not suffered much. The land lay right and not many tobacco plants had washed out of the ground. But I knew that a lot of tobacco round the country had been washed right out. My father had said so at breakfast.

My father was down at the bridge. When I came out of the gap in the osage hedge into the road, I saw him sitting on his mare over the heads of the other men who were standing around, admiring the flood. The creek was big here, even in low water; for only a couple of miles away it ran into the river, and when a real flood came, the red water got over the pike where it dipped down to the bridge, which was an iron bridge, and high over the floor and even the side railings of the bridge. Only the upper iron work would show, with the water boiling and frothing red and white around it. That creek rose so fast and so heavy because a few miles back it came down out of the hills, where the gorges filled up with water in no time when a rain came. The creek ran in a deep bed with limestone bluffs along both sides until it got within three quarters of a mile of the bridge, and when it came out from between those bluffs in flood it was boiling and hissing and steaming like water from a fire hose.

Whenever there was a flood, people from half the county would come down to see the sight. After a gully-washer there would not be any work to do anyway. If it didn't ruin your crop, you couldn't plow and you felt like taking a holiday to celebrate. If it did ruin your crop, there wasn't anything to do except to try to take your mind off the mortgage, if you were rich enough to have a mortgage, and if you couldn't afford a mortgage you needed something to take your mind off how hungry you would be by Christmas. So people would come down to the bridge and look at the flood. It made something different from the run of days.

There would not be much talking after the first few minutes of trying to guess how high the water was this time. The men and kids just stood around, or sat their horses or mules, as the case might be, or stood up in the wagon beds. They looked at the strangeness of the flood for an hour or two, and then somebody would say that he had better be getting on home to dinner and would start walking down the gray, puddled limestone pike, or would touch heel to his mount and start off. Everybody always knew what it would be like when he got down to the bridge, but people always came. It was like church or a funeral. They always came, that is, if it was summer and the flood unexpected. Nobody ever came down in winter to see high water.

When I came out of the gap in the bowdock hedge, I saw the crowd, perhaps fifteen or twenty men and a lot of kids, and saw my father sitting his mare, Nellie Gray. He was a tall, limber man and carried himself well. I was always proud to see him sit a horse, he was so quiet and straight, and when I stepped through the gap of the hedge that morning, the first thing that happened was, I remember, the warm feeling I always had when I saw him up on a horse, just sitting. I did not go toward him, but skirted the crowd on the far side, to get a look at the creek. For one thing, I was not sure what he would say about the fact that I was barefoot. But the first thing I knew, I heard his voice calling, "Seth!"

I went toward him, moving apologetically past the men, who bent their large, red or thin, sallow faces above me. I knew some of the men.

and knew their names, but because those I knew were there in a crowd, mixed with the strange faces, they seemed foreign to me, and not friendly. I did not look up at my father until I was almost within touching distance of his heel. Then I looked up and tried to read his face, to see if he was angry about my being barefoot. Before I could decide anything from that impassive, high-boned face, he had leaned over and reached a hand to me. "Grab on," he commanded.

I grabbed on and gave a little jump, and he said, "Up-see-daisy!" and whisked me, light as a feather, up to the pommel of his McClellan saddle.

"You can see better up here," he said, slid back on the cantle a little to make me more comfortable, and then, looking over my head at the swollen, tumbling water, seemed to forget all about me. But his right hand was laid on my side, just above my thigh, to steady me.

I was sitting there as quiet as I could, feeling the faint stir of my father's chest against my shoulders as it rose and fell with his breath, when I saw the cow. At first, looking up the creek, I thought it was just another big piece of driftwood steaming down the creek in the ruck of water, but all at once a pretty good-size boy who had climbed part way up a telephone pole by the pike so that he could see better yelled out, "Golly-damn, look at that-air cow!"

Everybody looked. It was a cow all right, but it might just as well have been driftwood; for it was dead as a chunk, rolling and rolling down the creek, appearing and disappearing, feet up or head up, it didn't matter which.

The cow started up the talk again. Somebody wondered whether it would hit one of the clear places under the top girder of the bridge and get through or whether it would get tangled in the drift and trash that had piled against the upright girders and braces. Somebody remembered how about ten years before so much driftwood had piled up on the bridge that it was knocked off its foundations. Then the cow hit. It hit the edge of the drift against one of the girders, and hung there. For a few seconds it seemed as though it might tear loose, but then we saw that it was really caught. It bobbed and heaved on its side there in a slow, grinding, uneasy fashion. It had a yoke around its neck, the kind made out of a forked limb to keep a jumper behind fence.

"She shore jumped one fence," one of the men said.

And another: "Well, she done jumped her last one, fer a fack."

They they began to wonder about whose cow it might be. They decided it must belong to Milt Alley. They said that he had a cow that was a jumper, and kept her in a fenced-in piece of ground up the creek. I had never seen Milt Alley, but I knew who he was. He was a squatter and lived up the hills a way, on a shirt-tail patch of set-on-edge land, in a cabin. He was pore white trash. He had lots of children. I had seen the children at school, when they came. They were thin-faced, with straight, sticky-looking, dough-colored hair, and they smelled something like old sour butter-milk, not because they drank so much buttermilk but because that is the sort of smell which children out of those cabins tend to have. The big Alley boy drew dirty pictures and showed them to the little boys at school.

That was Milt Alley's cow. It looked like the kind of cow he would have, a scrawny, old, sway-backed cow, with a yoke around her neck. I wondered if Milt Alley had another cow.

"Poppa," I said, "do you think Milt Alley has got another cow?"

"You say 'Mr. Alley,' " my father said quietly.

"Do you think he has?"

"No telling," my father said.

Then a big gangly boy, about fifteen, who was sitting on a scraggly little old mule with a piece of croker sack thrown across the saw-tooth spine, and who had been staring at the cow, suddenly said to nobody in particular, "Reckin anybody ever et drownt cow?"

He was the kind of boy who might just as well as not have been the son of Milt Alley, with his faded and patched overalls ragged at the bottom of the pants and the mud-stiff brogans hanging off his skinny, bare ankles at the level of the mule's belly. He had said what he did, and then looked embarrassed and sullen when all the eyes swung at him. He hadn't meant to say it, I am pretty sure now. He would have been too proud to say it, just as Milt Alley would have been too proud. He had just been thinking out loud, and the words had popped out.

There was an old man standing there on the pike, an old man with a white beard. "Son," he said to the embarrassed and sullen boy on the mule, "you live long enough and you'll find a man will eat anything when the time comes."

"Time gonna come fer some folks this year," another man said.

"Son," the old man said, "in my time I et things a man don't like to think on. I was a sojer and I rode with Gin'l Forrest, and them things we et when the time come. I tell you. I et meat what got up and run when you taken out yore knife to cut a slice to put on the fire. You had to knock it down with a carbeen butt, it was so active. That-air meat would jump like a bullfrog, it was so full of skippers."

But nobody was listening to the old man. The boy on the mule turned his sullen sharp face from him, dug a heel into the side of the mule and went off up the pike with a motion which made you think that any second you would hear mule bones clashing inside that lank and scrofulous hide.

"Cy Dundee's boy," a man said, and nodded toward the figure going up the pike on the mule.

"Reckin Cy Dundee's young-uns seen times they'd settle fer drownt cow," another man said.

The old man with the beard peered at them both from his weak, slow eyes, first at one and then at the other. "Live long enough," he said, "and a man will settle fer what he kin git."

Then there was silence again, with the people looking at the red, foam-flecked water.

My father lifted the bridle rein in his left hand, and the mare turned and walked around the group and up the pike. We rode on up to our big gate, where my father dismounted to open it and let me myself ride Nellie Gray through. When he got to the lane that led off from the drive about two hundred yards from our house, my father said, "Grab on." I grabbed on, and he let me down to the ground. "I'm going to ride down and look at my corn," he said. "You go on." He took the lane, and I stood there on the drive and watched him ride off. He was wearing cowhide boots and an old hunting coat, and I thought that that made him look very military, like a picture. That and the way he rode.

I did not go the house. Instead, I went by the vegetable garden and crossed behind the stables, and headed down for Dellie's cabin. I wanted to go down and play with Jebb, who was Dellie's little boy about two years older than I was. Besides, I was cold. I shivered as I walked, and I had goose-flesh. The mud which crawled up between my toes with every step I took was like ice. Dellie would have a fire, but she wouldn't make me put on shoes and stockings.

Dellie's cabin was of logs, with one side, because it was on a slope, set on limestone chunks, with a little porch attached to it, and had a little whitewashed fence around it and a gate with plow-points on a wire to clink when somebody came in, and had two big white oaks in the yard and some flowers and a nice privy in the back with some honeysuckle growing over it. Dellie and Old Jebb, who was Jebb's father and who lived with Dellie and had lived with her for twenty-five years even if they never had got married, were careful to keep everything nice around their cabin. They had the name all over the community for being clean and clever Negroes. Dellie and Jebb were what they used to call "white-folks' niggers." There was a big difference between their cabin and the other two cabins farther down where the other tenants lived. My father kept the other cabins weatherproof, but he couldn't undertake to go down and pick up after the litter they strewed. They didn't take the trouble to have a vegetable patch like Dellie and Jebb or to make preserves from wild plum, and jelly from crab apple the way Dellie did. They were shiftless, and my father was always threatening to get shed of them. But he never did. When they finally left, they just up and left on their own, for no reason, to go and be shiftless somewhere else. Then some more came. But meanwhile they lived down there, Matt Rawson and his family, and Sid Turner and his, and I played with their children all over the farm when they weren't working. But when I wasn't around they were mean sometimes to Little Jebb. That was because the other tenants down there were jealous of Dellie and Jebb.

I was so cold that I ran the last fifty yards to Dellie's gate. As soon as I had entered the yard, I saw that the storm had been hard on Dellie's flowers. The yard was, as I have said, on a slight slope, and the water running across had gutted the flower beds and washed out all the good black woods-earth which Dellie had brought in. What little grass there was in the yard was plastered sparsely down on the ground, the way the drainage water had left it. It reminded me of the way the fluff was plastered down on the skin of the drowned chicks that the strange man had been picking up, up in my mother's chicken yard.

I took a few steps up the path to the cabin, and then I saw that the drainage water had washed a lot of trash and filth out from under Dellie's house. Up toward the porch, the ground was not clean any more. Old pieces of rag, two or three rusted cans, pieces of rotten rope, some hunks of old dog dung, broken glass, old paper, and all sorts of things like that had washed out from under Dellie's house to foul her clean yard. It looked just as bad as the yards of the other cabins, or worse. It was worse, as a matter of fact, because it was a surprise. I had never thought of all that filth being under Dellie's house. It was not anything against Dellie that the stuff had been under the cabin. Trash will get under any house. But I did not think of that when I saw the foulness which had washed out on the ground which Dellie sometimes used to sweep with a twig broom to make nice and clean.

I picked my way past the filth, being careful not to get my bare feet on it, and mounted to Dellie's door. When I knocked, I heard her voice telling me to come in.

It was dark inside the cabin, after the daylight, but I could make out Dellie piled up in bed under a quilt, and Little Jebb crouched by the hearth, where a low fire simmered. "Howdy," I said to Dellie, "how you feeling?"

Her big eyes, the whites surprising and glaring in the black face, fixed on me as I stood there, but she did not reply. It did not look like Dellie, or act like Dellie, who would grumble and bustle around our kitchen, talking to herself, scolding me or Little Jebb, clanking pans, making all sorts of unnecessary noises and mutterings like an old-fashioned black steam thrasher engine when it has got up an extra head of steam and keeps popping the governor and rumbling and shaking on its wheels. But now Dellie just lay there on the bed, under the patch-work quilt, and turned the black face, which I scarcely recognized, and the glaring white eyes to me.

"How you feeling?" I repeated.

"I'se sick," the voice said croakingly out of the strange black face which was not attached to Dellie's big, squat body, but stuck out from under a pile of tangled bedclothes. Then the voice added: "Mighty sick."

"I'm sorry," I managed to say.

The eyes remained fixed on me for a moment, then they left me and the head rolled back on the pillow. "Sorry," the voice said, in a flat way which wasn't question or statement of anything. It was just the empty word put into the air with no meaning or expression, to float off like a feather or a puff of smoke, while the big eyes, with the whites like the peeled white of hard-boiled eggs, stared at the ceiling.

"Dellie," I said after a minute, "there's a tramp up at the house. He's got a knife."

She was not listening. She closed her eyes.

I tiptoed over to the hearth where Jebb was and crouched beside him. We began to talk in low voices. I was asking him to get out his train and play train. Old Jebb had put spool wheels on three cigar boxes and put wire links between the boxes to make a train for Jebb. The box that was the locomotive had the top closed and a length of broom stick for a smoke stack. Jebb didn't want to get the train out, but I told him I would go home if he didn't. So he got out the train, and the colored rocks, and fossils of crinoid stems, and other junk he used for the load, and we began to push it around, talking the way we thought trainmen talked, making a chuck-chucking sound under the breath for the noise of the locomotive and now and then uttering low, cautious toots for the whistle. We got so interested in playing train that the toots got louder. Then, before he thought, Jebb gave a good, loud *toot-toot*, blowing for a crossing.

"Come here," the voice said from the bed.

Jebb got up slow from his hands and knees, giving me a sudden, naked, inimical look.

"Come here!" the voice said.

Jebb went to the bed. Dellie propped herself weakly up on one arm, muttering, "Come closer."

Jebb stood closer.

"Last thing I do, I'm gonna do it," Dellie said. "Done tole you to be quiet."

Then she slapped him. It was an awful slap, more awful for the kind of weakness which it came from and brought to focus. I had seen her slap Jebb before, but the slapping had always been the kind of easy slap you would expect from a good-natured, grumbling Negro woman like Dellie. But this was different. It was awful. It was so awful that Jebb didn't make a sound. The tears just popped out and ran down his face, and his breath came sharp, like gasps.

Dellie fell back. "Cain't even be sick," she said to the ceiling. "Git sick and they won't even let you lay. They tromp all over you. Cain't even be sick." Then she closed her eyes.

I went out of the room. I almost ran getting to the door, and I did run across the porch and down the steps and across the yard, not caring whether or not I stepped on the filth which had washed out from under the cabin.

I ran almost all the way home. Then I thought about my mother catching me with the bare feet. So I went down to the stables.

I heard a noise in the crib, and opened the door. There was Big Jebb, sitting on an old nail keg, shelling corn into a bushel basket. I went in, pulling the door shut behind me, and crouched on the floor near him. I crouched there for a couple of minutes before either of us spoke, and watched him shelling the corn.

He had very big hands, knotted and grayish at the joints, with callused palms which seemed to be streaked with rust with the rust coming up between the fingers to show from the back. His hands were so strong and tough that he could take a big ear of corn and rip the grains right off the cob with the palm of his hand, all in one motion, like a machine. "Work long as me," he would say, "and the good Lawd'll give you a hand lak cass-ion won't nuthin' hurt." And his hands did look like cast iron, old cast iron streaked with rust.

He was an old man, up in his seventies, thirty years or more older than Dellie, but he was strong as a bull. He was a squat sort of man, heavy in the shoulders, with remarkably long arms, the kind of build they say the river natives have on the Congo from paddling so much in their boats. He had a round bullet-head, set on powerful shoulders. His skin was very black, and the thin hair on his head was now grizzled like tufts of old cotton batting. He had small eyes and a flat nose, not big, and the kindest and wisest old face in the world, the blunt, sad, wise face of an old animal peering tolerantly out on the goings-on of the merely human creatures before him. He was a good man, and I loved him next to my mother and father. I crouched there on the floor of the crib and watched him shell corn with the rusty cast-iron hands, while he looked down at me out of the little eyes set in the blunt face.

"Dellie says she's mighty sick," I said.

"Yeah," he said.

"What's she sick from?"

"Woman-mizry," he said.

"What's woman-mizry?"

"Hit comes on 'em," he said. "Hit just comes on 'em when the time comes."

"What is it?"

"Hit is the change," he said. "Hit is the change of life and time."

"What changes?"

"You too young to know."

"Tell me."

"Time come and you find out everything."

I knew that there was no use in asking him any more. When I asked him things and he said that, I always knew that he would not tell me. So

I continued to crouch there and watch him. Now that I had sat there a little while, I was cold again.

"What you shiver fer?" he asked me.

"I'm cold. I'm cold because it's blackberry winter," I said.

"Maybe 'tis and maybe 'tain't," he said.

"My mother says it is."

"Ain't sayen Miss Sallie doan know and ain't sayen she do. But folks doan know everything."

"Why isn't it blackberry winter?"

"Too late fer blackberry winter. Blackberries done bloomed."

"She said it was."

"Blackberry winter just a leetle cold spell. Hit come and then hit go away, and hit is growed summer of a sudden lak a gunshot. Ain't no tellen hit will go way this time."

"It's June," I said.

"June," he replied with great contempt. "That what folks say. What June mean? Maybe hit is come cold to stay."

"Why?"

"Cause this-here old yearth is tahrd. Hit is tahrd and ain't gonna perduce. Lawd let hit come rain one time forty days and forty nights, 'cause He wus tahrd of sinful folks. Maybe this-here old yearth say to the Lawd, Lawd, I done plum tahrd. Lawd, lemme rest. And Lawd say, Yearth, you done yore best, you give 'em cawn and you give 'em taters, and all they think on is they gut, and, Yearth, you kin take a rest."

"What will happen?"

"Folks will eat up everything. The yearth won't perduce no more. Folks cut down all the trees and burn 'em cause they cold, and the yearth won't grow no more. I been tellen 'em. I been tellen folks. Sayen, maybe this year, hit is the time. But they doan listen to me, how the yearth is tahrd. Maybe this year they find out."

"Will everything die?"

"Everything and everybody, hit will be so."

"This year?"

"Ain't no tellen. Maybe this year."

"My mother said it is blackberry winter," I said confidently, and got up.

"Ain't sayen nuthin' agin Miss Sallie," he said.

I went to the door of the crib. I was really cold. Running, I had got up a sweat and now I was worse.

I hung on the door, looking at Jebb, who was shelling corn again.

"There's a tramp came to the house," I said. I had almost forgotten the tramp.

"Yeah."

"He came by the back way. What was he doing down there in the storm?"

"They comes and they goes," he said, "and ain't no tellen."

"He had a mean knife."

"The good ones and the bad ones, they comes and they goes. Storm or sun, light or dark. They is folks and they comes and they goes lak folks."

I hung on the door, shivering.

He studied me a moment, then said, "You git on to the house. You ketch yore death. Then what yore mammy say?"

I hesitated.

"You git," he said.

When I came to the back yard, I saw that my father was standing by the back porch and the tramp was walking toward him. They began talking before I reached them, but I got there just as my father was saying, "I'm sorry, but I haven't got any work. I got all the hands on the place I need now. I won't need any extra until wheat thrashing."

The stranger made no reply, just looked at my father.

My father took out his leather coin purse, and got out a half-dollar. He held it toward the man. "This is for half a day," he said.

The man looked at the coin, and then at my father, making no motion to take the money. But that was the right amount. A dollar a day was what you paid them back in 1910. And the man hadn't even worked half a day.

Then the man reached out and took the coin. He dropped it into the right side pocket of his coat. Then he said, very slowly and without feeling: "I didn't want to work on your —— farm."

He used the word which they would have frailed me to death for using.

I looked at my father's face and it was streaked white under the sunburn. Then he said, "Get off this place. Get off this place or I won't be responsible."

The man dropped his right hand into his pants pocket. It was the pocket where he kept the knife. I was just about to yell to my father about the knife when the hand came back out with nothing in it. The man gave a kind of twisted grin, showing where the teeth had been knocked out above the new scar. I thought that instant how maybe he had tried before to pull a knife on somebody else and had got his teeth knocked out.

So now he just gave that twisted, sickish grin out of the unmemorable, grayish face, and then spat on the brick path. The glob landed just about six inches from the toe of my father's right boot. My father looked down at it, and so did I. I thought that if that glob had hit my father's boot something would have happened. I looked down and saw the bright glob, and on one side of it my father's strong cowhide boots, with the brass eyelets and the leather thongs, heavy boots splashed with good red mud and set solid on the bricks, and on the other side the pointed-toe, broken, black shoes, on which the mud looked so sad and out of place. Then I saw one of the black shoes move a little, just a twitch first, then a real step backward.

The man moved in a quarter circle to the end of the porch, with my father's steady gaze upon him all the while. At the end of the porch, the man reached up to the shelf where the wash pans were to get his little newspaper-wrapped parcel. Then he disappeared around the corner of the house and my father mounted the porch and went into the kitchen without a word.

I followed around the house to see what the man would do. I wasn't afraid of him now, no matter if he did have the knife. When I got around in front, I saw him going out the yard gate and starting up the drive toward the pike. So I ran to catch up with him. He was sixty yards or so up the drive before I caught up.

I did not walk right up even with him at first, but trailed him, the way a kid will, about seven or eight feet behind, now and then running two or three steps in order to hold my place against his longer stride. When I first came up behind him, he turned to give me a look, just a meaningless look, and then fixed his eyes up the drive and kept on walking.

When we had got around the bend in the drive which cut the house from sight, and were going along by the edge of the woods, I decided to come up even with him. I ran a few steps, and was by his side, or almost, but some feet off to the right. I walked along in this position for a while, and he never noticed me. I walked along until we got within sight of the big gate that let on the pike.

Then I said: "Where did you come from?"

He looked at me then with a look which seemed almost surprised that I was there. Then he said, "It ain't none of yore business."

We went on another fifty feet.

Then I said, "Where are you going?"

He stopped, studied me dispassionately for a moment, then suddenly took a step toward me and leaned his face down at me. The lips jerked back, but not in any grin, to show where the teeth were knocked out and to make the scar on the lower lip come white with the tension.

He said: "Stop following me. You don't stop following me and I cut yore throat, you little son-of-a-bitch."

Then he went on to the gate, and up the pike.

That was thirty-five years ago. Since that time my father and mother have died. I was still a boy, but a big boy, when my father got cut on the blade of a mowing machine and died of lockjaw. My mother sold the place and went to town to live with her sister. But she never took hold after my father's death, and she died within three years, right in middle life. My aunt always said, "Sallie just died of a broken heart, she was so devoted."

Dellie is dead, too, but she died, I heard, quite a long time after we sold the farm.

As for Little Jebb, he grew up to be a mean and ficey Negro. He killed another Negro in a fight and got sent to the penitentiary, where he is yet, the last I heard tell. He probably grew up to be mean and ficey from just being picked on so much by the children of the other tenants, who were jealous of Jebb and Dellie for being thrifty and clever and being white-folks' niggers.

Old Jebb lived forever. I saw him ten years ago and he was about a hundred then, and not looking much different. He was living in town then, on relief—that was back in the Depression—when I went to see him. He said to me: "Too strong to die. When I was a young feller just comen on and seen how things wuz, I prayed the Lawd. I said, Oh, Lawd, gimme strength and make me strong fer to do and in-dure. The Lawd hearkened to my prayer. He give me strength. I was in-duren proud fer being strong and me much man. The Lawd give me my prayer and my strength. But now He done gone off and fergot me and left me alone with my strength. A man doan know what to pray fer, and him mortal."

Jebb is probably living yet, as far as I know.

That is what has happened since the morning when the tramp leaned his face down at me and showed his teeth and said: "Stop following me. You don't stop following me and I cut yore throat, you little son-of-a-bitch." That was what he said, for me not to follow him. But I did follow him, all the years.

ROBERT PENN WARREN

"Blackberry Winter": A Recollection

I remember with peculiar distinctness the writing of this story, especially the balance, tension, interplay—or what you will—between a sense of compulsion, a sense that the story was writing itself, and the flashes of self-consciousness and self-criticism. I suppose that in all attempts at writing there is some such balance, or oscillation, but here the distinction between the two aspects of the process was peculiarly marked, between the ease and the difficulty, between the elation and, I am tempted to say, the pain. But the pain, strangely enough, seemed to be attached to the compulsion, as though in some way I did not want to go into that remembered world, and the elation attached to the critical effort

I had to make to ride herd on the wrangle of things that came milling into my head. Or perhaps the truth is that the process was more complicated than that and I shall never know the truth, even in the limited, provisional way the knowing of truth is possible in such matters.

It crosses my mind that the vividness with which I have always remembered the writing of this story may have something to do with the situation in which it was written. It was the fall or winter of 1945–46 just after the war, and even if one had had no hand in the blood-letting, there was the sense that the world, and one's own life, would never be the same again. I was then reading Herman Melville's poetry, and remember being profoundly impressed by "The Conflict of Convictions," a poem about the coming of the American Civil War. Whatever the rights and wrongs of the matter, the war, Melville said, would show "the slimed foundations" of the world. There was the sense in 1945, even with victory, that we had seen the slimed foundations, and as I now write this, the image that comes into my mind is the homely one from my story—the trash washed by the storm from under Dellie's cabin to foul her pridefully clean yard. And I should not be surprised if the picture in the story had its roots in the line from Melville as well as in such a fact, seen a hundred times in my rural boyhood. So the mixed feelings I had in our moment of victory in 1945, Melville's poem, and not only the image of Dellie's cabin, but something of the whole import of my little story, belong, it seems, in the same package.

For a less remote background, I had just finished two long pieces of work, a novel called *All the King's Men* and a critical study of Coleridge's poem *The Ancient Mariner*, both of which had been on my mind for years. Both those things were impersonal, about as impersonal as the work of any man's hand can be said to be. Even though much of my personal feeling had been drawn into both projects, they belonged to worlds very different from my own. At that time, too, I was living in a very cramped apartment over a garage, in a big, modern, blizzard-bit northern city, again a place very different from the world of my story.

In my daily life, I certainly was not thinking about and remembering that world. I suppose I was living in some anxiety about the fate of the two forthcoming pieces of work, on which I had staked much, and in the unspoken, even denied, conviction that some sort of watershed of life and experience was being approached. For one thing, the fortieth birthday, lately passed, and the sense of let-down after the long period of intense work, could account, in part at least, for that feeling.

Out of this situation the story began, but it began by a kind of accident. Some years earlier, I had written a story about a Tennessee sharecropper, a bad story that had never been published. Now I thought I saw a way to improve it. I don't know whether I actually sat down to rewrite the story that was to have the new avatar of "The Patented Gate and the

Mean Hamburger," or whether I got sidetracked into "Blackberry Winter" first. In any case, I was going back into a primal world of recollection. I was fleeing, if you wish. Hunting old bearings and bench-marks, if you wish. Trying to make a fresh start, if you wish. Whatever people do in their doubleness of living in a present and a past.

I recollect the particular thread that led me back into that past: the feeling you have when, after vacation begins, you are allowed to go barefoot. Not that I ever liked to go barefoot, not with my bony feet. But the privilege itself was important, a declaration of independence from the tyranny of winter and school and, even, your own family. It was like what the anthropologists call a rite of passage. But it had another meaning, too. It carried you back into a dream of nature, the woods not the house was now your natural habitat, the stream not the street. Looking out into the snow-banked alley of that iron latitude where I now lived, I had a vague, nostalgic feeling and wondered if spring would ever come. (It finally came—and then on May 5 there was again snow, and the heavy-headed blooms of lilac were beautiful with their hoods of snow and beards of ice.)

With the recollection of going barefoot came another, which had been recurrent over the years: the childhood feeling of betrayal when early summer gets turned upside-down, and all its promises are revoked by the cold-spell, the gully-washer. So by putting those two recollections together, the story got started. I had no idea where it was going, if anywhere. Sitting at the typewriter was merely a way of indulging nostalgia. But something has to happen in a story, if there is to be more than a dreary lyric poem posing as a story to promote the cause of universal boredom and deliquescent prose. Something had to happen, and the simplest thing ever to have happen is to say: *Enter, mysterious stranger.* And so he did.

The tramp who thus walked into the story had been waiting a long time in the wings of my imagination—an image drawn, no doubt, from a dozen unremembered episodes of childhood, the city bum turned country tramp, suspicious, resentful, contemptuous of hick dumbness, bringing his own brand of violence into a world where he half-expected to find another kind, enough unlike his own to make him look over his shoulder down the empty lane as dusk came on, a creature altogether lost and pitiful, a dim image of what, in one perspective, our human condition is. But then, at that moment, I was merely thinking of the impingement of his loose-footedness and lostness on a stable and love-defined world of childhood.

Before the tramp actually appeared, I had, however, known he was coming, and without planning I began to write the fourth paragraph of the story, about the difference between what time is when we have grown up and what it was when we stood on what, in my fancy phrase in the story, I called the glistening auroral beach of the world—a phrase which belonged, by the way, to an inland boy who had never seen a beach but whose dreams were all of the sea. Now the tramp came up, not merely out of the woods, but out of the darkening grown-up world of time.

The tramp had, literally, come up through the river woods, and so in the boy's literal speculations he sees the tramp coming through the woods. By now, however, the natural thematic distinction touched on in relation to time is moving into a pattern, the repetition in fiction of the established notion in a new guise. So when the boy sees the mental image of the tramp coming through the woods, there is the distinction set up between the way a man, particularly such a man as this, would go through woods, and the way a boy can stand in the woods in absolute quiet, almost taking root and growing moss on himself, trying to catch the rhythm, as it were, of that vegetative life, trying to breathe himself into that mode of being.

But what would this other, woodland, vegetative world of being carry with it in human terms—in terms, that is, of what a story must be about? I can promise that the passage was written on impulse, but an impulse conditioned by the idea that there had to be an expressed difference between boy-in-woods and tramp-in-woods, the tramp who doesn't know what a poult is and thinks the final degradation is to mess with a flower bed. And so here we are back to the contrast between the tramp's world and that of childhood innocence appearing in some sense of a rapport between the child and nature, his feeling that he himself might enter that very life of nature.

As soon as the passage was written I knew its import; I was following my nose, trusting, for what they were worth, my powers of association, hoping that those powers would work in relation to a pattern that had begun to emerge as a series of contrasts. And it was natural, therefore, after a few paragraphs about the strangeness and fish-out-of-waterness of the tramp, his not knowing about dogs for example, to have the mother's self-sufficiency set against the tramp's rude, resentful uncertainty, and then have her portrait at the time of the episode set against the time when she would be dead, and only a memory—though back then, of course, in the secure world of changelessness and timelessness, it had never crossed the boy's mind that "she would ever be dead."

The instant I wrote that clause I knew, not how the story would end, for I was still writing by guess and by God, but on what perspective of feeling it would end. I knew that it would end with a kind of detached summary of the work of time, some hint of the adult's grim orientation toward that fact. From now on, the items that came on the natural wash of recollection came not only with their, to me, nostalgic quality, but also with the freighting of the grimmer possibilities of change—the flood, which to the boy is only an exciting spectacle but which will mean hunger to others, the boy's unconscious contempt for poor white-trash like Milt Alley, the recollection of hunger by the old man who had ridden with Forrest, Dellie suffering in her "woman mizry." But before I had got to

Dellie, I already had Old Jebb firmly in mind, with some faint sense of the irony of having his name remind one—or at least me—of the dashing Confederate cavalryman killed at Yellow Tavern.

Perhaps what I finally did with Dellie stemmed, in fact, from the name I gave Old Jebb. Even if the boy would see no irony in that echo of J. E. B. Stuart's fame, he would get a shock when Dellie slapped her beloved son, and would sense that that blow was, in some deep way, a blow at him. I knew this, for I knew the inside of that prideful cabin, and the shock of early recognition that beneath mutual kindliness and regard some dark, tragic, unresolved something lurked. And with that scene with Dellie, I felt I was forecasting the role of the tramp in the story. The story, to put it in another way, was now shifting emphasis from the lyricism of nostalgia to a concern with the jags and injustices of human relationships. What had earlier come in unconsciously, reportorially, in regard to Milt Alley now got a conscious formulation.

I have said that the end was by now envisaged as a kind of summary of the work of time on the human relationships. But it could not afford to be a mere summary: I wanted some feeling for the boy's family and Jebb's family to shine through the flat surface. Now it struck me that I might build this summary with Jebb as a kind of pilot for the feeling I wanted to get; that is, by accepting, in implication at least, something of Jebb's feeling about his own life, we might become aware of our human communion. I wanted the story to give some notion that out of change and loss a human recognition may be redeemed, more precious for being no longer innocent. So I wrote the summary.

When I had finished the next to the last paragraph I still did not know what to do with my tramp. He had already snarled at the boy, and gone, but I sensed that in the pattern of things his meaning would have to coalesce with the meaning I hoped to convey in the summary about the characters. Then, for better or worse, there it was. In his last anger and frustration, the tramp had said to the boy: "You don't stop following me and I cut yore throat, you little son-of-a-bitch."

Had the boy then stopped or not? Yes, of course, literally, in the muddy lane. But at another level—no. In so far as later he had grown up, had really learned something of the meaning of life, he had been bound to follow the tramp all his life, in the imaginative recognition, with all the responsibility which such a recognition entails, of this lost, mean, defeated, cowardly, worthless, bitter being as somehow a man.

So what had started out for me as, perhaps, an act of escape, of fleeing back into the simplicities of childhood, had turned, as it always must if we accept the logic of our lives, into an attempt to bring something meaningfully out of that simple past into the complication of the present. And what had started out as a personal indulgence had tried to be, in the end, an impersonal generalization about experience, as a story must always try to be if it accepts the logic of fiction. And now, much later, I see that the story and the novel which I had then only lately finished, as well as the study of Coleridge, all bore on the same end.

I would give a false and foolish impression if I were to imply that I think this to be the only way a story should be written, or that this is the only way I myself have ever written stories. As a matter of fact, most of my stories and all of my novels (except two unpublished ones) have started very differently, from some objective situation or episode, observed or read about, something that caught my eye and imagination so that feeling and interpretation began to flow in. And I sometimes think it strange that the last story I ever wrote and presumably the last I shall ever write (for poems are great devourers of stories) should have sprung so instinctively from the world of simple recollection—not a blackberry winter at all, but a kind of Indian summer.

I would give a false impression, too, if I were to imply that this story is autobiographical. It is not. I never knew these particular people, only that world and people like them. And no tramp ever leaned down at me and said for me to stop following him or he would cut my throat. But if one had, I hope that I might have been able to follow him anyway, in the way the boy in the story does.

Appendix: Technical Problems and Principles in the Composition of Fiction— a Summary

IF one learns anything about fiction from reading even a limited number of short stories and novels, it is that there is no single, special technique or formula for writing good fiction. Rather, one learns that every good writer develops a method which, in so far as he is a good writer, is specially adapted to the kind of effect which he is trying to give. He has his own view of the world; certain kinds of persons interest him, and certain problems and issues; the experiences and observations from which his fiction is nourished differ from the experiences and observations of other writers.

This does not mean that his fiction should be autobiographical, or semiautobiographical, or be limited in its scene to the world which he has been able to observe at first hand.* This interpretation would imply that fiction is nothing but a special kind of reporting, and would dismiss as unimportant the power of imagination by which a writer can create a scene which he has never observed, as in a historical novel—or can make comprehensible the character of, let us say, a murderer, when he has never known a murderer. But this exercise of imagination is very different from the dishonesty, the self-falsification, which, in its crudest form, may lead a writer to adopt certain attitudes or methods because they are fashionable. It is also very different from the mechanical manipulation of characters and scenes according to a set formula—the kind of manipulation which one can see in ordinary magazine fiction. In this kind of fiction one can detect certain

---

* It is a good general principle, however, that the relatively inexperienced writer should work in terms of life which he has been able to observe at first hand or about which he has some special knowledge.

stereotyped characters, scenes, and ideas which appear over and over again in different stories, with only a kind of superficial novelty such as would be gained, say, by transposing a typical "western" into a new setting, the jungles of Brazil, the slums of Chicago, or the bush of Australia, or by keeping accustomed settings and characters and working out new turns of plot. Such fiction depends on mechanical suspense, on surprise in event, on flattering the reader's prejudices and ideas, on appealing to *stock responses* (see Glossary). The writers of such fiction depend on the use of a bag of tricks. Their work is quickly exhausted because of this fact; it does not spring from any real perceptions about human experience.

A good writer knows in his very bones that fiction involves not the mere exploiting of a bag of tricks, but the careful study of the possible relationships among the numerous elements which go to make up a piece of fiction. He knows that characterization, setting and atmosphere, plot, style, tone, symbolism, theme, and various other elements must be functionally related to each other to create a real unity—a unity in which every part bears an expressive relation to other parts. We can see, for example, that the very style of Anderson's "I Want to Know Why" contributes something to the total effect of the story; it is constantly telling us something about the boy himself (p. 325). We can see how a very different style in Joyce's "Araby," another story about an adolescent boy, is contributing to a very different effect (p. 192). We can see why elaborate analysis of the hero's past life is necessary in Caroline Gordon's "Old Red," but is not necessary in Pirandello's "War" (p. 646). We can see how, because of its underlying intellectual complication and irony, Kipling's "The Man Who Would Be King" differs from the ordinary thriller, in which violent action is scarcely meaningful.

The good writer knows that there is no single, ideal "form" for the short story—a fixed and sanctified way of handling things—or even a set of forms, already determined, into which he can fit his own story. He knows that, when he sets out to write a story, he is really engaged in a process of exploration and experiment: he is exploring the nature of his characters and the meaning of their acts, and, too, he is exploring his own feelings about them. He knows that any shift in the organization of his story, or any variation in style, will alter, however slightly, the total response of the reader. For instance, we have seen how the hard, crisp, factual style of Hemingway's "The Killers" and its sharp, cinematic flashes of scenes are to be associated in the process of conveying his general view of the world (p. 310); and we can contrast with these factors the highly wrought, complicated, meditative style of Joyce's "Araby," and the close analyses of the hero's feelings which fill out the scenes themselves. The whole "feel" of the two stories is different—and this difference, which may seem unimportant at first glance, is important, and central rather than accidental, because it is through such differences that the fundamental interpretations of an author may be registered.

But if there is not an ideal form for the short story—or set of forms—the reader who is also interested in writing may well ask: *What is the use of studying stories if I cannot learn from them exactly how to write?* The answer might be put in this way: *There is no ideal form, or set of forms, for the short story, but there are certain principles to which one may become more sensitive by studying stories.* These principles involve the relationships existing among the elements of a story, the adjusting of means to ends, the organization of material to create an expressive unity.

It is the hope of the authors of this book that the more important principles have already been illustrated in the discussions and interpretations of the stories included here, but there may be some utility in presenting certain questions which arise in the composition of a story. It is not to be understood, however, that in the actual process of composition an author always encounters such questions in this order, for different writers have different ways of moving into their stories, different methods of exploring their material, as well as different degrees of critical self-consciousness.

BEGINNING AND EXPOSITION

But let us assume that the writer has a pretty good general idea of his contemplated story: he has a grasp of the basic natures and motivations of his characters, he has decided on the general sequence of events, he knows, roughly at least, what his own attitude toward the material is. But where shall he begin? He is aware that his characters have histories reaching far back beyond the moment of his story. Some writers, we know, have used the method of preparing full biographies of their characters, even though they knew that most of the material in these imaginary biographies would not appear in the finished story; but any writer must have some notion of the history of his characters, enough at least to make him feel that he knows them. But, obviously, a story cannot begin at its absolute beginning. The writer wants to strike into his story at a point which will lead fairly quickly and logically to the crucial moment, the climax, the point of decision on which will hinge the fate of the characters. But in almost every case—or perhaps to some degree in every case—some explanation of the background is required to make the story intelligible. The characters must be introduced, the setting must be established, the basic situation defined. In other words, a certain amount of *exposition* must be presented.

But how much? The answer to this question is always to be determined by the demands of the particular case. In Pirandello's "War," Chekhov's "The Lament," or Hemingway's "The Killers," very little information about the past of the characters is required. In these stories the "ordinariness" of the characters contributes to the significance of the events.

The parents in the railway compartment in "War" are primarily *parents*, ordinary parents, and the reactions they express show the various attitudes toward bereavement which one ordinarily encounters. Even the words of the main character, the man in the fawn-colored overcoat, are not remarkable, for we can well imagine how he has arrived at his view, from newspapers, funeral services, patriotic poems, and the like; it is simply an extreme expression of an ordinary form of consolation. And what makes the story a story is the sudden and dramatic discovery that the cliché of consolation is not working, that it has not conquered the sense of loss. But this sense of loss, too, is common—it is shared by all present.

Thus, in this story, it is not the fact of special histories and backgrounds which is important, but the fact that the histories and backgrounds are *not* special. They do not have to be explained. So in "The Lament" the old man is just a poor and humble old man who has lost his son; his ordinariness, the fact that he does not have to be explained, is significant. The loneliness and pathos of the old man are more significant because he makes no special claim upon us; it is as though Chekhov were saying that it is particularly the poor and the outcast, the people without histories worth telling, who demand sympathy. So with Nick in "The Killers"; he is simply an ordinary boy in an ordinary American town. We sense his history without hearing it. And though the Nicks in real life undoubtedly do have definite personalities of their own, such a personality is not important for the purpose of this story.

But one can see how it is important for us to know much more about the history of the boy in "I Want to Know Why." This boy is more special. He is more reflective; he has begun to raise certain definite questions about the attitudes of society and about his own place in the world. His case is more extreme than that of Nick, and his sensitivity must be more fully realized by the reader. The same is true of Miss Emily, in Faulkner's story, or of Aleck Maury in Caroline Gordon's "Old Red." In fact, the past of the characters in these stories is so important that it is difficult to say exactly where preparatory exposition leaves off and immediate significance begins. One observes, for instance, how in these three stories the past is skillfully interwoven with the present. The element of time is important here; the crisis of each story sums up, as it were, a process which has been going on for years.

DESCRIPTION AND SETTING

Just as, in managing the exposition in a story, the writer selects only what is significant for the final purpose of the story, so he must select the significant items in presenting his settings. Description of setting is not to be judged simply in terms of realistic accuracy; it is to be judged in terms of what it accomplishes for a story. But setting can be used for a number of purposes.

First, and most obviously, a setting which is recognizable, and which at the same time is rendered vividly and memorably, tends to increase the credibility of character and action; that is, if the reader accepts the setting as real, he tends more readily to accept, in a preliminary way at least, the inhabitants of the setting and their behavior. The most successfully rendered setting in the world will not make a reader accept characters and actions which are palpably improbable or preposterous; but the successfully rendered setting does increase, by a kind of transference, the general susceptibility of the reader. Many writers are inclined to bank too heavily on this susceptibility created by realism of setting, and to forget that such susceptibility is only preliminary and not final; the good reader is, after all, concerned with psychological and not physical realism, with internal and not external credibility.*

Second, the setting of a story can have a more direct relation to the general meaning of a story. It is easy to see how O. Henry, in "The Furnished Room," is trying to make the description of the room indicate to us the anonymity and isolation of the individual in a great city. And it is easy to see how Bret Harte in "Tennessee's Partner" is straining, by his use of natural setting, for emotional effects which are not validated in the story itself (p. 183). More successful instances can be found in "The Lament," in which, especially in the opening sentences, the setting is used to create the general atmosphere of loneliness (p. 207); or in Maupassant's "Love," in which the description of the landscape is symbolically related to the theme of the story (pp. 288–289). The greater degree of success in the use of setting found in the stories by Chekhov and Maupassant as compared with those by O. Henry and Bret Harte may depend, in part at least, on the fact that Chekhov and Maupassant do not insist on the significance of the setting as such, do not strain for effect, but depend on the accumulation of details which are realistically valid in themselves, but which, at the same time, are suggestive of the main impulse. The reader tends to accept the setting at the straight realistic level, but the setting, because of the particular relevance of the details selected, is also creating an atmosphere appropriate to the general intention of the story.

Third, it may sometimes be the case that the setting may work for more definite purposes than that of creating an appropriate atmosphere. Let us look, for example, at "I Want to Know Why." A good deal of attention is given to the detailed rendering of the scene at the training track in the early morning: "At the tracks you sit on the fence with men, whites and niggers, and they chew tobacco and talk, and then the colts are brought out. It's early and the grass is covered with shiny dew and in

---

* Fiction which is overtly fantastic, such as "In the Penal Colony" is a special case. See pp. 389–390.

another field a man is plowing and they are frying things in a shed where the track niggers sleep, and you know how a nigger can giggle and laugh and say things that make you laugh."

Or: "Well, out of the stables they come and the boys are on their backs and it's lovely to be there. You hunch down on top of the fence and itch inside you. Over in the sheds the niggers giggle and sing. Bacon is being fried and coffee made. Everything smells lovely. Nothing smells better than coffee and manure and horses and niggers and bacon frying and pipes being smoked out of doors on a morning like that. It just gets you, that's what it does."

One thing that is important about the setting here is the fact that the boy himself feels that he must dwell lovingly on each item. The way the setting is presented indicates the sensitivity of the boy, and his pleasure in the world of the senses; and we see how this is important in defining the boy's special character for us and in defining his belief in natural goodness which is altered by the experience at the "rummy farmhouse." In a like fashion, some of the descriptive material in "Old Red" serves as a kind of index to the character of the old man: his pleasure is not merely in catching fish for whatever value they may have, but in exercising his skill, his discipline, in enjoying the physical world in which fishing is possible. In other words, his attitude has a large aesthetic component, in that he enjoys the world by direct contact with it and not by what he can use it for. The nearest thing to a direct statement of this idea occurs at the pond, after the description, when he sees the Negro shack and thinks that Negroes always know how to pick out the good places. This remark comes to us charged, as it were, with the quiet beauty of the scene which has been described. But we can also remember in this regard, how he refers to a stream he had fished in his youth as his "first love." And in the end we see him symbolically merged into the world of nature.

ATMOSPHERE

In discussing setting we have used the word *atmosphere*. This term is usually applied in connection with stories which have a considerable element of description, especially description which is obviously intended to evoke a certain mood, as in "A Piece of News." In fact, some critics of the short story put such stories into a special category—"the atmosphere story"—just as they put other stories into categories called "the plot story," "the character story," and "the theme story." Now, as a matter of fact, all such categories may be misleading, for all stories involve plot, character, theme, and, likewise, atmosphere. But the category of "atmosphere story" is particularly misleading. What we call the atmosphere of a story—and the word is a loose metaphor for the total feel or mood of a story—is the product of all the other factors, of the nature of the plot, of setting, of character delineation, of style and symbolism, of the very rhythms of the prose. We may take atmosphere to be a result rather than a cause, and a result of the operation of many causes. Therefore description, and especially description of setting, can scarcely be taken as the fundamental cause of atmosphere in a story. Even in "A Piece of News," the atmosphere of which we have discussed (pp. 129–131), the atmosphere depends more upon the particular characters and actions than upon the preliminary description. People tend to use the word *atmosphere* in connection with stories in which the mysterious and poetic elements are played up, but such a story as "The Killers" has just as positively its own atmosphere. And in this case, it is easy to see that the atmosphere is not dependent upon set descriptions but upon the very style (pp. 310–311), the attitudes of the characters, the symbolic force of the scene with Mrs. Bell, and so on (p. 306).

SELECTION AND SUGGESTION

After this digression concerning atmosphere, we may return to another aspect of the problem of setting and description. Just as a writer cannot give the total past in his exposition, so he cannot give the total present in his scene. His problem is to select the relevant details, the items which will suggest the whole scene, and in certain cases give clues to character, situation, and theme. Chekhov once told a writer to cut out his long passage describing the moonlight in a scene and give simply the glint of the moon on a piece of broken bottle. Such a perception might do more to give the sense of a scene than would a full rendering, because more vivid, more sharply focused, more stimulating to the imagination. The special items listed by the boy in "I Want to Know Why" in describing the early morning at the training track give us a sense of the place, but the boy tells us nothing, in any strict sense, about the landscape, the track itself, or the actual buildings. And we have already pointed out how the opening sentences of "The Lament" suggest the theme of the story (p. 247).

The description of persons in a story raises many of the same problems raised by description of setting. In the first place, a complete description is impossible, or if possible, awkward and unwieldy; since one cannot present the appearance fully and photographically, one must depend upon the sharpness of selection of detail, upon suggestiveness in regard to appearance, character, or idea. Inspect, for instance, the description of the main character in "War," or of the main character in Joseph Conrad's "Amy Foster," or of Miss Emily in Faulkner's story. Or observe the great economy in the description of the gangsters in "The Killers." The details given are few: they eat with their gloves on; the very anonymity and uniformity of their appearance is significant; in their tight-buttoned blue overcoats and derby hats, they look "like a vaudeville team." They have, as it were, no "faces," no personalities; in other words, they are dehumanized. A full description, personalizing each of them and distinguishing between them carefully, would have, in a sense, violated their very meaning in the story. We notice that the only real distinction made between them is on the point of their attitude toward the "job," their attitudes toward their code, and this distinction ties into the main idea of the story (pp. 305–306).

In discussing the previous topics, we have several times referred to *selection*. But this principle applies not only to exposition and description; it applies with equal force to plot structure. The individual items in the chain of events in which presumably the character of a story would participate, in real life, during the span of time covered by the story, are not of equal significance; in fact, the writer does not try to follow, in most cases, an unbroken chronicle of events, but omits from the story itself many possible events, meals, casual meetings, routine occupations, and the like. He selects the events which have meaning, and meaning in terms of the basic impulse of the story, not simply in isolation or in relation to some idea not involved in the story. Even among the events which are actually to appear in the story, the writer exercises discriminations of emphasis and subordination. He selects a certain event to serve as the key to his whole plot sequence. Other events lead to, and sometimes lead away from, such a key event, but among these other events there is also operating a process of selection in terms of emphasis and subordination, for these other events are not all at the same level of importance.

KEY MOMENT

If a writer has not determined his key event, or if the key event is not truly a key, the structure of the story will be loose and vague, the effect will be one of diffuseness, and the reader will be puzzled rather than enlightened. We can examine any satisfactory story and locate the key event, or the key moment. In "The Man Who Would Be King," it occurs when Dravot, on the rope bridge, calls back to the tribesmen to cut. It is the moment when the man who would be king truly becomes king. In "The Lament" it is the moment when the old cabdriver, who has gone back to the stables to see about his horse, suddenly begins to tell the horse about the death of his son. In "War" it is the moment when the man in the fawn-colored overcoat bursts into unexpected sobs. Such a moment brings into focus all previous events and interprets all previous events. It is the moment of illumination for the whole story. It is the germ of the story, and contains in itself, by implication at least, the total meaning of the story.

CLIMAX

We have just said that the key moment, the moment of illumination, implies the total meaning of a story. The very use of the word *meaning* here suggests that the key event, or key moment, is not simply the decisive episode in any merely physical sense—not the moment when, for instance, the hero finally confronts the villain and grapples with him on the edge of the cliff. For instance, we can see that the moment, in "The Man Who Would Be King," when the intended bride of Dravot bites him and blood flows to demonstrate that he is not god but man, is the decisive moment in the purely physical sense, in the strict plot sense. But that moment does not illuminate the meaning of the story; it merely tells us about the success or failure of the adventure at its practical level. Of course, in some stories, the decisive moment for the plot, as ordinarily conceived, may be identified with the moment of illumination. Such seems to be the case in "The Lament," "War," and "Old Red."

CONFLICT

How does the writer build toward the moment of illumination? He cannot move in an uncontested line to that moment, for if he does, he has no story. All of us tend to think of a story in terms of problem and solution, conflict and repose, tension and resolution, suspense and satisfaction, question and answer, mystery and revelation. A story is a movement through complexity to unity, through complication to simplicity, through confusion to order. The moment of illumination, then, is the moment when the underlying unity is perceived as inherent in the complexity, the simplicity in complication, order in confusion. It is the moment when the relationships among the elements become clear, the moment when the story is seen to have a form, a structure. But this sense of the unity, the form, the structure, the meaning, must be achieved by the movement through complexity, complication, confusion, meaninglessness. To sum up, we are generally told that story means conflict.

There are many types of conflict. There is conflict between man and man, man and society, one idea and another. There is conflict in the external world and conflict in a man's own mind. Now it might be argued that no narrative which presents a purely physical conflict, and nothing more, can be called fiction, a story in the proper sense of the word. For instance, we have said that the narrative of the attack on the fort by Jim Beckworth is not fiction (pp. 3–4). Our reason for refusing to call it fiction was that Jim Beckworth has no motive attributed to his action, that he has, in other words, no character. But now, as a corollary of that statement, we can say that the conflict as given is purely physical and therefore meaningless. If a writer were to try to make a story out of the incident, he would characterize Jim Beckworth, would investigate his motives; and as soon as he did that, he would imply sympathy or antipathy for the man; he would begin to imply evaluation, and, therefore, a conflict of ideas behind the physical events of the incident. In any story, however crude and simple, say the ordinary thriller or adventure story, as soon as even rudimentary characterization is established, as soon as sympathies and antipathies emerge, a conflict or contrast in ideas has become, by implication at least, a component in the story. "Hero" and "villain" mean good and bad, admirable and despicable; the words imply a conflict. In good fiction, however, distinctions are never so easy and crude as in the thriller, and the process of the story, at the level of ideas, may be the effort to make distinctions which are even provisionally tenable.

Let us look at a relatively simple story, "The Man Who would Be King," with this general consideration in mind. There is an obvious external conflict, that between the adventurers and the tribesmen; then there is the internal conflict in Dravot's mind, that between his original motivation and the newly discovered motivation, a conflict between vanity and greed on the one hand and responsibility on the other. At the same time, in the story, there is a conflict or contrast between two ideas of kingship (pp. 56–57). A story like "Old Red" is more complex. There is the conflict between family ties and personal inclination; the conflict between the individual and society; the conflict between the practical and the aesthetic views of life; the conflict between ambition and enjoyment; the conflict between the values of the modern world of efficiency and "getting on" and a past world, more easy-going. The conflicts in this story are more complex than in "The Man Who Would Be King," but they are not so positively resolved. Aleck Maury comes to a definition of himself, just as Dravot does, but in the case of Aleck Maury we cannot feel that the conflict of ideas behind the story is positively resolved in a "good," as in the case of Dravot. Dravot's final cry on the bridge sums up the view that true kingship is spiritual. But at the end of "Old Red," the background conflicts are still, in a sense, held in ironical suspension, and we are not totally committed to either side; we have simply become aware of the dramatic ramifications of the conflicts, and, perhaps, of the face that the "good" can only be determined by a recognition of, or synthesis of, certain elements in the competing claims. The same is true in "Noon Wine."

COMPLICATION

We began this discussion of conflict in fiction by asking the question, how does the writer build toward his moment of illumination? He does this by establishing an ascending series of moments of *complication*, moments of tension. For instance, in "The Girls in Their Summer Dresses" the first moment of complication occurs when Michael first notices a passing girl. Or we can take as the moments of complication in "The Lament" the various attempts of the old cabdriver to speak of his bereavement.

We have said that such moments of complication form an ascending series. Usually this is true in a quite literal sense—the complications become greater in intensity as the plot moves toward the moment of decision, the climax. Such a direct scaling upward may be observed, for instance in "I Want to Know Why." But sometimes this principle is not literally applied, for the increase in intensity may be simply the result of accumulation of complications, though the individual complications in themselves may be approximately equivalent. Such is the case in "The Lament," for it is difficult to see any great difference in intensity between the first and subsequent moments of complication; the increase in intensity is simply a result of the cumulative effect on the old man.* Furthermore, especially in long and complex stories, such as "Amy Foster," there may be a good deal of fluctuation in intensity among the moments of complication, although the general tendency is upward if one takes the process in the whole.

Earlier in this discussion, we mentioned the fact that a writer sometimes works from, as well as toward, the moment of decision and the moment of illumination. In "I Want to Know Why" it may be said that the moment of decision and the moment of illumination are identical—the moment when the boy looks into the window of the "rummy farmhouse." But the story does not end, as it might conceivably do, at that scene. The author returns to the scene of the training tracks, the place where the boy had known his innocent happiness, and sets up a contrast between the past attitude and the present attitude. Furthermore, we find introduced in this last paragraph, though introduced almost casually, a statement concerning the illumination, an explanation of it: "It's because a man like Jerry Tillford, *who knows what he does* . . ." This is implicit in the scene at the farmhouse, but the author feels the necessity of making explicit the idea which has been dramatized. Here the continuation of the story is not a winding up of the action, for the action has been completely ended; it is merely a rounding out of the basic contrast of ideas in the story, an additional clarification.

The situation is different in "The Killers." The moment of decision, the climax, may be said to come in Ole Andreson's room, and the moment of illumination at the very end of the story, in the last few words exchanged between George and Nick. In other words, after the scene in Ole Andreson's room the line of action directly concerned with the mission of the gangsters is decided, and at the same time Nick has confronted the crucial fact of the situation, the real horror, which is in Andreson's attitude. The story now moves toward the moment of illumination.

PATTERN OR DESIGN

After these comments upon plot, we are ready to turn to the question of plot as an aspect of pattern or design in fiction (see pp. 156–157). The

---

* There is, however, some difference in intensity, strictly speaking, between the last moment of complication and the preceding ones in "The Lament." In the last moment of complication, the old man is not appealing for attention to strangers, but to his own kind, who might be expected to have a readier sympathy for him.

idea of pattern implies repetition. In terms of plot, an actual incident is not repeated; we have rather a variety of incidents in sequence. The repetition depends on the fact that each incident in the pattern of plot, no matter how different from the last, recalls us, directly or indirectly, to the central question, presents to us an aspect of the central conflict, affirms again the "line" of interest which makes us feel that the incidents have some significance. "The Lament" gives us a very simple example: each meeting of the old cabdriver repeats the fact of his isolation. In the interpretation of "I Want to Know Why," it was pointed out how the references to Negroes and to Henry Rieback's father and the incident at the farmhouse all present aspects of the same question. In "Old Red," too, we can see how, no matter how casual each incident may seem to be at first glance, it always returns us to the main problem—the problem of the old man's relation to the world.

Though pattern involves repetition, it does not, in a fictional sense, mean mechanical repetition, as does the decorative pattern on a carpet or vase. In the first place, the items, taken in themselves, are different. The various incidents which obstruct the boy's effort to go to the bazaar, in "Araby," are different among themselves, but they have a similarity in function, in a plot sense—the function of obstruction—and have similar ties to the idea of the boy's relation to the world. So the writer of a story has to fulfill conflicting demands in creating his pattern, the demand for variety on the one hand and the demand for repetition on the other. If he fails to fulfill the first demand, his story will seem artificial and contrived; if he fails to fulfill the second, it will seem aimless and diffuse. In the second place, the repetition involved in a fictional pattern is not mechanical, because the individual items represent stages in a progression, because they are stages in a process. The items are all related to the line of interest, to the question, but each item introduces a modification, even if the modification is merely a modification of intensity through cumulative effect. In this sense, the pattern is a pattern of logical, and psychological change, logical as it relates to the theme of the story, psychological as it relates to the motivation and development of character within the story. Sometimes the logical, and sometimes the psychological, aspect of the pattern may be the more obvious. For instance, in "The Killing of the Dragon" or "In the Penal Colony" the logical aspect of pattern is generally at the threshold of our attention; and in "Old Red" or "I Want to Know Why," the psychological aspect is at the threshold. But always both aspects are present in the total pattern. It is merely a matter of general emphasis.

DENOUEMENT

In terms of the aspects of pattern which we call plot, this progression of action leads to what is called the *denouement*—the point at which the fate of the character is clear, the moment of success or failure, or perhaps, the moment when the character comprehends his own final position, as in "Old Red," or when we finally comprehend the position, as in "Noon Wine." In terms of theme, the pattern leads to the moment of illumination, which *may* or *may not* coincide with the denouement, just as it may or may not coincide with the climax of action (pp. 651–652).

CHARACTER AND ACTION

The general consideration of pattern involves a consideration of character; this is, of course, only a way of saying that character and plot imply each other, or that character and meaning imply each other. In other words, when the writer thinks of a character, he cannot think of him simply as a static portrait, or a psychological description, like the portrait of Marguerite Blessington. He must, rather, think of him as a complex of potentialities for action. A character is a complex of potentialities for action, for many different kinds of action, but not for all kinds of action, only for certain kinds of action which can finally be rendered consistent with each other. A hero may become a villain, or a villain a hero, but the reader must not be permitted to feel that such changes are arbitrary, that they represent real contradictions; rather, he must be made to feel that both kinds of action, the good and the bad, were potential in the character and are consistent with each other. That is, there must be a psychological pattern, even in cases of apparent reversal of character, as in the case of "War" or "The Man Who Would Be King."

How does the writer present this psychological pattern? There are many ways, and few, if any, stories can afford to confine themselves to a single way. Since action, movement, change is a central fact in fiction, the most significant way for presenting character is through action. The reader wants to see character realized concretely—through action. But action includes a number of things, violent physical action, the smallest gesture, a thought, a word, a decision. Analysis of motive, psychological portraiture, physical description are also important means of presenting character, but they are always subsidiary because their true function is to point to the moment when character and action are one, when we can realize that character *is* action. Therefore, in using these subsidiary means of presenting character, the writer must remain aware of his true intention; he is not merely trying to give the picture of a man but of a man who is capable of certain actions, certain particular actions. When the writer of a thriller says that the villain has "hard eyes" or a "cruel mouth like a scar," he is acting on a sound impulse. The trouble is simply that he is doing his job very crudely. The reader knows that all villains are not so easily advertised. But the reader, though he may reject the thriller's portraiture, also feels that there are significant relationships between appearance and character, even though he is prepared to admit that they are subtle and fleeting. The good writer sets out to detect such subtle and fleeting relationships when he uses description as a means for the presentation of character. The same principle holds good when a writer gives a small, apparently trivial detail. For instance, in "Noon Wine" the way poor Mr. Thompson churns is a key to his character.

FOCUS OF INTEREST

All the topics we have thus far discussed concern the organization of the material which goes to make up a story. But there are other topics concerning organization which have not yet been touched on, or have been touched on only by implication. These topics are closely related to each other. Let us call them (1) *focus of interest*, (2) *focus of character*, and (3) *focus of narration*. They represent certain questions which the writer confronts as he begins to put his story into shape.

When the writer begins his story he is up against the simple problem of catching the reader's attention. At the first moment, mere vividness of presentation may suffice, but it will not suffice for long. There must be some *focus of interest* to carry the reader along. The reader's curiosity is complex. He has many questions in mind, or in the back of his mind. He wants answers to a whole set of questions: *what? who? when? why? what does it mean?* The total answer is, of course, the total story, but it cannot render itself all at once, and different questions must come into focus at different times in the course of a story. And in different stories, the different questions have different degrees of importance. We can see, for example, that the *where* is intended to have great importance in "The Furnished Room" or "A Piece of News," and practically none in "The Necklace." And we can see that the *when* has immediate importance in "Christ in Flanders." We can see that the *who* is of immediate importance in "Old Red" or "Araby" or "I Want to Know Why" or "A Rose for Emily." Or we can see that the *what* is of immediate importance in "The Lament," and that the *what does it mean* has immediate importance in "War" or "Christ in Flanders" or "In the Penal Colony."

By this it is not to be understood that every story does not involve all of these questions, but simply that certain questions are strongly focused in certain stories and less strongly focused in others. We said that the *what* is of great importance in "The Lament." This simply implies that the particular character of the old man is not played up; that the place might be any great city almost anywhere; that the situation with its loneliness and general defect of sympathy is at the threshold of attention. But this does not imply that the *what does it mean* is not fundamental; that question, however, is held in suspension without being specified. In "War," which, like "The Lament," does not bring the *who* or *where* or *when* into sharp focus, we find, however, that the *what*, the particular line of event, the situation, is not played up; instead, the *what does it mean* is put into sharp focus, for the characters debate in specific terms the question of the appropriate attitude of parents toward the giving of children to their country. In "I Want to Know Why" the *what does it mean* is kept in sharp focus (as the title indicates), but the *who* (the special character of the boy) is also played up, and the *where* (the special world of the racing town). But even in a story like "The Lament," in which the *what does it mean* is not sharply focused, the question is still fundamental. The whole matter is a matter of emphases in relationships among the questions; and it is often the case that a question which is not brought into sharp focus may be, for the whole story, more important than a question which is brought, temporarily perhaps, into sharp focus. In a good story, in which the underlying relationships among the elements are functionally established, the one question will always involve other questions; that is, the good story is unified. But for purposes of controlling the material, and directing the reader's interest, the writer must face the problem of focus. How it is to be solved in any given instance is determined by the nature of the particular story. Skill in handling the problem can best be achieved by the close analysis of other stories, by asking the question *why does the writer focus this and not the other?* and referring the question to the basic intention of the story for answer.

FOCUS OF CHARACTER

The problem of the *focus of character* may be stated thus: *whose story is it?* A story is not simply a series of events. The events are of importance to some special person, or some special group of persons. But even when it is a question of the importance of the events to a group of persons, the importance to some one person in the group is usually brought into the sharpest focus. For instance, in "War" the discussion in the railway compartment is of importance to all present, for all are parents who may be deprived of their children by war. But, first, the importance of the situation to the fat woman is emphasized, and finally, the importance to the man in the fawn-colored overcoat. There is, then, a scaling down of importance from the man in the fawn-colored overcoat, through the fat woman, to the nameless companions. Or in "The Killers" the final importance of the events is attached to Nick, and not to George, the cook, or even Ole Andreson. This does not mean that the events are necessarily seen through the eyes of the main character, but that the relation between the character and the events is a fundamental principle of organization in the story. For example, in "The Man Who Would Be King" the events are seen through the eyes of Peachey, but the relation between Dravot and the events is the fundamental principle of organization—the core of meaning.

In most short stories one character is clearly central. A story like

"The Killers," in which the focus of character is not made until late in the development of the narrative, is relatively rare. One can see that in most of the stories in the present collection, some one character dominates the story from its early stages. Considerations of space—the fact that one does not have time to establish many characters—have something to do with this situation in the short story. In novels and novelettes, however, though the general principle of focus of character still holds good, subsidiary characters and their relation to the main situation and main idea may be more freely developed.

When the writer approaches the rough materials of his story, he must always determine the focus of character, for this is one of the organizing principles of his narrative, one of the things which will give his narrative a form. He asks, *whose story is it?* And before he can answer that question he must answer another question, *whose fate is really at stake?* Out of the total context of the events which are, potentially at least, involved in the story, he then selects those items which, at one level or another, are pertinent to the fate of the character and pertinent to our understanding of that fate.

FOCUS OF NARRATION: POINT OF VIEW

We have said above that the events of a story are not necessarily seen through the eyes of the main character; and this consideration leads us to the problem of the *focus of narration*. Who sees the story? Or, who tells the story? There are many combinations of focus possible in extended pieces of fiction, such as novels, but for purposes of convenience we can distinguish certain basic types.

First, the main character may tell his own story. In such a case the focus of character and the focus of narration are identical. We have a clear case of this in "I Want to Know Why." Second, the story may be told by an observer who is, to a greater or lesser degree, a participant in the action. For instance, the narrator of "A Rose for Emily" is a citizen of the town in which the heroine lives, and serves as observer. Both of these types of focus of narration involve a first-person account of the events of the story. When the account passes from the first person to the third person, we have a third type of focus, that of the observer-author. We have a case of this in "The Killers." In this story the author tells us everything that happens in the objective physical sense, and everything that is said, but he does not tell us what passes in the mind of any of the characters. Fourth, the story may be told by the omniscient author, or analytic author, the author who does undertake to present the working of the mind of one, or more, of the characters, and who may investigate and interpret motives and feelings. "The Lament" or "Old Red" presents a simple case of this method, a case in which the author confines himself to the penetration of one mind, that of the main character, with other persons presented objectively, that is, as through the method of the observer-author. This situation is the usual one in stories told by the omniscient author, for the scope of the short story can rarely permit the investigation of the consciousness of more than one character. In such cases, the focus of narration supports the focus of character, and tends to make for a unified effect. But in some stories, and in many novels, the omniscient author works in terms of more than one character.*

It is usually said that first-person narration, types one and two as given here, tends to make for greater credibility in that the mere affirmation, "I saw such-and-such," or "I did such-and-such," or "I felt such-and-such," is more readily acceptable to the reader than a rendering without the support of what pretends to be first-hand testimony. But the reader is not so innocent that he is actually taken in by the pretense of first-hand testimony. He is not deceived into thinking that the "I" of a story is a real person reporting actual events. He knows that this method represents a convention, just as the other methods do. And he will certainly know from experience, if he has read much fiction, that the illusion of reality can be achieved in the other methods by sharpness of detail, emotional evocation and suggestion, and penetrating analysis. Furthermore, he knows that the mere fact of illusion in fiction is not crucial; the reader, again, is not deceived into taking the fictional illusion for reality, for the illusion is willingly assented to by the reader, and is itself a convention; that is, he knows that the illusion of fiction differs from the experience of actuality in that the illusion has a structure more closely wrought and meaningful than one ordinarily encounters in actuality, in that fiction represents an interpretation of experience. So granting that the first-person methods may increase the credibility of the story, that factor can never be taken as fundamental in the choice of the focus of narration.

But what factors do seem to be fundamental in the choice of one of the two types of focus of narration which involve the first person? It would be very hard to generalize on this point. One is forced, rather, to investigate particular instances, and to try to discern the logic of the method as applied in those instances. In "I Want to Know Why" the problem is complex. First, the use of the boy's own language and comment gives the author the advantage of being able to define the boy's basic character, his

---

*If the student has difficulty in keeping these four types of focus straight, perhaps the following scheme, which we have used earlier (p. 148), may prove helpful:

	Internal analysis of events	Outside observation of events
Narrator as a character in the story	1. Main character tells his story	2. Minor character tells character's story
Narrator not a character in the story	4. Analytic or omniscient author tells story	3. Author tells story as observer

special sensitivity, without resorting to analysis. The author does not have to say that the boy is sensitive and perceptive; he simply lets the boy describe a morning at the training track or lets him try to tell about his feeling for horses. He does not have to say that the boy is unusually serious and reflective; he simply lets the boy tell how he wants to be O.K. and how he is puzzled about certain problems. The boy's sensitivity and reflective cast of mind enter into the whole texture of the story; we get them immediately and not in terms of analysis or description. Exposition here, preparation for the final situation, is accomplished directly and not indirectly. Second, the theme of the story, the distinction between "good" at the level of nature and "good" at the truly human level, though important and far-reaching in its consequences, is so commonplace that in real life it tends to be accepted as a platitude and then forgotten. By showing us the boy at the moment of discovery, at the moment when he is wrestling with the question, the author tries to revivify the issue. That is, the first-hand rendering of the boy's puzzlement and confusion of mind, as contrasted with, say, an analytical treatment which would imply that the narrator at least—the omniscient author, for example—had a clear conception of the nature of the problem, greatly increases the immediacy and freshness. The method implies some such statement as this: most adults in thinking that they have a clear conception of the moral issue (which is at the root of the story) really shelve the issue, forget it, or ignore it; therefore, to dramatize the significance of the issue, one must take it in terms of its first impact, before familiarity or the ready-made solutions of society have dulled the awareness. So the fact that the intelligence of the narrator, the boy, is not entirely adequate to the problem put before it and honestly admits its inadequacy (as the title indicates) is a kind of ironical rebuke to the complacency of those intelligences (of the readers, of society, and the like) which claim to have the ready answer; the rebuke exists because the complacent intelligences, though presumably having the answer, have ceased to regard the issue as important, and the irony exists because the young and inexperienced intelligence, in terms of its very inexperience, in terms of its fumbling, rebukes the old and wise.

What is the logic of the use of the first-person observer in "A Rose for Emily"? In our interpretation of the story it was said that the relation between Miss Emily and the town was important (p. 352). Therefore the use of one of the townspeople to tell the story enables the author to indicate constantly in a dozen small ways (metaphors, incidental comments, and the like) the attitude of the town toward Miss Emily and of Miss Emily toward the town. If a third-person focus were used, this relationship might be specified and analyzed, but it would scarcely be so pervasive—it would not enter fully into the very texture of the narrative. Furthermore, the very fact that the narrator is limited in his opportunities for observation, that he only sees Miss Emily in scattered flashes, provides a highly dramatic frame for the story—a device for suspense. The mounting curiosity in the town provides, as it were, the pattern which the reader will follow in his own effort to approach Miss Emily, to understand her and the significance of her act.

Or what is the logic behind the use of Peachey as observer-narrator for the main action of "The Man Who Would Be King"? Dravot's story could be told from the third person, and might still be quite effective. But one thing, now present, would be missing: Peachey's attempt to understand Dravot. It is the effect on Peachey which finally points up the full significance of Dravot's development—Peachey's vision of Dravot leading him through the mountains, Peachey's refusal to sell the crown, and so on. Therefore, Peachey's position is somewhat like the position of the narrator in "A Rose for Emily." His reactions provide a basis of reference by which the significance of the main action can be indicated.

In addition to such special functions of the first-person narrative in the above stories, it may be said that the use of the first person may provide a ready-made scheme for selection. That is, the opportunities for observation and experience by the character who tells the story are somewhat limited, whether the story is his own story or that of someone else. The boy in "I Want to Know Why," for instance, is limited in the commentary which he can make on his own situation—cannot fully understand it. Or the narrator in "A Rose for Emily" only sees Miss Emily and the foreman on the street; he cannot be a party to their private conversations, and he cannot enter into her thoughts. Therefore, in the case of the first-person narrator, the writer has his field of selection already narrowed; and in the further exercise of the principle of selection, he must be governed by his consideration of the impact of events upon the narrator. So the fact of the first person—his limited opportunity for observation and interpretation, his special character—gives a certain kind of unity to a story. But this kind of unity can only be achieved in certain instances. The writer must ask himself: *Does the narrator have the opportunity of observing or experiencing all that is finally pertinent to the story?* And: *Is the narrator capable of serving, directly or indirectly, as a means of interpreting the action?* Then, after deciding these questions, he must ask another: *Is the style of the narration consistent with the character of the narrator?* (For instance, compare the style in "I Want to Know Why" with that of "Araby"—p. 317 and p. 185.) And: *Is the style which is consistent with the character of the narrator capable of rendering the effects I want?* (For example, the style of "I Want to Know Why" could not consistently admit the last paragraphs of "Araby" [p. 189].)

The focus of the observer-author obviously shares one basic limitation with that of the first-person observer: it does not admit of any direct account of mental process, states of feeling, or motives of persons under observation, except in terms of surmise by the observer. At the same time,

unlike the focus of the first-person observer, it permits unlimited opportunity for observation. The first-person observer is a *person*, and he can
see only what would be possible for a person to see, but the observer-author
can follow his character to a desert island or a locked room. But this method
must dispense with the advantage which the method of the first-person
observer may, as we have pointed out (pp. 661–662), give: the use of the
narrator as a kind of interpreter—a kind of refractor for the action, a basis
of reference by which the significance of the main action may be indicated.
In the method of observer-author, all must depend directly on presentation
of background, external action, gesture, and speech. The method tends
to reduce the story to a series of objective scenes much after the manner of
a play, as in "The Killers." Therefore, the writer, in considering such a
method for a story, must ask himself: *Can I dispense with the advantage of
the "refractor" and still make my point?* For instance, suppose such a
writer had in mind the materials which we find in "A Rose for Emily," and
wanted, like Faulkner, to emphasize the town-Emily relationship. He
might work out the whole story of Emily scenically, and even give more of
Emily's career than Faulkner does. He might even put in two or three
scenes between Emily and the townspeople. But he might find, in the end,
that he had been unable by such a method to convey the constant sense of
the eyes of the community upon her, and had been unable to define the
strangely mixed reverential and condemnatory attitude of the community.
So he might be forced to come back to the narrator who is, as it were, the
eyes and voice of the community. But in "The Killers" the author is able
to present his total meaning without a refractor, or interpreter; the material is such that it can be worked out in self-contained scenes, with no
commentary beyond that implied in the special style (pp. 310–311).

But the observer-author method would be impossible in "Old Red,"
just as would be the method of observer-narrator. For in this case, the
true stage of the action is inside the head of the old man; we are dealing with
the psychological process by which he arrives at self-definition. The same
thing is true of "Noon Wine" or "The Lament." We see that these stories
share one characteristic: all of them depend, as stories, upon the analysis
of states of feeling of the main character, upon subtle psychological
changes. When this sort of "inwardness of character" is involved, obviously
one cannot use the focus of first-person observer or of observer-author.
Conceivably in such cases, the first-person hero might tell his own story,
for he himself knows, presumably, what he thinks and feels. But does he always have the maturity and detachment and skill in psychological analysis
necessary to understand himself? We have said that in "I Want to Know
Why" the fact that the hero is fumbling with the question, that he has, presumably, less experience and psychological expertness than the reader,
creates an irony which is functional in the story (p. 660–661). But in other
stories we can understand how commentary, either direct or indirect, on

the part of the omniscient author may be necessary. For instance, if the old man in "The Lament" should tell his own story, it would be almost impossible to avoid extreme sentimentality; the omniscient author can adopt an attitude of detachment, he can give us an account without overtly appealing to our feelings, he can summarize and analyze, he can keep his distance from the events, but if the old man himself were to tell the story, the mere fact of his telling it might imply a sort of self-pity, or at least an excessive self-consciousness which is not in keeping with the character.

DISTANCE

These last remarks on "The Lament" and the whole discussion of the focus of narration, suggest another problem with which the writer must deal, or rather, suggest two problems, that of *distance* and that of *tone*.

The word *distance* used in this sense is, of course, a metaphor, just as is the word *atmosphere*. But we do have the feeling that in some stories the writer is "closer" to his character than in others, that he wants the reader's feelings and attitudes to be more nearly equated with those of the character, that he wants the reader's sympathies to be more immediately implicated. We can see how the problem of the focus of narration may involve this problem of distance. First-person narration tends to shorten the distance between the reader and the fictional character; for instance, the character narrating his own story tends to give us the world strictly in his own terms, in his own feelings and attitudes, and he can scarcely see himself in a large context. He tends to reveal himself rather than to pass judgment upon himself, to give comments about himself, or to analyze himself. Such judgments, comments, and analyses exist in such a story, but they exist by implication, and the reader must formulate them for himself. Judgment and analysis depend upon detachment, upon a standard outside the character being judged and analyzed. Obviously such a method as that of the observer-author, which merely records objectively dialogue, setting, and action without ever going into the consciousness of characters, tends to imply a greater distance than either type which uses the first-person narrator; for even the first-person observer, though he may comment and pass judgment upon the main character, nevertheless, immediately involves the reader in the world in which the main character moves—as in "The Man Who Would Be King" or in "A Rose for Emily." But the fourth type of focus, that of the omniscient author, may involve very great or very little distance.

On this point, let us compare "Old Red" with "The Necklace." In the first story, we plunge immediately into the old man's view of the world about him, and as the story goes on, added details and events come to us primarily through him. When the past appears in the story, it is introduced in terms of the old man's recollection, in terms of his attempt to make his

past make sense. By contrast, in "The Necklace," when the past is introduced in the very opening paragraphs, we have a bare, clipped summary
given in terms of the writer's mind, and with his analyses and commentaries. He gives us the essential facts of the past, with a kind of brutal
directness and economy, as though he were thinking, "Well, there's not a
great deal in this woman's past worth recounting; so I'll only give you the
essentials—the rest would probably bore you." The whole story is written
from a considerable distance, a distance which permits the compact summaries, the sharp commentaries, the rigorous selection of incident. For
instance, the passage of ten years is indicated in a sentence. It is not to be
understood that such a degree of distance is always to be taken as implying
a highly critical or unsympathetic attitude toward a character. At the very
end of "The Necklace" we discover a sympathy for the heroine—as we
understand the moral regeneration which the period of deprivation has
brought about.

As has been said above, the problem of distance is closely related to
that of *tone*. Again, as in the case of distance, one may come to an understanding of the term by considering it as a metaphor. When, in ordinary
conversation, somebody says something, we depend on the tone of voice
as well as on the actual words to tell us exactly what the speaker means.
For example, the word *yes* may not mean yes at all. Because of an ironical
inflection, it may mean quite the contrary, or it may mean a grudging and
bitter assent. The tone of voice indicates the attitude of the speaker toward
what is being said.

But obviously a writer cannot indicate his attitude by any such direct
means. He must fall back on all sorts of devices to indicate his attitude. And
usually, the underlying attitude of the writer is not given by statement, but
by a complex of such devices. We have already indicated how in "The
Necklace" the attitude of the writer is involved in the matter of distance.
And we can see how, in such a story as "The Secret Life of Walter
Mitty," the mixture of sympathy and amusement may be related to the
particular degree of distance taken by the writer. He lets Mr. Mitty speak
for himself, or rather, he give us in full detail certain sections of Mr.
Mitty's thoughts. He comes very close to Mr. Mitty, but at the same time he
renders Mr. Mitty preposterous and ridiculous. The style of Mr. Mitty's
thoughts is the style of adventure stories in cheap magazines, or movie
thrillers, and that style indicates the degree of seriousness which we are
to attach to Mr. Mitty's meditations. But at the same time there is a certain
sympathy for the henpecked little man whose only escape from the tyranny
of his wife and the dullness of his routine is by means of these ridiculous
day-dreams. Here the style of Mr. Mitty's thoughts is the primary device
used to indicate the writer's attitude. And, as we have already seen, the
style of "The Killers" (p. 310) or that of "Araby" (p. 192) is important

in indicating the underlying attitude. We hav already pointed out the special tone involved in "In the Penal Colony" and its relation to the questions of style and distance.

SCALE

In addition to all of the foregoing questions which the writer must confront, consciously or unconsciously, there are the problems of *scale* and *pace*, problems which involve a number of the preceding problems.

The problem of *scale* simply means this: *How long should the particular story be?* This question has two aspects, one mechanical and the other interpretive. The first aspect involves the degree of complication inherent in the story material. "The Man Who Would Be King" must, obviously, be longer than, say, "The Lament" or "Christ in Flanders." In "The Lament" nothing is necessary to the point of the action except a few immediate events: we need to know nothing of the son except the fact of his death, nothing about the old man except his overmastering impulse to tell of his bereavement. In "The Man Who Would Be King," however, we must have more than the events taken at the crisis: we need to know what Dravot was and what motives he had at the beginning of the adventure, if we are to appreciate the change which overtakes him, and we need to know the effect on Peachey. In other words, here the fact of change or development is important, and therefore must be documented. We must get a sense of the process, which involves time and the history of the character. Of course, there are ways to foreshorten the fictional "time"; that is, to give the impression of the passage of time, with consequent change, without the presentation of full documentation. In "Old Red" the sense of the past is rendered by a series of *cutbacks* (see Glossary) presented through the mind of the main character, and in "A Rose for Emily" the observer-narrator gives summaries which foreshorten the time. In "Araby," as has been previously stated, the nature of the style implies a foreshortening of time; but this story really avoids the problem of development, for it takes an incident from the past and simply interprets it as a single, inclusive symbol for a subsequent development, in no way specified, in the life of the character. But it is to be observed that in the actual body of the action, no account of development *antecedent* to the action is required. The foreshortening is a foreshortening of future and not past time, in relation to the main body of the action. So the situation in these stories is, in so far as there is no need for exploration of a past which exists before the main action, similar to that in "The Lament," and different from that in "The Man Who Would Be King." In other words, the scale of these stories can be "short" and not "long"—relatively speaking.

A similar situation is encountered in "A Rose for Emily." The author might have been compelled to give a much fuller account, perhaps a novelette, if he had attempted a direct psychological treatment of Emily. But for various reasons (p. 352), he is not concerned with the full psychological analysis of Emily. His observer-narrator, the citizen of the town, can give him all that is necessary for his interpretation, and by this means he can reduce the scale of the story.

PACE

The problem of *pace* is closely associated with that of scale. In a short piece of fiction, the handling can more nearly move at the same rate of speed throughout without incurring the danger of monotony than in a longer piece. In regard to speed, we may think along these lines: summary is faster in rendering an action than is narrative; narrative tends to be faster than full rendering in terms of scene (for instance, we see how the narrative method rather than the scenic method in "A Rose for Emily" tends to reduce the scale); scene tends to be faster than analysis; and so on. Almost all stories involve a combination of these methods. For instance, "The Killers," which is almost purely scenic in method, does have of necessity a certain amount of narrative. But few stories, even quite short ones, are as single in method as "The Killers." Such a story as "Old Red," as we can easily see, involves all of them. Pace, then, we may take to be a term for indicating the relationships existing among these various methods in a given piece of fiction, the proportioning of analysis to action, of summary to scene, and the like. If the author relies on one method too exclusively the pace tends to become monotonous. The changes of pace, which really represent changes in emphasis and *may* represent changes in distance, tend to sharpen the reader's attention. But the changes in pace cannot be determined arbitrarily. As has been suggested above, the change of pace represents a change in emphasis. Obviously, the scenic method provides more emphasis than the method of summary, but even within any given method varying degrees of emphasis, and consequent changes of pace, are possible. And frequently a writer in rendering a single situation will mix the methods in an extremely complicated fashion, dialogue, narrative, flashbacks of memory, summary, and the like being used in building up the immediate effect. For example, we can turn to "Old Red."

We have tried to describe some of the problems which a writer encounters as he composes a piece of fiction, and have tried to indicate, in the interpretations of the individual stories in this volume and in this appendix, some of the solutions which have been arrived at in particular cases. But the solutions are always solutions for particular cases. All that one can do is to study the particular cases in the hope that such an effort will result in the sharpening of his own capacity for discrimination, that it will help him to see the relationships existing among the elements which go to make up a piece of fiction. Then, perhaps, he can, in his own writing, achieve a closer co-ordination of means and ends. But he must realize that no fictional problem can, finally, be solved in isolation from the other problems involved in the same composition, just as he must realize that the various elements as they appear in the particular work are not distinct but are organically unified. Henry James, in his essay on "The Art of Fiction," states this point very clearly. Speaking of the elements of fiction, he says:

"People often talk of these things as if they had a kind of internecine distinctness, instead of melting into each other at every breath, and being intimately associated parts of one general effort of expression. I cannot imagine composition existing in a series of blocks, nor conceive, in any novel worth discussing at all, of a passage of description that is not in its intention narrative, a passage of dialogue that is not in its intention descriptive, a touch of truth of any sort that does not partake of the nature of incident, or an incident that derives its interest from any other source than the general and only source of the success of a work of art—that of being illustrative. A novel is a living thing, all one and continuous, like any other organism, and in proportion as it lives will it be found, I think, that in each of the parts there is something of each of the other parts. The critic who over the close texture of a finished work shall pretend to trace a geography of items will mark some frontiers as artificial, I fear, as any that have been known to history."

In other words, a piece of fiction is a tissue of significances, some great and some small, but all of them aspects, finally, of the total significance of the piece. And one must remember that this total significance is not merely some idea which can be abstracted from the "story" and stated in general terms. It is the fact of the idea's living in action, in the "story," which makes the idea significant, for the underlying significance of all fiction may be the faith of the writer that experience itself is significant and is not a mere flux of unrelated items. That is, in other terms, he has a faith that man is a responsible being, and he tries to validate this faith by the responsible and vital organization of his art.

Biographical Notes

SHERWOOD ANDERSON (1876–1941) was born in Camden, Ohio. His father was an aimless, improvident wanderer, a talker and teller of tales, a type that appears in Anderson's fiction. Anderson had a limited formal education, served in Cuba during the Spanish-American War, worked as manager of a paint factory in Elmyra, Ohio, then as an advertising copy writer in Chicago, where he became a protégé of the Chicago group of writers, including Carl Sandburg and Theodore Dreiser. He achieved fame with his collection of stories *Winesburg, Ohio,* in 1919; and with *The Triumph of the Egg,* two years later, became generally recognized as a master of that form. His other work includes novels, autobiography, memoirs, verse, and journalism.

MARCEL AYMÉ (1902–) is a distinguished French novelist and playwright. His schooling was irregular—he detested school—and he had a go at various jobs before he found his vein as a writer. He achieved great success as a young man and at the age of twenty-seven his fourth novel won the Théophraste Renaudot prize for the best novel of the year. He is noted as a stylist and as a satirist. His principal novels that have been translated into English include *The Green Mare,* 1938, *The Miraculous Barber,* 1951, and *The Secret Stream,* 1954. *Across Paris,* 1959, is his first volume of short stories to be published in English.

ISAAC BABEL (1894–1939?) was born in Odessa, Russia, of a lower middle-class Jewish family. As a young man he went to St. Petersburg and lived as an impoverished Bohemian. Maxim Gorki was the first to encourage Babel by printing two of his volumes. During the Revolution and civil war, Babel fought with the cavalry. In 1923 he began to win success with short stories published in magazines. He published *Odessa Tales* in 1924 and a brilliant collection, *Red Cavalry,* in 1926. Since 1936 there has been no mention of his name in any Soviet publication. It is believed that he may have died in a concentration camp in 1939 or 1940.

HONORÉ DE BALZAC (1799–1850) was born at Tours, in France, to a prosperous family that abandoned him to a monastic school, and for years neglected him. After his school years he spent a long period in Paris, in dire poverty, struggling to learn the craft of writing, reading prodigiously and writing, under various pseudonyms, a dozen novels, which he later repudiated. When he was thirty, he began to receive recognition, and in the next twenty years poured out a flood of novels, stories, and plays, more than 350 titles, this in addition to work as a journalist and editor. Some hundred of his novels are interrelated to give a coherent picture of the world of his time, under the title *La Comédie Humaine*, a monumental achievement.

SAUL BELLOW (1915–) was born in Quebec, but raised in Chicago, where he attended public school and the University of Chicago, with graduate work at Northwestern University. He has been intermittently a university professor, and is one of the most impressive of the younger novelists. His best known books are *The Adventures of Augie March*, which received the National Book Award in 1954, and *Henderson, the Rain King*.

AMBROSE BIERCE (1842–1914?) was born in Ohio, the son of a poverty-stricken, pious farmer, whom he detested. He attended the Kentucky Military Institute for one year, entered the Civil War as a drummer boy, and after being twice wounded, emerged as a brevet major, and went to San Francisco and a career in journalism, where his reputation as a writer was made. But he lived and worked several years in England, and Washington, D.C., as a correspondent for Hearst. His personal life was unhappy, and in 1913 he disappeared into Mexico.

RAY BRADBURY (1920–) was born in Waukegan, Illinois. He comes of a line of editors and publishers, and as a young man began himself to write, producing science fiction. *Dark Carnival, The Martian Chronicles*, and *The Illustrated Man* are representative titles. But quite early—in 1945—Bradbury became interested in writing serious fiction, though his subjects still tend to be concerned with fantasy and the grotesque. *The Golden Apples of the Sun*, from which the story included in this volume is taken, appeared in 1958.

DINO BUZZATI (1906–) was born in Bellune, Italy. After studying for the law, he took up a career in journalism and for many years has beeen prominent on the staff of the *Corriere della Sera* of Milan. He has published a number of collections of stories, and his reputation in that form has long since been firmly established in Europe. His latest collection received the important Strega Prize, in Italy.

ALBERT CAMUS (1913–1960) was born in Algeria, of peasant stock. He worked his way through the university, but at the same time was devoting much energy to a theatrical stock company which he had organized. During the German occupation of France he was active in the Resistance and afterward remained deeply involved in political journalism. But his career in the theater and as a writer of fiction proceeded with marked success. He received the Nobel Prize in 1957.

TRUMAN CAPOTE (1924–) was born in New Orleans, Louisiana, and characteristically writes of that region. He is the author of two novels, two collections of stories, two plays, and two books of travel, one concerning Russia.

JOHN CHEEVER (1912–) was born in Quincy, Massachusetts, the son of an English immigrant and a Massachusetts Yankee. He was educated at Thayer Academy. At sixteen he began to publish fiction, and has produced over a hundred stories and one novel, *The Wapshot Chronicle*, which received the National Book Award in 1958. His stories have been collected in three volumes, *The Way Some People Live*, *The Enormous Radio*, and *The Housebreaker of Shady Hill*.

ANTON CHEKHOV (1860–1904) was born at Taganrog, on the Sea of Azov, in Russia, the grandson of a serf. Educated as a doctor, he rarely practiced his profession, but devoted himself almost from the first to literature. His stories found a ready public, and in time exerted a profound effect on that form in all countries. Though his first play, *Ivanov*, belongs to his middle twenties, it was more than ten years before his second, *The Sea Gull*, established him as a dramatist. From that time, though he was increasingly plagued by ill health, he devoted himself chiefly to the theater, his other plays being *Uncle Vanya*, *The Three Sisters*, and *The Cherry Orchard*, which have had an immense influence on the modern drama.

GABRIELLE CLAUDINE COLETTE (1873–1954) spent her childhood in the countryside of Burgundy. Her first books, the Claudine volumes, appeared under his first husband's pen name, Willy. After her divorce in 1906 she went on the stage and performed as a dancer and a mime. She continued her writing and produced fiction which won her a place in the Royal Academy of Belgium in 1934 and the Goncourt Academy in 1945. On her death she was accorded a state funeral, the only woman author so honored in the history of the five French republics. From the beginning she was able to write effortlessly. She is regarded as a brilliant stylist. Of her many novels, one may mention as representative *The Vagrant*, *The Gentle Libertine*, and *Cheri*.

JOHN COLLIER (1901–) was born in London, was privately educated, began writing verse at nineteen, and was soon being published. For several years he was poetry editor of *Time and Tide,* but his reputation is based on his stories.

JOSEPH CONRAD (1857–1924) was a Pole, but his boyhood dreams of adventure at sea led him first to an involvement in revolutionary plots and gunrunning in France, and later to a long and adventurous career as an officer in the British merchant marine. He was nearing middle life before he devoted himself fully to writing, but within a few years had established himself as one of the most powerful and original writers of his time. His best known novels are perhaps *Lord Jim, Nostromo, Under Western Eyes,* and *Victory;* but some of his pieces of short fiction, such as "The Heart of Darkness," "The Secret Sharer," and the story included here, show his genius in an equally striking form.

STEPHEN CRANE (1871–1900) was born in Newark, New Jersey, attended a military school and, briefly, Lafayette College and Syracuse University. Perhaps his training as a journalist on the New York *Herald* and the *Tribune* was the most significant influence in forming his scrupulously realistic notion of fiction. Crane was enormously precocious, writing two of his most impressive books before he was 25, *Maggie, a Girl of the Streets* and *The Red Badge of Courage.* He was a master of the short story and a famous war correspondent, covering the Spanish-American War and the Greco-Turkish War. His verse is, however, undistinguished. He died abroad, in self-imposed exile, feeling himself rejected by the American life of the period.

BARONESS KAREN VON BLIXEN-FINECKE, née DINESEN ("Isak Dinesen") (1885–) was born in Denmark. As a young woman she studied painting and did not take up writing until she went out to Kenya Colony with her husband, Baron Blixen. Her book *Out of Africa,* 1938, tells of her years on a large farm in east Africa. Her first collection of stories, *Seven Gothic Tales,* 1934, was an immediate success. Other fiction by Isak Dinesen includes *Winter's Tales,* 1942, and a novel published in the United States under the title, *The Angelic Avengers.*

WILLIAM FAULKNER (1897–) was born in Mississippi, of a family distinguished in the political history of the state. Perfunctorily and briefly he attended the University of Mississippi. He served with the Canadian Air Force in World War I, and in the years before literary recognition came, worked as a barn-storming aviator and at various odd jobs. Since then he has operated a farm and done a good deal of script writing for Hollywood. He is a passionately devoted hunter, and the world of hunting appears over and over in his work, most notably in his masterly long tale, "The Bear." *Sanctuary* brought him his first recognition, but his best novels are probably *The Sound and the Fury, Light in August, Absalom, Absalom!* and *The Hamlet*. He has written some of the most memorable short stories in our literature and one play, a dramatization of his novel, *Requiem for a Nun*. He has received the Nobel Prize.

F. SCOTT FITZGERALD (1896–1940) was born in Saint Paul, Minnesota. He attended an eastern preparatory school, and Princeton University, where his literary talent began to appear but where irregular work caused his suspension, in his junior year, for low marks. After a brief period in the Army, and in an advertising agency in New York, he wrote his first novel, *This Side of Paradise*, which heralded the advent of the Jazz Age. For the next ten years there was a flood of short stories, and several novels. His best novel is, perhaps, *The Great Gatsby*, but *Tender Is the Night* and *The Last Tycoon*, left unfinished at his death, are highly regarded by many critics.

CAROLINE GORDON (1895–) was born on Merry Mont farm, Todd County, Kentucky, and was educated in the classical school for boys which was conducted by her father at Clarksville, Tennessee. The story in this collection, "Old Red," is a kind of preliminary sketch of what is perhaps her best novel, *Alec Maury, Sportsman*, a fictionalized portrait of her father. Miss Gordon has published eight novels, and one collection of stories, *The Forest of the South*.

BRET HARTE (1836–1902) was born in Albany, New York, of Dutch and English ancestry. His father was a school teacher, and perhaps this fact, coupled with years of illness in childhood, led to the boy's extensive reading in the English classics. He began work at thirteen to help out the family, and by sixteen was self-supporting. At nineteen he went to California, where he worked as a teacher, apothecary clerk, tutor, express messenger, type-setter, and editor, all the while writing stories and poems. The frontier life of California gave him his characteristic subject, a subject of interest to the eastern part of America and to Europe. After a brief period as editor of *The Overland Monthly*, which he had founded, and as a professor at the University of California, he went East for a triumphal lecture tour, and on to England, where he cut a figure in literary circles. He was consul at Crefeld, Germany, and at Glasgow. He died in England.

ERNEST HEMINGWAY (1898–), born in Oak Park, Illinois, the son of a physician, served in World War I as ambulance driver, and later with the Italian Arditi, and after the war, worked as a foreign correspondent. In the 1920's, he made a sensational impact with his highly individual stories and his two early novels. *The Sun Also Rises* and *A Farewell to Arms*. In the midst of his literary career he returned to journalism as a correspondent covering the Spanish Civil War, an experience reflected in the famous novel *For Whom the Bell Tolls*. He received the Nobel Prize in 1954.

O. HENRY is the pen name of William Sydney Porter (1862–1910). O. Henry was born in Greensboro, North Carolina, attended school there until fifteen, when he went to work in a drug store, and at the age of twenty went to Texas. In Texas he worked as a clerk, draughtsman, bookkeeper, bank teller, and journalist, editing a humorous weekly and then going to the Houston *Daily Post* as a columnist and cartoonist. In 1895 he was indicted for embezzlement from the bank where he had been teller, and though his guilt was, probably, only technical, he fled to New Orleans, and thence to South America and Mexico, where he travelled with the notorious Jennings brothers, on money they had stolen. Two years later, because of the illness of his wife, he returned to the United States, and after her death stood trial, and was sentenced to five years in the Columbus, Ohio, penitentiary. In prison he began his serious career as a writer, and upon being released for good behavior, went to New York to become a professional fiction writer. He was enormously prolific, enormously successful, and a consumer of enormous quantities of whisky. He died at the age of forty-eight, of tuberculosis.

SHIRLEY JACKSON (1919–) is a native of California, but more recently has lived in the East. She has written novels and essays, but is best known for her stories.

JAMES JOYCE (1882–1941) was born in Dublin, and first won fame with his collection of stories called *Dubliners*. The title is significant, for in all his subsequent work, including the celebrated *Ulysses* and *Finnegan's Wake*, the city of Dublin is the vital fact. Joyce's influence has been prodigious, and some critics are inclined to rate him as the most significant novelist of the century.

FRANZ KAFKA (1883–1924) was born at Prague of German-Jewish stock, with a father who was violent and overbearing and opposed the son's literary aspirations. Kafka studied for the law, and was employed in an insurance company, but continued his literary work. The last seven years of his life was a period of illness and depression, and when he died he instructed that the writings he left be destroyed. But his friend Max Brod, to whom he had given the instructions, published them, and the recognition which had eluded Kafka in life came after his death.

RUDYARD KIPLING (1865–1936) was born in Bombay, India, his father, an artist, being curator of the museum at Lahore. After attending school at the United Services College, in Devonshire, England (the scene of his *Stalky and Co.*), he returned to India, and became, at seventeen, an under-editor of the Lahore *Civil and Military Gazette*, beginning the career of journalism that helped him learn Indian life and form his sharp and succinct style. Some of his best work was done in his early years, for example "The Man Who Would Be King," which was written before he was twenty-five, and world fame came early to him, both as a poet and writer of fiction. He received the Nobel Prize in 1907. He travelled widely, and lived for several years in Vermont (he had married an American woman).

RING (Ringgold Wilmer) LARDNER (1885–1933) was born in Niles, Michigan. He began life as a sportswriter, and much of his fiction reflects the world of sport. He is famous for his vigorous use of the vernacular, for his introduction of new types into fiction, and for a humorous and sardonic tone. In addition to his many short stories, he collaborated in two plays, one with George M. Cohan and the other with George S. Kaufman.

D. H. LAWRENCE (1885–1930) was born in Nottinghamshire, England, the son of a coal miner. For a time he taught in elementary school, trying to find himself as a painter and writer. With recognition, he became a wanderer, partly from curiosity and restlessness, and partly in the vain attempt to cure his tuberculosis, travelling in Europe, Mexico, Australia, and the United States. He was an enormously versatile writer, producing stories and novels, books of travel, criticism and essays, and poetry. By the time of his death, in Vence, France, his reputation seemed permanently established.

MARY McCARTHY (1912–), born in Seattle, was early orphaned, and the experiences of her childhood have provided the material of one of her more interesting books, *Memories of a Catholic Girlhood*, 1957. She was educated in private schools and at Vassar. Her work as a writer began early, and includes various forms, short stories, travel books, art criticism, autobiography, theater reviewing, and novels. She is best known for her satirical fiction, which deals chiefly with the life of New York intellectuals and artists, and those on the fringe of that world. She was at one time married to Edmund Wilson, the distinguished critic, by whom she has one son.

CARSON McCULLERS (1917–) was born in Columbus, Georgia, as Carson Smith, McCullers being the name of her husband. At seventeen she went to New York with the intention of studying music at the Julliard Foundation, but drifted into part-time jobs and attended night school. She began to publish stories, and when she was twenty-three, her first novel, *The Heart Is a Lonely Hunter*, made a sensation. In addition to two other novels, and a number of stories, she has written two plays, one of which, the dramatization of her novel *The Member of the Wedding*, has had a considerable success.

THOMAS MANN (1875–1955) was born at Lübeck, Germany, of the solid merchant class, and the contrast between that world and the artistic temperament has provided the theme for his first novel *Buddenbrooks* (which appeared when he was twenty-six) and also for much of his subsequent work. He achieved a prodigious reputation, and received the Nobel Prize in 1929. His best known novels are *Buddenbrooks*, *The Magic Mountain*, and the cycle dealing with the Biblical Joseph; but some critics are inclined to regard his short fiction as his best work. He opposed Hitler and spent many of his later years as an exile.

KATHERINE MANSFIELD (1888–1923) was born in Wellington, New Zealand, with the name of Kathleen Mansfield Beauchamp. She attended Queen's College, in London, edited the college magazine, studied music and became a competent cellist, and later toured as a super in opera. Her first stories appeared when she was twenty-two. She married John Middleton Murry, the critic, collaborated with him and D. H. Lawrence in founding a review, *The Signature*, and continued her own writing. By 1920 with the publication of the volume *Bliss and Other Stories*, her reputation was made. For several years she had been suffering from tuberculosis, and died at the age of thirty-five, in France, where she had gone for treatment.

GUY DE MAUPASSANT (1850–1893) was the son of a Paris stock broker and the godson of Gustav Flaubert, who supervised his literary training. From the age of thirty Maupassant was an acknowledged master of the short story, and in ten torrential years produced some thirty volumes, including two world-famous novels. Maupassant had inherited severe nervous disease, which was aggravated by drugs, dissipation, and over-exercise. After an attempted suicide, he died of paresis.

FLANNERY O'CONNOR (1925–) was born in Savannah, Georgia. Her novel *Wise Blood*, published in 1952, received wide attention. Her stories, which had been appearing in the quarterlies and little magazines, were collected in 1955 under the title *A Good Man Is Hard to Find*. She has held grants from the National Institute of Arts and Letters, from the Ford Foundation, and has held a Kenyon Fellowship in Fiction. She makes her home in Milledgeville, Georgia.

FRANK O'CONNOR (1903–) was born in Cork, Ireland, and attended the Christian Brothers School there, but was too poor to go to the university. He began to write early, worked as a librarian to maintain himself, and attracted the attention of literary men like Yeats and AE (George Russell).

His reputation is based on his stories, but he has also written verse and a critical study of Turgenev.

LUIGI PIRANDELLO (1867–1936), though living much of his adult life in Rome, was a Sicilian by birth and heritage. Through a long unhappy marriage, and a long and uncongenial career as a teacher, Pirandello produced an enormous amount of work in the short story, the novel, and the drama. Recognition, however, did not come until he was in his fifties, and then the fame of his plays *Six Characters in Search of an Author* and *As You Desire Me* overshadowed his great achievement as a writer of fiction. He received the Nobel Prize in 1934.

KATHERINE ANNE PORTER (1894–), a descendant of Daniel Boone, was born in the little community of Indian Creek, Texas. Brought up in Texas and Louisiania, she was educated in small convent schools. Her formal education ended at seventeen, but she continued to read widely with the passionate desire to become a writer. After some newspaper work and various nondescript jobs, and years of publishing occasional stories, she found distinguished recognition with the publication of the collection of stories *Flowering Judas* (1930), which has now become a classic of our time. Her other collections, which have maintained her high level of performance, are *Pale Horse, Pale Rider* (three short novels), and *The Leaning Tower and Other Stories*. She has published one book of essays, and some translations. She has travelled widely, worked as a script writer for moving pictures, lectured, and taught. She has received a number of distinguished awards.

JAMES PURDY (1923–) was born in Ohio, and attended the University of Chicago, as well as universities in Mexico and Spain. His collection of stories *Don't Call Me by My Right Name* (1956) was received with unusual enthusiasm by many critics. He is the author of a novel, *Malcolm*.

WILLIAM SANSOM (1912–) was born in England and attended schools there and on the continent. *Fireman Flower*, his first collection of stories, appeared in 1944. Since that time he has published over a dozen books, including several novels, *The Body*, 1947, *The Face of Innocence*, 1951, and *A Bed of Roses*, 1954. Other important collections of his stories include *The Passionate North*, 1950, and *A Touch of the Sun*, 1952.

IRWIN SHAW (1913–) was born in Brooklyn and was educated at Brooklyn College. During his college years and immediately afterward, he worked at a variety of jobs, but he had an early success in the theater and as a script writer in Hollywood. He has produced a number of stories, two novels, and his work for the movies and the stage.

JESSE HILTON STUART (1907–) was born in W-Hollow in the mountains of eastern Kentucky. He attended the Lincoln Memorial University at Harrogate, Tennessee, and after a year's work at Vanderbilt University, he taught school. His first volume, *Man with a Bull-Tongue Plow*, was a collection of poems and attracted wide attention on its publication in 1934. Since that time Stuart has become better known as a writer of stories and novels. He held a Guggenheim Fellowship in 1937 and was awarded a prize by the Academy of Arts and Sciences in 1941. A serious heart attack has prompted him to write his autobiography.

DYLAN THOMAS (1914–1953) was born in Wales and attended the Swansea Grammar School. He worked for a time as a newspaperman and held a post with the British Broadcasting Company. His first volume of poems appeared in 1934 when he was twenty. Thomas's talent was quickly discerned and long before his early death he was regarded as one of the brilliant writers of England and America. His poetry is dithyrambic and bardic. His life and personality have become legendary. His short stories have been overshadowed by his fame as a poet, but his pictures of village and country life in Wales have their own quality.

JAMES THURBER (1894–) was born in Columbus, Ohio, a city that appears in a number of his stories. After graduating from Ohio State University, he began newspaper work in Columbus, but shortly went to France, on the Paris edition of the *Herald Tribune*. In 1926 he began contributing to *The New Yorker* magazine his famous series of drawings, stories, commentaries, and sketches, which have established him as a distinguished stylist and one of the foremost humorists of our time. He has done, in collaboration with Elliot Nugent, one play *The Male Animal*.

ROBERT PENN WARREN (1905–) was born in Guthrie, Kentucky, and attended Vanderbilt University, the University of California, Yale University, and Oxford. For a number of years he was a teacher, or part-time teacher, at various colleges and universities, the last being Yale. He is the author of a number of novels and collections of verse, and critical essays. He has been awarded Pulitzer prizes for fiction (*All the King's Men*) and for poetry (*Promises*).

EUDORA WELTY (1909–) was born in Jackson, Mississippi, where she continues to live. She was educated at the Mississippi State College for Women and at the University of Wisconsin; and for a short time, she studied advertising at Columbia University. Though her first ambition was to be a painter, she began to write as a child. With her first book of stories, *A Curtain of Green* (1941), she was widely acclaimed for an extraordinary talent. Since that time she has published a number of novels and collections of stories, and has received general recognition, including the Howells Medal awarded by the American Academy of Arts and Letters, and the Pulitzer Prize.

ANGUS WILSON (1913–) was born in England. He attended Westminster School and Merton College, Oxford. He was in the Foreign Office for a time and then had a post in the British Museum. His first collection of short stories, *The Wrong Set*, 1949, had an immediate success. Other volumes of his fiction include *Such Darling Dodos* (stories) and *Hemlock and After* (a novel).

THOMAS CLAYTON WOLFE (1900–1938) was born in Asheville, North Carolina. He attended the University of North Carolina, where his major interest was in play writing, an interest which he subsequently pursued at Harvard. His fame, however, was achieved in the novel. *Look Homeward, Angel* (1929) made a profound impact. Later novels are *Of Time and the River*, *The Web and the Rock*, and *You Can't Go Home Again*, the latter two published posthumously.

Glossary

ABSTRACT: Abstractions are qualities and characteristics isolated as pure ideas. A piece of *sugar* is a concrete substance with its own qualities but we may *abstract* (literally *draw away*) from it *whiteness, hardness, sweetness*. Literature characteristically deals with the concrete rather than the abstract, and also the specific rather than the general. All of which is not to say that ideas, which are capable of being stated abstractly—love, courage, justice—are not involved in literature, but such ideas rarely emerge as abstractions; rather, they are incorporated in the concrete elements—in the case of fiction, in the particular characters and situations and events. The general observations that one may abstract from the particulars of a story—observations about human nature or about life—are not to be taken as the equivalent of the story. The abstraction—and the generalization—are something less than—merely a part of—the concrete particularity of the story itself. See pp. 21, 274–275.

ACTION: A series of events having unity and significance. See pp. 77–78, 656–657.

ACTION STORY: A story in which the principal interest lies in plot suspense, such as adventure or detective fiction. See pp. 3–4, 55–56, 77–78.

ALLEGORICAL: See ALLEGORY.

ALLEGORY: An allegory is a kind of narrative in which the characters, objects, and events are to be taken, not as real but as standing for some set of ideas. That is, each item in the narrative is equated with some item among the ideas. For example, in Bunyan's *The Pilgrim's Progress*, the character Christian, who leaves his home to journey to the Celestial City, is to be taken as the type of all people who try to lead the Christian life, and each event that takes place on the journey stands for some problem in the spiritual life. See PARABLE, and see pp. 73–74, 286–288, 389–390.

ALLITERATION: Repetition of consonants, particulary of initial consonants as in *lullaby* or "*l*evels of the *l*ake." See p. 64.

ANECDOTE: A brief narrative of some incident or event. See p. 3.

ANTICLIMAX: A break in the climactic order of events or effects; a falling off from the expected intensification of effect. See CLIMAX and IRONY. See also pp. 181–182, 651–652.

ATMOSPHERE: The general pervasive feeling aroused by the various factors in a piece of fiction, such as setting, character, theme, and the like; the general

681

effect of the handling of the total work. To be distinguished from SETTING and from TONE. Considerations of the metaphorical origin of the two terms, *atmosphere* and *tone*, may be helpful here. *Tone* is to be referred ultimately to the author's attitude (the tone of voice of a speaker as qualifying what he says) toward what is being presented, whereas *atmosphere* is to be referred to the general qualification provided by the materials themselves (an atmosphere of sunshine, of cheerfulness, an atmosphere of gloom, and the like). There is, however, a good deal of overlapping and vagueness about the use of these terms in ordinary discussion. The student, in referring to a particular case in fiction, should ask himself whether he wishes to emphasize the author's attitude or the mere effect of the materials as such. See pp. 76, 79, 132, 189, 529, 649–650.

CLICHÉ: Usually used in reference to a phrase which has lost its force because of continual use; for example, "in the arms of Morpheus," or "a dull, sickening thud." But the term is also applied occasionally to fictional situations or events which have become hackneyed and stereotyped. The cliché represents one kind of appeal to a STOCK RESPONSE on the part of the reader. But, of course, clichés may be used justifiably by the author, for ironical effect, or because a certain kind of character would normally use clichés in his speech, or for other reasons. In general, it may be said that a cliché is bad when used with the intention of creating a vivid and memorable effect; it fails in such cases because it does not represent a fresh perception. See pp. 64, 183, 305, 650–651.

CLIMAX: The highest point in an ascending series; in fiction, for example, the point at which the forces in conflict reach the highest intensification. See pp. 81, 156, 651–652.

COHERENCE: The hanging together—the interconnectedness—of the parts of a piece of fiction. TRUTH OF COHERENCE has to do with the internal consistency of a piece of literature. See pp. 27–28, 82–83, 173, 277.

COINCIDENCE: An accidental coming together of certain events. (See SURPRISE ENDING.) The use of coincidence is, in one sense, unavoidable in fiction, for the original situation in any story may be defined as a coincidence. But the use of coincidence is, generally speaking, illegitimate when it functions to solve the fictional problem; that is, when the events which bring about the resolution of a plot have no logical connection with preceding events. See pp. 26, 98, 105, 113, 132, 368.

COMPLICATION: The interplay between character and event which builds up a tension and develops a problem out of the original situation given in the story. See pp. 81, 172, 653–654.

CONCRETE: See ABSTRACT.

CONFLICT: All fiction involves, at one level or another, conflict. The characters struggle against enviroment or with each other (external conflict) or are engaged in struggles with themselves (internal conflict). One important approach to the understanding of any story is to determine the nature of the conflict involved and the pattern that the opposing forces assume. See pp. 78–81, 172–173, 652–653.

CONNOTATION: See DENOTATION

CONVENTION: Any method, device, or rule that is accepted by explicit or tacit agreement. For example, the fact that the letter *t* shall have a certain consonantal value, or that a touchdown shall count for six points depends upon nothing intrinsic but is determined by convention. All the arts, including that of fiction, make use of *conventions*. For example, the omniscient author's ability to enter into the innermost thoughts of several of his characters depends upon a convention. The author continually makes use of traditional conventions handed down to him from the past. His work, however, is termed CONVENTIONAL in a bad sense when it fails to justify the conventional items it employs by relating them freshly to the new problem.

CONVENTIONAL: See CONVENTION.

CUTBACK: A passage in a narrative which breaks the chronological sequence to deal with earlier events. (For example, the method of "Old Red" involves numerous cutbacks. See pp. 80, 248, 666.

DENOTATION: The exact thing or idea indicated by word. The denotation is not only the primary meaning, but it is the specific and abstract meaning. Scientific prose needs no more than the denotations of words, and the attempt to build up a scientific and technical language is in harmony with this situation. But the CONNOTATIONS of a word are the things suggested by or associated with the word. These connotations, though necessarily vague and inexact (as compared with denotations) are nevertheless powerful and important, and the skillful writer whose intention is literary rather than scientific makes full use of them. See pp. 190–191.

DENOUEMENT: The final resolution or untying of the plot. It sometimes, but not always, coincides with the climax. See pp. 81, 655–656.

DISTANCE: The term is used to mean the degree of detachment with which the characters in a story are viewed. See pp. 664–666.

DRAMATIC: Strictly speaking, fictional method is said to be dramatic when the author gives a purely OBJECTIVE rendering of his material, without indulging either in editorial comment and generalization of his own or in the analysis of the feelings and thoughts of his characters. The clearest case of such a method in this book is "The Killers" (p. 296). But in such a story as "The Lament" (p. 203), though the method is less strictly dramatic, the old man's grief is not commented upon by the author until he has presented the grief in terms of action. Where a dramatic method is used the reader must infer the inner situation from the external action and dialogue. But the term is used more loosely to indicate merely the presence of strong tension and sharp conflict in a story or novel; and it is used more loosely still to indicate concrete presentation as opposed to abstract statement.

EPISODE: A separate incident in a larger piece of action. In "The Lament" (see pp. 206–207), for example, the visit to the stable to see the horse constitutes an episode.

EPISODIC: A piece of fiction is said to be *episodic* when there is not a strongly emphasized causal continuity between one episode and the next. Episodic structure is, logically, loose structure, in so far as plot is concerned.

EXPOSITION: The process of giving the reader necessary information concerning characters and events existing before the action proper of a story begins. See pp. 81, 168–170, 646–647.

FABLE: A tale, usually rather simple and often illustrating some maxim about human nature. See. p. 73.

FICTION: See pp. 1–28, 667–668.

FIRST-PERSON NARRATION: See FOCUS OF NARRATION. See also pp. 147–150, 659–664.

FOCUS: The center around which the material of an imaginative work is concentrated. The focus may shift from moment to moment in a piece of fiction or it may remain constant. For example, the focus may be primarily upon character, upon an idea, upon a setting, or the like. See p. 657.

FOCUS OF CHARACTER: A piece of fiction is not merely a sequence of events. The events are of special concern to some person, or group of persons, involved in them, and the structure of the narrative depends, in one sense, upon the reference to the person, or persons, most fundamentally concerned. See pp. 171–172, 304–305, 658–659.

FOCUS OF NARRATION (POINT OF VIEW): The focus of narration has to do with who tells the story. We may make four basic distinctions: (1) a character may tell his own story in the first person; (2) a character may tell, in the first person, a story which he has observed; (3) the author may tell what happens in the purely objective sense—deeds, words, gestures—without going into the minds of the characters and without giving his own comment; (4) the author may tell what happens with full liberty to go into the minds of characters and to give his own comment. These four types of narration may be called: (1) first-person, (2) first-person observer, (3) author-observer, and (4) omniscient author. Combinations of these methods are, of course, possible. See pp. 146–150, 192, 529–530, 659–664.

FORESHADOWING: The process of giving the reader an intimation of some event which is to follow later in the action.

FORM: The arrangement of various elements in a work of literature; the organization of various materials (ideas, images, characters, setting, and the like) to give a single effect. It may be said that a story is successful—that it has achieved form—when all of the elements are functionally related to each other, when each part contributes to the intended effect. Form is not to be thought of merely as a sort of container for the story; it is, rather, the total principle of organization and affects every aspect of the composition. (See pp. 1–28, 645–646.) STRUCTURE and STYLE are also used to indicate the author's arrangement of his materials to give his effect. *Structure*, however, is usually used with more special reference to the ordering of the larger elements such as episodes, scenes, and details of action, in contrast to the arrangement of words, for which the term *style* is ordinarily employed. In the fullest sense, both the terms become synonymous with form, but in this book *style* is used merely to refer to the selection and ordering of language. See pp. 191–192, 310–312, 329–330, 645–646, 662, 664–665.

FUNCTIONAL: Having to do with the development of the total effect of a piece of fiction. The term is used in this book to denote those elements of a story which actually play a part in building up the complex and rich unity of a story in contrast to those used merely because they are fashionable, or feed some external interest, or are merely sensational or decorative or engaging. See pp. 645–646, 667–668.

IMAGERY: The representation of any sense experience. Imagery does not consist merely of "mental pictures," but may make an appeal to any of the senses. In keeping with its insistance upon the concrete and the particular, all literature, including fiction, makes much use of imagery, not only in obvious descriptive fashion but also in figurative language. The most common forms of figurative language are SIMILES and METAPHORS. A *simile* is a direct comparison between two things, and such a comparison is introduced by *like* or *as*. A *metaphor* does not announce the comparison and proceeds indirectly to indicate an identification of the two items involved. Although such details of style may seem trivial in fiction, their effects are subtle and important. Sometimes the fundamental attitude of an author (see TONE), and hence the fundamental meaning of a piece of fiction, may be largely conveyed in terms of such details. See pp. 190–191, 207–208, 310–311, 661–666. See also ATMOSPHERE.

INEVITABILITY: The sense that the result presented is the only possible result of the situation previously given. It cannot be strictly maintained that inevitability in fiction is absolute, if one is to judge by realistic standards. The element of chance, or what appears as chance, in human affairs is too great to admit of such an interpretation. The term is simply used in most discussions to indicate a high degree of logic in the handling of the development of plot or character.

IRONICAL: See IRONY.

IRONY: Irony always involves contrast, a discrepancy between the expected and the actual, between the apparent and the real. Such contrast may appear in many forms. A speaker uses irony, for example, when he deliberately says something which he does not mean, but indicates by his tone what he does mean. UNDERSTATEMENT—the saying of less than one feels the occasion would warrent—and PARADOX—the saying of something which is apparently untrue but which on examination proves to be true, or partially true—both of these are forms of irony. In addition to such forms of IRONY OF STATEMENT, there are also various forms of IRONY OF SITUATION. The irony of situation involves a discrepancy between what we expect the outcome of an action to be, to what would seem to be the fitting outcome, and the actual outcome. In dealing with this term, the student should always remember that there are a thousand subtle shadings of irony, and must, therefore, not take it in too restricted a sense, for example, in the sense of obvious sarcasm. See "Letter to the Teacher," and pp. 21–23, 56, 97, 113, 157, 202, 210, 392.

LOGIC: In fiction, the relation that exists between character and character, or character and setting. See p. 80. See also INEVITABILITY.

MELODRAMATIC: An effect is said to be melodramatic when the violent or the sensational seems to be used for its own sake without adequate reference to the motivation of the characters or to other elements in the story. But the mere fact of violence, it should be pointed out, does not constitute melodrama. If the violence is logical and meaningful, it is not melodramatic. See pp. 1–28, 56–57, 350–354.

METAPHOR: See IMAGERY.

MOTIVATION: The purpose, or mixture of purposes, or even the more or less unconscious impulses that determine the behavior of a character. See pp. 26–28, 208–209.

OBJECTIVE: In relation to fiction, the pair of terms OBJECTIVE and SUBJECTIVE, is used in two connections. In the first, they are used with reference to the author, and in the second they are used with reference to a character, or characters, in the work of fiction. In the first connection, an *objective* treatment by the author implies an attitude of detachment toward the material which is being presented, a refusal to comment and interpret directly. (See DISTANCE, DRAMATIC, and SCALE.) A *subjective* treatment, on the other hand, is one which is highly colored by the author's own feelings and beliefs. Of course, the amount of subjectivity or objectivity is always a matter of degree. Since all fiction involves, ultimately, the author's interpretations, feelings, judgments, and the like, there is strictly speaking no absolutely objective presentation, but we can say that, in terms of method the distinction can be made. In reference to the character, or characters, in a work of fiction, the terms can be applied more absolutely. When there is no direct presentation of the thoughts or feelings of a character, the treatment is said to be objective; when such presentation is made, the treatment is said to be subjective. But most pieces of fiction tend to mix the two methods, some events being rendered objectively, some characters being treated objectively, and some subjectively. See pp. 659–664.

PACE: The rate of speed with which the various parts of the story are made to move, ranging from summary to fully reported scene. See pp. 114–115, 667.

PARABLE: A story, usually simple, which makes an obvious point or has a rather obvious symbolic meaning. The method of parable is closely related to that of ALLEGORY, but the tendency is to use the term *allegory* to indicate a more systematic and complicated structure of equivalents. See pp. 73–74, 286–288, 389–390.

PARADOX: See IRONY.

PATHOS: The sense of pity. The author, however, must be on his guard to make sure that the pathos in a story emerges legitimately from the situation given. When there is no reasonable basis in character and situation for the pathos, one has an effect of SENTIMENTALITY. The quality of being *pathetic* is to be distinguished from that of being *tragic*. In a tragic situation the sense of pity is complicated by an effect of struggle and conflict. The pathetic effect may be given by the spectacle of a weak person suffering; the tragic effect requires that the sufferer have strength enough to struggle vigorously against his situation.

PATTERN: The significant repetition—such as the repetition of incidents and events in a plot. See pp. 89, 156–157, 654–655. See also PLOT.

PERSONIFICATION: The attribution of the qualities of a person to an inanimate object or idea.

PLOT: The structure of action *as presented* in fiction or drama. Plot, as PLOT PATTERN, is one aspect of the total design of a story. See 1–28, 77–84, 651–656.

POINT OF VIEW: This term is loosely used to refer to the author's basic attitudes and ideas; for example, one may speak of a detached point of view, a sympathetic point of view, a Christian point of view. More strictly, the term is used to refer to the teller of the story—to the mind through which the material of the story is presented. The story may be told in the first or in the third person, and the teller may be the mere observer or much more than that. See pp. 146–150, 192, 529–530, 659–664. See also FOCUS OF NARRATION.

PROPAGANDA: Propaganda literature is literature which tends to state its theme abstractly and tends to insist upon its "message" at the expense of other elements. Usually it can be said that such literature oversimplifies its material in order to emphasize a particular interpretation. (For a fuller discussion, see "Letter to the Teacher," pp. xvi–xvii.)

REALISTIC: Having a strong sense of fact or actuality. The term is used in this text to refer to the presentation of ordinary, easily observable details which give an impression of fidelity to experience. *Realistic* is to be contrasted with ROMANTIC, which implies the remote, the exotic, the exaggerated. (There is no attempt in this book to go into the distinction between *romantic* and *classic*.)

RHYTHM: Movement with a recurrent beat or stress. Though prose rhythms are not so marked as those in poetry, most of which is written in *verse*, the rhythms in a piece of prose are frequently important and may indeed be highly expressive.

SCALE: The relative amount of detail of treatment allowed to the various parts in a story. See pp. 113–114, 666–667.

SELECTION: See pp. 148–149, 329–330, 650–651. See also FORM and STYLE.

SELECTIVITY: See SELECTION.

SENTIMENTALITY: Emotional response in excess of the occasion; emotional response that has not been prepared for in the story in question. See pp. 98, 183–184, 191, 207–210, 232. See also TONE.

SETTING: The physical background, the element of place, in a story. See pp. 189, 547–551, 647–649.

SIMILE: See IMAGERY.

STOCK RESPONSE: The automatic or conventional or generally uncritical response of a reader to some word, phrase, situation, character, or subject in literature. See also CLICHÉ.

STRUCTURE: See FORM.

STYLE: See FORM.

SUBJECTIVE: See OBJECTIVE.

SURPRISE ENDING: An ending in a story that comes with some sense of shock to the reader. (For the grounds for distinguishing between legitimate and illegitimate surprise endings, see pp. 98, 105, 113, 122–123, 132.) See also COINCIDENCE.

SYMBOL: An object, character, or incident which stands for something else, or suggests something else, is a *symbol* of that thing. See pp. 24, 56, 74 note.

THEME: The "point" or "meaning" of a story or novel. See pp. 26–27, 56–57, 76, 272–278.

TONE: The tone is the reflection in the story of the author's attitude toward his material and toward his audience. (It is to be distinguished from ATMOSPHERE, which see.) See pp. 63–64, 76, 391–392, 665. See also SENTIMENTALITY.

TRAGEDY: See PATHOS. See also pp. 23, 56–57, 354.

UNDERSTATEMENT: See IRONY. See also p. 140.

UNITY: The sense of wholeness or oneness. See pp. 24–27, 80, 82, 173, 668.